ELDRI
TIDE AND PIL
202

Our One Hundred Fiftieth Year of Continuous Publication

CONTENTS

☛ **NOTE:** The information in this volume has been compiled from U. S. Government sources and others, and carefully checked. The Publishers cannot assume any liability for errors, omissions, or changes.

Printed in U.S.A.   Copyright 2023 by Eldridge Maritime LLC   ISBN 978-1-883465-30-8

ELDRIDGE Through the Years

As ELDRIDGE marks its 150th year, we're taking an extended look back at the history and evolution of the publication. In the beginning, there were Government tables... but only for tides. Before steam power became prevalent, coastwise commerce relied on sail-powered vessels, most of them bluff-bowed schooners, to carry timber, stone, coal, and other heavy cargoes. These burdensome vessels were very slow, even in a good breeze, and a favorable or adverse current mattered far more than the height of the tide. George W. Eldridge, sent to Vineyard Haven to sell his father's charts from his catboat, heard the call from the waterfront, where many schooners routinely anchored to await a favorable current west, toward New York, or east toward Boston and Downeast. The inaugural edition of what today we call ELDRIDGE gave skippers what they needed.

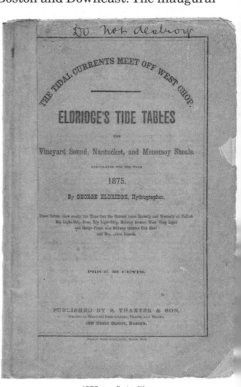

1875, our first edition

The first edition in 1875, ELDRIDGE'S TIDE TABLES FOR VINEYARD SOUND, NANTUCKET, AND MONOMOY SHOALS, was a modest booklet with 48 pages, priced at 50 cents. The cover listed George Eldridge, Hydrographer, as the Publisher, as he had the better-known name due to his growing chart business and piloting guides, but his son George W. had done most of the work: compiling current tables from direct observations. Inside there were tables for three points in Vineyard and Nantucket Sounds: Pollock Rip, Gay Head, and West Chop; there were also tide listings for much of the East Coast, using Chatham as the principal reference port. All information was provincial, centered on Cape Cod and Martha's Vineyard for a very local audience whose waters were busy with commerce, and which father and son knew well, as father George lived in Chatham and son George W. in Vineyard Haven.

The 1907 edition, titled ELDRIDGE'S TIDE-BOOK AND MARINE DIRECTORY and listing for one dollar, based the times of tide and current change using only Vineyard Haven as the reference port. The directory portion, a clear attempt to widen readership and increase revenue, must have worked, because fully 127 pages were devoted to ads for steam windlasses, coal, manila and hemp cordage, binnacles, Chelsea clocks, and predictably, father George Eldridge's increasingly popular charts.

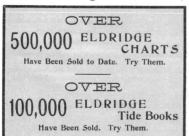

Advertisement from the 1907 edition

In 1910 George W. handed over the management of his book to family members, wanting time to

Notes

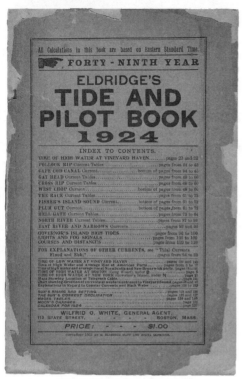

1924, courses and distances are added

grow the chart business and invent improved aids to navigation. At his death in 1914 the leading role fell to son-in-law Wilfrid O. White, who was becoming an expert in marine navigation. A significant change would come in the 1924 edition with a new title, ELDRIDGE'S TIDE AND PILOT BOOK, and the inclusion of courses and distances from the Chesapeake to Maine. The inclusion of courses must have created a great deal of plotting and proofreading; since all compass cards contained points and some included degrees, courses were described using the traditional notation of compass points (imagine trying to steer NExE 5/8E) as well as degrees magnetic. Vineyard Haven remained the reference port for all tide and current changes. Now a true piloting guide, the book had many notes about navigating in and out of harbors and how to take advantage of currents. Boating for pleasure was in its infancy and mainly for the wealthy, so most of the ads were for industrial items, like boilers, towboats, and uniforms for the captain and crew.

By the 1930s it was becoming clear that Vineyard Haven was no longer suitable as the reference port for all the newly listed ports, so it became Boston's turn. All listed harbors based their times of tides as offsets on Boston. By now readership was steadily expanding south and west, and New York was booming as a market for the book. As a result, a special section of ELDRIDGE with tide and current tables for New York, the pages in light blue for quick reference, began appearing. In a late response to the opening of the Cape Cod Canal in 1916, the currents for that busy waterway finally found their pages. Electronic navigation was becoming widely used as pleasure boating began to bloom, and radio direction finders and electronic fathometers found their way to the back cover. Publisher Wilfrid O. White began to take several pages of ads for his recently patented spherical compass.

World War II stifled much pleasure boating, except for small boats engaged in fishing, ferrying, and sailboat racing. The end of the war brought real changes, with a new boom in yachting reflected in the ads in ELDRIDGE: Edson; John G. Alden; Yachting, Motor Boating, and The Rudder magazines; Bausch & Lomb; and Chelsea Clock Co. Wilfrid's spherical compasses fill four pages as the pleasure boating market continued to surge. However, as a sign that prosperity had a way to go, a Wages Table in the 1947 edition lists pay from a low of $2.50 per month—equivalent to $35 in 2023—to a high of $300. Fitzroy's Barometer Instructions occupy two pages. Courses continue in compass points and degrees.

As Wilfrid entered his late 60s and looked forward to retiring, he and sons Gordon and Robert were increasingly focused on the engineering and production of all kinds of navigation instruments, especially spherical compasses. At one point he confessed to finding the publication of ELDRIDGE a bit of a distraction and was overheard muttering "That darned book!" And so he turned to his daughter Sydna, who began to assist in the book's preparation. She was to serve as an unnamed editor for about 30 years.

With the passing of Wilfrid in 1955, the role of Publisher fell to his youngest, Robert Eldridge White. An apt successor, he was an experienced navigator, adept with calculations, and inquiring of mind. He had a secret strength in wife Marion Jewett White, known as Molly, who played a quiet (she refused to be listed as co-Publisher) but substantial role in getting each year's edition to press. In 1959, "ELDRIDGE'S" became simply "ELDRIDGE." A new table called Ratios of Boat Speed to Current Speed showed how, at various angles to the bow, one's speed was affected by currents of several velocities. A recent feature, drawn by the Publisher, was a current diagram of the waters between Long Island and Cape Cod, with Newport at the center, showing how to ride a fair current all the way from L.I. Sound to Nantucket Sound, and the reverse. The Rule of the Road - "When all three

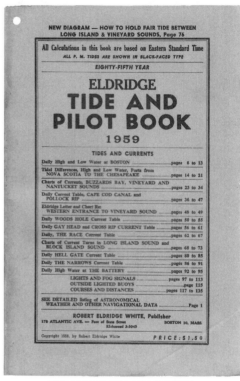

1959, ELDRIDGE'S becomes ELDRIDGE

lights I see ahead, I turn to Starboard and show my Red ..." - filled an early page. (Years later we removed the Rule but it was quickly reintroduced in response to outcry from out readers.) Boston continued as the reference port for all Times of High Water up and down the coast. New York pages remained in blue. One article continues to give Chronometer Instructions. Yacht Club flags Frequently Seen While Cruising has a page, but this was ultimately discontinued years later for being too arbitrary. Atlantic Coast Radiobeacon Signals gets a page.

The 1960s saw the continued growth of popular boating. Advertising changed to focus on pleasure boaters. The lengthy Courses and Distances section dropped compass points from course listings as almost all compass cards now used degrees. (Later, it would be removed altogether as GPS became ubiquitous.) By the end of the 1980's, the book had grown to 272 pages and included sections on Emergency First Aid and Racons.

In 1990 Robert Eldridge White passed away and Molly was compelled to step out of her quiet role and, for the first time in the book's long history, the Publisher

Continued on p. 178   **5**

INLAND NAVIGATION RULES

●

Good Seamanship Rule (Rule 7): Every vessel shall use all available means appropriate to the prevailing circumstances and conditions to determine if risk of collision exists. If there is any doubt, such risk shall be deemed to exist.

General right-of-way (Rule 18): Vessel categories are listed in <u>decreasing</u> order of having the right-of-way:

- Vessel not under command (most right of way)
- Vessel restricted in ability to maneuver, in a narrow fairway or channel
- Vessel engaged in fishing with nets, lines, or trawls (but not trolling lines)
- Sailing vessel (sails only)
- Power-driven vessel (least right of way)

Vessels Under Power

Overtaking (Rule 13): A vessel overtaking another is the "give-way" vessel and must stay clear of the overtaken or "stand-on" vessel. The overtaking vessel is to sound one short blast if it intends to pass on the other vessel's starboard side, and two short blasts if it intends to pass on the other's port side. The overtaken vessel must respond with the identical sound signal if it agrees, and must maintain course and speed during the passing situation.

Meeting head-on (Rule 14): When two vessels are meeting approximately head-on, neither has right-of-way. Unless it is otherwise agreed, each vessel should turn to starboard and pass port to port.

Memorized for generations by mariners, the verse below tells what to do when power vessels meet at night.

The Rule of the Road

When all three lights I see ahead,
I turn to **Starboard** and show my **Red:**
Green to Green, Red to Red,
Perfect Safety – **Go Ahead.**

But if to **Starboard Red appear,**
It is my duty to keep clear –
To act as judgment says is proper:
To **Port** or **Starboard, Back** or **Stop** her.

And if upon my **Port** is seen
A Steamer's **Starboard** light of **Green,**
I hold my course and watch to see
That **Green** to **Port** keeps Clear of me.

Both in safety and in doubt
Always keep a good look out.
In danger, with no room to turn,
Ease her, **Stop** her, **Go Astern.**

Crossing (Rule 15): When two vessels approaching each other are neither in an overtaking or meeting situation, they are deemed to be crossing. The power vessel which has the other on its starboard side is the give-way vessel and must change course, slow down, or stop. The vessel which is on the right, is in the right.

Vessels Under Sail

Port-Starboard (Rule 12): A vessel on the port tack shall keep clear of one on the starboard tack.

Windward-Leeward (Rule 12): When both vessels are on the same tack, the vessel to windward shall keep clear of a vessel to leeward.

Sail vs. Power (Rule 18): Generally, a sailboat has right of way over a powerboat. However: (1) a sailboat overtaking a powerboat must keep clear; (2) sailboats operating in a narrow channel shall keep clear of a power vessel which can safely navigate only within a narrow channel; (3) sailboats must give way to a vessel which is fishing, a vessel restricted in its ability to maneuver, and a vessel not under command.

FEDERAL SAFETY EQUIPMENT REQUIREMENTS

(These are minimum requirements. Some states require additional equipment.)

Sound Signaling Devices

Under 39.4' or 12 meters:
> Must have some means of making an efficient sound signal

Over 39.4' or 12 meters to 65' or 20 meters:
> Must have a whistle or horn

Over 65' or 20 meters:
> Must have a whistle or horn and a bell

Visual Distress Signals

Under 16' or 5 meters:
> Night: 1 electric SOS flashlight or 3 day/night red flares

Over 16' or 5 meters:
> Day only: 1 orange flag, 3 floating or hand-held orange smoke signals
> Day and night: 3 hand-held, or 3 pistol, or 3 hand-held rocket, or 3 red flares

The following signals indicate distress or need of assistance:

- A gun or other explosive signal fired at intervals of about 1 minute
- A continuous sounding with any fog-signaling apparatus
- Rockets or shells, fired one at a time or at short intervals
- SOS transmitted by any signaling method
- "Mayday" on the radiotelephone (channel 16)
- International Code Signal flags "NC"
- An orange square flag with a black square over a black ball
- Flames on the vessel
- Rocket parachute flare or hand-held flare
- Orange colored smoke
- Slowly and repeatedly raising and lowering outstretched arms
- Signals transmitted by EPIRB
- High intensity white light flashing 50-70 times per minute

Personal Flotation Devices (must be USCG approved)

Under 16' or 5 meters:
> 1 Type I, II, III, or V per person, USCG approved

Over 16' or 5 meters:
> 1 Type I, II, III, or V per person, and 1 Type IV per boat, USCG approved

Portable Fire Extinguishers (approved)

Under 26' 1 B-I, if no fixed extinguisher system in machinery space.
> (Not required on out-boards built so that vapor entrapment cannot occur.)

26-39'   2 B-I or 1 B-II if no fixed exting. system; 1 B-I, with a fixed exting. system.

40-65'   3 B-I or 1 B-II & 1 B-I, if no fixed exting. system; 2 B-I or 1 B-II with a fixed exting. system.

Back-Fire Flame Arrestor

One approved device per carburetor of all inboard gasoline engines.

At least 2 ventilator ducts fitted with cowls or their equivalent to ventilate efficiently the bilges of every engine and fuel tank compartment of boats using gasoline or other fuel with a flashpoint less than 110°F.

NAVIGATION LIGHTS
Definition of Lights

Masthead Light — a white light fixed over the centerline showing an unbroken light over an arc of 225°, from dead ahead to 22.5° abaft the beam on either side.

Sidelights — a green light on the starboard side and a red light on the port side showing an unbroken light over an arc of the horizon of 112.5°, from dead ahead to 22.5° abaft the beam on either side.

Sternlight — a white light placed as nearly as practicable at the stern showing an unbroken light over an arc of the horizon of 135°, 67.5° from dead aft to each side of the vessel.

All-round Light — an unbroken light over an arc of the horizon of 360°.

Towing Light — a yellow light with same characteristics as the sternlight.

Note: R. and Y. Flashing Lights are now authorized for vessels assigned to Traffic Control, Medical Emergencies, Search and Rescue, Fire-Fighting, Salvage, and Disabled Vessels.

When under way, in all weathers from sunset to sunrise, every vessel shall carry and exhibit the following lights

When Under Power Alone or When Under Power and Sail Combined

Under 39.4' or 12 meters:
Masthead light visible 2 miles
Sidelights visible 1 mile
Sternlight visible 2 miles (or in lieu of separate masthead light and sternlight, an all-round white light visible 2 miles)

Over 39.4' or 12 meters to 65' or 20 meters:
Masthead light visible 3 miles
Sidelights visible 2 miles
Sternlight visible 2 miles

Sailing Vessels Under Way (Sail Only)

Under 22' or 7 meters:
Either the lights listed below for sailing vessels under 65'; or a white light to be exhibited (for example, by shining it on the sail) in sufficient time to prevent collision
Under 65' or 20 meters: *may be combined in one tricolor lantern carried near top of mast*
Sidelights visible 2 miles
Sternlight visible 2 miles

At Anchor

Vessels under 50 meters (165') must show an all-round white light visible 2 miles.
Vessels under 7 meters (22') need no light unless they are near a channel, a fairway, an anchorage or area where other vessels navigate.

Fishing

Vessels Trawling shall show, in addition to the appropriate lights above, 2 all-round lights in a vertical line, the upper green and the lower white.
Vessels Fishing (other than trawling) shall show, in addition to the appropriate lights above, 2 all-round lights, the upper red and the lower white.

When Towing or Being Towed

Towing Vessel: 2 masthead lights (if tow is less than 200 meters); 3 masthead lights in a vertical line forward (if tow exceeds 200 meters); sidelights; sternlight; a yellow tow light in vertical line above sternlight; a diamond shape where it can best be seen (if tow exceeds 200 meters).
Vessel Being Towed: sidelights; sternlight; a diamond shape where it can best be seen (if tow exceeds 200 meters).

SOUND SIGNALS FOR FOG

Ask your Chart Dealer for the latest Navigation Rules—Inland/International

Frequently, in fog, small sail or power boats cannot be heard or picked up by other vessels' radar. The Coast Guard strongly recommends that, to avoid collisions, all vessels carry Radar Reflectors mounted as high as possible.

All signals prescribed by this article for vessels under way shall be given:

> **First:** By Power-driven Vessels – On the Whistle or Horn.
> **Second:** By Sailing Vessels or Vessels being Towed – On the Fog Horn.

A prolonged blast shall mean a blast of 4 to 6 seconds' duration.
A short blast shall mean a blast of about one second's duration.

A power-driven vessel making way through the water shall sound at intervals of no more than 2 minutes 1 prolonged blast.

A power-driven vessel under way, but stopped and making no way through the water, shall sound at intervals of no more than 2 minutes 2 prolonged blasts with about 2 seconds between them.

A sailing vessel under way shall sound at intervals of not more than 2 minutes 1 prolonged blast followed by 2 short blasts regardless of tack.

A fishing vessel or a power-driven vessel towing or pushing another vessel shall sound every 2 minutes 1 prolonged blast followed by 2 short blasts. A vessel being towed shall sound 1 prolonged blast followed by 3 short blasts.

A vessel at anchor shall ring a bell rapidly for about 5 seconds at intervals of not more than 1 minute and may in addition sound 3 blasts — 1 short, 1 prolonged, 1 short — to give warning of her position to an approaching vessel. Vessels under 20 meters (65') shall not be required to sound these signals when anchored in a special anchorage area.

A vessel aground shall give the bell signal and shall, in addition, give 3 separate and distinct strokes of the bell both before and after the rapid ringing of the bell.

MANEUVERING AND WARNING SIGNALS

Inland Rules:

> 1 short blast: I intend to leave you on my port side.
> 2 short blasts: I intend to leave you on my starboard side.
> 3 short blasts: I am backing
> 5 or more short and rapid blasts: danger or doubt

Response: If in agreement, upon hearing the 1 or 2 blast signal, a vessel shall sound the same signal and take the steps necessary to effect a safe passing. If not agreeable, or if in doubt, sound the danger/doubt signal.

International Rules:

> 1 short blast: I am altering my course to starboard.
> 2 short blasts: I am altering my course to port.
> 2 prolonged, 1 short blast: I am overtaking you on your starboard side.
> 2 prolonged, 2 short blasts: I am overtaking you on your port side.

Response in overtaking: prolonged blast, short blast, prolonged blast, short blast if agreeable. If not agreeable, or if in doubt, sound the danger/doubt signal.

> 3 short blasts: I am backing
> 5 or more short and rapid blasts: danger or doubt.

Why Tides and Currents Often Behave Differently

Frequently Asked Questions

"Why do the times of high water and current change differ?" Shouldn't an ebb current begin right after a high tide? Although tides (vertical height of water) and currents (horizontal movement) are inextricably related, they often behave rather differently.

If the Earth had a uniform seabed and no land masses, it is likely that a high tide at one point would occur simultaneously with a change in the current direction. However, the existence of continents, a complex sea bottom, the great ocean currents, and different prevailing winds around the world, make the picture extremely complex.

For an example of how a time of high tide can differ greatly from the time of a current change, see the Relationship of High Water and Ebb Current, p. 161. Picture a fjord or long indentation into the coastline, with a narrow opening to the ocean. When a flood current is reaching its peak, or the tide is high outside the mouth of this fjord, the fjord is still filling, unable to keep pace with conditions on the outer coast.

Why do the heights of tides differ so much from one place to the next? Turn to Time of High Water at various ports, pp. 12-20, and compare the Rise in Feet of tides for Nova Scotia's outer coast — 2.6 to 4.8 feet — to those for the Bay of Fundy, just below, that range of up to 38.4 feet. Why the difference? The answer is geography, both above and below water. Tidal ranges of points on the edge of an outer coast (Nantucket, for instance) tend to be moderate, while estuaries and deep bays with narrowing contours often experience a funneling effect which exaggerates the tidal range. Another explanation is proximity to the continental shelf: the closer a port is to the shelf, the more likely it is to experience a lower tidal range; the farther from the shelf, the more likely it is that a harbor is subject to surges, as when a wave crest hits the shallow water at a beach.

Do stronger currents indicate higher tides? There are other anomalies between tides and currents. Woods Hole, MA often has very strong currents through its narrow passage, sometimes as fast as 7 knots, but the tidal range is less than 2 feet. Conversely, Boston Harbor has a mean tidal range of about 9.6 feet, but the average currents at the opening, between Deer Island and Hull, do not exceed 2 knots. There is no necessary correlation between current strength and range of tide.

Why did the tidal or current prediction in ELDRIDGE differ from what I saw? Unless there was an error in our source data from NOAA, the answer is either (1) weather-related, as when a storm either retards or advances a tidal event, or (2) the discrepancy is small enough to be explained by the approximate nature of tide and current predictions, and figures are sometimes rounded off. We appreciate hearing from readers of any observed discrepancies or errors. Contact us by emailing pilot@eldridgetide.com, or calling 617-449-7393.

How To Use The Tide And Current Tables And Current Charts

High and Low Water Tide Tables

In addition to presenting tide tables for nine reference ports, from Portland to Miami, we show the approximate time of High Water and the mean (average) height of high at some 350 substations.

- On pp. 12-20, find your harbor, or the nearest one to it, and note the time difference between it and the reference port.
- Apply this time difference to the reference table for that date. On average the Low Water will follow by about 6 hours, 12 minutes.
- When the height of High Water in the reference table is higher or lower than the average, it will be correspondingly higher or lower at your harbor.

Current Tables

There are eight current tables covering from Massachusetts to the Chesapeake. At over 300 other points, on pp. 22-29, we show the approximate time of current change, the directions of ebb and flood, and the average maximum velocities.

- Find the place you are concerned with, or the listed position nearest to it, and note the time difference between it and the reference location.
- Apply this time difference to the reference table for that date. On average, the current will change approximately every 6 hours, 12 minutes.
- When the velocity of the current in the reference table exceeds the average maximum, the current in your area will also exceed the average maximum.

Naming Currents

While it is traditional to name currents as Ebb or Flood, these terms can easily confuse. We recommend using the direction as the name of the current. It is more helpful to refer to an Easterly current, which means it is Eastbound or runs toward the East, than it is to name it as an Ebb or Flood Current, which leaves the listener guessing its direction.

Current Charts and Diagrams

- Find the appropriate current chart and note the table to which it is refer-enced. For instance, the Long Island Sound charts (pp. 98-103) reference the Race tables.
- Turn to this table, which shows the time of start of Flood and start of Ebb, and find the time of the start of the advantageous current for that day.
- The difference between having a fair current or a head current means hours and dollars to the slower moving vessel such as a trawler or auxiliary sailboat. See Smarter Boating, p. 36.

Effect of the Moon

It is wise to pay particular attention to the phase or position of the Moon. "Astronomical" tides and currents occur around the times of full and new moons, especially when the Moon is at perigee, or closest to the Earth. Tides will be both higher and lower than average, and currents will run stronger than average. See pp. 238-239.

TIME OF HIGH WATER

Time figures shown are the *average* differences throughout the year. Rise in feet is mean range.
(Low Water times are given *only* when they vary more than 20 min. from High Water times.)

NOTE: *Asterisk indicates that NOAA has removed these substations from its listing because the data are judged to be of questionable accuracy. We have published NOAA's most recently available figures with this warning: Mariners are cautioned that the starred information is only approximate and not supported by NOAA or the Publishers of Eldridge.

*For **Canadian Ports**, if your watch is set for Atlantic Time, use the time differences listed here; if your watch is set for Eastern Time, subtract one hour from these time differences.*

	Hr.	Min.			Rise in feet
NOVA SCOTIA, Outer Coast					
Guysborough	3	00	before	PORTLAND	3.8
Whitehaven Harbour	3	15	"	"	3.7
Liscomb Harbour	3	20	"	"	4.2
Sheet Harbour	3	15	"	"	4.2
Ship Harbour	3	15	"	"	4.2
Jeddore Harbour	3	15	"	"	4.3
Halifax	3	10	"	"	4.4
Sable Island, north side	3	20	"	"	2.6
Sable Island, south side	3	15	"	"	3.9
Chester, Mahone Bay	3	10	"	"	4.4
Mahone Harbour, Mahone Bay	3	10	"	"	4.5
Lunenburg	3	05	"	"	4.2
Riverport, La Have River	3	00	"	"	4.5
Liverpool Bay	3	00	"	"	4.3
Lockeport	**high 2 45** before, low 3	10	"	"	4.6
Shelburne	2	40	"	"	4.8
NOVA SCOTIA & NEW BRUNSWICK, Bay of Fundy					
Lower E. Pubnico	1	15	before	PORTLAND	8.7
Yarmouth Harbour	0	25	"	"	11.5
Annapolis Royal, Annapolis R.	0	55	after	"	22.6
Parrsboro, Minas Basin, Partridge Is.	1	35	"	"	34.4
Burntcoat Head, Minas Basin	1	55	"	"	38.4
Amherst Point, Cumberland Basin	1	25	"	"	35.6
Grindstone Is, Petitcodiac River	1	10	"	"	31.1
Hopewell Cape, Petitcodiac River **high 1 00** after, low	1	25	"	"	33.2
Saint John	0	45	"	"	20.8
Indiantown, Saint John River **high 2 15** after, low 3	10	"	"		1.2
L'Etang Harbor	0	50	"	"	18.4

REVERSING FALLS, SAINT JOHN, N.B.

The most turbulence in the gorge occurs on days when the tides are largest. On largest tides the outward fall is between 15 and 16 1/2 feet and is accompanied by a greater turbulence than the inward fall which is between 11 and 12 1/2 feet. The outward fall is at its greatest between two hours before and one hour after low water at St. John; the inward fall is greater just before the time of high water. For complete tidal information of Canadian ports see Tide Tables of the Atlantic Coast of Canada. (Purchase tables from nautical dealers in Canadian ports or from the Queen's Printer, Department of Public Printing, Ottawa).

PORTLAND Tables, pp. 30-35

When a high tide exceeds avg. ht., the *following* low tide will be lower than avg.
*Times and Hts. are approximate. *Important*: See NOTE, top p. 12.

TIME OF HIGH WATER

Time figures shown are the *average* differences throughout the year. Rise in feet is mean range.
(Low Water times are given *only* when they vary more than 20 min. from High Water times.)

U.S. ATLANTIC COAST, from Maine southward

TIDE STATIONS

	Hr.	Min.			Rise in feet
MAINE					
Eastport	0	15	*before*	PORTLAND	18.4
Cutler, Little River	0	30	"	"	13.5
Shoppee Pt., Englishman Bay	0	25	"	"	12.1
Steele Harbor Island	0	25	"	"	11.6
*Jonesport	0	20	"	"	11.5
Green Island, Petit Manan Bar	0	25	"	"	10.6
Prospect Harbor	0	20	"	"	10.5
Winter Harbor, Frenchman Bay	0	15	"	"	10.1
Bar Harbor, Mt. Desert Island	0	20	"	"	10.6
Southwest Harbor, Mt. Desert Is. **high 0 20** *before, low*..0		45	"	"	10.2
Bass Harbor **high 0 15** *before, low*..0		45	"	"	9.9
Blue Hill Harbor, Blue Hill Bay	0	10	"	"	10.1
Burnt Coat Harbor, Swans Island	0	15	"	"	9.5
Penobscot Bay					
Center Harbor, Eggemoggin Reach	0	10	"	"	10.1
Little Deer Isle, Eggemoggin Reach	0	05	"	"	10.0
Isle Au Haut **high 0 20** *before, low*..0		45	"	"	9.3
Stonington, Deer Isle	0	15	"	"	9.7
Matinicus Harbor, Wheaton Is. ... **high 0 15** *before, low*..0		45	"	"	9.0
Vinalhaven	0	10	"	"	9.3
North Haven	0	10	"	"	9.7
Pulpit Harbor, North Haven Is.	0	10	"	"	9.9
Castine	0	05	"	"	10.1
Bucksport, Penobscott River	0	15	"	"	10.8
Bangor, Penobscot River **high 0 25** *before, low*..same as				"	13.4
Belfast	0	15	*before*	"	10.2
*Camden	0	10	"	"	9.6
Rockland	0	10	"	"	9.8
MAINE, Outer Coast					
Tenants Harbor	0	10	*before*	PORTLAND	9.3
Monhegan Island	0	10	"	"	8.8
Port Clyde, St. George River	0	10	"	"	8.9
Thomaston, St. George River	0	05	"	"	9.4
New Harbor, Muscongus Bay	0	10	"	"	8.8
Friendship Harbor	0	15	"	"	9.0
Waldoboro, Medomak River	0	10	"	"	9.5
East Boothbay, Damariscotta River	same as			"	8.9
Boothbay Harbor	0	05	*before*	"	8.8
Wiscasset, Sheepscot River	0	10	*after*	"	9.4
Robinhood, Sasanoa River	0	15	"	"	8.8
Phippsburg, Kennebec River	0	25	"	"	8.0
Bath, Kennebec River	1	10	"	"	6.4
Casco Bay					
*Small Point Harbor	0	10	*before*	"	8.8
Cundy Harbor, New Meadows River	same as			"	8.9
South Harpswell, Potts Harbor	same as			"	8.9
South Freeport	0	10	*after*	"	9.0

PORTLAND Tables, pp. 30-35

When a high tide exceeds avg. ht., the *following* low tide will be lower than avg.
*Times and Hts. are approximate. *Important*: See NOTE, top p. 12.

13

TIME OF HIGH WATER

Time figures shown are the *average* differences throughout the year. Rise in feet is mean range.
(Low Water times are given *only* when they vary more than 20 min. from High Water times.)

	Hr. Min.			Rise in feet
MAINE, Cont.				
Falmouth Foreside................................same as			PORTLAND	9.2
Great Chebeague Island.........................same as			"	9.1
Portland Head Light ....same as			"	8.9
Cape Porpoise 0 15		after	"	8.7
Kennebunkport..0 05		"	"	8.8
York Harbor 0 10		"	"	8.6
NEW HAMPSHIRE				
Portsmouth 0 20		after	PORTLAND	7.8
Gosport Harbor, Isles of Shoals ....same as			"	8.5
Hampton Harbor......................................0 25		after	"	8.3
MASSACHUSETTS, Outer Coast				
Newburyport, Merrimack River.. **high 0 30** *after, low* 1 10		after	PORTLAND	7.8
Plum Island Sound, S. End .... **high 0 10** *after, low* 0 35		"	"	8.6
Annisquam, Lobster Cove 0 10		"	"	8.8
Rockport..0 05		"	"	8.7
Gloucester Harbor ....same as			BOSTON	8.8
*Manchester...same as			"	8.8
Salem...0 05		before	"	8.9
*Marblehead...same as			"	9.1
Lynn, Lynn Harbor..................................same as			"	9.2
Neponset, Neponset R..............................same as			"	9.5
Weymouth, Fore River Bridge 0 10		after	"	9.5
Hingham..0 10		"	"	9.5
Hull..0 05		"	"	9.3
Cohasset Harbor (White Head)...............same as			"	8.8
Scituate, Scituate Harbor.......................same as			"	8.9
Cape Cod Bay				
Duxbury Harbor.......................... **high 0 05** *after, low* 0 35		after	"	9.9
Plymouth..0 10		"	"	9.8
Cape Cod Canal, East Entrance...............same as			"	8.7
Barnstable Harbor, Beach Point 0 20		after	"	9.5
Wellfleet..0 20		"	"	10.0
Provincetown 0 15		"	"	9.1
Cape Cod				
Stage Harbor, Chatham .... **high 0 45** *after, low* 0 20		"	"	4.0
Chatham Hbr, Aunt Lydias Cove.......................1 05		"	"	5.8
Pleasant Bay, Chatham.............. **high 2 30** *after, low* 3 25		"	"	3.2
Nantucket Sound				
Wychmere Harbor........................ **high 0 50** *after, low* 0 25		"	"	3.7
Dennisport .... **high 1 05** *after, low* 0 40		"	"	3.4
South Yarmouth, Bass River.............................1 45		"	"	2.8
Hyannis Port............................... **high 1 00** *after, low* 0 25		"	"	3.2
Cotuit Highlands........................ **high 1 15** *after, low* 0 45		"	"	2.5
Falmouth Heights...0 15		before	"	1.3
Nantucket Island				
Great Point..0 35		after	"	3.1
Nantucket 1 05		"	"	3.0
Muskeget Island, North side...................0 20		"	"	2.0

PORTLAND Tables, pp. 30-35, BOSTON Tables, pp. 38-43

When a high tide exceeds avg. ht., the *following* low tide will be lower than avg.
*Times and Hts. are approximate. *Important*: See NOTE, top p. 12.

TIME OF HIGH WATER

Time figures shown are the *average* differences throughout the year. Rise in feet is mean range.
(Low Water times are given *only* when they vary more than 20 min. from High Water times.)

TIDE STATIONS

	Hr.	Min.			Rise in feet
MASSACHUSETTS, Martha's Vineyard					
Lake Tashmoo (inside)....................................	2	35	before	BOSTON	2.0
Vineyard Haven...	3	35	after	NEWPORT	1.6
Oak Bluffs..	3	55	"	"	1.7
Edgartown	4	20	"	"	2.1
Wasque Point, Chappaquiddick.. **high** 2 00 *after, low* 3 20			"	"	1.1
Squibnocket Point....................... **high** 0 45 *before, low*..same as				"	2.9
Nomans Land............................. **high** 0 20 *before, low*..0 20			after	"	3.0
Gay Head..................................... **high** 0 05 *before, low*..0 45			"	"	2.9
Cedar Tree Neck .... **high** 0 10 *after, low* 1 30			"	"	2.2
Menemsha Bight....................... **high** *same as, low* 0 35			"	"	2.7
Vineyard Sound					
Little Hbr., Woods Hole................ **high** 0 30 *after, low* 2 20			"	"	1.4
Quick's Hole, N. side 0 10			before	"	3.5
Penikese...0 15			"	"	3.4
Cuttyhunk 1 20			after	"	3.4
Buzzards Bay					
Cuttyhunk Pond Entr...............................same as				"	3.4
W. Falmouth Harbor, Chappaquoit Pt. 0 05			after	"	3.8
Pocasset Hbr., Barlows Landing 0 20			"	"	4.0
Monument Beach..0 25			"	"	4.0
Wareham River..0 20			"	"	4.1
Great Hill...0 10			"	"	4.0
Marion, Sippican Harbor...............................0 10			"	"	4.0
Mattapoisett Harbor.....................................0 15			"	"	3.9
Clarks Point..0 20			"	"	3.6
New Bedford..0 05			"	"	3.7
South Dartmouth.......................................0 30			"	"	3.7
Westport Harbor, Westport River. **high** 0 10 *after, low* 0 35			"	"	3.0
RHODE ISLAND & MASS, Narragansett Bay					
Sakonnet, Sakonnet River........... **high** 0 10 *before, low*..0 15			after	NEWPORT	3.2
Beavertail Point, Conanicut Island ....same as				"	3.3
Conanicut Point, Conanicut Island ....same as				"	3.8
Prudence Island (south end)..............................0 05			after	"	3.7
Bristol Harbor 0 05			"	"	4.1
Fall River, MA...0 10			"	"	4.4
Bay Spring, Bullock Cove..................................0 05			"	"	4.3
Providence, State Pier no. 1...............................0 05			"	"	4.4
Pawtucket, Seekonk River 0 15			"	"	4.6
East Greenwich...0 10			"	"	4.1
Wickford...same as				"	3.7
Narragansett Pier....................... **high** 0 10 *before, low*..0 10			after	"	3.2
RHODE ISLAND, Outer Coast					
Pt. Judith, Harbor of Refuge....... **high** *same as, low*........0 35			after	NEWPORT	3.0
Block Island, Old Harbor............ **high** 0 15 *before, low*..0 15			"	"	2.9
Watch Hill Pt. .... **high** 0 40 *after, low* 1 15			"	"	2.6
CONNECTICUT, L.I. Sound					
Stonington 2 15			before	BRIDGEPORT	2.7
Noank...2 05			"	"	2.3
New London, Thames River (State Pier)..........1 45			"	"	2.6
Norwich, Thames River....................................1 25			"	"	3.0

BOSTON Tables, pp. 38-43, NEWPORT Tables, pp. 84-89, BRIDGEPORT Tables, pp. 104-109

When a high tide exceeds avg. ht., the *following* low tide will be lower than avg.
*Times and Hts. are approximate. *Important*: See NOTE, top p. 12.

TIME OF HIGH WATER

Time figures shown are the *average* differences throughout the year. Rise in feet is mean range.
(Low Water times are given *only* when they vary more than 20 min. from High Water times.)

	Hr.	Min.			Rise in feet
CONNECTICUT, L.I. Sound, Cont.					
Saybrook Jetty, Connecticut Riv... **high 0 35** *before, low* .1		00	*before*	BRIDGEPORT	3.5
Essex, Connecticut River.....................................0		05	"	"	3.0
Madison 0		25	"	"	4.9
Branford, Branford River 0		10	"	"	5.9
New Haven Harbor, New Haven Reach............................0		05	"	"	6.2
Milford Harbor.......................................same as				"	6.3
Sniffens Point, Housatonic River 0		10	*after*	"	6.4
South Norwalk 0		10	"	"	7.1
Stamford...0		05	"	"	7.2
Cos Cob Harbor 0		10	"	"	7.2
*Greenwich ....same as				"	7.4
NEW YORK, Long Island Sound, North Side					
Rye Beach 0		25	*before*	KINGS POINT	7.3
New Rochelle 0		15	"	"	7.3
Throgs Neck, Fort Schuyler............................same as				"	7.1
Whitestone, East River 0		10	*after*	"	7.1
College Point, Flushing Bay................................0		15	"	"	6.8
Hunts Point, East River 0		10	"	"	6.9
North Brother Island, East River 0		20	"	"	6.6
Port Morris, Stony Pt., East River 0		10	"	"	6.2
NEW YORK, Long Island, North Shore					
Willets Point...same as				KINGS POINT	7.2
Port Washington, Manhasset Bay.......................0		10	*before*	"	7.3
Glen Cove, Hempstead Harbor.............................0		25	"	"	7.3
Oyster Bay Harbor, Oyster Bay............................0		10	*after*	BRIDGEPORT	7.3
Cold Spring Harbor, Oyster Bay..........................0		05	*before*	"	7.3
Eatons Neck Point 0		05	*after*	"	7.1
Lloyd Harbor, Huntington Bay 0		05	"	"	7.0
Northport, Northport Bay ....same as				"	7.3
Port Jefferson Harbor Entrance....................same as				"	6.6
Mattituck Inlet...0		05	*after*	"	5.1
Shelter Island Sound					
Orient..1		10	*before*	"	2.5
Greenport.......................... **high 0 35** *before, low* ..1		00	"	"	2.4
Southold 0		05	"	"	2.3
Sag Harbor 0		50	"	"	2.4
New Suffolk, Peconic Bay.....................................0		35	*after*	"	2.6
South Jamesport, Peconic Bay..............................0		55	"	"	2.8
Threemile Harbor, Entr., Gardiners Bay 1		15	*before*	"	2.5
Montauk Harbor Entr. 2		05	"	"	1.9
Long Island, South Shore					
Shinnecock Inlet, Ocean.............. **high 0 15** *before, low* ..1		10	*before*	SANDY HOOK	3.1
Moriches Inlet. Coast Guard Sta 0		45	*after*	"	2.2
Democrat Point, Fire Island Inlet........................0		35	*before*	"	2.6
Patchogue, Great South Bay 3		25	*after*	"	1.1
Bay Shore, Watchogue Creek Entrance............................2		20	"	"	1.0
Babylon.......................... **high 2 10** *after, low* 2		40	"	"	0.6
Jones Inlet (Point Lookout) 0		20	*before*	"	3.6
Bellmore Creek, Hempstead Bay **high 1 30** *after, low* 2		00	*after*	"	2.0

BRIDGEPORT Tables, pp. 104-109, KINGS POINT Tables, pp. 110-115, SANDY HOOK Tables, pp. 140-145

When a high tide exceeds avg. ht., the *following* low tide will be lower than avg.
*Times and Hts. are approximate. *Important*: See NOTE, top p. 12.

TIME OF HIGH WATER

Time figures shown are the *average* differences throughout the year. Rise in feet is mean range.
(Low Water times are given *only* when they vary more than 20 min. from High Water times.)

TIDE STATIONS

	Hr. Min.			Rise in feet
NEW YORK, Long Island, South Shore, Cont.				
Freeport, Baldwin Bay	0 45	after	SANDY HOOK	3.0
E. Rockaway Inlet	0 15	before	"	4.4
Barren Is., Rockaway Inlet, Jamaica Bay	0 05	"	"	5.0
NEW YORK & NEW JERSEY				
New York Harbor				
Coney Island	0 10	before	SANDY HOOK	4.7
Fort Hamilton, The Narrows	0 05	after	"	4.7
Tarrytown, Hudson River	1 55	"	BATTERY	3.2
Poughkeepsie, Hudson River	4 40	"	"	3.1
Kingston, Hudson River	5 30	"	"	3.7
NY & NJ, the Kills and Newark Bay				
Constable Hook, Kill Van Kull	0 15	before	"	4.6
Port Elizabeth	0 05	after	"	5.1
Bellville, Passaic River **high 0 10** after, low	0 50	"	"	5.6
Kearny Pt., Hackensack River	0 15	"	"	5.2
Hackensack, Hackensack River	1 05	"	"	6.0
Lower NY Bay, Raritan Bay				
Great Kills Harbor	same as		SANDY HOOK	4.9
South Amboy, Raritan River	same as		"	5.1
New Brunswick, Raritan River	0 40	after	"	5.7
Keyport	same as		"	5.0
Atlantic Highlands, Sandy Hook Bay	0 10	before	"	4.7
Highlands, Shrewsbury R., Rte. 36 bridge, Sandy Hook	0 15	after	"	4.2
Red Bank, Navesink River, Sandy Hook Bay				
high 1 20 after, low	2 00	"	"	3.5
Sea Bright, Shrewsbury River, Sandy Hook Bay	1 10	"	"	3.2
NEW JERSEY, Outer Coast				
Shark River Island, Fixed RR. Bridge, Shark River	0 10	before	"	4.3
Manasquan Inlet, USCG Station	0 20	"	"	4.0
Brielle, Rte. 35 bridge, Manasquan River	0 15	"	"	3.9
Barnegat Inlet,USCG Station, Barnegat Bay	0 05	"	"	2.2
Manahawkin Drawbridge **high 2 50** after, low	3 40	after	"	1.3
Beach Haven, USCG Station, Little Egg Harbor	1 20	"	"	2.2
Absecon Creek, Rte. 30 bridge	1 10	"	"	3.9
Atlantic City, Ocean	0 25	before	"	4.0
Beesleys Pt., Great Egg Hbr. Bay **high 0 30** after, low	1 10	after	"	3.6
Townsends Inlet, Ocean Dr. bridge	same as		"	4.0
Stone Harbor, Great Channel, Hereford Inlet	0 30	after	"	4.2
Cape May Harbor, Cape May Inlet	same as		"	4.5
NEW JERSEY & DELAWARE BAY				
Delaware Bay, Eastern Shore				
Brandywine Shoal Light **high 0 30** after, low	1 00	after	BATTERY	4.9
Cape May Point, Sunset Beach **high 0 15** after, low	0 40	"	"	4.8
Dennis Creek, 2.5 mi. above Entr. **high 1 15** after, low	2 00	"	"	5.2
Mauricetown, Maurice R. **high 2 40** after, low	3 15	"	"	4.4
Millville, Maurice R. **high 3 55** after, low	4 20	"	"	5.0

SANDY HOOK Tables, pp. 140-145, BATTERY Tables, pp. 128-133

When a high tide exceeds avg. ht., the *following* low tide will be lower than avg.
*Times and Hts. are approximate. *Important*: See NOTE, top p. 12.

TIME OF HIGH WATER

Time figures shown are the *average* differences throughout the year. Rise in feet is mean range.
(Low Water times are given *only* when they vary more than 20 min. from High Water times.)

	Hr.	Min.			Rise in feet
NEW JERSEY & DELAWARE BAY, Cont.					
Delaware Bay, Western Shore					
*Cape Henlopen...0	10	after	BATTERY	4.1
Lewes (Breakwater Harbor)........ **high 0 20** *after, low* 0	45	"	"	4.1
*St. Jones River Ent. .... **high 1 10** *after, low* 1	55	"	"	4.8
Delaware River					
*Liston Point, Delaware................................2	05	"	"	5.7
Salem, Salem River, NJ 4	00	"	"	4.2
Reedy Point, Delaware 3	15	"	"	5.3
C&D Summit Bridge, Delaware...................2	35	"	"	3.5
Chesapeake City, MD..2	15	"	"	2.9
New Castle, Delaware .... **high 3 35** *after, low* 4	05	"	"	5.2
Wilmington Marine Terminal..... **high 3 55** *after, low* 4	30	"	"	5.3
Philadelphia, PA, USCG Station.........................5	40	"	"	6.0
Burlington, NJ .... **high 6 25** *after, low* 7	00	"	"	7.2
Trenton, NJ................................. **high 6 45** *after, low* 7	45	"	"	8.2

	Hr.	Min.			Rise in feet
DELAWARE, MARYLAND & VIRGINIA					
Indian River Inlet, USCG Station, Delaware .... **high 0 55** *after, low* 0	25	after	SANDY HOOK	2.5
Ocean City Fishing Pier...............................0	20	before	"	3.4
Harbor of Refuge, Chincoteague Bay..................0	15	after	"	2.4
Chincoteague Channel, south end 0	25	"	"	2.2
Chincoteague Island, USCG Station.....................0	45	"	"	1.6
Metompkin Inlet...0	30	"	"	3.6
Wachapreague, Wachapreague Channel................0	45	"	"	4.0
*Quinby Inlet Entrance.................................0	05	"	"	4.0
Great Machipongo Inlet, inside 0	40	"	"	3.9
Chesapeake Bay, Eastern Shore					
Cape Charles Harbor 0	40	after	BATTERY	2.3
Crisfield, Little Annemessex River.....................4	30	"	"	1.9
Salisbury, Wicomico River 7	10	"	"	3.0
Middle Hooper Island 4	40	before	BALTIMORE	1.5
Taylors Island, Little Choptank River, Slaughter Creek ..3	10	"	"	1.3
*Sharps Is. Lt..3	50	"	"	1.3
Cambridge, Choptank River 2	35	"	"	1.6
Dover Bridge, Choptank River 0	30	"	"	1.7
Oxford, Tred Avon River................................2	50	"	"	1.4
Easton Pt., Tred Avon River...........................2	40	"	"	1.6
St. Michaels, Miles River...............................2	10	"	"	1.4
Kent Island Narrows.......................................1	25	"	"	1.2
*Bloody Pt. Bar Lt...2	40	"	"	1.1
Worton Creek Entrance 1	20	after	"	1.3
Town Point Wharf, Elk River 3	10	"	"	2.2
Chesapeake Bay, Western Shore					
Havre de Grace, Susquehanna River.....................3	20	after	"	1.9
*Pooles Is...0	55	"	"	1.2
Annapolis, Severn River (US Naval Academy).................1	35	before	"	1.0
*Sandy Point 1	20	"	"	0.8
Thomas Pt. Shoal Lt.......................................2	05	"	"	0.9
*Drum Point, Pawtuxent River 4	50	"	"	1.2
Solomons Island, Pawtuxent River......................4	40	"	"	1.2

BATTERY Tables, pp. 128-133, SANDY HOOK Tables, pp. 140-145, BALTIMORE Tables, pp. 162-165

When a high tide exceeds avg. ht., the *following* low tide will be lower than avg.

*Times and Hts. are approximate. *Important*: See NOTE, top p. 12.

TIME OF HIGH WATER

Time figures shown are the *average* differences throughout the year. Rise in feet is mean range.
(Low Water times are given *only* when they vary more than 20 min. from High Water times.)

DELAWARE, MARYLAND & VIRGINIA, Cont.

	Hr.	Min.			Rise in feet
Point Lookout	5	30	before	BALTIMORE	1.2
Sunnybank, Little Wicomico River	6	30	after	BATTERY	0.8
Glebe Point, Great Wicomico River	4	15	"	"	1.2
Windmill Point, Rappahannock River	2	50	"	"	1.2
*Orchard Point, Rappahannock River	3	20	"	"	1.4
*New Point Comfort, Mobjack Bay	0	45	"	"	2.3
Tue Marshes Light, York River	0	50	"	"	2.2
*Perrin River, York River	1	05	"	"	2.3
Yorktown, Goodwin Neck, York River	1	00	"	"	2.2
Hampton Roads, Sewells Pt.	0	45	"	"	2.4
Norfolk, Elizabeth River	1	05	"	"	2.8
Newport News, James River	1	15	"	"	2.6
*Windmill Pt., James River	6	20	"	"	2.3
Chesapeake Bay Br. Tunnel	0	15	before	"	2.6

NORTH CAROLINA

	Hr.	Min.			Rise in feet
Roanoke Sound Channel	1	10	after	BATTERY	0.5
Oregon Inlet Marina	0	15	before	"	0.9
Oregon Inlet, USCG Station	0	50	"	"	2.0
Oregon Inlet Channel	0	35	"	"	1.2
Cape Hatteras Fishing Pier	1	05	"	"	3.0
Hatteras Inlet	0	55	"	"	2.0
Ocracoke Inlet	0	55	"	"	1.9
Beaufort Inlet Channel Range	0	55	"	"	3.2
Morehead City	0	40	"	"	3.1
Bogue Inlet	0	50	"	"	2.2
New River Inlet	0	50	"	"	3.0
*New Topsail Inlet ... **high 0 40** before, low	0	10	"	"	3.0
Bald Head, Cape Fear River	0	50	"	"	4.5
Wilmington ... **high 1 20** after, low	1	45	after	"	4.3
Lockwoods Folly Inlet	1	00	"	"	4.2

SOUTH CAROLINA

	Hr.	Min.			Rise in feet
Little River Neck, north end	1	30	after	BATTERY	4.6
Hog Inlet Pier	0	45	"	"	5.0
Myrtle Beach, Springmaid Pier	0	50	"	"	5.0
Pawleys Island Pier (ocean)	0	55	"	"	4.9
Winyah Bay Entrance, south jetty	0	50	before	"	4.6
South Island Plantation, C.G. Station	0	10	after	"	3.8
Georgetown, Sampit River ... **high 1 00** after, low	1	40	"	"	3.7
North Santee River Inlet	0	30	before	"	4.5
Charleston (Custom House Wharf)	0	25	"	"	5.2
Folly River, north, Folly Island ... **high** same as, low	0	35	"	"	5.4
Rockville, Bohicket Creek, North Edisto River	0	15	"	"	5.8
Edisto Marina, Big Bay Creek entr., South Edisto River	0	25	"	"	6.0
Harbor River Bridge, St. Helena Sound	0	20	"	"	6.1
Hutchinson Island, Ashepoo River, St. Helena Sound	0	20	after	"	6.0
Fripps Inlet, Hunting Island Bridge, St. Helena Sound	0	30	before	"	6.1
Port Royal Plantation, Hilton Head Is.	0	25	"	"	6.1
Battery Creek, Beaufort River Port Royal Sd, 4 mi. above entr. ... **high 1 00** after, low	0	15	after	"	7.6

BALTIMORE Tables, pp. 162-165, BATTERY Tables, pp. 128-133

When a high tide exceeds avg. ht., the *following* low tide will be lower than avg.
*Times and Hts. are approximate. *Important*: See NOTE, top p. 12.

TIDE STATIONS

19

TIME OF HIGH WATER

Time figures shown are the *average* differences throughout the year. Rise in feet is mean range.
(Low Water times are given *only* when they vary more than 20 min. from High Water times.)

	Hr.	Min.			Rise in feet
SOUTH CAROLINA, Cont.					
Beaufort, Beaufort River .... **high 0 55** *after, low* 0 30			*after*	*BATTERY*	7.4
Braddock Point, Hilton Head Island, Calibogue Sd. 0 15			*before*	"	6.7
GEORGIA					
Savannah River Entrance, Fort Pulaski 0 15			*before*	*BATTERY*	6.9
Tybee Creek Entrance...0 20			"	"	6.8
Wilmington River, north entrance.......................................0 25			*after*	"	7.6
Isle of Hope, Skidaway River ...... **high 0 35** *after, low* 0 10			"	"	7.8
Egg Islands, Ossabaw Sound 0 10			*before*	"	7.2
Walburg Creek Entr., St. Catherines Sd...........................*same as*				"	7.1
Blackbeard Island...*same as*				"	6.9
Blackbeard Creek, Blackbeard Island..					
.... **high 0 05** *after, low* ...0 30			*after*	"	6.5
Old Tower, Sapelo Island, Doboy Sound 0 05			*before*	"	6.8
Threemile Cut Entrance, Darien River..............................0 30			*after*	"	7.1
St. Simons Sound Bar...0 20			*before*	"	6.5
Frederica River, St. Simons Sound....................................0 35			*after*	"	7.2
Brunswick, East River, Howe St. Pier, St. Simons Sound 0 20			"	"	7.1
Jekyll Is. Marina, Jekyll Creek, St. Andrew Sound 0 35			"	"	6.8
Cumberland Wharf, Cumberland River 0 30			*after*	"	6.8
FLORIDA, East Coast					
St. Marys Entrance, north jetty, Cumberland Sd..............*same as*				*BATTERY*	5.8
Fernandina Beach, Amelia R...... **high 0 30** *after, low* 0 05			*after*	"	6.0
Amelia City, South Amelia River.......................................0 50			"	"	5.4
Nassau River Entrance............... **high 0 10** *after, low* 0 50			"	"	5.2
Mayport, (Bar Pilot Dock).......... **high 0 15** *after, low* 0 15			*before*	"	4.6
St. Augustine, City Dock..0 10			*after*	"	4.5
Ponce Inlet, Halifax River .... **high 0 05** *after, low* 0 30			*after*	*MIAMI*	2.8
Cape Canaveral........................... **high 1 05** *before, low* ..0 45			*before*	"	3.5
Port Canaveral, Trident Pier......................................*same as*				"	3.5
Sebastian Inlet bridge................. **high 0 50** *before, low* ..0 25			*before*	"	2.2
St. Lucie, Indian River .... **high 0 40** *after, low* 1 45			*after*	"	1.1
Vero Beach, ocean...0 45			*before*	"	3.4
Fort Pierce Inlet, south jetty..0 25			"	"	2.6
Stuart, St. Lucie River .... **high 2 15** *after, low* 3 30			*after*	"	0.9
Jupiter Inlet, south jetty...0 10			*before*	"	2.5
North Palm Beach, Lake Worth .. **high 0 15** *before, low* ..0 15			*after*	"	2.8
Port of Palm Beach, Lake Worth . **high 0 20** *before, low* ..0 05			"	"	2.7
Lake Worth Pier, ocean .... **high 0 45** *before, low* ..0 20			*before*	"	2.7
Hillsboro Inlet, C.G. Light Station 0 05			"	"	2.5
Hillsboro Inlet Marina................ **high 0 05** *before, low* ..0 25			*after*	"	2.5
Lauderdale-by-the-Sea, fish pier.....................................0 25			*before*	"	2.6
Bahia Mar Yacht Club .... **high 0 05** *before, low* ..0 35			*after*	"	2.4
Port Everglades, Turning Basin.......................................0 20			*before*	"	2.5
North Miami Beach, fishing pier.....................................0 10			"	"	2.5
Miami, Miamarina, Biscayne Bays **high 0 20** *after, low* 0 50			*after*	"	2.2
Dinner Key Marina, Biscayne Bay **high 0 55** *after, low* 1 50			"	"	1.9
Key Biscayne Yt. Club, Biscayne B **high 0 45** *after low*....1 30			"	"	2.0
Ocean Reef Hbr., Key Largo .... **high 0 10** *before, low* ..0 15			"	"	2.3
Tavernier Harbor, Hawk Ch...0 15			"	"	2.0
Key West 0 50			*before*	*BOSTON*	1.3

BATTERY Tables, pp. 128-133, MIAMI Tables, pp. 166-169, BOSTON Tables, pp. 38-43
When a high tide exceeds avg. ht., the *following* low tide will be lower than avg.
*Times and Hts. are approximate. *Important*: See NOTE, top p. 12.

Piloting in a Cross Current

See also p. 58, Coping with Currents

When we are piloting in a body of water with an active current from ahead or astern, our course is not affected and the arithmetic for speed is easy. (See p. 36.) When the current comes at an angle to the bow or stern, unless our speed is far greater than the current, we need to alter course to compensate.

First, what not to do: When in a cross current it is a major mistake simply to steer toward our destination. The current will carry us more and more off course, with the heading or bearing to our destination changing all the time. We may finally get there, but we will have traveled considerably farther, on what is termed a hooked course, and possibly have entered dangerous water while doing so.

By GPS: With GPS it's all too easy to find the new heading. We enter our destination waypoint and press GoTo. There are several screens to choose from. First, carefully check the Map screen to see if there are any hazards or obstructions between us and our destination. The Highway screen, considered perhaps the most useful display, will show if we are on course by displaying the highway as straight ahead. The screen will also indicate how far to the left or right of our course we are. This is crosstrack error. We steer to that side which brings us back onto the center of the highway, and then continue to steer in such a way that we stay in the middle. We have changed our heading to achieve the desired COG, course over ground. Now the Course and Bearing numbers should be the same, and we have compensated for cross current.

By eye: Without the help of electronics but with good visibility, we know we need to alter course toward the current until a foreground object, let's say a point on the shore, remains steady in relation to an object farther away, perhaps a distant steeple. This alignment is called a range. Once we find the corrected heading, we can use our compass to maintain it, checking those objects periodically in case current or wind conditions change.

By a chart: With compromised visibility and again without electronics, the problem is solved the traditional way with a paper chart. First, consult the proper current table to determine the speed and direction of the current for the hour(s) in question. (Keep in mind that speeds and times are predictions only. They are approximate and can be altered by weather.) Plot the course, let's say 090°, as if there is no current. Then construct a one-hour vector diagram. From the departure point, construct a line in the direction of the current, let's say 180°, whose length is the distance the current would carry an object in one hour. If the predicted current is 2 knots, that's 2 n.m. Now we set our dividers for a distance which represents how far our boat speed will take us through the water in one hour, let's say 8 n.m. We will put one point of the dividers on the far end of the line representing current, and then swing the dividers until the second point intercepts the line of our intended course. The direction of that third line represents what our boat's heading needs to be (the course to steer) to maintain the original course we drew. The intercept point represents about where our boat will be along the intended course line (COG) at the end of one hour. If this leg is longer or shorter than one hour, it doesn't matter. The course to steer is the same as we determined in our one-hour vector plot, until conditions change.

TIME OF CURRENT CHANGE

(See Note at bottom of Boston Tables, pp. 38-43: Rule-of-Thumb for Current Velocities.)

CURRENTS IN THE GULF OF MAINE - In the Gulf of Maine, on the western side, the Flood Current splits at Cape Ann, Mass., and floods north and east along the shore towards the Bay of Fundy. At the same time, on the eastern side of the Gulf, at the southern tip of Nova Scotia, the Flood Current runs to the west and then north and eastwards along the shore into the Bay of Fundy. The Ebb Current is just the reverse. In addition to these large principal currents, along the Maine Coast, at least at the mouths of principal bays, there is a shoreward set during the Flood and an offshore set during the Ebb, although this set is of considerably less velocity.

West of Mount Desert, the average along-shore current is rarely more than a knot but the farther east one goes, the greater are the average velocities to be expected, up to 2 knots or more. When heading west, therefore, start off at the time shown for High Water in your area (see p. 13) and have a fair Ebb current for 6 hours. Headed east, start at the time for Low Water in your area (about 6 ½ hours after High Water) and carry the beneficial Flood current. East of Schoodic Point, the average currents are up to 2 knots and taking advantage of them will save considerable time and fuel.

Off shore, in the Gulf of Maine, unlike the along-shore currents that come to dead slack and _reverse_, there are so-called _rotary_ currents. These currents constantly change direction in a clockwise flow completing the circle in about 12 ½ hours. The maximum currents are when it is flooding in the northeasterly direction or ebbing in a southwesterly direction; minimum currents occur halfway between. There is no slack water.

Entering the Bay of Fundy through Grand Manan Channel, one finds that the average velocities are from 1-2 ½ knots, although in the narrower channels off the Bay, velocities are higher (Friar Roads at Eastport has average velocities of 3 knots of more). The Current in the Bay Floods to the Northeast and Ebbs to the Southwest.

In using this table, bear in mind that **actual times of Slack or Maximum occasionally differ from the predicted times** by as much as half an hour and in rare instances as much as an hour. Referring the Time of Current Change at the subordinate stations listed below, to the predicted Current Change at the reference station gives the _approximate_ time only. Therefore, to make sure of getting the full advantage of a favorable current or slack water, the navigator should reach the entrance or strait at least half an hour before the predicted time. (This is essentially the same precautionary note found in the U.S. Tidal Currents Table Book.)

Figures shown below are **average maximum** velocities in knots. To find the Time of Current Change (Start of Flood and Start of Ebb) at a selected point, refer to the table heading that particular section (in bold type) and add or subtract the time listed.

TIME DIFFERENCES Flood Starts; Ebb Starts Hr. Min.	MAXIMUM FLOOD		MAXIMUM EBB	
	Dir.(true) in degrees	Avg. Max. in knots	Dir.(true) in degrees	Avg. Max. in knots
MAINE COAST – based on Portland, pp. 30-35				
(Flood starts at Low Water; Ebb starts at High Water)				
Isle Au Haut, 0.8 mi. E of Richs Pt. F-0 05, E-0 25	336	1.4	139	1.5
Damariscotta R., off Cavis Pt. .... F+1 20, E+0 20	350	0.6	215	1.0
Sheepscot R., off Barter Is............ F+1 20, E+0 30	005	0.8	200	1.1
Lowe Pt., NE of, Sasanoa R. .... F+1 20, E+0 55	327	1.7	152	1.8
Lower Hell Gate, Knubble Bay* F+1 40, E+0 55	290	3.0	155	3.5

*Velocities up to 9.0 kts. have been observed in the vicinity of the Boilers.

Important: See NOTE, bottom p. 29.

TIME OF CURRENT CHANGE
(See Note at bottom of Boston Tables, pp. 38-43: Rule-of-Thumb for Current Velocities.)

	TIME DIFFERENCES Flood Starts; Ebb Starts Hr. Min.	MAXIMUM FLOOD Dir.(true) in degrees	Avg. Max. in knots	MAXIMUM EBB Dir.(true) in degrees	Avg. Max. in knots
KENNEBEC RIVER – based on Portland, pp. 30-35					
(Flood starts at Low Water; Ebb starts at High Water)					
Hunniwell Pt., NE of	F+2 10, E+1 45	332	2.4	151	2.9
Bald Head, 0.3 mi. SW of	F+2 25, E+1 35	321	1.6	153	2.3
Bluff Head, W of	F+2 35, E+2 05	014	2.3	184	3.4
Fiddler Ledge, N of	F+2 45, E+2 00	267	1.9	113	2.6
Doubling Pt., S of	F+2 30, E+2 00	300	2.6	127	3.0
Bath Iron Works	F+2 40, E+2 10	004	1.9	178	2.5
CASCO BAY – based on Portland, pp. 30-35					
(Flood starts at Low Water; Ebb starts at High Water)					
Broad Sound, W. of Eagle Is.	+0 10	351	1.0	187	1.1
Hussey Sound, Cow Islands	+ 0 30	012	1.1	178	0.8
Portland Hbr. entr, 19ft depth	F+0 55, E+0 15	313	0.7	137	1.1
Portland, Fore River Bridge	F+0 50, E+0 05	229	0.5	065	0.4
PORTSMOUTH HARBOR – based on Boston, pp. 38-43					
(Flood starts at Low Water; Ebb starts at High Water)					
Portsmouth Hbr. entr.	+1 40	342	1.2	194	1.5
Fort Point	F+2 10, E+1 35	328	1.6	098	2.0
Clark Is., S of	+2 10	270	1.6	085	2.3
Henderson Pt., W of	+1 50	285	2.4	138	2.8
MASSACHUSETTS COAST – based on Boston, pp. 38-43					
(Flood starts at Low Water; Ebb starts at High Water)					
Merrimack River entr.	+0 55	285	2.2	105	1.4
Newburyport, Merrimack R.	+1 20	288	1.5	098	1.4
Plum Is. Sound entr.	+0 30	316	1.6	184	1.5
Gloucester Hbr., Blynman Canal entr.	F-0 05, E-0 40	310	3.0	130	3.3
Marblehead Channel	F+0 20, E-0 30	280	0.3	171	0.3
Hypocrite Channel	+0 20	262	0.9	070	1.0
BOSTON HARBOR – based on Boston, pp. 38-43					
(Flood starts at Low Water; Ebb starts at High Water)					
Pt. Allerton, 0.4 mi. NW.	-0 05	265	0.7	080	0.8
Deer Island Lt.	F+0 10, E-0 20	264	1.3	112	1.2
Nantasket Rds					
Hull Gut	F-0 05, E-0 35	162	1.9	340	2.5
West Head (W. Gut) 0.2mi. SW	F-0 05, E+0 35	167	1.4	322	1.4
Weir R. entr., Worlds End, N of	+0 20	076	0.7	272	0.8
Bumkin Is., 0.4mi. W. of	F-0 05	195	0.5	303	0.3
Weymouth Back R., betw. Grape I. and Lower Neck	-0 15	094	0.7	281	0.9
CAPE COD BAY – based on Boston, pp. 38-43					
(Flood starts at Low Water; Ebb starts at High Water)					
Barnstable Harbor	+0 10	192	1.2	004	1.4
NANTUCKET SOUND – based on Pollock Rip Channel, pp. 66-71					
Pollock Rip Channel, E end	-0 20	053	2.0	212	1.8

Important: See NOTE, bottom p. 29.

CURRENT STATIONS

TIME OF CURRENT CHANGE
(See Note at bottom of Boston Tables, pp. 38-43: Rule-of-Thumb for Current Velocities.)

	TIME DIFFERENCES Flood Starts; Ebb Starts Hr. Min.	MAXIMUM FLOOD		MAXIMUM EBB	
		Dir.(true) in degrees	Avg. Max. in knots	Dir.(true) in degrees	Avg. Max. in knots
*POLLOCK RIP CHANNEL at Butler Hole - See table, pp. 66-71					
Monomoy Point, 0.2 mi. W of	+0 10	170	1.7	346	2.0
Halfmoon Shoal, 3.5 mi. E of	+1 10	088	1.1	295	1.0
Great Point, 0.5 mi. W of	F+0 25, E+1 15	029	1.1	195	1.2
Tuckernuck Shoal, off E end	+1 15	113	0.9	287	0.9
Nantucket Hbr. entr. chan.	F+3 20, E+2 45	171	1.2	350	1.5
Muskeget Is. chan., 1 mi. NE of	F+1 30, E+1 00	108	1.1	295	1.5
Muskeget Rock, 1.3 mi. SW of	+1 05	024	1.3	192	1.0
Muskeget Channel	+1 35	021	3.8	200	3.3
Betw. Long Shoal-Norton Shoal	+1 30	100	1.4	260	1.1
Cape Poge Lt., 1.7 mi. SSE of	+0 55	025	1.6	215	1.3
Cross Rip Channel	+1 50	091	1.3	272	0.9
Cape Poge, 3.2 mi. NE of	+2 35	095	1.6	300	1.2
Betw. Broken Gr.-Horseshoe Sh.	F+1 45, E+1 15	107	1.1	276	0.9
Point Gammon, 1.2 mi. S of	+1 10	105	1.1	260	1.0
Lewis Bay entr. chan.	+2 45	004	0.9	184	1.3
Betw. Wreck Shoal-Eldridge Shoal	+1 45	062	1.7	245	1.4
Hedge Fence Lighted Gong Buoy 22	+2 45	108	1.4	268	1.2
Betw. E. Chop-Squash Meadow	F+2 10, E+1 45	131	1.4	329	1.8
East Chop, 1 mi. N of	F+2 40, E+2 15	116	2.2	297	2.2
West Chop, 0.8 mi. N of	F+2 50, E+2 20	096	3.1	282	3.0
Betw. Hedge Fence and L'hommedieu Shoal	F+2 30, E+2 00	106	2.1	276	2.2
Waquoit Bay entr.	+3 30	348	1.5	203	1.4
L'hommedieu Shoal, N of W end	+2 20	080	2.3	268	2.3
Nobska Point, 1.8 mi. E of	+2 05	063	2.3	240	1.7
VINEYARD SOUND – based on Pollock Rip Channel, pp. 66-71					
West Chop, 0.2 mi. W of	F+1 20, E+1 50	059	2.7	241	1.4
Nobska Point, 1 mi. SE of	+2 30	071	2.6	259	2.4
Norton Point, 0.5 mi. N of	+2 00	050	3.4	240	2.4
Tarpaulin Cove, 1.5 mi. E of	F+2 50, E+2 10	055	1.9	232	2.3
Robinsons Hole, 1.2 mi. SE of	+2 20	060	1.9	240	2.1
Gay Head, 3 mi. N of	+2 05	074	1.1	255	1.2
Gay Head, 1.5 mi. NW of	+1 35	012	2.0	249	2.0
VINEYARD SOUND-BUZZARDS BAY – based on Woods Hole, pp. 52-57					
Robinsons Hole, Naushon Pt.	+0 40	151	3.0	332	2.9
Quicks Hole, S end	F+1 20, E+0 30	140	1.9	300	2.0
Quicks Hole, Middle	F+1 30, E+1 00	157	2.3	327	1.8
Quicks Hole, N end	F+1 40, E+0 55	165	2.0	002	2.6
Canapitsit Channel	F+1 30, E+0 30	131	1.7	312	1.6
BUZZARDS BAY – based on Woods Hole, pp. 52-57					
Westport River entr.	-1 20	290	2.2	108	2.5

Gooseberry Nk., 2 mi. SSE of (41°27'N- 71°01'W) *Rotary current, no slack water.*
  Avg. max. 0.6 kts, approx. dir. 52° true 3:20 hrs. after Flood starts at Pollock Rip.
  Avg. max. 0.5 kts, approx. dir. 232° true 2:45 hrs. after Ebb starts at Pollock Rip.					

Betw. Ribbon Reef-Sow &Pigs Rf.	F-1 45, E-3 45	062	0.8	237	1.2
Penikese Is., 0.8 mi. NW of	F-3 00, E-1 55	050	1.2	254	1.1
Betw. Gull Is.-Nashawena Is.	F-3 40, E-3 00	091	0.9	247	1.1
Dumpling Rocks, 0.2 mi. SE of	F-3 10, E-2 30	066	0.8	190	1.1
BUZZARDS BAY – based on Cape Cod Canal, pp. 46-51					
Abiels Ledge	F+0 10, E-0 20	069	1.3	236	1.8
CAPE COD CANAL - table, pp. 46-51		070	4.0	250	4.5

*See Tidal Current Chart Buzzards Bay, Vineyard and Nantucket Sounds, pp. 72-83

Important: See NOTE, bottom p. 29.

(See Note at bottom of Boston Tables, pp. 38-43: Rule-of-Thumb for Current Velocities.)

	TIME DIFFERENCES Flood Starts; Ebb Starts Hr. Min.	MAXIMUM FLOOD Dir.(true) in degrees	MAXIMUM FLOOD Avg. Max. in knots	MAXIMUM EBB Dir.(true) in degrees	MAXIMUM EBB Avg. Max. in knots
*NARRAGANSETT BAY – based on Pollock Rip Channel, pp. 66-71					
Tiverton, Stone Bridge, Sakonnet	F-3 00, E-2 25	010	2.7	190	2.7
Tiverton, RR Bridge, Sakonnet R.	F-3 25, E-2 50	000	2.3	180	2.4
Castle Hill, W of East Passage	F-0 05, E-1 05	013	0.7	237	1.2
Bull Point, E of	-1 10	001	1.2	206	1.5
Rose Is., NE of	F-1 55, E-1 15	310	0.8	124	1.0
Rose Is., W of	F-0 40, E-1 20	001	0.7	172	1.0
Dyer Is., W of	-1 00	023	0.8	216	1.0
Mount Hope Bridge	-1 15	047	1.1	230	1.4
Kickamuit R., Mt. Hope Bay	F-2 05, E-1 20	000	1.4	191	1.7
Warren R., Warren	-0 20	358	1.0	171	0.9
Beavertail Point, 0.8 mi NW of	F-0 10, E-1 30	003	0.5	188	1.0
Betw. Dutch Is.-Beaver Head	-1 55	030	1.0	233	1.0
Dutch Is., W of	-1 25	014	1.3	206	1.2
India Pt. RR Bridge, Seekonk R.	-1 40	020	1.0	180	1.4
BLOCK ISLAND SOUND – based on The Race, pp. 92-97					
Pt. Judith Pond entr.	-3 10	351	1.8	186	1.5
Sandy Pt., Block Is. 1.5 mi N of	F-0 25, E-1 05	315	1.9	063	2.1
Lewis Pt., 1.0 mi. SW of	F-1 30, E-0 25	298	1.9	136	1.8
Lewis Pt., 1.5 mi. W of	F-1 35, E-0 50	318	1.4	170	1.7
Southwest Ledge	-0 25	321	1.5	141	2.1
Watch Hill Pt., 2.2 mi. E of	F-0 30, E+0 45	260	1.2	086	0.7
Montauk Pt., 1.2 mi. E of	F-1 20, E-0 40	346	2.8	162	2.8
Montauk Pt., 1 mi. NE of	F-2 05, E-1 15	356	2.4	145	1.9
Betw. Shagwong Reef-Cerberus Shoal	-0 30	241	1.9	056	1.8
Betw. Cerberus Sh.-Fishers Is.	F-1 00, E+0 05	264	1.3	096	1.3
Gardiners Is., 3 mi. NE of	F-0 50, E-0 25	305	0.9	138	1.0
GARDINERS BAY etc. – based on The Race, pp. 92-97					
Goff Point, 0.4 mi. NW of	-1 35	225	1.2	010	1.6
Acabonack Hbr. entr., 0.6 mi. ESE of	F-1 35, E-1 05	345	1.4	140	1.2
Gardiners Pt. Ruins, 1.1 mi. N of	-0 10	270	1.2	066	1.8
Betw. Gardiners Point-Plum Is.	-0 25	288	1.4	100	1.6
Jennings Pt., 0.2 mi. NNW of	+0 35	290	1.6	055	1.5
Cedar Pt., 0.2 mi. W of	F-0 10, E+0 30	195	1.8	005	1.6
North Haven Peninsula, N of	F+0 10, E+0 40	230	2.4	035	2.1
Paradise Pt., 0.4 mi. E of	+0 35	145	1.5	345	1.5
Little Peconic Bay entr.	+0 45	240	1.6	015	1.5
Robins Is., 0.5 mi. S of	F+0 30, E+0 55	245	1.7	065	0.6
FISHERS ISLAND SOUND – based on The Race, pp. 92-97					
Napatree Point, 0.7 mi. SW of	-0 50	284	1.7	113	2.2
Little Narragansett Bay entr.	-2 05	092	1.3	268	1.3
Ram Island Reef, S of	-0 50	255	1.3	088	1.6
LONG ISLAND SOUND – based on The Race, pp. 92-97					
**THE RACE (near Valiant Rock) – See pp. 92-97		291	3.3	106	4.2
Race Point, 0.4 mi. SW of	-0 25	288	2.6	135	3.5
Little Gull Is., 1.1 mi. ENE of	+0 05	301	4.0	130	4.7
Little Gull Is., 0.8 mi. NNW of	F+0 25, E-2 20	258	1.9	043	2.9
Great Gull Is., SW of	-0 35	320	2.3	147	3.3
New London St. Pier, Thames R.	-1 20	358	0.4	178	0.4
Goshen Pt., 1.9 mi. SSE of	-0 55	285	1.2	062	1.6
Bartlett Reef, 0.2 mi. S of	F-2 05, E-1 05	255	1.4	090	1.3
Twotree Is. Channel	F-1 00, E-0 35	267	1.2	099	1.6

Floods somewhat unstable. Flood currents differing from predicted should be expected.
** See Tidal Current Chart Long Is. and Block Is. Sounds, pp. 98-103*

Important: See NOTE, bottom p. 29.

TIME OF CURRENT CHANGE

(See Note at bottom of Boston Tables, pp. 38-43: Rule-of-Thumb for Current Velocities.)

	TIME DIFFERENCES Flood Starts; Ebb Starts Hr. Min.	MAXIMUM FLOOD Dir.(true) in degrees	Avg. Max. in knots	MAXIMUM EBB Dir.(true) in degrees	Avg. Max. in knots
LONG ISLAND SOUND – based on The Race, pp. 92-97 (cont.)					
Black Point, 0.8 mi. S of	F-0 40, E-0 15	260	1.3	073	1.4
Betw. Black Pt.-Plum Is.	+0 35	236	2.1	076	2.4
Plum Is., 0.8 mi. NNW of	F+0 10, E-1 05	247	1.7	065	2.4
Plum Gut	-1 00	306	1.9	116	3.0
Hatchett Pt., 1.1 mi. WSW of	F-2 30, E-0 40	240	1.3	045	1.2
Saybrook Bkwtr., 1.5 mi. SE of	F-1 20, E-0 45	260	1.9	070	2.0
Conn. River I-95 Bridge	F+1 15, E+0 20	356	0.9	166	1.8
Mulford Pt., 3.1 mi. NW of	+0 05	269	1.9	066	2.3
Cornfield Point, 2.8 mi. SE of	F-1 30, E-0 30	249	1.9	085	1.4
Cornfield Point, 1.1 mi. S of	-0 50	293	1.4	108	1.6
Kelsey Point, 1 mi. S of	F-1 35, E-1 05	249	2.0	118	1.5
Six Mile Reef, 2 mi. E of	F-0 30, E+0 05	235	1.6	040	2.1
Sachem Head, 1 mi. SSE of	-0 30	255	1.1	065	1.0
New Haven Harbor entr.	F-0 20, E+0 05	277	0.7	122	0.5
Housatonic R., Milford Pt., 0.2 mi. W of	F+0 00, E+0 25	330	1.2	135	1.2
Point No Point, 2.1 mi. S of	F-0 20, E+0 05	251	1.3	074	1.2
Port Jefferson Harbor entr.	-0 10	150	1.6	336	1.0
Crane Neck Point, 0.5 mi. NW of	F-0 45, E-1 40	256	1.3	016	1.5
Eatons Neck Pt., 1.3 mi. N of	+0 20	283	1.4	075	1.4
Lloyd Point, 1.3 mi. NNW of	+1 30	255	1.0	055	0.9
EAST RIVER – based on Hell Gate, pp. 116-121					
Cryders Pt., 0.4 mi. NNW of	-0 25	110	1.3	285	1.1
College Pt. Rf., .25 mi. NW of	F-0 30, E+0 10	074	1.5	261	1.4
Rikers Is. Chann. off La Guardia Field	+0 05	088	1.1	261	1.3
Hunts Point, SW of	+0 05	108	1.7	280	1.3
S. Brother Is. NW of	-0 10	054	1.5	252	1.2
Off Winthrop Ave., Astoria	+0 05	040	3.4	220	2.5
Mill Rock, NE of	-0 25	103	2.3	288	0.6
Mill Rock, W of	F-0 25, E+0 00	000	1.2	180	1.0
HELL GATE (off Mill Rock) – table, pp. 116-121		050	3.4	230	4.6
Roosevelt Is., W of, off 75th St.	0 00	037	3.8	215	4.7
Roosevelt Is., E of, off 36th Ave.	-0 05	030	3.5	210	3.4
Roosevelt Is., W of, off 67th St.	+0 15	011	3.6	230	4.0
Pier 67 (Off 19th St.)	-0 10	355	1.8	179	1.9
Williamsburg Br., 0.3 mi. N of	-0 05	020	2.7	220	2.9
Brooklyn Bridge, 0.1 mi. SW of	-0 05	046	2.9	222	3.5
LONG ISLAND, South Coast – based on The Narrows, pp. 122-127					
Shinnecock Inlet	F+0 15, E-0 -35	350	2.5	170	2.3
Fire Is. Inlet, 0.5 mi. S. of Oak Bch.	+0 25	082	2.4	244	2.4
Jones Inlet	-0 50	035	3.1	217	2.6
East Rockaway Inlet	-1 15	042	2.2	227	2.3
JAMAICA BAY – based on The Narrows, pp. 122-127					
Rockaway Inlet entr.	-1 35	085	1.8	244	2.7
Barren Is., E of	F-1 30, E-2 05	004	1.2	192	1.7
Beach Channel (bridge)	F-1 25, E-1 00	062	1.9	225	2.0
Grass Hassock Channel	-1 00	052	1.0	228	1.0
NEW YORK HARBOR ENTRANCE – based on The Narrows, pp. 122-127					
Ambrose Channel	-0 30	303	1.6	123	1.7
Norton Pt., WSW of	+0 15	341	1.0	166	1.2
THE NARROWS – table, pp. 122-127		325	1.3	142	1.6

Important: **See NOTE, bottom p. 29.**

TIME OF CURRENT CHANGE
(See Note at bottom of Boston Tables, pp. 38-43: Rule-of-Thumb for Current Velocities.)

	TIME DIFFERENCES Flood Starts; Ebb Starts Hr. Min.	MAXIMUM FLOOD Dir.(true) Avg. Max. in degrees in knots		MAXIMUM EBB Dir.(true) Avg. Max. in degrees in knots	
NEW YORK HARBOR, Upper Bay – based on The Narrows, pp. 122-127					
Bay Ridge, W of	F+0 10, E+0 40	354	1.4	185	1.5
Red Hook Channel	F-0 40, E-0 05	353	1.0	170	0.7
Robbins Reef Light, E of	F+0 40, E+0 00	016	1.3	204	1.6
Red Hook, 1 mi. W of	+0 55	024	1.3	206	2.3
Statue of Liberty, E of	F+1 20, E+0 55	031	1.4	205	1.9
HUDSON RIVER, Midchannel – based on The Narrows, pp. 122-127					
George Washington Bridge	+1 30	010	1.8	203	2.5
Spuyten Duyvil	+1 15	020	1.6	200	2.1
Riverdale	+2 00	015	1.4	200	2.0
Dobbs Ferry	+2 20	010	1.3	190	1.7
Tarrytown	+2 30	000	1.1	180	1.5
West Point, off Duck Is.	+3 30	010	1.0	190	1.1
NEW YORK HARBOR, Lower Bay – based on The Narrows, pp. 122-127					
Sandy Hook Channel	F-1 30, E-1 10	286	1.6	094	0.9
Sandy Hook Channel, 0.4 mi. W of N. tip	-1 30	235	2.0	050	1.6
Coney Is. Lt., 1.5 mi. SSE of	-1 00	310	1.1	125	1.3
Rockaway Inlet Jetty, 1 mi. SW of	F-1 55, E-1 30	287	1.2	142	1.4
Coney Is. Channel, W end	F-1 00, E-0 30	293	1.1	102	1.2
SANDY HOOK BAY – based on The Narrows, pp. 122-127					
Highlands Bridge, Shrewsbury R.	+0 35	170	2.6	000	2.5
Seabright Br., Shrewsbury R.	F+1 20, E+0 50	185	1.4	000	1.7
RARITAN RIVER – based on The Narrows, pp. 122-127					
Washington Canal, N entr.	F-0 50, E-1 35	240	1.5	060	1.5
South River entr.	F-1 30, E-0 30	180	1.1	000	1.0
ARTHUR KILL & KILL VAN KULL – based on The Narrows, pp. 122-127					
Tottenville, Arthur Kill River	-0 45	023	1.0	211	1.1
Tufts Pt.-Smoking Pt.	-0 25	109	1.2	267	1.2
Elizabethport	+0 30	090	1.4	262	1.1
Bergen Pt., East Reach	F-1 10, E-1 40	274	1.1	094	1.2
New Brighton	-1 25	262	1.3	072	1.9
NEW JERSEY COAST – based on Del. Bay Entr., pp. 146-151					
Manasquan Inlet	F-1 00, E-1 40	300	1.7	120	1.8
Manasquan R. Hwy. Br. Main Ch.	F-1 00, E-1 40	230	2.2	050	2.1
Pt. Pleasant Canal, north bridge*	F+1 25, E+0 20	170	1.8	350	2.0
Barnegat Inlet	F+0 40, E-0 10	270	2.2	090	2.5
Manahawkin Drawbridge	+2 05	030	1.1	210	0.9
McCrie Shoal	-1 00	280	1.3	100	1.4
Cape May Harbor entr.	-1 55	324	1.6	142	1.7
Cape May Canal, E end	-2 15	310	1.9	130	1.9
DELAWARE BAY & RIVER – based on Del. Bay Entr., pp. 146-151					
Cape May Channel	-1 35	306	1.5	150	2.3
DELAWARE BAY ENTR. – table, pp. 146-151		342	1.8	152	1.7
Cape Henlopen, 0.7 mi. ESE of	F-0 25, E-1 05	331	1.8	139	2.4
Cape Henlopen, 2 mi. NE of	F+0 00, E-0 30	315	2.0	145	2.3
Cape Henlopen, 5 mi. N of	+0 10	344	2.0	173	1.9

Waters are extremely turbulent. Currents of 6 to 7 knots have been reported near the bridges.

Important: **See NOTE, bottom p. 29.**

TIME OF CURRENT CHANGE
(See Note at bottom of Boston Tables, pp. 38-43: Rule-of-Thumb for Current Velocities.)

	TIME DIFFERENCES Flood Starts; Ebb Starts Hr. Min.	MAXIMUM FLOOD Dir.(true) in degrees	Avg. Max. in knots	MAXIMUM EBB Dir.(true) in degrees	Avg. Max. in knots
DELAWARE BAY & RIVER – based on Del. Bay Entr., pp. 146-151 (cont.)					
Mispillion River Mouth	F+2 15, E+1 20	025	1.5	190	1.0
Bay Shore chan., City of Town Bank	F-0 50, E-1 10	006	0.9	183	1.0
Fourteen Ft. Bk., Lt., 1.2 mi. E of	-0 05	339	1.3	174	1.5
Maurice River entr.	+0 35	012	1.1	192	1.0
Kelly Island, 1.5 mi. E of	+0 25	348	0.9	164	1.2
Miah Maull rge. at Cross Ledge rge.	+1 00	335	1.5	160	1.8
False Egg Is. Pt., 2 mi. off	F+0 05, E-0 15	342	1.1	158	1.3
Ben Davis Pt. Shoal., SW of	F+1 30, E+1 05	321	1.8	147	1.9
Cohansey R., 0.5 mi. above entr.	+1 05	074	1.2	254	1.4
Arnold Point, 2.2 mi. WSW of	+2 00	324	2.1	145	1.9
Smyrna River entr.	+1 30	250	1.2	070	1.5
Stony Point chan., W of	F+2 55, E+1 50	324	1.5	151	1.9
Appoquinimink R. entr.	F+2 10, E+1 35	231	1.0	048	1.2
Reedy Is., off end of pier	F+2 35, E+2 05	027	2.4	194	2.6
Alloway Creek entr., 0.2 mi. above	F+2 00, E+1 35	129	2.1	325	2.1
Reedy Point	F+2 55, E+2 05	354	2.1	160	2.3
Salem River entr.	F+3 15, E+2 40	062	1.5	245	1.6
Bulkhead Sh. chan., off Del. City	F+2 50, E+2 15	308	2.1	138	2.1
Pea Patch Is., chan., E of	F+2 55, E+2 35	319	2.3	148	2.3
New Castle, chan., abreast of	F+3 00, E+2 10	051	1.9	230	2.4
CHESAPEAKE BAY – based on The Race, pp. 92-97					
(over 90% correlation within 15 min. throughout year)					
Chesapeake Bay entr., Buoy LB2CH	+0 10	297	1.1	112	1.1
Cape Henry Light, 4.6 mi. N of	F-0 30, E+0 10	294	1.3	104	1.3
Cape Henry Light, 8.3 mi. NW of	F+0 05, E+0 25	329	1.0	133	1.1
Tail of the Horseshoe	+0 05	300	0.9	110	1.0
Chesapeake Channel (Bridge Tunnel)	F+0 00, E+0 20	335	1.8	145	1.5
Fisherman Is., 1.7 nmi. S of	-0 20	297	1.0	126	1.4
York Spit Channel N buoy "26"	F+1 20, E+0 55	010	0.8	195	1.1
Old Plantation Flats Lt., 0.5 mi. W of	+1 20	005	1.2	175	1.3
Wolf Trap Lt., 0.5 mi. W of	F+1 30, E+1 05	015	1.0	190	1.2
Stingray Point, 5.5 mi. E of	+2 15	343	1.0	179	0.9
Stingray Point, 12.5 mi. E of	F+2 00, E+1 33	030	1.0	175	0.8
Smith Point Lt., 6.0 mi. N of	F+4 05, E+3 10	350	0.4	135	1.0
Cove Point - See Chesapeake Bay Current Diagram, p. 160					
Pooles Island - See Chesapeake Bay Current Diagram, p. 160					
Worton Point - See Chesapeake Bay Current Diagram, p. 160					
CHESAPEAKE & DELAWARE CANAL - table, pp. 154-159		097	2.0	278	1.9
HAMPTON ROADS – based on The Race, pp. 92-97					
(over 90% correlation within 15 min. throughout year)					
Thimble Shoal Channel (West End)	-0 20	293	0.9	116	1.2
Old Point Comfort, 0.2 mi. S of	-0 45	240	1.7	075	1.4
Willoughby Spit, 0.8 mi. NW of	-1 35	260	0.7	040	1.0
Sewells Point, chan., W of	F-0 55, E-3 00	195	0.9	000	1.2
Newport News, chan., middle	F-0 20, E-0 50	244	1.1	076	1.1

Important: See NOTE, bottom p. 29.

	TIME DIFFERENCES Flood Starts; Ebb Starts Hr. Min.	MAXIMUM FLOOD Dir.(true) in degrees	Avg. Max. in knots	MAXIMUM EBB Dir.(true) in degrees	Avg. Max. in knots
C&D CANAL POINTS – based on C&D Canal, pp. 154-159					
Back Creek, 0.3 nmi. W of Sandy Pt.	-0 10	057	1.2	244	1.4
Reedy Point Radio Tower, S of......	F-1 00, E-0 15	078	1.9	263	1.3
VA, NC, SC, GA & FL, outer coast – based on Hell Gate, pp. 116-121					
(over 90% correlation within 15 min. throughout year)					
Hatteras Inlet	+0 50	307	2.1	148	2.0
Ocracoke Inlet chan. entr...........	F+1 00, E+0 10	000	1.7	145	2.4
Beaufort Inlet Approach	F+0 20, E-0 55	358	0.3	161	1.4
Cape Fear R. Bald Head Shoal	F-0 55, E-1 20	013	0.6	208	1.7
Winyah Bay entr.	F+0 05, E-0 25	320	1.9	140	2.0
North Santee R. entr.	F-0 40, E-1 25	010	1.5	165	1.8
South Santee R. entr.	-1 15	045	1.5	240	1.6
Charleston Hbr. entr., betw. jetties..............	-1 30	320	1.8	121	1.8
Charleston Hbr., off Ft. Sumter..................	-1 35	313	1.7	127	2.0
Charleston Hbr. S. ch. 0.8 mi.					
ENE of Ft. Johnson	F-0 55, E-1 35	275	0.8	115	2.6
Charleston Hbr., Drum Is., E of (bridge)...	-1 15	020	1.2	183	2.0
North Edisto River entr.	-0 35	332	2.9	142	3.7
South Edisto River entr.	-1 25	350	1.8	146	2.2
Ashepoo R. off Jefford Cr. entr...................	-0 35	016	1.5	197	1.6
Port Royal Sd., SE chan. entr.........	F-2 05, E-1 35	310	1.3	150	1.6
Hilton Head..	-1 10	324	1.8	146	1.8
Beaufort River entr....................................	-1 15	010	1.3	195	1.4
Savannah River entr..................................	-0 50	286	2.0	110	2.0
Vernon R. 1.2 mi. S of Possum Pt..	F-1 25, E-0 50	324	1.1	166	1.7
Raccoon Key & Egg Is. Shoal bet.................	-0 50	254	1.6	129	2.0
St. Catherines Sound entr.............	F-1 40, E-0 30	291	1.8	126	1.7
Sapelo Sound entr..........................	F-1 30, E-0 45	290	1.7	118	2.2
Doboy Sound entr.	-1 15	289	1.6	106	1.8
Altamaha Sd., 1 mi. SE of					
Onemile Cut..........................	F-0 20, E-1 45	272	1.0	092	1.9
St. Simons Sound Bar Channel....	F-1 15, E-0 30	308	0.8	119	1.7
St. Andrews Sound entr.	F-1 20, E-0 40	268	2.1	103	2.2
Cumberland Sd., St. Mary's River,					
Ft. Clinch, 0.3 nmi. N..................	F-1 15, E -0 50	275	1.4	087	1.6
Drum Point Is., rge. D chan..........	F-0 50, E -0 20	350	1.1	170	1.5
Nassau Sd., midsound,					
1 mi. N of Sawpit Cr. entr.	-0 20	312	1.7	135	1.7
FLORIDA EAST COAST – based on The Narrows, pp. 122-127					
(over 90% correlation within 15 min. throughout year)					
St. Johns R. entr. betw. jetties......................	+0 30	262	2.0	081	2.0
Mayport...	+0 35	211	2.2	026	3.3
St. Johns Bluff..	+1 10	244	1.6	059	2.4
FLORIDA EAST COAST – based on Hell Gate, pp. 116-121					
(over 90% correlation within 15 min. throughout year)					
Fort Pierce Inlet entr.	+0 30	258	2.7	080	2.8
Lake Worth Inlet, entr................................	-0 55	267	1.6	086	1.3
Miami Hbr., Bakers Haulover Cut	-0 10	270	2.9	090	2.5
Miami Hbr. entr.	-0 15	293	2.3	113	2.4

CURRENT STATIONS

NOTE: Velocities shown are from U.S. Gov't. figures. It is obvious, however, to local mariners and other observers, that coastal inlets may have far greater velocities than indicated here. Strong winds and opposing tides can cause even more dangerous conditions, and great caution should be used. Separate times for Flood and Ebb are given only when the times are more than 20 minutes apart.

2024 HIGH & LOW WATER
PORTLAND, ME
43°39.4'N, 70°14.8'W

Standard Time | Standard Time

D A Y O F M O N T H	D A Y O F W E E K	JANUARY								D A Y O F M O N T H	D A Y O F W E E K	FEBRUARY					
		HIGH				LOW						HIGH				LOW	
		a.m.	Ht.	p.m.	Ht.	a.m.	p.m.					a.m.	Ht.	p.m.	Ht.	a.m.	p.m.
1	M	2:25	8.3	2:29	8.8	8:18	8:49			1	T	3:00	8.6	3:21	8.0	9:11	9:24
2	T	3:09	8.3	3:16	8.4	9:06	9:31			2	F	3:42	8.6	4:10	7.7	10:00	10:10
3	W	3:53	8.3	4:06	8.1	9:56	10:15			3	S	4:29	8.6	5:06	7.4	10:53	11:01
4	T	4:40	8.3	4:59	7.8	10:49	11:02			4	S	5:22	8.6	6:07	7.4	11:52	11:58
5	F	5:26	8.4	5:56	7.6	11:44	11:52			5	M	6:20	8.9	7:12	7.5	...	12:56
6	S	6:16	8.6	6:55	7.6	...	12:42			6	T	7:22	9.3	8:12	7.9	1:00	1:57
7	S	7:07	8.9	7:52	7.8	12:45	1:38			7	W	8:20	9.8	9:07	8.4	2:00	2:53
8	M	7:58	9.4	8:44	8.0	1:39	2:30			8	T	9:15	10.4	9:58	9.0	2:56	3:44
9	T	8:47	9.8	9:33	8.4	2:30	3:19			9	F	10:07	11.0	10:47	9.6	3:49	4:33
10	W	9:36	10.3	10:21	8.8	3:19	4:07			10	S	10:59	11.3	11:35	10.1	4:42	5:21
11	T	10:25	10.8	11:09	9.1	4:08	4:54			11	S	11:50	11.4	...	...	5:34	6:08
12	F	11:15	11.1	11:57	9.5	4:58	5:42			12	M	12:23	10.5	12:40	11.2	6:25	6:55
13	S	...	...	12:05	11.2	5:49	6:30			13	T	1:11	10.7	1:32	10.8	7:18	7:44
14	S	12:45	9.8	12:56	11.1	6:41	7:18			14	W	2:00	10.6	2:27	10.1	8:13	8:34
15	M	1:35	9.9	1:49	10.7	7:34	8:08			15	T	2:53	10.4	3:26	9.4	9:11	9:29
16	T	2:27	10.0	2:45	10.2	8:31	9:01			16	F	3:49	10.0	4:30	8.7	10:13	10:28
17	W	3:22	10.0	3:46	9.6	9:32	9:56			17	S	4:50	9.6	5:37	8.2	11:20	11:32
18	T	4:19	9.9	4:50	9.0	10:36	10:54			18	S	5:55	9.3	6:47	7.9	...	12:30
19	F	5:18	9.8	5:57	8.6	11:42	11:55			19	M	7:03	9.1	7:53	7.9	12:41	1:39
20	S	6:20	9.7	7:05	8.3	...	12:51			20	T	8:05	9.2	8:50	8.1	1:48	2:38
21	S	7:22	9.6	8:09	8.3	1:00	1:56			21	W	9:00	9.3	9:39	8.3	2:45	3:29
22	M	8:20	9.7	9:06	8.3	2:02	2:53			22	T	9:47	9.5	10:22	8.5	3:33	4:12
23	T	9:13	9.8	9:57	8.4	2:57	3:44			23	F	10:30	9.6	11:00	8.7	4:17	4:51
24	W	10:02	9.8	10:42	8.5	3:47	4:31			24	S	11:08	9.6	11:35	8.9	4:56	5:25
25	T	10:46	9.9	11:24	8.6	4:32	5:13			25	S	11:43	9.5	...	...	5:32	5:56
26	F	11:27	9.8	...	...	5:13	5:50			26	M	12:07	9.0	12:17	9.4	6:06	6:26
27	S	12:02	8.6	12:05	9.7	5:52	6:25			27	T	12:38	9.1	12:51	9.1	6:40	6:56
28	S	12:37	8.7	12:41	9.5	6:29	6:58			28	W	1:08	9.1	1:25	8.8	7:15	7:28
29	M	1:11	8.7	1:17	9.2	7:06	7:31			29	T	1:39	9.1	2:03	8.5	7:52	8:03
30	T	1:46	8.7	1:55	8.8	7:45	8:06										
31	W	2:22	8.6	2:35	8.4	8:26	8:43										

Dates when Ht. of **Low** Water is below Mean Lower Low with Ht. of lowest given for each period and Date of lowest in ( ):

10th–17th: -1.5' (13th)   7th–16th: -1.8' (11th)
23rd–26th: -0.2'

Average Rise and Fall 9.1 ft.

When a high tide exceeds avg. ht., the *following* low tide will be lower than avg.

2024 HIGH & LOW WATER
PORTLAND, ME
43°39.4'N, 70°14.8'W

*Daylight Time starts March 10 at 2 a.m.　　　　**Daylight Saving Time**

DAY OF MONTH	DAY OF WEEK	MARCH HIGH a.m.	Ht.	MARCH HIGH p.m.	Ht.	MARCH LOW a.m.	MARCH LOW p.m.	DAY OF MONTH	DAY OF WEEK	APRIL HIGH a.m.	Ht.	APRIL HIGH p.m.	Ht.	APRIL LOW a.m.	APRIL LOW p.m.
1	F	2:15	9.0	2:44	8.1	8:33	8:43	1	M	4:14	9.1	5:03	7.8	10:47	10:57
2	S	2:56	8.9	3:32	7.8	9:20	9:30	2	T	5:13	9.1	6:06	7.8	11:47	...
3	S	3:44	8.8	4:27	7.5	10:13	10:23	3	W	6:18	9.2	7:13	8.1	12:01	12:52
4	M	4:41	8.8	5:30	7.4	11:13	11:23	4	T	7:28	9.4	8:18	8.6	1:08	1:58
5	T	5:43	8.9	6:39	7.6	...	12:20	5	F	8:34	9.9	9:15	9.4	2:16	2:58
6	W	6:52	9.3	7:44	8.1	12:30	1:27	6	S	9:34	10.3	10:07	10.1	3:18	3:52
7	T	7:56	9.9	8:41	8.8	1:36	2:26	7	S	10:30	10.7	10:56	10.8	4:15	4:41
8	F	8:55	10.5	9:33	9.5	2:36	3:19	8	M	11:23	10.9	11:44	11.3	5:08	5:30
9	S	9:49	11.0	10:23	10.2	3:32	4:08	9	T	...	...	12:15	10.9	6:00	6:17
10	S	*11:41	11.3	...	...	*5:25	*5:56	10	W	12:31	11.5	1:06	10.6	6:50	7:05
11	M	12:10	10.8	12:33	11.3	6:17	6:43	11	T	1:19	11.4	1:57	10.2	7:41	7:53
12	T	12:57	11.2	1:23	11.1	7:08	7:30	12	F	2:07	11.1	2:50	9.6	8:32	8:44
13	W	1:44	11.2	2:15	10.6	7:59	8:18	13	S	2:58	10.5	3:46	9.0	9:27	9:38
14	T	2:33	11.0	3:08	9.9	8:52	9:08	14	S	3:54	9.9	4:47	8.5	10:26	10:38
15	F	3:24	10.6	4:06	9.2	9:49	10:03	15	M	4:55	9.3	5:49	8.1	11:28	11:42
16	S	4:21	10.0	5:09	8.6	10:50	11:03	16	T	6:00	8.9	6:53	8.0	...	12:33
17	S	5:22	9.4	6:15	8.1	11:55	...	17	W	7:05	8.6	7:54	8.1	12:50	1:37
18	M	6:29	9.0	7:24	7.8	12:08	1:05	18	T	8:08	8.6	8:48	8.3	1:56	2:34
19	T	7:39	8.8	8:29	7.9	1:19	2:14	19	F	9:03	8.7	9:34	8.6	2:54	3:22
20	W	8:43	8.8	9:25	8.1	2:27	3:13	20	S	9:51	8.8	10:14	9.0	3:43	4:03
21	T	9:37	9.0	10:12	8.4	3:25	4:02	21	S	10:33	8.9	10:51	9.3	4:25	4:39
22	F	10:24	9.2	10:53	8.8	4:13	4:43	22	M	11:13	8.9	11:24	9.5	5:04	5:12
23	S	11:05	9.3	11:29	9.0	4:55	5:19	23	T	11:51	8.9	11:57	9.7	5:39	5:45
24	S	11:43	9.3	...	...	5:33	5:52	24	W	...	...	12:28	8.9	6:14	6:17
25	M	12:02	9.2	12:19	9.3	6:08	6:22	25	T	12:29	9.8	1:03	8.8	6:48	6:51
26	T	12:33	9.4	12:53	9.1	6:41	6:52	26	F	1:01	9.8	1:39	8.6	7:24	7:27
27	W	1:03	9.5	1:26	9.0	7:14	7:22	27	S	1:37	9.8	2:18	8.5	8:03	8:07
28	T	1:32	9.5	2:01	8.7	7:48	7:55	28	S	2:16	9.7	3:01	8.3	8:46	8:52
29	F	2:04	9.4	2:37	8.5	8:24	8:31	29	M	3:02	9.6	3:52	8.2	9:35	9:43
30	S	2:40	9.4	3:18	8.2	9:05	9:13	30	T	3:55	9.5	4:49	8.2	10:29	10:41
31	S	3:23	9.2	4:07	7.9	9:52	10:01								

Dates when Ht. of **Low** Water is below Mean Lower Low with Ht. of lowest given for each period and Date of lowest in ( ):

　　7th–16th: -1.8' (12th)　　　　　　5th–13th: -1.9' (10th)

Average Rise and Fall 9.1 ft.

When a high tide exceeds avg. ht., the *following* low tide will be lower than avg.

2024 HIGH & LOW WATER
PORTLAND, ME
43°39.4'N, 70°14.8'W

Daylight Saving Time   **Daylight Saving Time**

DAY OF MONTH	DAY OF WEEK	MAY HIGH a.m.	Ht.	p.m.	Ht.	LOW a.m.	p.m.	DAY OF MONTH	DAY OF WEEK	JUNE HIGH a.m.	Ht.	p.m.	Ht.	LOW a.m.	p.m.
1	W	4:56	9.4	5:49	8.4	11:28	11:44	1	S	6:49	9.5	7:27	9.9	12:37	1:03
2	T	6:00	9.4	6:51	8.8	...	12:29	2	S	7:54	9.4	8:24	10.4	1:42	2:02
3	F	7:07	9.5	7:52	9.3	12:51	1:30	3	M	8:57	9.4	9:18	10.8	2:45	2:58
4	S	8:14	9.7	8:49	10.0	1:59	2:29	4	T	9:57	9.5	10:09	11.0	3:43	3:52
5	S	9:15	10.0	9:41	10.6	3:01	3:24	5	W	10:51	9.5	11:00	11.1	4:37	4:43
6	M	10:11	10.2	10:31	11.1	3:58	4:15	6	T	11:45	9.5	11:49	11.0	5:29	5:34
7	T	11:06	10.2	11:20	11.4	4:52	5:04	7	F	...	...	12:36	9.4	6:20	6:24
8	W	11:59	10.2	...	...	5:43	5:54	8	S	12:39	10.8	1:25	9.2	7:09	7:12
9	T	12:08	11.4	12:50	10.0	6:34	6:42	9	S	1:27	10.5	2:13	9.0	7:57	8:01
10	F	12:56	11.2	1:41	9.7	7:24	7:31	10	M	2:14	10.1	3:01	8.8	8:44	8:50
11	S	1:45	10.9	2:32	9.3	8:14	8:21	11	T	3:03	9.7	3:51	8.6	9:32	9:41
12	S	2:35	10.3	3:25	8.8	9:06	9:14	12	W	3:53	9.3	4:41	8.5	10:20	10:35
13	M	3:29	9.8	4:21	8.5	10:01	10:11	13	T	4:45	8.9	5:29	8.5	11:07	11:29
14	T	4:26	9.3	5:18	8.3	10:57	11:11	14	F	5:38	8.5	6:17	8.6	11:54	...
15	W	5:25	8.8	6:14	8.2	11:53	...	15	S	6:32	8.2	7:05	8.7	12:24	12:41
16	T	6:24	8.5	7:09	8.3	12:12	12:48	16	S	7:28	8.0	7:53	8.9	1:21	1:29
17	F	7:22	8.4	8:00	8.5	1:14	1:41	17	M	8:23	7.9	8:38	9.1	2:15	2:17
18	S	8:19	8.3	8:47	8.8	2:12	2:30	18	T	9:14	8.0	9:22	9.4	3:05	3:03
19	S	9:10	8.3	9:29	9.1	3:04	3:13	19	W	10:02	8.1	10:04	9.6	3:51	3:47
20	M	9:56	8.4	10:07	9.4	3:49	3:53	20	T	10:48	8.2	10:46	9.9	4:34	4:30
21	T	10:39	8.5	10:44	9.6	4:29	4:30	21	F	11:32	8.4	11:29	10.2	5:17	5:14
22	W	11:20	8.6	11:20	9.8	5:08	5:07	22	S	...	...	12:16	8.6	6:00	5:58
23	T	11:59	8.6	11:57	10.0	5:45	5:44	23	S	12:14	10.4	1:00	8.8	6:44	6:45
24	F	...	...	12:40	8.6	6:24	6:23	24	M	1:00	10.6	1:46	9.0	7:29	7:33
25	S	12:35	10.1	1:20	8.6	7:04	7:05	25	T	1:47	10.6	2:33	9.2	8:15	8:24
26	S	1:16	10.2	2:03	8.6	7:46	7:49	26	W	2:37	10.6	3:23	9.4	9:04	9:19
27	M	2:00	10.2	2:49	8.6	8:31	8:37	27	T	3:31	10.3	4:16	9.6	9:55	10:17
28	T	2:49	10.1	3:40	8.7	9:21	9:31	28	F	4:29	10.0	5:11	9.9	10:48	11:18
29	W	3:43	10.0	4:35	8.9	10:14	10:30	29	S	5:30	9.6	6:06	10.1	11:42	...
30	T	4:43	9.8	5:32	9.1	11:09	11:32	30	S	6:33	9.3	7:03	10.2	12:21	12:38
31	F	5:45	9.6	6:29	9.5	...	12:05								

Dates when Ht. of **Low** Water is below Mean Lower Low with Ht. of lowest given for each period and Date of lowest in ( ):

5th–12th: -1.5' (8th, 9th)   3rd–9th: -1.0' (6th, 7th)
                                            23rd–28th: -0.6' (25th, 26th)

Average Rise and Fall 9.1 ft.

When a high tide exceeds avg. ht., the *following* low tide will be lower than avg.

2024 HIGH & LOW WATER
PORTLAND, ME
43°39.4'N, 70°14.8'W

Daylight Saving Time   Daylight Saving Time

DAY OF MONTH	DAY OF WEEK	JULY HIGH a.m.	Ht.	HIGH p.m.	Ht.	LOW a.m.	LOW p.m.	DAY OF MONTH	DAY OF WEEK	AUGUST HIGH a.m.	Ht.	HIGH p.m.	Ht.	LOW a.m.	LOW p.m.
1	M	7:38	9.0	8:02	10.4	1:26	1:38	1	T	9:33	8.5	9:44	10.1	3:20	3:24
2	T	8:43	8.9	8:59	10.5	2:31	2:38	2	F	10:28	8.6	10:36	10.1	4:16	4:19
3	W	9:44	8.9	9:54	10.6	3:31	3:35	3	S	11:19	8.7	11:25	10.2	5:07	5:08
4	T	10:41	8.9	10:46	10.6	4:26	4:29	4	S	...	...	12:04	8.8	5:53	5:54
5	F	11:32	8.9	11:37	10.6	5:18	5:20	5	M	12:09	10.1	12:46	8.9	6:34	6:37
6	S	...	...	12:22	8.9	6:08	6:09	6	T	12:50	10.0	1:24	8.9	7:12	7:17
7	S	12:24	10.4	1:08	8.9	6:54	6:55	7	W	1:29	9.8	2:00	9.0	7:47	7:56
8	M	1:10	10.2	1:51	8.9	7:37	7:40	8	T	2:07	9.5	2:35	9.0	8:21	8:35
9	T	1:53	10.0	2:33	8.8	8:18	8:24	9	F	2:45	9.1	3:11	9.0	8:55	9:17
10	W	2:35	9.6	3:15	8.8	8:58	9:09	10	S	3:26	8.7	3:49	8.9	9:32	10:00
11	T	3:19	9.2	3:57	8.7	9:38	9:56	11	S	4:10	8.3	4:31	8.9	10:12	10:47
12	F	4:05	8.8	4:40	8.7	10:19	10:44	12	M	4:58	7.9	5:15	8.8	10:56	11:38
13	S	4:53	8.4	5:24	8.8	11:01	11:34	13	T	5:51	7.7	6:05	8.8	11:44	...
14	S	5:43	8.1	6:08	8.8	11:44	...	14	W	6:48	7.5	7:00	8.9	12:33	12:37
15	M	6:36	7.8	6:56	8.9	12:27	12:31	15	T	7:49	7.5	7:59	9.2	1:34	1:36
16	T	7:33	7.6	7:47	9.0	1:22	1:23	16	F	8:49	7.8	8:57	9.6	2:35	2:35
17	W	8:31	7.7	8:38	9.2	2:19	2:16	17	S	9:43	8.2	9:51	10.2	3:30	3:31
18	T	9:24	7.8	9:28	9.6	3:12	3:08	18	S	10:33	8.8	10:42	10.7	4:21	4:24
19	F	10:14	8.1	10:17	10.0	4:01	3:58	19	M	11:22	9.4	11:33	11.1	5:09	5:16
20	S	11:03	8.4	11:05	10.4	4:49	4:47	20	T	...	...	12:10	9.9	5:56	6:07
21	S	11:50	8.8	11:54	10.8	5:36	5:36	21	W	12:24	11.3	12:57	10.4	6:42	6:59
22	M	...	...	12:37	9.2	6:22	6:26	22	T	1:14	11.2	1:44	10.8	7:29	7:51
23	T	12:43	11.0	1:24	9.6	7:08	7:17	23	F	2:05	10.9	2:32	10.9	8:16	8:45
24	W	1:32	11.1	2:11	10.0	7:54	8:09	24	S	2:59	10.4	3:24	10.8	9:06	9:42
25	T	2:23	10.9	3:00	10.2	8:42	9:03	25	S	3:57	9.9	4:20	10.5	10:00	10:43
26	F	3:16	10.5	3:52	10.3	9:32	10:01	26	M	4:59	9.2	5:19	10.2	10:57	11:47
27	S	4:14	10.0	4:46	10.4	10:24	11:01	27	T	6:04	8.7	6:22	9.9	11:59	...
28	S	5:15	9.5	5:42	10.3	11:19	...	28	W	7:12	8.4	7:29	9.7	12:55	1:06
29	M	6:18	9.0	6:41	10.2	12:04	12:17	29	T	8:19	8.3	8:34	9.6	2:04	2:14
30	T	7:25	8.6	7:44	10.1	1:11	1:20	30	F	9:20	8.4	9:32	9.7	3:08	3:15
31	W	8:32	8.5	8:46	10.0	2:18	2:24	31	S	10:13	8.6	10:23	9.8	4:02	4:08

Dates when Ht. of **Low** Water is below Mean Lower Low with Ht. of lowest given for each period and Date of lowest in ( ):

   3rd–8th: -0.5' (5th, 6th)   19th–25th: -1.3' (22nd)
   21st–27th: -1.1' (24th)

Average Rise and Fall 9.1 ft.

When a high tide exceeds avg. ht., the *following* low tide will be lower than avg.

2024 HIGH & LOW WATER
PORTLAND, ME
43°39.4'N, 70°14.8'W

	Daylight Saving Time									Daylight Saving Time				

DAY OF MONTH	DAY OF WEEK	SEPTEMBER					DAY OF MONTH	DAY OF WEEK	OCTOBER					
		HIGH		LOW					HIGH				LOW	
		a.m.	Ht.	p.m.	Ht.	a.m.	p.m.			a.m.	Ht.	p.m.	Ht.	a.m.	p.m.
1	S	10:59	8.8	11:08	9.9	4:49	4:54	1	T	11:09	9.2	11:25	9.5	4:59	5:14
2	M	11:40	9.0	11:49	9.8	5:30	5:37	2	W	11:43	9.4	...	...	5:33	5:51
3	T	...	...	12:17	9.1	6:07	6:15	3	T	12:02	9.4	12:16	9.5	6:05	6:26
4	W	12:28	9.7	12:51	9.2	6:40	6:52	4	F	12:39	9.2	12:47	9.5	6:36	6:59
5	T	1:03	9.5	1:23	9.3	7:12	7:27	5	S	1:12	9.0	1:17	9.5	7:07	7:33
6	F	1:39	9.2	1:55	9.3	7:43	8:03	6	S	1:47	8.7	1:49	9.4	7:40	8:10
7	S	2:14	8.9	2:27	9.2	8:15	8:40	7	M	2:23	8.4	2:25	9.3	8:16	8:50
8	S	2:52	8.6	3:03	9.1	8:51	9:21	8	T	3:04	8.1	3:07	9.1	8:56	9:35
9	M	3:33	8.2	3:43	9.0	9:30	10:07	9	W	3:51	7.9	3:56	9.0	9:43	10:28
10	T	4:20	7.9	4:30	8.9	10:15	10:58	10	T	4:45	7.7	4:52	9.0	10:37	11:26
11	W	5:13	7.6	5:24	8.8	11:06	11:55	11	F	5:44	7.7	5:54	9.1	11:36	...
12	T	6:11	7.5	6:23	8.9	...	12:02	12	S	6:47	8.0	7:00	9.3	12:27	12:40
13	F	7:15	7.7	7:27	9.2	12:57	1:04	13	S	7:48	8.5	8:04	9.7	1:29	1:46
14	S	8:17	8.0	8:29	9.7	2:01	2:08	14	M	8:45	9.2	9:04	10.2	2:28	2:48
15	S	9:14	8.6	9:27	10.3	2:59	3:08	15	T	9:36	10.1	9:59	10.6	3:21	3:44
16	M	10:05	9.4	10:20	10.8	3:51	4:03	16	W	10:25	10.8	10:52	10.8	4:11	4:37
17	T	10:53	10.1	11:12	11.1	4:40	4:56	17	T	11:13	11.3	11:44	10.9	4:59	5:29
18	W	11:41	10.8	...	...	5:27	5:48	18	F	...	...	12:01	11.6	5:47	6:21
19	T	12:03	11.2	12:28	11.2	6:14	6:40	19	S	12:37	10.7	12:50	11.6	6:36	7:13
20	F	12:55	11.1	1:16	11.4	7:01	7:31	20	S	1:29	10.4	1:40	11.4	7:25	8:05
21	S	1:47	10.8	2:05	11.3	7:50	8:25	21	M	2:23	9.9	2:32	10.9	8:17	9:01
22	S	2:41	10.2	2:57	11.0	8:41	9:21	22	T	3:20	9.3	3:30	10.3	9:13	10:01
23	M	3:39	9.6	3:54	10.5	9:36	10:23	23	W	4:22	8.8	4:33	9.7	10:14	11:05
24	T	4:42	9.0	4:57	10.0	10:36	11:28	24	T	5:26	8.5	5:39	9.3	11:20	...
25	W	5:48	8.6	6:03	9.5	11:41	...	25	F	6:30	8.3	6:44	9.0	12:10	12:27
26	T	6:55	8.3	7:11	9.3	12:37	12:50	26	S	7:31	8.4	7:47	8.9	1:14	1:33
27	F	8:01	8.3	8:16	9.3	1:45	1:59	27	S	8:27	8.6	8:44	8.9	2:12	2:33
28	S	8:59	8.5	9:13	9.4	2:46	2:59	28	M	9:14	8.9	9:33	9.0	3:02	3:24
29	S	9:48	8.8	10:02	9.5	3:37	3:50	29	T	9:56	9.2	10:16	9.0	3:45	4:08
30	M	10:31	9.0	10:45	9.5	4:21	4:34	30	W	10:33	9.4	10:57	9.0	4:22	4:48
								31	T	11:07	9.6	11:35	8.9	4:56	5:24

Dates when Ht. of **Low** Water is below Mean Lower Low with Ht. of lowest given for each period and Date of lowest in ( ):

16th–23rd: -1.5' (19th, 20th)   15th–22nd: -1.8' (18th)

Average Rise and Fall 9.1 ft.

When a high tide exceeds avg. ht., the *following* low tide will be lower than avg.

2024 HIGH & LOW WATER
PORTLAND, ME
43°39.4'N, 70°14.8'W

*Standard Time starts Nov. 3 at 2 a.m.   Standard Time

DAY OF MONTH	DAY OF WEEK	NOVEMBER						DAY OF MONTH	DAY OF WEEK	DECEMBER					
		HIGH			LOW					HIGH				LOW	
		a.m.	Ht.	p.m.	Ht.	a.m.	p.m.			a.m.	Ht.	p.m.	Ht.	a.m.	p.m.
1	F	11:40	9.7	...	...	5:29	5:59	1	S	10:44	9.7	11:26	8.5	4:31	5:10
2	S	12:12	8.8	12:13	9.7	6:02	6:33	2	M	11:21	9.8	...	...	5:08	5:48
3	S	12:48	8.7	-A-	...	*5:35	*6:08	3	T	12:04	8.4	12:01	9.9	5:47	6:27
4	M	12:25	8.5	12:20	9.6	6:11	6:46	4	W	12:44	8.4	12:40	9.9	6:28	7:09
5	T	1:01	8.3	12:58	9.5	6:49	7:27	5	T	1:25	8.4	1:25	9.8	7:13	7:55
6	W	1:42	8.1	1:42	9.4	7:31	8:13	6	F	2:11	8.4	2:15	9.7	8:02	8:44
7	T	2:29	8.0	2:32	9.3	8:20	9:05	7	S	3:03	8.5	3:10	9.5	8:58	9:37
8	F	3:24	8.0	3:29	9.2	9:15	10:01	8	S	3:58	8.8	4:11	9.3	9:58	10:32
9	S	4:22	8.2	4:31	9.2	10:16	10:59	9	M	4:55	9.1	5:14	9.2	11:01	11:28
10	S	5:21	8.5	5:36	9.3	11:20	11:58	10	T	5:52	9.6	6:19	9.2	...	12:06
11	M	6:20	9.1	6:41	9.5	...	12:26	11	W	6:50	10.1	7:24	9.2	12:27	1:11
12	T	7:17	9.8	7:43	9.8	12:57	1:29	12	T	7:46	10.5	8:25	9.4	1:26	2:12
13	W	8:10	10.5	8:40	10.1	1:52	2:27	13	F	8:40	10.9	9:22	9.5	2:22	3:08
14	T	9:00	11.1	9:35	10.2	2:44	3:21	14	S	9:32	11.1	10:16	9.6	3:15	4:01
15	F	9:49	11.5	10:28	10.3	3:34	4:13	15	S	10:23	11.2	11:08	9.5	4:07	4:53
16	S	10:39	11.6	11:21	10.1	4:24	5:05	16	M	11:14	11.1	11:59	9.4	4:58	5:43
17	S	11:29	11.5	...	...	5:14	5:56	17	T	...	...	12:04	10.9	5:49	6:33
18	M	12:13	9.9	12:19	11.2	6:05	6:48	18	W	12:48	9.2	12:53	10.5	6:38	7:21
19	T	1:05	9.5	1:11	10.7	6:56	7:41	19	T	1:37	9.0	1:42	10.0	7:28	8:09
20	W	2:00	9.1	2:06	10.1	7:50	8:38	20	F	2:27	8.7	2:33	9.4	8:20	8:58
21	T	2:57	8.7	3:05	9.6	8:49	9:36	21	S	3:17	8.6	3:27	8.9	9:14	9:47
22	F	3:56	8.5	4:06	9.1	9:50	10:34	22	S	4:08	8.5	4:21	8.4	10:10	10:36
23	S	4:54	8.4	5:07	8.7	10:53	11:30	23	M	4:58	8.4	5:17	8.0	11:08	11:25
24	S	5:50	8.4	6:06	8.4	11:56	...	24	T	5:48	8.5	6:15	7.8	...	12:06
25	M	6:43	8.6	7:04	8.3	12:24	12:56	25	W	6:38	8.6	7:12	7.7	12:16	1:04
26	T	7:31	8.8	7:56	8.3	1:15	1:49	26	T	7:27	8.8	8:06	7.8	1:08	1:57
27	W	8:15	9.1	8:43	8.4	2:00	2:36	27	F	8:13	9.0	8:54	7.9	1:56	2:44
28	T	8:54	9.3	9:27	8.4	2:41	3:17	28	S	8:56	9.3	9:39	8.0	2:41	3:26
29	F	9:31	9.5	10:08	8.5	3:19	3:56	29	S	9:38	9.5	10:21	8.2	3:23	4:07
30	S	10:08	9.6	10:47	8.5	3:55	4:33	30	M	10:19	9.8	11:03	8.4	4:04	4:47
								31	T	11:00	10.0	...	...	4:45	5:28

A also at *11:46 a.m. (9.7)

Dates when Ht. of **Low** Water is below Mean Lower Low with Ht. of lowest given for each period and Date of lowest in ( ):

13th–19th: -1.8' (16th)   12th–18th: -1.4' (15th)
                                           31st: -0.3'

Average Rise and Fall 9.1 ft.

When a high tide exceeds avg. ht., the *following* low tide will be lower than avg.

Smarter Boating in Currents

If your vessel is a sailboat or a displacement powerboat your normal cruising speed is probably under 10 knots. In this range, current can become a significant factor. (See the Current Tables for the Cape Cod Canal and the Race, and the Current Diagrams for Vineyard Sound, showing some currents of 4 to 5 knots.) You can save a remarkable amount of time and, if under power, a great deal of fuel expense by using the current for maximum efficiency.

SAIL: Slow vs. Flow

The arithmetic is simple. If your 35' sailboat has a boat speed (BS) through the water of 5 knots under power or sail, then a 2-knot current directly against you means your speed made good (SMG) is 3 knots, and the same current going with you boosts that to 7 knots. Tacking into or with a current changes the simple arithmetic shown here (see Coping With Currents, p. 58.) The time difference can be great: a destination 10 miles away is 3 hours 20 minutes against the current, but only 1 hour 26 minutes with the current. Leaving earlier or later to go with the current leaves more time (almost 2 hours) to relax either at your departure point or destination. Of course if you're just out for a sail on a beautiful day, the arithmetic may not matter! If your sailboat is under power, keep reading.

POWER: Ego vs. Eco

As long as speed thrills, as we know it does, some boaters will demand it. But the trend is headed the other way. Today it is more about being economical, not egomaniacal. By far the most dramatic saving in fuel cost, or nautical miles per gallon (NMPG), comes from cutting back on the throttle; however, there are further savings from using the current to your advantage, especially with slower vessels.

Consider a trawler that burns 10 gallons of fuel per hour at a speed of 8 knots. If the cost of fuel is, say, $4 per gallon, that's $40 per hour. For a destination 24 nautical miles away, going directly against a current of 2 knots, her SMG is only 6 knots, requiring 4 hours for the trip, and costing her owner $160. If the skipper had gone with a current of 2 knots, then her SMG would be 10 knots, her transit time 2 hours 24 minutes, with a fuel expense of only $96. The time saved, 1 hour 36 minutes, allows more time for relaxation (TFR) either before departure or after arrival, and the $64 saved could buy a nice meal ashore. That's smarter boating!

Consult the table below for SMG and time/fuel consequences in currents.

SMG *WITH* CURRENT, and Time/Fuel GAINS

Current Speed Kts *With* +		+1 kt	+2 kts	+3 kts	+4 kts
Boat Speed: 4 kts	SMG =	5 kts	6 kts	7 kts	8 kts
Time/Fuel **Gain**		20%	33%	43%	50%
Boat Speed: 6 kts	SMG =	7 kts	8 kts	9 kts	10 kts
Time/Fuel **Gain**		14%	25%	33%	40%
Boat Speed: 8 kts	SMG =	9 kts	10 kts	11 kts	12 kts
Time/Fuel **Gain**		11%	20%	28%	33%
Boat Speed: 10 kts	SMG =	11 kts	12 kts	13 kts	14 kts
Time/Fuel **Gain**		9%	17%	24%	29%

SMG *AGAINST* CURRENT, and Time/Fuel LOSSES

Current Speed Kts *Against* -		-1 kt	-2 kts	-3 kts	-4 kts
Boat Speed: 4 kts	SMG =	3 kts	2 kts	1 kts	0 kts
Time/Fuel **Loss**		33%	100%	300%	---
Boat Speed: 6 kts	SMG =	5 kts	4 kts	3 kts	2 kts
Time/Fuel **Loss**		20%	50%	100%	200%
Boat Speed: 8 kts	SMG =	7 kts	6 kts	5 kts	4 kts
Time/Fuel **Loss**		14%	33%	60%	100%
Boat Speed: 10 kts	SMG =	9 kts	8 kts	7 kts	6 kts
Time/Fuel **Loss**		11%	25%	43%	67%

Boston Harbor Currents

This diagram shows the direction of the Flood Currents in Boston Harbor at the Maximum* Flood velocity, generally 3.5 hours after Low Water at Boston. The Ebb Currents flow in precisely the opposite direction (note one exception, shown by dotted arrow east of Winthrop), and reach these maximum velocities about 4 hours after High Water at Boston. The velocities of the Ebb Currents are about the same as those of the Flood Currents. Where the Ebb Current differs by .2 kts., the velocity of the Ebb is shown in parentheses.

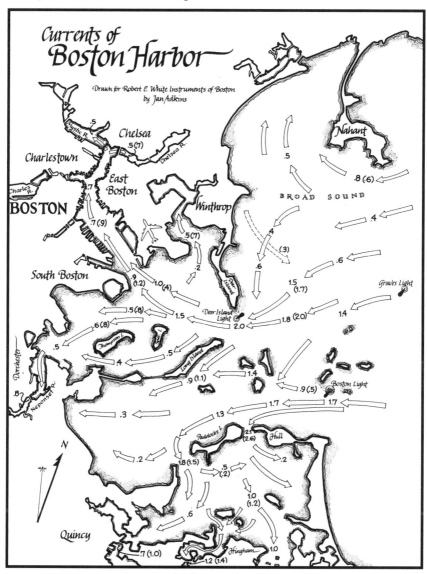

Currents of
Boston Harbor

Drawn for Robert E. White Instruments of Boston
by Jan Adkins

*The Velocities shown on this Current Diagram are the **maximums** normally encountered each month at Full Moon and at New Moon. At other times the velocities will be lower. As a rule of thumb, the velocities shown are those found on days when High Water at Boston is 11.0' to 11.5' (see Boston High Water Tables pp. 38-43). When the height of High Water is 10.5', subtract 10% from the velocities shown; at 10.0', subtract 20%; at 9.0', 30%; at 8.0', 40%; below 7.5', 50%.

2024 HIGH & LOW WATER
BOSTON, MA
42°21.3'N, 71°03'W

Standard Time   Standard Time

DAY OF MONTH	DAY OF WEEK	JANUARY HIGH a.m.	Ht.	p.m.	Ht.	LOW a.m.	p.m.	DAY OF MONTH	DAY OF WEEK	FEBRUARY HIGH a.m.	Ht.	p.m.	Ht.	LOW a.m.	p.m.
1	M	2:35	8.6	2:42	9.1	8:32	9:03	1	T	3:17	8.8	3:38	8.3	9:30	9:47
2	T	3:19	8.5	3:30	8.7	9:20	9:47	2	F	4:01	8.8	4:28	8.0	10:20	10:34
3	W	4:04	8.5	4:20	8.4	10:11	10:34	3	S	4:48	8.8	5:22	7.7	11:14	11:25
4	T	4:52	8.6	5:13	8.1	11:04	11:22	4	S	5:41	8.9	6:20	7.6	...	12:10
5	F	5:39	8.7	6:07	7.9	11:58	...	5	M	6:35	9.1	7:21	7.7	12:20	1:10
6	S	6:28	8.9	7:03	7.9	12:11	12:52	6	T	7:34	9.5	8:20	8.1	1:18	2:09
7	S	7:19	9.2	7:58	8.0	1:02	1:47	7	W	8:31	10.1	9:15	8.6	2:16	3:04
8	M	8:09	9.6	8:51	8.2	1:54	2:40	8	T	9:25	10.7	10:06	9.2	3:11	3:56
9	T	8:59	10.1	9:41	8.6	2:45	3:31	9	F	10:18	11.2	10:56	9.8	4:04	4:45
10	W	9:47	10.6	10:30	8.9	3:35	4:19	10	S	11:09	11.5	11:45	10.3	4:56	5:33
11	T	10:36	11.0	11:18	9.3	4:24	5:07	11	S	...	...	12:01	11.6	5:48	6:21
12	F	11:26	11.3	...	...	5:14	5:55	12	M	12:34	10.7	12:53	11.4	6:40	7:09
13	S	12:07	9.6	12:17	11.4	6:05	6:43	13	T	1:22	10.9	1:45	11.0	7:32	7:57
14	S	12:57	9.9	1:09	11.3	6:57	7:32	14	W	2:12	10.9	2:38	10.4	8:25	8:48
15	M	1:47	10.1	2:02	11.0	7:50	8:22	15	T	3:03	10.6	3:35	9.7	9:22	9:41
16	T	2:38	10.2	2:57	10.4	8:45	9:14	16	F	3:59	10.3	4:37	9.0	10:22	10:38
17	W	3:32	10.2	3:56	9.8	9:44	10:08	17	S	4:58	9.9	5:42	8.4	11:26	11:39
18	T	4:28	10.1	4:58	9.2	10:46	11:05	18	S	6:01	9.5	6:51	8.1	...	12:32
19	F	5:26	10.0	6:02	8.8	11:49	...	19	M	7:07	9.3	7:59	8.0	12:42	1:40
20	S	6:26	9.9	7:09	8.5	12:03	12:53	20	T	8:12	9.3	8:59	8.2	1:46	2:43
21	S	7:27	9.8	8:15	8.4	1:03	1:58	21	W	9:08	9.4	9:48	8.4	2:45	3:35
22	M	8:27	9.8	9:13	8.4	2:04	2:58	22	T	9:55	9.6	10:30	8.6	3:35	4:18
23	T	9:21	9.9	10:04	8.5	3:00	3:50	23	F	10:36	9.7	11:07	8.9	4:19	4:55
24	W	10:08	10.0	10:49	8.6	3:50	4:36	24	S	11:15	9.8	11:42	9.0	4:59	5:30
25	T	10:52	10.0	11:31	8.7	4:36	5:17	25	S	11:51	9.7	...	...	5:38	6:04
26	F	11:34	10.0	...	...	5:18	5:56	26	M	12:15	9.2	12:28	9.6	6:16	6:38
27	S	12:09	8.8	12:13	9.9	5:59	6:33	27	T	12:49	9.3	1:04	9.4	6:53	7:12
28	S	12:46	8.8	12:52	9.7	6:40	7:09	28	W	1:22	9.3	1:41	9.1	7:31	7:48
29	M	1:22	8.9	1:31	9.4	7:20	7:46	29	T	1:57	9.3	2:20	8.8	8:11	8:26
30	T	1:59	8.9	2:10	9.1	8:01	8:24								
31	W	2:36	8.9	2:52	8.7	8:44	9:04								

Dates when Ht. of **Low** Water is below Mean Lower Low with Ht. of lowest given for each period and Date of lowest in ( ):

    10th–17th: -1.5' (13th)   8th–15th: -1.7' (11th)

Average Rise and Fall 9.5 ft.
When a high tide exceeds avg. ht., the *following* low tide will be lower than avg. Since there is a high degree of correlation between the height of High Water and the velocities of the Flood and Ebb Currents for that same day, we offer a rough rule of thumb for estimating the current velocities, for ALL the Current Charts and Diagrams in this book. **Rule of Thumb:** Refer to Boston High Water. If the height of High Water is 11.0' or over, use the Current Chart velocities as shown. When the height is 10.5', subtract 10%; at 10.0', subtract 20%; at 9.0', 30%; at 8.0', 40%; below 7.5', 50%.

2024 HIGH & LOW WATER
BOSTON, MA
42°21.3'N, 71°03'W

Daylight Time starts March 10 at 2 a.m.　　　　**Daylight Saving Time**

DAY OF MONTH	DAY OF WEEK	MARCH HIGH a.m.	Ht.	HIGH p.m.	Ht.	LOW a.m.	LOW p.m.	DAY OF MONTH	DAY OF WEEK	APRIL HIGH a.m.	Ht.	HIGH p.m.	Ht.	LOW a.m.	LOW p.m.
1	F	2:35	9.2	3:03	8.4	8:54	9:07	1	M	4:34	9.4	5:20	8.0	11:09	11:21
2	S	3:17	9.1	3:51	8.0	9:43	9:54	2	T	5:32	9.4	6:21	8.0	...	12:08
3	S	4:05	9.0	4:46	7.8	10:37	10:48	3	W	6:35	9.5	7:24	8.3	12:22	1:10
4	M	5:01	9.1	5:46	7.7	11:36	11:46	4	T	7:41	9.8	8:26	8.9	1:26	2:11
5	T	6:00	9.2	6:49	7.8	...	12:37	5	F	8:44	10.2	9:24	9.6	2:30	3:09
6	W	7:04	9.6	7:52	8.3	12:48	1:39	6	S	9:44	10.6	10:16	10.4	3:31	4:03
7	T	8:06	10.1	8:50	9.0	1:51	2:37	7	S	10:40	11.0	11:06	11.1	4:27	4:54
8	F	9:05	10.7	9:42	9.7	2:50	3:31	8	M	11:32	11.2	11:54	11.6	5:20	5:42
9	S	9:59	11.2	10:31	10.4	3:46	4:20	9	T	...	...	12:24	11.1	6:11	6:30
10	S	*11:51	11.5	...	...	*5:38	*6:09	10	W	12:42	11.8	1:16	10.9	7:02	7:18
11	M	12:20	11.0	12:43	11.5	6:30	6:56	11	T	1:30	11.7	2:07	10.4	7:53	8:07
12	T	1:08	11.4	1:35	11.3	7:21	7:44	12	F	2:19	11.3	2:59	9.9	8:44	8:57
13	W	1:56	11.5	2:26	10.8	8:12	8:32	13	S	3:10	10.8	3:54	9.3	9:37	9:49
14	T	2:45	11.3	3:19	10.2	9:04	9:21	14	S	4:03	10.2	4:52	8.7	10:33	10:46
15	F	3:35	10.8	4:14	9.5	9:59	10:15	15	M	5:03	9.6	5:55	8.3	11:34	11:47
16	S	4:30	10.2	5:15	8.8	10:58	11:12	16	T	6:06	9.1	6:58	8.2	...	12:36
17	S	5:30	9.7	6:20	8.3	...	12:01	17	W	7:11	8.9	7:59	8.2	12:50	1:38
18	M	6:35	9.2	7:28	8.0	12:14	1:08	18	T	8:13	8.8	8:54	8.5	1:53	2:35
19	T	7:43	9.0	8:35	8.0	1:18	2:15	19	F	9:10	8.9	9:41	8.8	2:52	3:25
20	W	8:49	9.0	9:34	8.2	2:24	3:17	20	S	9:58	9.1	10:21	9.2	3:43	4:07
21	T	9:45	9.2	10:20	8.6	3:24	4:08	21	S	10:41	9.2	10:57	9.5	4:27	4:44
22	F	10:32	9.4	11:00	8.9	4:14	4:48	22	M	11:19	9.3	11:31	9.8	5:07	5:20
23	S	11:12	9.5	11:35	9.2	4:57	5:24	23	T	11:57	9.3	...	...	5:45	5:55
24	S	11:50	9.6	...	...	5:36	5:57	24	W	12:05	9.9	12:35	9.2	6:22	6:32
25	M	12:08	9.4	12:26	9.6	6:13	6:31	25	T	12:40	10.1	1:13	9.1	7:00	7:09
26	T	12:41	9.6	1:02	9.4	6:50	7:05	26	F	1:16	10.1	1:52	9.0	7:40	7:48
27	W	1:14	9.7	1:38	9.3	7:27	7:40	27	S	1:54	10.1	2:33	8.8	8:21	8:29
28	T	1:48	9.7	2:15	9.1	8:04	8:16	28	S	2:35	10.0	3:17	8.6	9:05	9:14
29	F	2:23	9.7	2:54	8.8	8:44	8:54	29	M	3:21	10.0	4:07	8.5	9:54	10:05
30	S	3:01	9.6	3:37	8.5	9:26	9:36	30	T	4:13	9.9	5:03	8.5	10:48	11:03
31	S	3:44	9.5	4:25	8.2	10:14	10:25								

Dates when Ht. of **Low** Water is below Mean Lower Low with Ht. of lowest given for each period and Date of lowest in ( ):

8th–15th: -1.8' (12th)　　　　　　6th–13th: -1.8' (10th)

Average Rise and Fall 9.5 ft.
When a high tide exceeds avg. ht., the *following* low tide will be lower than avg. Since there is a high degree of correlation between the height of High Water and the velocities of the Flood and Ebb Currents for that same day, we offer a rough rule of thumb for estimating the current velocities, for ALL the Current Charts and Diagrams in this book. **Rule of Thumb:** Refer to Boston High Water. If the height of High Water is 11.0' or over, use the Current Chart velocities as shown. When the height is 10.5', subtract 10%; at 10.0', subtract 20%; at 9.0', 30%; at 8.0', 40%; below 7.5', 50%.

Daylight Saving Time		Daylight Saving Time	

D A Y O F M O N T H	D A Y O F W E E K	MAY						D A Y O F M O N T H	D A Y O F W E E K	JUNE					
		HIGH				LOW				HIGH				LOW	
		a.m.	Ht.	p.m.	Ht.	a.m.	p.m.			a.m.	Ht.	p.m.	Ht.	a.m.	p.m.
1	W	5:12	9.8	6:02	8.7	11:46	...	1	S	7:00	9.8	7:35	10.3	12:51	1:17
2	T	6:15	9.8	7:01	9.1	12:05	12:45	2	S	8:03	9.8	8:32	10.7	1:52	2:13
3	F	7:19	9.9	8:00	9.6	1:08	1:43	3	M	9:05	9.8	9:26	11.1	2:53	3:09
4	S	8:24	10.1	8:57	10.3	2:11	2:41	4	T	10:05	9.8	10:18	11.3	3:51	4:03
5	S	9:24	10.3	9:50	10.9	3:12	3:36	5	W	10:58	9.9	11:08	11.4	4:46	4:55
6	M	10:21	10.5	10:40	11.4	4:09	4:27	6	T	11:51	9.8	11:58	11.3	5:37	5:45
7	T	11:14	10.6	11:29	11.7	5:02	5:17	7	F	...	...	12:43	9.6	6:28	6:34
8	W	...	...	12:06	10.5	5:53	6:06	8	S	12:47	11.1	1:33	9.5	7:17	7:23
9	T	12:17	11.7	12:58	10.3	6:44	6:55	9	S	1:36	10.8	2:22	9.3	8:05	8:12
10	F	1:06	11.5	1:50	9.9	7:34	7:44	10	M	2:25	10.4	3:10	9.1	8:52	9:00
11	S	1:56	11.1	2:41	9.6	8:24	8:33	11	T	3:13	10.0	3:57	8.9	9:39	9:51
12	S	2:46	10.6	3:33	9.1	9:15	9:25	12	W	4:03	9.6	4:46	8.8	10:27	10:43
13	M	3:38	10.1	4:27	8.8	10:08	10:19	13	T	4:55	9.2	5:35	8.8	11:16	11:37
14	T	4:34	9.6	5:23	8.5	11:03	11:17	14	F	5:48	8.8	6:24	8.9	...	12:04
15	W	5:32	9.1	6:19	8.5	11:58	...	15	S	6:41	8.6	7:11	9.0	12:31	12:52
16	T	6:31	8.9	7:13	8.6	12:16	12:52	16	S	7:35	8.4	7:58	9.2	1:25	1:39
17	F	7:28	8.7	8:04	8.8	1:14	1:43	17	M	8:29	8.3	8:45	9.4	2:17	2:27
18	S	8:24	8.6	8:51	9.1	2:10	2:32	18	T	9:20	8.4	9:31	9.7	3:09	3:15
19	S	9:16	8.7	9:35	9.4	3:03	3:18	19	W	10:09	8.5	10:14	10.0	3:57	4:01
20	M	10:02	8.8	10:14	9.7	3:50	4:00	20	T	10:54	8.6	10:57	10.3	4:43	4:46
21	T	10:45	8.9	10:52	10.0	4:33	4:40	21	F	11:39	8.8	11:40	10.5	5:27	5:30
22	W	11:26	8.9	11:30	10.2	5:14	5:20	22	S	...	...	12:24	8.9	6:11	6:15
23	T	...	...	12:07	8.9	5:54	6:00	23	S	12:25	10.8	1:10	9.1	6:57	7:02
24	F	12:08	10.3	12:48	8.9	6:36	6:41	24	M	1:12	10.9	1:57	9.3	7:43	7:51
25	S	12:49	10.4	1:31	8.9	7:18	7:23	25	T	2:01	10.9	2:44	9.5	8:29	8:42
26	S	1:31	10.5	2:15	8.9	8:02	8:09	26	W	2:52	10.9	3:34	9.8	9:18	9:35
27	M	2:17	10.5	3:02	8.9	8:48	8:57	27	T	3:45	10.6	4:26	10.0	10:09	10:32
28	T	3:06	10.4	3:52	9.0	9:37	9:50	28	F	4:42	10.3	5:20	10.2	11:02	11:32
29	W	3:59	10.3	4:46	9.2	10:30	10:48	29	S	5:42	10.0	6:15	10.4	11:56	...
30	T	4:57	10.1	5:42	9.5	11:25	11:49	30	S	6:43	9.6	7:11	10.6	12:33	12:52
31	F	5:58	10.0	6:39	9.9	...	12:21								

Dates when Ht. of **Low** Water is below Mean Lower Low with Ht. of lowest given for each period and Date of lowest in ( ):

5th–11th: -1.4' (8th, 9th)   4th–9th: -0.9' (6th)

23rd–27th: -0.4' (24th–26th)

Average Rise and Fall 9.5 ft.
When a high tide exceeds avg. ht., the *following* low tide will be lower than avg. Since there is a high degree of correlation between the height of High Water and the velocities of the Flood and Ebb Currents for that same day, we offer a rough rule of thumb for estimating the current velocities, for ALL the Current Charts and Diagrams in this book. **Rule of Thumb:** Refer to Boston High Water. If the height of High Water is 11.0' or over, use the Current Chart velocities as shown. When the height is 10.5', subtract 10%; at 10.0', subtract 20%; at 9.0', 30%; at 8.0', 40%; below 7.5', 50%.

2024 HIGH & LOW WATER
BOSTON, MA
42°21.3'N, 71°03'W

Daylight Saving Time   Daylight Saving Time

| DAY OF MONTH | DAY OF WEEK | JULY | | | | | | DAY OF MONTH | DAY OF WEEK | AUGUST | | | | | |
| | | HIGH | | | LOW | | | | | HIGH | | | LOW | | |
		a.m.	Ht.	p.m.	Ht.	a.m.	p.m.			a.m.	Ht.	p.m.	Ht.	a.m.	p.m.
1	M	7:46	9.4	8:09	10.7	1:34	1:49	1	T	9:40	8.8	9:50	10.3	3:24	3:29
2	T	8:49	9.2	9:06	10.8	2:36	2:47	2	F	10:37	8.9	10:43	10.4	4:21	4:24
3	W	9:50	9.2	10:01	10.9	3:36	3:44	3	S	11:26	9.0	11:31	10.4	5:12	5:14
4	T	10:48	9.2	10:53	10.9	4:32	4:37	4	S	...	...	12:11	9.1	5:57	6:00
5	F	11:39	9.2	11:43	10.8	5:24	5:28	5	M	12:16	10.3	12:52	9.2	6:38	6:44
6	S	...	...	12:28	9.2	6:13	6:17	6	T	12:58	10.2	1:31	9.3	7:17	7:26
7	S	12:31	10.7	1:15	9.2	6:59	7:04	7	W	1:39	10.0	2:08	9.3	7:55	8:07
8	M	1:18	10.5	1:59	9.1	7:43	7:49	8	T	2:19	9.8	2:45	9.4	8:32	8:49
9	T	2:03	10.2	2:41	9.1	8:25	8:34	9	F	2:59	9.4	3:23	9.3	9:10	9:31
10	W	2:47	9.9	3:23	9.1	9:07	9:20	10	S	3:41	9.1	4:03	9.3	9:50	10:17
11	T	3:31	9.6	4:05	9.1	9:49	10:07	11	S	4:26	8.7	4:46	9.2	10:32	11:05
12	F	4:17	9.2	4:49	9.1	10:32	10:57	12	M	5:15	8.3	5:32	9.1	11:18	11:57
13	S	5:06	8.8	5:34	9.1	11:17	11:48	13	T	6:07	8.0	6:22	9.2	...	12:07
14	S	5:56	8.4	6:20	9.1	...	12:03	14	W	7:02	7.9	7:15	9.3	12:51	1:00
15	M	6:48	8.2	7:08	9.2	12:39	12:51	15	T	8:00	7.9	8:11	9.6	1:48	1:55
16	T	7:43	8.0	7:58	9.3	1:32	1:41	16	F	8:58	8.1	9:07	10.0	2:46	2:52
17	W	8:38	8.0	8:49	9.6	2:27	2:32	17	S	9:52	8.6	10:01	10.5	3:41	3:47
18	T	9:32	8.2	9:39	10.0	3:20	3:24	18	S	10:43	9.1	10:53	11.0	4:32	4:40
19	F	10:23	8.4	10:28	10.4	4:11	4:15	19	M	11:31	9.7	11:43	11.4	5:20	5:32
20	S	11:11	8.8	11:16	10.8	5:00	5:04	20	T	...	...	12:19	10.3	6:08	6:23
21	S	11:58	9.1	...	...	5:47	5:53	21	W	12:34	11.5	1:07	10.8	6:55	7:14
22	M	12:04	11.1	12:46	9.6	6:34	6:42	22	T	1:26	11.5	1:55	11.1	7:42	8:06
23	T	12:54	11.3	1:34	10.0	7:20	7:33	23	F	2:18	11.2	2:44	11.3	8:30	8:59
24	W	1:45	11.3	2:22	10.3	8:07	8:25	24	S	3:11	10.8	3:35	11.2	9:20	9:54
25	T	2:36	11.1	3:11	10.6	8:55	9:18	25	S	4:07	10.2	4:29	10.9	10:12	10:53
26	F	3:29	10.8	4:01	10.7	9:45	10:14	26	M	5:07	9.6	5:27	10.6	11:09	11:55
27	S	4:25	10.3	4:55	10.7	10:37	11:13	27	T	6:11	9.0	6:29	10.2	...	12:09
28	S	5:24	9.8	5:51	10.6	11:32	...	28	W	7:18	8.7	7:34	9.9	1:00	1:11
29	M	6:27	9.3	6:49	10.5	12:14	12:29	29	T	8:26	8.6	8:39	9.9	2:06	2:14
30	T	7:31	8.9	7:50	10.4	1:17	1:28	30	F	9:29	8.6	9:39	9.9	3:11	3:16
31	W	8:37	8.8	8:51	10.3	2:21	2:29	31	S	10:22	8.8	10:31	10.0	4:07	4:11

Dates when Ht. of **Low** Water is below Mean Lower Low with Ht. of lowest given for each period and Date of lowest in ( ):

4th–6th: -0.3' (5th)   19th–25th: -1.1' (21st, 22nd)
21st–26th: -0.9' (24th)

Average Rise and Fall 9.5 ft.
When a high tide exceeds avg. ht., the *following* low tide will be lower than avg. Since there is a high degree of correlation between the height of High Water and the velocities of the Flood and Ebb Currents for that same day, we offer a rough rule of thumb for estimating the current velocities, for ALL the Current Charts and Diagrams in this book. **Rule of Thumb:** Refer to Boston High Water. If the height of High Water is 11.0' or over, use the Current Chart velocities as shown. When the height is 10.5', subtract 10%; at 10.0', subtract 20%; at 9.0', 30%; at 8.0', 40%; below 7.5', 50%.

2024 HIGH & LOW WATER
BOSTON, MA
42°21.3'N, 71°03'W

Daylight Saving Time   Daylight Saving Time

DAY OF MONTH	DAY OF WEEK	SEPTEMBER HIGH a.m.	Ht.	HIGH p.m.	Ht.	LOW a.m.	LOW p.m.	DAY OF MONTH	DAY OF WEEK	OCTOBER HIGH a.m.	Ht.	HIGH p.m.	Ht.	LOW a.m.	LOW p.m.
1	S	11:07	9.1	11:16	10.1	4:54	4:58	1	T	11:15	9.5	11:32	9.7	5:04	5:18
2	M	11:47	9.3	11:56	10.0	5:34	5:41	2	W	11:49	9.7	...	...	5:38	5:56
3	T	...	...	12:23	9.4	6:11	6:21	3	T	12:08	9.6	12:23	9.9	6:12	6:34
4	W	12:36	9.9	12:58	9.6	6:46	7:00	4	F	12:46	9.5	12:56	9.9	6:47	7:11
5	T	1:12	9.8	1:32	9.6	7:21	7:39	5	S	1:22	9.3	1:31	9.9	7:22	7:49
6	F	1:50	9.6	2:07	9.6	7:57	8:18	6	S	2:00	9.1	2:07	9.8	7:59	8:28
7	S	2:28	9.3	2:43	9.6	8:33	8:58	7	M	2:40	8.8	2:45	9.6	8:37	9:10
8	S	3:08	8.9	3:21	9.5	9:11	9:41	8	T	3:22	8.4	3:27	9.5	9:19	9:57
9	M	3:51	8.6	4:02	9.3	9:52	10:28	9	W	4:09	8.2	4:15	9.4	10:06	10:49
10	T	4:38	8.2	4:50	9.2	10:38	11:20	10	T	5:03	8.0	5:11	9.4	11:00	11:46
11	W	5:31	8.0	5:42	9.2	11:30	...	11	F	6:01	8.1	6:11	9.4	11:59	...
12	T	6:28	7.9	6:40	9.3	12:16	12:26	12	S	7:00	8.4	7:13	9.7	12:45	1:00
13	F	7:28	8.0	7:39	9.6	1:14	1:25	13	S	7:58	8.9	8:14	10.1	1:43	2:02
14	S	8:27	8.4	8:40	10.1	2:13	2:25	14	M	8:54	9.6	9:14	10.5	2:40	3:02
15	S	9:23	9.0	9:37	10.6	3:10	3:24	15	T	9:46	10.4	10:09	10.9	3:33	3:58
16	M	10:15	9.7	10:31	11.1	4:03	4:19	16	W	10:35	11.1	11:02	11.1	4:24	4:51
17	T	11:03	10.5	11:22	11.4	4:52	5:11	17	T	11:23	11.7	11:54	11.2	5:13	5:43
18	W	11:50	11.1	...	...	5:40	6:02	18	F	...	...	12:11	12.0	6:01	6:34
19	T	12:14	11.5	12:38	11.6	6:27	6:54	19	S	12:46	11.0	1:01	12.0	6:50	7:26
20	F	1:06	11.4	1:27	11.8	7:15	7:46	20	S	1:39	10.6	1:52	11.8	7:39	8:18
21	S	1:58	11.1	2:17	11.7	8:04	8:38	21	M	2:33	10.1	2:44	11.3	8:31	9:12
22	S	2:52	10.5	3:08	11.4	8:54	9:33	22	T	3:29	9.6	3:39	10.7	9:24	10:10
23	M	3:48	9.9	4:03	10.9	9:48	10:32	23	W	4:29	9.1	4:40	10.1	10:22	11:11
24	T	4:49	9.3	5:04	10.3	10:46	11:35	24	T	5:33	8.7	5:44	9.6	11:25	...
25	W	5:55	8.8	6:09	9.9	11:48	...	25	F	6:37	8.6	6:49	9.3	12:14	12:29
26	T	7:02	8.6	7:16	9.6	12:40	12:53	26	S	7:38	8.6	7:52	9.1	1:16	1:33
27	F	8:08	8.6	8:22	9.5	1:46	1:58	27	S	8:34	8.8	8:50	9.1	2:13	2:32
28	S	9:08	8.7	9:21	9.6	2:49	2:59	28	M	9:22	9.1	9:40	9.2	3:04	3:25
29	S	9:58	9.0	10:10	9.7	3:42	3:53	29	T	10:03	9.4	10:24	9.2	3:48	4:11
30	M	10:39	9.3	10:53	9.7	4:26	4:38	30	W	10:39	9.7	11:03	9.3	4:26	4:51
								31	T	11:14	9.9	11:41	9.2	5:03	5:29

Dates when Ht. of **Low** Water is below Mean Lower Low with Ht. of lowest given for each period and Date of lowest in ( ):

17th–23rd: -1.4' (19th, 20th)   15th–21st: -1.7' (18th)

Average Rise and Fall 9.5 ft.

When a high tide exceeds avg. ht., the *following* low tide will be lower than avg. Since there is a high degree of correlation between the height of High Water and the velocities of the Flood and Ebb Currents for that same day, we offer a rough rule of thumb for estimating the current velocities, for ALL the Current Charts and Diagrams in this book. **Rule of Thumb:** Refer to Boston High Water. If the height of High Water is 11.0' or over, use the Current Chart velocities as shown. When the height is 10.5', subtract 10%; at 10.0', subtract 20%; at 9.0', 30%; at 8.0', 40%; below 7.5', 50%.

2024 HIGH & LOW WATER
BOSTON, MA
42°21.3'N, 71°03'W

Standard Time starts Nov. 3 at 2 a.m.   Standard Time

D A Y O F M O N T H	D A Y O F W E E K	NOVEMBER HIGH a.m.	Ht.	p.m.	Ht.	LOW a.m.	p.m.	D A Y O F M O N T H	D A Y O F W E E K	DECEMBER HIGH a.m.	Ht.	p.m.	Ht.	LOW a.m.	p.m.
1	F	11:48	10.0	...	...	5:38	6:07	1	S	10:54	10.1	11:33	8.7	4:44	5:21
2	S	12:18	9.1	12:23	10.1	6:14	6:45	2	M	11:33	10.1	...	...	5:24	6:01
3	S	12:57	9.0	*12:01	10.0	*5:51	*6:24	3	T	12:14	8.6	12:13	10.2	6:05	6:43
4	M	12:37	8.8	12:37	10.0	6:30	7:04	4	W	12:57	8.6	12:56	10.2	6:48	7:27
5	T	1:16	8.6	1:17	9.9	7:10	7:47	5	T	1:40	8.6	1:42	10.1	7:33	8:13
6	W	1:59	8.4	2:01	9.8	7:53	8:33	6	F	2:27	8.7	2:32	10.0	8:23	9:02
7	T	2:47	8.3	2:50	9.6	8:42	9:25	7	S	3:17	8.8	3:26	9.8	9:18	9:54
8	F	3:39	8.3	3:46	9.6	9:37	10:20	8	S	4:11	9.1	4:25	9.6	10:17	10:49
9	S	4:36	8.5	4:47	9.6	10:37	11:17	9	M	5:06	9.4	5:26	9.5	11:18	11:45
10	S	5:33	8.9	5:49	9.7	11:39	...	10	T	6:02	9.9	6:29	9.5	...	12:20
11	M	6:30	9.4	6:51	9.9	12:13	12:40	11	W	6:59	10.4	7:32	9.5	12:41	1:21
12	T	7:26	10.1	7:51	10.1	1:09	1:41	12	T	7:55	10.8	8:32	9.6	1:38	2:21
13	W	8:19	10.8	8:49	10.3	2:04	2:39	13	F	8:49	11.2	9:29	9.7	2:33	3:17
14	T	9:10	11.4	9:44	10.5	2:57	3:33	14	S	9:41	11.4	10:23	9.7	3:27	4:11
15	F	9:59	11.8	10:37	10.5	3:48	4:25	15	S	10:32	11.5	11:16	9.7	4:19	5:02
16	S	10:49	12.0	11:29	10.4	4:37	5:17	16	M	11:23	11.4	...	...	5:09	5:53
17	S	11:39	11.8	...	...	5:27	6:08	17	T	12:08	9.6	12:14	11.1	6:00	6:42
18	M	12:22	10.1	12:30	11.5	6:18	7:00	18	W	12:58	9.4	1:03	10.7	6:49	7:30
19	T	1:16	9.7	1:23	11.0	7:09	7:52	19	T	1:47	9.2	1:53	10.2	7:39	8:18
20	W	2:09	9.3	2:16	10.5	8:02	8:45	20	F	2:35	8.9	2:43	9.7	8:29	9:06
21	T	3:05	9.0	3:13	9.9	8:57	9:41	21	S	3:25	8.8	3:35	9.2	9:22	9:56
22	F	4:03	8.7	4:12	9.4	9:56	10:38	22	S	4:15	8.7	4:29	8.7	10:17	10:45
23	S	5:01	8.6	5:13	9.0	10:57	11:34	23	M	5:05	8.7	5:24	8.3	11:13	11:34
24	S	5:56	8.7	6:11	8.7	11:57	...	24	T	5:54	8.7	6:19	8.1	...	12:08
25	M	6:47	8.8	7:08	8.6	12:26	12:54	25	W	6:43	8.8	7:15	8.0	12:23	1:03
26	T	7:36	9.1	8:01	8.6	1:15	1:48	26	T	7:32	9.0	8:09	8.0	1:13	1:57
27	W	8:20	9.3	8:49	8.6	2:02	2:37	27	F	8:20	9.3	8:59	8.1	2:02	2:46
28	T	9:01	9.6	9:32	8.7	2:45	3:21	28	S	9:04	9.5	9:44	8.2	2:49	3:32
29	F	9:39	9.8	10:13	8.7	3:26	4:01	29	S	9:47	9.8	10:27	8.4	3:33	4:15
30	S	10:16	10.0	10:53	8.7	4:05	4:41	30	M	10:28	10.1	11:10	8.5	4:17	4:57
								31	T	11:10	10.3	...	...	5:00	5:40

Dates when Ht. of **Low** Water is below Mean Lower Low with Ht. of lowest given for each period and Date of lowest in ( ):

13th–19th: -1.6' (16th)   12th–18th: -1.3' (15th)
31st: -0.2'

Average Rise and Fall 9.5 ft.
When a high tide exceeds avg. ht., the *following* low tide will be lower than avg. Since there is a high degree of correlation between the height of High Water and the velocities of the Flood and Ebb Currents for that same day, we offer a rough rule of thumb for estimating the current velocities, for ALL the Current Charts and Diagrams in this book. **Rule of Thumb:** Refer to Boston High Water. If the height of High Water is 11.0' or over, use the Current Chart velocities as shown. When the height is 10.5', subtract 10%; at 10.0', subtract 20%; at 9.0', 30%; at 8.0', 40%; below 7.5', 50%.

43

Cape Cod Canal

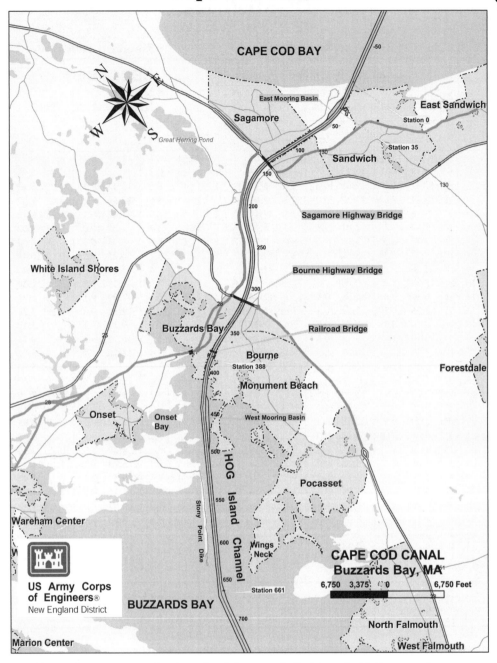

CAPE COD BAY

East Mooring Basin

Sagamore

East Sandwich
Station 0

Great Herring Pond

Station 35

Sandwich

Sagamore Highway Bridge

White Island Shores

Bourne Highway Bridge

Buzzards Bay

Railroad Bridge

Bourne
Station 388

Monument Beach

Forestdale

Onset

Onset Bay

West Mooring Basin

HOG Island Channel

Pocasset

Stony Point Dike

Wareham Center

US Army Corps of Engineers®
New England District

Wings Neck

CAPE COD CANAL
Buzzards Bay, MA

6,750   3,375   0   6,750 Feet

Station 661

BUZZARDS BAY

Marion Center

North Falmouth

West Falmouth

Small boat basins are on both ends of the canal. On E. end, 13-ft. mean low water, on S. side of Sandwich, available for mooring small boat traffic. On W. end, channel 13-ft. at mean low water, 100 ft. wide leads from NE side of Hog Is. Ch. abreast of Hog Is. to harbor in Onset Bay. Fuel, supplies and phone services at both locations.

See Cape Cod Canal Currents pp. 46-51.

Cape Cod Canal Regulations

For complete regulations see 33 CFR, Part 207 and 36 CFR, Part 327

No excessive wake — Speed Limit 10 m.p.h. (8.7 kts.)

Vessels going with the current have right of way over those going against it.

Clearance under all bridges: 135 feet at mean high water. Available clearance can be reduced by construction work on the bridges so mariners are advised to contact the Marine Traffic Controller for current clearance dimensions prior to transit. Buzzards Bay Railroad Bridge is maintained in up, or open position, except when lowered for trains or maintenance.

Obtaining Clearance

Vessels 65 feet and over shall not enter the Canal until clearance has been given by radio from the Marine Traffic Controller. These vessels shall request clearance at least 15 minutes prior to entering the Canal at any point.

Vessels up to 65 feet in length shall be operated so as not to interfere with the navigation of vessels of greater length.

Vessels of any kind unable to make a through transit of the Canal against a head current of 6 kts. within a time limit of 2-1/2 hrs. are required to obtain helper tug assistance or wait for a fair current prior to receiving clearance from the Controller.

Vessels shall not obstruct navigation by stopping or unnecessarily idling at low speed in the channel.

Two-way traffic through the Canal for all vessels is allowed when Controller on duty considers conditions suitable.

Communications are available at all hours by VHF radio or by phoning 978-318-8500. **Call on Channel 13 to establish contact**. Transmissions may then be switched to Channel 14 as the working channel. Channel 16 is also available but should be limited to emergency situations. Vessels shall maintain a radio guard on Channel 13 during the entire passage. Note: the Railroad Bridge does not stand by VHF Radio

Traffic Lights are at Eastern End at Sandwich (Cape Cod Bay entrance) and at Western End near Wings Neck (Buzzards Bay entrance). When traffic lights are extinguished: all vessels over 65 feet are cautioned not to enter Canal until clearance given, as above.

Entering From EASTERN END: (Lights on S. side of entrance to Canal.)

RED LIGHT: Any type of vessel 65 feet in length and over must stop clear of the Cape Cod Bay entrance channel.

YELLOW LIGHT: Vessels 65 feet in length and over and drawing less than 25 feet may proceed as far as the East Mooring Basin where they must stop.

GREEN LIGHT: Vessels may proceed westward through the Canal.

Entering From WESTERN END: (Lights near Wings Neck at W. Entr. to Hog Is. Channel)

RED LIGHT: Vessels 65 feet and over in length and drawing less than 25 feet must keep southerly of Hog Island Channel Entrance Buoys Nos. 1 and 2 and utilize the general anchorage areas adjacent to the improved channel. Vessel traffic drawing 25 feet and over are directed not to enter the Canal channel at the Cleveland Ledge Light entrance and shall lay to or anchor in Buzzards Bay until clearance is granted by the Marine Traffic Controller or a green traffic light at Wings Neck is displayed.

YELLOW LIGHT: Vessels may proceed through Hog Island Channel as far as the West Mooring Basin where they must stop.

GREEN LIGHT: Vessels may proceed eastward through the Canal.

Prohibited Activities

Jet skis, sea planes, paddle-driven craft and sailing vessels not under power are prohibited from transiting the Canal.

Fishing from a vessel within the channel limits of the Canal is prohibited.

Swimming, snorkeling or scuba diving anywhere within the Canal limits is prohibited

Anchoring within the channel limits of the Canal, except in emergencies with notice given to the Traffic Controller, is prohibited.

2024 CURRENT TABLE
CAPE COD CANAL
41°44.56'N, 70°36.85'W at R.R. Bridge

Standard Time   Standard Time

DAY OF MONTH	DAY OF WEEK	CURRENT TURNS TO						DAY OF MONTH	DAY OF WEEK	CURRENT TURNS TO					
		EAST Flood Starts			WEST Ebb Starts					EAST Flood Starts			WEST Ebb Starts		
		a.m.	p.m.	Kts.	a.m.	p.m.	Kts.			a.m.	p.m.	Kts.	a.m.	p.m.	Kts.
JANUARY								**FEBRUARY**							
1	M	7:24	7:48	p3.5	1:30	1:36	p4.0	1	T	8:12	8:30	p3.6	2:12	2:24	3.8
2	T	8:12	8:30	p3.4	2:18	2:24	p3.8	2	F	9:00	9:12	p3.6	2:48	3:12	a3.8
3	W	9:00	9:18	p3.3	3:00	3:06	p3.6	3	S	9:48	10:00	p3.6	3:30	4:06	a3.8
4	T	9:49	10:00	p3.4	3:42	3:54	3.4	4	S	10:37	11:00	p3.7	4:18	5:00	a4.0
5	F	10:36	10:48	p3.5	4:24	4:42	a3.4	5	M	11:30	11:54	p3.9	5:06	6:00	a4.2
6	S	11:24	11:36	p3.7	5:06	5:36	a3.6	6	T	...	12:24	3.9	6:00	6:54	a4.5
7	S	...	12:06	3.5	5:48	6:24	a3.9	7	W	12:48	1:18	p4.3	7:00	7:48	a4.9
8	M	12:24	12:54	a3.9	6:36	7:18	a4.3	8	T	1:42	2:06	p4.7	7:54	8:36	a5.4
9	T	1:12	1:42	p4.2	7:24	8:06	a4.8	9	F	2:30	3:00	p5.0	8:48	9:30	a5.9
10	W	2:00	2:30	p4.6	8:12	9:00	a5.3	10	S	3:24	3:48	5.3	9:36	10:18	a6.2
11	T	2:48	3:18	p4.9	9:00	9:48	a5.7	11	S	4:12	4:36	a5.4	10:30	11:06	a6.4
12	F	3:42	4:06	5.1	9:54	10:36	a6.0	12	M	5:00	5:30	a5.4	11:24	...	6.4
13	S	4:30	4:54	5.2	10:48	11:30	a6.2	13	T	5:54	6:18	a5.2	12:01	12:18	p6.1
14	S	5:18	5:48	5.2	11:36	...	6.3	14	W	6:48	7:06	a4.9	12:48	1:12	5.7
15	M	6:12	6:42	a5.1	12:24	12:30	p6.2	15	T	7:42	8:00	a4.4	1:36	2:06	a5.4
16	T	7:06	7:30	a4.9	1:12	1:30	p5.8	16	F	8:42	8:54	a4.0	2:30	3:06	a5.1
17	W	8:06	8:30	4.5	2:06	2:24	p5.4	17	S	9:42	10:00	a3.7	3:24	4:06	a4.6
18	T	9:06	9:24	4.2	3:00	3:24	a5.0	18	S	10:42	11:00	a3.8	4:18	5:12	a4.3
19	F	10:06	10:24	a4.0	3:54	4:24	a4.8	19	M	11:42	...	4.0	5:18	6:12	a4.1
20	S	11:06	11:24	a3.9	4:48	5:30	a4.6	20	T	12:01	12:42	p4.2	6:18	7:06	a4.1
21	S	...	12:06	4.1	5:42	6:30	a4.5	21	W	1:00	1:30	p4.5	7:18	8:00	a4.4
22	M	12:18	1:00	p4.3	6:42	7:30	a4.5	22	T	1:48	2:24	p4.6	8:06	8:48	a4.6
23	T	1:18	1:54	p4.6	7:36	8:24	a4.7	23	F	2:42	3:12	p4.6	8:54	9:36	a4.7
24	W	2:12	2:42	p4.7	8:30	9:12	a4.8	24	S	3:24	3:54	p4.4	9:42	10:18	a4.7
25	T	3:00	3:30	p4.7	9:18	10:00	a4.8	25	S	4:06	4:36	p4.2	10:24	10:54	a4.7
26	F	3:48	4:18	p4.5	10:06	10:48	a4.8	26	M	4:48	5:12	p4.1	11:06	11:36	a4.6
27	S	4:36	5:00	p4.3	10:48	11:30	a4.7	27	T	5:30	5:48	p4.1	11:42	...	4.5
28	S	5:18	5:48	p4.0	11:36	...	4.6	28	W	6:06	6:24	p4.0	12:12	12:24	p4.4
29	M	6:06	6:24	p3.9	12:12	12:18	p4.4	29	T	6:48	7:00	p4.0	12:48	1:06	a4.3
30	T	6:48	7:06	p3.8	12:54	1:00	p4.2								
31	W	7:30	7:48	p3.7	1:36	1:42	p4.0								

The Kts. (knots) columns show the **maximum** predicted velocities of the stronger one of the Flood Currents and the stronger one of the Ebb Currents for each day.

The letter "a" means the velocity shown should occur **after** the **a.m.** Current Change. The letter "p" means the velocity shown should occur **after** the **p.m.** Current Change (even if next morning). No "a" or "p" means a.m. and p.m. velocities are the same for that day.

Avg. Max. Velocity: Flood 4.0 Kts., Ebb 4.5 Kts.

Max. Flood 3 hrs. after Flood Starts, ±20 min.

Max. Ebb 3 hrs. after Ebb Starts, ±20 min.

Average rise and fall: canal east end, 8.7 ft. (time of high water same as Boston); west end, at Monument Beach, 4.0 ft. (time of high water 15 min. after Newport).

See pp. 22-29 for Current Change at other points.

2024 CURRENT TABLE
CAPE COD CANAL
41°44.56'N, 70°36.85'W at R.R. Bridge

Daylight Time starts Mar. 10 at 2 a.m.   **Daylight Saving Time**

MARCH

Day of Month	Day of Week	EAST Flood Starts a.m.	p.m.	Kts.	WEST Ebb Starts a.m.	p.m.	Kts.
1	F	7:30	7:42	p3.9	1:24	1:48	a4.3
2	S	8:12	8:30	p3.7	2:00	2:36	a4.3
3	S	9:00	9:24	p3.7	2:48	3:30	a4.3
4	M	10:01	10:30	p3.8	3:36	4:30	a4.3
5	T	11:00	11:30	p4.0	4:36	5:30	a4.4
6	W	...	12:01	4.0	5:36	6:30	a4.6
7	T	12:24	12:54	p4.4	6:36	7:24	a5.0
8	F	1:18	1:48	p4.8	7:36	8:18	a5.5
9	S	2:12	2:42	5.1	8:30	9:06	a6.0
10	S	*4:06	*4:30	a5.4	*10:24	*10:54	a6.3
11	M	4:54	5:18	a5.5	11:12	11:42	a6.3
12	T	5:42	6:06	a5.4	...	12:06	6.2
13	W	6:30	6:54	a5.1	12:30	1:00	a6.0
14	T	7:24	7:42	a4.7	1:18	1:54	a5.8
15	F	8:18	8:36	a4.3	2:12	2:48	a5.4
16	S	9:18	9:36	a3.8	3:00	3:48	a4.9
17	S	10:18	10:36	a3.7	3:54	4:48	a4.4
18	M	11:18	11:42	a3.8	4:54	5:48	a3.9
19	T	...	12:18	3.9	5:54	6:48	a3.7
20	W	12:42	1:18	p4.1	6:54	7:42	p4.0
21	T	1:36	2:06	p4.3	7:54	8:36	p4.3
22	F	2:30	2:54	p4.4	8:42	9:18	4.4
23	S	3:12	3:42	p4.3	9:30	10:06	4.5
24	S	4:00	4:18	p4.2	10:12	10:42	a4.5
25	M	4:36	5:00	p4.2	10:54	11:18	a4.5
26	T	5:18	5:36	p4.2	11:30	11:54	4.5
27	W	5:54	6:06	p4.3	...	12:12	4.5
28	T	6:30	6:42	p4.3	12:30	12:48	a4.6
29	F	7:06	7:24	p4.2	1:00	1:36	a4.7
30	S	7:48	8:06	p4.1	1:36	2:18	a4.8
31	S	8:30	9:00	3.9	2:24	3:12	a4.8

APRIL

Day of Month	Day of Week	EAST Flood Starts a.m.	p.m.	Kts.	WEST Ebb Starts a.m.	p.m.	Kts.
1	M	9:24	10:00	3.9	3:12	4:06	a4.7
2	T	10:30	11:06	3.9	4:12	5:06	a4.6
3	W	11:36	...	4.0	5:12	6:06	a4.7
4	T	12:07	12:36	4.2	6:18	7:06	a4.8
5	F	1:06	1:36	p4.5	7:18	8:00	a5.2
6	S	2:00	2:30	p4.9	8:18	8:54	a5.5
7	S	2:54	3:18	5.1	9:12	9:42	a5.9
8	M	3:42	4:06	a5.3	10:06	10:30	6.0
9	T	4:36	4:54	a5.3	10:54	11:18	6.0
10	W	5:24	5:42	a5.2	11:48	...	5.7
11	T	6:12	6:30	a4.9	12:06	12:42	a5.9
12	F	7:06	7:18	a4.5	12:54	1:36	a5.6
13	S	7:54	8:18	a4.1	1:42	2:30	a5.2
14	S	8:54	9:18	a3.8	2:36	3:30	a4.7
15	M	9:54	10:18	a3.8	3:36	4:24	a4.2
16	T	10:54	11:18	a3.8	4:30	5:24	a3.7
17	W	11:54	...	3.8	5:30	6:18	p3.6
18	T	12:18	12:48	p4.0	6:30	7:12	p3.9
19	F	1:12	1:36	p4.0	7:24	8:00	p4.1
20	S	2:00	2:24	p4.0	8:12	8:48	p4.2
21	S	2:42	3:06	p3.9	9:00	9:24	p4.2
22	M	3:24	3:42	p4.0	9:42	10:06	p4.3
23	T	4:06	4:18	p4.1	10:24	10:36	p4.5
24	W	4:42	4:54	p4.3	11:00	11:12	p4.7
25	T	5:18	5:30	p4.4	11:42	11:48	p4.9
26	F	5:54	6:12	p4.4	...	12:24	4.5
27	S	6:30	6:54	4.4	12:24	1:06	a5.1
28	S	7:18	7:42	a4.4	1:06	1:54	a5.2
29	M	8:06	8:36	a4.3	1:54	2:48	a5.2
30	T	9:00	9:36	a4.2	2:54	3:48	a5.1

The Kts. (knots) columns show the **maximum** predicted velocities of the stronger one of the Flood Currents and the stronger one of the Ebb Currents for each day.

The letter "a" means the velocity shown should occur **after** the a.m. Current Change. The letter "p" means the velocity shown should occur **after** the p.m. Current Change (even if next morning). No "a" or "p" means a.m. and p.m. velocities are the same for that day.

Avg. Max. Velocity: Flood 4.0 Kts., Ebb 4.5 Kts.

Max. Flood 3 hrs. after Flood Starts, ±20 min.

Max. Ebb 3 hrs. after Ebb Starts, ±20 min.

Average rise and fall: canal east end, 8.7 ft. (time of high water same as Boston); west end, at Monument Beach, 4.0 ft. (time of high water 15 min. after Newport).

See pp. 22-29 for Current Change at other points.

2024 CURRENT TABLE
CAPE COD CANAL
41°44.56'N, 70°36.85'W at R.R. Bridge

Daylight Saving Time   **Daylight Saving Time**

		MAY								JUNE					
		CURRENT TURNS TO								**CURRENT TURNS TO**					
D A Y O F M O N T H	D A Y O F W E E K	EAST Flood Starts			WEST Ebb Starts			D A Y O F M O N T H	D A Y O F W E E K	EAST Flood Starts			WEST Ebb Starts		
		a.m.	**p.m.**	Kts.	a.m.	**p.m.**	Kts.			a.m.	**p.m.**	Kts.	a.m.	**p.m.**	Kts.
1	W	10:06	**10:42**	4.2	3:54	**4:42**	a5.0	1	S	11:48	**...**	4.5	5:36	**6:12**	a5.1
2	T	11:12	**11:42**	p4.3	4:54	**5:42**	a5.0	2	S	12:18	**12:42**	4.5	6:36	**7:06**	p5.1
3	F	...	**12:12**	4.4	6:00	**6:42**	a5.1	3	M	1:18	**1:36**	4.5	7:36	**8:00**	p5.3
4	S	12:43	**1:12**	p4.6	7:00	**7:36**	a5.2	4	T	2:13	**2:30**	a4.6	8:36	**8:54**	p5.5
5	S	1:42	**2:00**	p4.8	7:54	**8:30**	5.4	5	W	3:06	**3:18**	a4.8	9:30	**9:42**	p5.6
6	M	2:30	**2:54**	4.9	8:54	**9:18**	p5.7	6	T	4:00	**4:12**	a4.8	10:24	**10:30**	p5.5
7	T	3:24	**3:42**	a5.0	9:48	**10:06**	p5.9	7	F	4:48	**5:00**	a4.8	11:18	**11:24**	p5.4
8	W	4:18	**4:30**	a5.0	10:42	**10:54**	p5.9	8	S	5:36	**5:54**	a4.7	...	**12:06**	4.7
9	T	5:06	**5:18**	a4.9	11:36	**11:42**	p5.7	9	S	6:24	**6:48**	a4.5	12:12	**1:00**	a5.1
10	F	5:54	**6:12**	a4.7	...	**12:24**	4.9	10	M	7:18	**7:36**	a4.2	1:00	**1:48**	a4.8
11	S	6:42	**7:00**	a4.4	12:30	**1:18**	a5.4	11	T	8:06	**8:30**	a4.0	1:54	**2:42**	a4.5
12	S	7:36	**8:00**	a4.1	1:24	**2:12**	a5.0	12	W	9:00	**9:24**	a3.8	2:48	**3:30**	a4.2
13	M	8:30	**8:54**	a3.9	2:18	**3:06**	a4.5	13	T	9:54	**10:18**	a3.6	3:36	**4:18**	a3.9
14	T	9:30	**9:54**	a3.8	3:12	**4:00**	a4.1	14	F	10:42	**11:12**	a3.4	4:30	**5:06**	a3.6
15	W	10:24	**10:54**	a3.7	4:06	**4:54**	a3.7	15	S	11:30	**...**	3.3	5:18	**5:54**	a3.4
16	T	11:24	**11:48**	a3.7	5:06	**5:48**	3.5	16	S	12:01	**12:18**	p3.3	6:12	**6:42**	p3.3
17	F	...	**12:12**	3.7	6:00	**6:36**	p3.6	17	M	12:48	**1:06**	p3.4	7:00	**7:24**	p3.5
18	S	12:42	**1:00**	p3.6	6:48	**7:24**	p3.7	18	T	1:36	**1:48**	p3.5	7:48	**8:00**	p3.8
19	S	1:30	**1:48**	p3.5	7:36	**8:06**	p3.7	19	W	2:18	**2:30**	p3.8	8:36	**8:42**	p4.2
20	M	2:12	**2:24**	p3.6	8:24	**8:48**	p3.9	20	T	2:54	**3:12**	p4.0	9:18	**9:18**	p4.7
21	T	2:54	**3:06**	p3.9	9:06	**9:24**	p4.2	21	F	3:36	**3:54**	p4.3	10:06	**10:00**	p5.1
22	W	3:30	**3:42**	p4.1	9:48	**9:54**	p4.6	22	S	4:18	**4:36**	p4.6	10:48	**10:48**	p5.5
23	T	4:12	**4:24**	p4.3	10:30	**10:30**	p4.9	23	S	5:00	**5:24**	p4.8	11:36	**11:36**	p5.8
24	F	4:48	**5:00**	p4.5	11:12	**11:12**	p5.2	24	M	5:48	**6:12**	p5.0	...	**12:24**	5.2
25	S	5:24	**5:48**	p4.6	11:59	**11:54**	p5.4	25	T	6:36	**7:06**	5.0	12:30	**1:12**	a6.0
26	S	6:06	**6:30**	a4.7	...	**12:42**	4.8	26	W	7:30	**8:00**	a5.0	1:18	**2:06**	a6.0
27	M	6:54	**7:24**	a4.7	12:42	**1:36**	a5.6	27	T	8:24	**8:54**	a4.8	2:18	**3:00**	a6.0
28	T	7:48	**8:18**	a4.6	1:36	**2:30**	a5.6	28	F	9:24	**9:54**	a4.7	3:12	**3:54**	a5.7
29	W	8:42	**9:18**	4.5	2:36	**3:24**	a5.6	29	S	10:18	**10:54**	a4.5	4:12	**4:48**	a5.4
30	T	9:42	**10:18**	a4.5	3:36	**4:18**	a5.4	30	S	11:18	**...**	4.4	5:12	**5:42**	a5.0
31	F	10:48	**11:18**	a4.5	4:36	**5:18**	a5.3								

The Kts. (knots) columns show the **maximum** predicted velocities of the stronger one of the Flood Currents and the stronger one of the Ebb Currents for each day.

The letter "a" means the velocity shown should occur **after** the **a.m.** Current Change. The letter "p" means the velocity shown should occur **after** the **p.m.** Current Change (even if next morning). No "a" or "p" means a.m. and p.m. velocities are the same for that day.

Avg. Max. Velocity: Flood 4.0 Kts., Ebb 4.5 Kts.

Max. Flood 3 hrs. after Flood Starts, ±20 min.

Max. Ebb 3 hrs. after Ebb Starts, ±20 min.

Average rise and fall: canal east end, 8.7 ft. (time of high water same as Boston); west end, at Monument Beach, 4.0 ft. (time of high water 15 min. after Newport).

See pp. 22-29 for Current Change at other points.

2024 CURRENT TABLE
CAPE COD CANAL

41°44.56'N, 70°36.85'W at R.R. Bridge

Daylight Saving Time · Daylight Saving Time

		JULY								AUGUST				
		CURRENT TURNS TO						**CURRENT TURNS TO**						
		EAST Flood Starts			WEST Ebb Starts					EAST Flood Starts			WEST Ebb Starts		
DAY OF MONTH	DAY OF WEEK	a.m.	**p.m.**	Kts.	a.m.	**p.m.**	Kts.	DAY OF MONTH	DAY OF WEEK	a.m.	**p.m.**	Kts.	a.m.	**p.m.**	Kts.
1	M	12:01	**12:18**	4.2	6:18	**6:42**	p4.9	1	T	1:36	**1:48**	a4.3	8:00	**8:06**	p4.6
2	T	12:54	**1:12**	a4.2	7:18	**7:36**	p5.0	2	F	2:30	**2:48**	a4.5	9:00	**9:06**	p4.8
3	W	1:54	**2:06**	a4.4	8:18	**8:30**	p5.1	3	S	3:18	**3:36**	a4.7	9:48	**9:54**	p4.9
4	T	2:49	**3:00**	a4.6	9:18	**9:24**	p5.2	4	S	4:13	**4:30**	a4.8	10:36	**10:48**	p5.0
5	F	3:42	**3:54**	a4.8	10:12	**10:12**	p5.2	5	M	5:00	**5:12**	a4.8	11:24	**11:30**	p5.0
6	S	4:30	**4:48**	a4.8	11:00	**11:06**	p5.1	6	T	5:42	**6:00**	a4.6	...	**12:12**	4.7
7	S	5:18	**5:36**	a4.7	11:48	**11:54**	p5.0	7	W	6:24	**6:48**	a4.3	12:18	**12:54**	a4.9
8	M	6:06	**6:24**	a4.6	...	**12:36**	4.6	8	T	7:06	**7:30**	a4.1	1:00	**1:36**	a4.7
9	T	6:54	**7:12**	a4.3	12:42	**1:24**	a4.8	9	F	7:48	**8:12**	a3.9	1:48	**2:18**	a4.4
10	W	7:42	**8:00**	a4.0	1:30	**2:12**	a4.6	10	S	8:30	**9:00**	a3.7	2:30	**3:00**	a4.1
11	T	8:30	**8:54**	a3.7	2:18	**2:54**	a4.3	11	S	9:12	**9:48**	a3.5	3:12	**3:36**	3.7
12	F	9:12	**9:42**	a3.5	3:06	**3:42**	a4.0	12	M	10:00	**10:36**	a3.4	4:00	**4:18**	p3.6
13	S	10:00	**10:30**	a3.4	3:54	**4:24**	a3.7	13	T	10:48	**11:24**	a3.3	4:54	**5:00**	p3.6
14	S	10:48	**11:18**	a3.3	4:42	**5:06**	3.3	14	W	11:42	...	3.3	5:42	**5:48**	p3.7
15	M	11:36	...	3.3	5:30	**5:48**	p3.4	15	T	12:12	**12:36**	p3.5	6:42	**6:42**	p4.0
16	T	12:06	**12:18**	p3.3	6:24	**6:36**	p3.5	16	F	1:06	**1:30**	p3.8	7:30	**7:36**	p4.4
17	W	12:54	**1:06**	p3.5	7:12	**7:18**	p3.9	17	S	1:54	**2:18**	p4.2	8:24	**8:30**	p5.0
18	T	1:42	**1:54**	p3.7	8:00	**8:06**	p4.3	18	S	2:48	**3:06**	p4.7	9:12	**9:18**	p5.5
19	F	2:24	**2:42**	p4.1	8:54	**8:54**	p4.8	19	M	3:36	**4:00**	p5.2	10:06	**10:12**	p6.0
20	S	3:12	**3:30**	p4.5	9:42	**9:42**	p5.3	20	T	4:24	**4:48**	p5.5	10:54	**11:00**	p6.4
21	S	3:54	**4:18**	p4.9	10:24	**10:30**	p5.8	21	W	5:12	**5:36**	p5.6	11:42	**11:54**	p6.5
22	M	4:42	**5:06**	p5.2	11:12	**11:18**	p6.1	22	T	6:00	**6:24**	5.5	...	**12:30**	6.0
23	T	5:30	**5:54**	p5.3	...	**12:01**	5.6	23	F	6:48	**7:18**	a5.3	12:48	**1:18**	a6.0
24	W	6:18	**6:42**	5.3	12:12	**12:54**	a6.3	24	S	7:36	**8:12**	a5.0	1:42	**2:06**	a6.0
25	T	7:12	**7:36**	a5.2	1:06	**1:42**	a6.3	25	S	8:30	**9:06**	a4.6	2:36	**3:00**	5.4
26	F	8:00	**8:30**	a5.0	2:00	**2:36**	a6.1	26	M	9:24	**10:06**	a4.1	3:36	**3:54**	p4.9
27	S	8:54	**9:30**	a4.8	2:54	**3:24**	a5.7	27	T	10:30	**11:12**	p3.8	4:36	**4:48**	p4.5
28	S	9:54	**10:30**	a4.4	3:54	**4:18**	a5.2	28	W	11:30	...	3.4	5:42	**5:48**	p4.2
29	M	10:48	**11:36**	a4.1	4:54	**5:18**	p4.8	29	T	12:12	**12:36**	a4.0	6:42	**6:54**	p4.1
30	T	11:54	...	3.8	6:00	**6:12**	p4.6	30	F	1:12	**1:36**	a4.2	7:42	**7:48**	p4.3
31	W	12:36	**12:54**	a4.0	7:00	**7:12**	p4.5	31	S	2:06	**2:30**	a4.5	8:36	**8:48**	p4.6

The Kts. (knots) columns show the **maximum** predicted velocities of the stronger one of the Flood Currents and the stronger one of the Ebb Currents for each day.

The letter "a" means the velocity shown should occur **after** the **a.m.** Current Change. The letter "p" means the velocity shown should occur **after** the **p.m.** Current Change (even if next morning). No "a" or "p" means a.m. and p.m. velocities are the same for that day.

Avg. Max. Velocity: Flood 4.0 Kts., Ebb 4.5 Kts.

Max. Flood 3 hrs. after Flood Starts, ±20 min.

Max. Ebb 3 hrs. after Ebb Starts, ±20 min.

Average rise and fall: canal east end, 8.7 ft. (time of high water same as Boston); west end, at Monument Beach, 4.0 ft. (time of high water 15 min. after Newport).

See pp. 22-29 for Current Change at other points.

2024 CURRENT TABLE
CAPE COD CANAL
41°44.56'N, 70°36.85'W at R.R. Bridge

Daylight Saving Time   Daylight Saving Time

		SEPTEMBER							OCTOBER					
		CURRENT TURNS TO							CURRENT TURNS TO					
		EAST Flood Starts			WEST Ebb Starts					EAST Flood Starts			WEST Ebb Starts	
DAY OF MONTH	DAY OF WEEK	a.m.	p.m.	Kts.	a.m.	p.m.	Kts.	DAY OF MONTH	DAY OF WEEK	a.m.	p.m.	Kts.	a.m.	p.m.	Kts.
1	S	3:00	3:18	a4.7	9:24	9:36	p4.8	1	T	3:18	3:42	a4.5	9:42	9:54	4.7
2	M	3:48	4:06	a4.7	10:12	10:24	p4.9	2	W	4:00	4:24	a4.4	10:24	10:36	a4.7
3	T	4:30	4:48	a4.7	10:54	11:06	p4.9	3	T	4:42	5:06	a4.2	11:06	11:18	a4.6
4	W	5:13	5:36	a4.5	11:36	11:48	4.7	4	F	5:19	5:42	a4.2	11:42	...	4.5
5	T	5:54	6:18	a4.2	...	12:18	4.5	5	S	6:00	6:18	a4.2	12:01	12:12	p4.5
6	F	6:36	6:54	a4.1	12:30	12:54	a4.5	6	S	6:36	7:00	a4.1	12:42	12:48	p4.5
7	S	7:12	7:36	a4.0	1:12	1:36	4.3	7	M	7:12	7:36	a3.9	1:24	1:24	p4.5
8	S	7:48	8:18	a3.8	1:54	2:12	p4.2	8	T	7:54	8:18	a3.8	2:06	2:06	p4.5
9	M	8:30	9:00	a3.6	2:42	2:48	p4.1	9	W	8:42	9:06	a3.7	2:54	2:54	p4.4
10	T	9:18	9:48	a3.5	3:24	3:30	p4.0	10	T	9:36	10:06	3.6	3:48	3:48	p4.4
11	W	10:06	10:36	a3.4	4:18	4:18	p4.0	11	F	10:36	11:06	p3.8	4:42	4:48	p4.4
12	T	11:06	11:36	3.5	5:12	5:12	p4.0	12	S	11:36	...	4.0	5:42	5:48	p4.6
13	F	...	12:06	3.7	6:06	6:12	p4.3	13	S	12:06	12:36	p4.3	6:36	6:48	p5.0
14	S	12:36	1:00	p4.0	7:06	7:12	p4.7	14	M	1:06	1:30	p4.7	7:30	7:48	p5.4
15	S	1:30	1:54	p4.5	8:00	8:06	p5.2	15	T	2:00	2:24	p5.0	8:24	8:42	p5.8
16	M	2:24	2:48	p4.9	8:48	9:00	p5.8	16	W	2:48	3:18	p5.3	9:12	9:36	p6.0
17	T	3:12	3:36	p5.3	9:42	9:54	p6.2	17	T	3:36	4:06	p5.4	10:00	10:30	6.0
18	W	4:00	4:24	p5.6	10:30	10:48	p6.4	18	F	4:24	4:54	p5.4	10:48	11:24	a6.2
19	T	4:48	5:18	p5.6	11:18	11:36	p6.3	19	S	5:12	5:48	a5.2	11:36	...	6.1
20	F	5:36	6:06	5.4	...	12:01	6.2	20	S	6:06	6:36	4.8	12:18	12:24	p5.9
21	S	6:24	6:54	a5.2	12:30	12:48	6.0	21	M	6:54	7:30	4.4	1:12	1:18	p5.5
22	S	7:12	7:48	a4.8	1:24	1:42	p5.7	22	T	7:48	8:24	p4.0	2:06	2:12	p5.0
23	M	8:06	8:42	a4.3	2:24	2:30	p5.3	23	W	8:48	9:24	p3.9	3:00	3:06	p4.5
24	T	9:06	9:42	p3.8	3:18	3:30	p4.7	24	T	9:48	10:24	p3.9	4:00	4:06	p4.0
25	W	10:06	10:48	p3.8	4:18	4:24	p4.2	25	F	10:54	11:24	p3.9	4:54	5:06	p3.8
26	T	11:12	11:48	p3.9	5:18	5:30	p3.9	26	S	11:54	...	3.3	5:54	6:06	p3.8
27	F	...	12:18	3.3	6:18	6:30	p3.9	27	S	12:24	12:48	a4.0	6:48	7:00	4.0
28	S	12:48	1:12	a4.2	7:18	7:30	p4.2	28	M	1:12	1:36	a4.1	7:36	7:54	4.2
29	S	1:42	2:06	a4.4	8:12	8:24	p4.5	29	T	2:00	2:24	a4.2	8:24	8:42	a4.4
30	M	2:36	2:54	a4.5	9:00	9:12	p4.7	30	W	2:48	3:12	a4.1	9:12	9:24	a4.4
								31	T	3:30	3:54	a4.0	9:48	10:12	a4.4

The Kts. (knots) columns show the **maximum** predicted velocities of the stronger one of the Flood Currents and the stronger one of the Ebb Currents for each day.

The letter "a" means the velocity shown should occur **after** the **a.m.** Current Change. The letter "p" means the velocity shown should occur **after** the **p.m.** Current Change (even if next morning). No "a" or "p" means a.m. and p.m. velocities are the same for that day.

Avg. Max. Velocity: Flood 4.0 Kts., Ebb 4.5 Kts.

Max. Flood 3 hrs. after Flood Starts, ±20 min.

Max. Ebb 3 hrs. after Ebb Starts, ±20 min.

Average rise and fall: canal east end, 8.7 ft. (time of high water same as Boston); west end, at Monument Beach, 4.0 ft. (time of high water 15 min. after Newport).

See pp. 22-29 for Current Change at other points.

2024 CURRENT TABLE
CAPE COD CANAL

41°44.56'N, 70°36.85'W at R.R. Bridge

*Standard Time starts Nov. 3 at 2 a.m. — Standard Time

NOVEMBER

DAY OF MONTH	DAY OF WEEK	EAST Flood Starts a.m.	p.m.	Kts.	WEST Ebb Starts a.m.	p.m.	Kts.
1	F	4:06	4:30	a4.0	10:24	10:48	a4.4
2	S	4:42	5:12	a4.1	11:00	11:30	a4.5
3	S	*4:24	*4:48	a4.1	*10:36	*11:12	a4.6
4	M	5:01	5:24	4.1	11:12	11:54	a4.8
5	T	5:42	6:00	4.1	11:48	...	4.9
6	W	6:24	6:48	4.1	12:42	12:36	p4.9
7	T	7:18	7:36	4.0	1:30	1:30	p4.9
8	F	8:12	8:36	p4.1	2:18	2:24	p4.9
9	S	9:12	9:42	p4.2	3:12	3:24	p4.9
10	S	10:12	10:42	p4.4	4:12	4:24	p5.0
11	M	11:12	11:36	p4.6	5:06	5:24	p5.2
12	T	...	12:06	4.7	6:06	6:24	p5.3
13	W	12:30	1:06	p4.9	7:00	7:24	p5.5
14	T	1:24	1:54	p5.1	7:48	8:18	a5.7
15	F	2:12	2:48	p5.1	8:36	9:12	a5.9
16	S	3:06	3:36	p5.0	9:24	10:06	a6.0
17	S	3:54	4:30	p4.9	10:12	11:00	a5.9
18	M	4:48	5:18	p4.6	11:06	11:54	a5.6
19	T	5:36	6:12	p4.3	...	12:01	5.3
20	W	6:30	7:06	p4.1	12:48	12:54	p4.9
21	T	7:30	8:00	p4.0	1:42	1:48	p4.4
22	F	8:24	9:00	p3.9	2:36	2:42	p4.1
23	S	9:24	9:54	p3.9	3:30	3:36	3.8
24	S	10:24	10:48	p3.8	4:24	4:36	3.7
25	M	11:18	11:36	p3.7	5:12	5:30	a3.8
26	T	...	12:06	3.3	6:00	6:18	a3.9
27	W	12:24	12:54	a3.6	6:48	7:12	a3.9
28	T	1:12	1:42	a3.6	7:30	7:54	a4.0
29	F	1:54	2:18	a3.7	8:12	8:42	a4.1
30	S	2:30	3:00	a3.8	8:48	9:24	a4.3

DECEMBER

DAY OF MONTH	DAY OF WEEK	EAST Flood Starts a.m.	p.m.	Kts.	WEST Ebb Starts a.m.	p.m.	Kts.
1	S	3:12	3:36	4.0	9:24	10:00	a4.6
2	M	3:54	4:12	p4.2	10:00	10:42	a4.8
3	T	4:30	4:54	4.3	10:42	11:30	a5.1
4	W	5:19	5:36	p4.5	11:24	...	5.3
5	T	6:00	6:24	4.5	12:12	12:12	p5.4
6	F	6:54	7:18	4.5	1:06	1:06	p5.5
7	S	7:48	8:12	4.5	1:54	2:06	p5.5
8	S	8:48	9:12	4.5	2:48	3:00	p5.4
9	M	9:48	10:12	p4.6	3:42	4:00	p5.3
10	T	10:48	11:12	p4.6	4:42	5:06	p5.1
11	W	11:48	...	4.5	5:36	6:06	a5.1
12	T	12:06	12:42	4.6	6:30	7:06	a5.3
13	F	1:00	1:36	p4.7	7:24	8:06	a5.5
14	S	1:54	2:30	p4.8	8:12	9:00	a5.6
15	S	2:48	3:24	p4.9	9:06	9:54	a5.6
16	M	3:42	4:12	p4.8	9:54	10:42	a5.5
17	T	4:30	5:00	p4.6	10:48	11:36	a5.3
18	W	5:24	5:54	p4.4	11:42	...	5.1
19	T	6:12	6:42	p4.2	12:24	12:30	p4.8
20	F	7:06	7:36	p4.0	1:18	1:24	p4.5
21	S	8:00	8:24	p3.8	2:06	2:18	4.2
22	S	8:54	9:18	p3.7	2:54	3:06	3.9
23	M	9:48	10:12	p3.4	3:48	4:00	a3.5
24	T	10:42	11:00	p3.3	4:36	4:54	a3.5
25	W	11:36	11:48	p3.3	5:24	5:48	a3.4
26	T	...	12:18	3.0	6:06	6:36	a3.4
27	F	12:30	1:06	a3.3	6:48	7:24	a3.6
28	S	1:18	1:48	3.4	7:30	8:12	a3.9
29	S	2:00	2:24	3.7	8:06	8:54	a4.2
30	M	2:42	3:06	p4.0	8:48	9:36	a4.6
31	T	3:24	3:48	p4.4	9:30	10:18	a5.0

The Kts. (knots) columns show the **maximum** predicted velocities of the stronger one of the Flood Currents and the stronger one of the Ebb Currents for each day.

The letter "a" means the velocity shown should occur **after** the a.m. Current Change. The letter "p" means the velocity shown should occur **after** the p.m. Current Change (even if next morning). No "a" or "p" means a.m. and p.m. velocities are the same for that day.

Avg. Max. Velocity: Flood 4.0 Kts., Ebb 4.5 Kts.

Max. Flood 3 hrs. after Flood Starts, ±20 min.

Max. Ebb 3 hrs. after Ebb Starts, ±20 min.

Average rise and fall: canal east end, 8.7 ft. (time of high water same as Boston); west end, at Monument Beach, 4.0 ft. (time of high water 15 min. after Newport).

See pp. 22-29 for Current Change at other points.

2024 CURRENT TABLE
WOODS HOLE, MA, The Strait
41°31.16'N, 70°40.97'W

		Standard Time						Standard Time			
		JANUARY						**FEBRUARY**			
		CURRENT TURNS TO						CURRENT TURNS TO			
		SOUTHEAST Flood Starts			NORTHWEST Ebb Starts			SOUTHEAST Flood Starts			NORTHWEST Ebb Starts
D A Y O F M O N T H	D A Y O F W E E K	a.m.	**p.m.**	Kts.	a.m.	**p.m.**	Kts.	a.m.	**p.m.**	Kts.	a.m.	**p.m.**	Kts.
1	M	8:06	**8:42**	p1.7	2:06	**2:12**	p2.5	9:06	**9:18**	p1.8	2:48	**3:00**	2.5
2	T	9:00	**9:24**	p1.7	2:48	**2:54**	p2.4	10:00	**10:06**	p1.8	3:30	**3:48**	a2.5
3	W	9:54	**10:12**	p1.7	3:30	**3:42**	p2.3	10:54	**10:54**	p1.8	4:12	**4:42**	a2.4
4	T	10:43	**10:54**	p1.7	4:18	**4:30**	2.2	11:49	**11:48**	p1.9	5:00	**5:42**	a2.5
5	F	11:30	**11:36**	p1.8	5:00	**5:18**	a2.2	...	**12:36**	1.6	5:54	**6:42**	a2.6
6	S	...	**12:24**	1.5	5:48	**6:12**	a2.3	12:42	**1:30**	a1.9	6:48	**7:36**	a2.8
7	S	12:24	**1:12**	a1.8	6:36	**7:12**	a2.5	1:30	**2:24**	a2.1	7:48	**8:36**	a3.0
8	M	1:06	**2:00**	a1.9	7:24	**8:06**	a2.7	2:24	**3:12**	2.2	8:42	**9:24**	a3.3
9	T	1:54	**2:42**	a2.0	8:12	**8:54**	a3.0	3:18	**4:00**	2.4	9:36	**10:12**	a3.6
10	W	2:42	**3:30**	a2.2	9:00	**9:48**	a3.3	4:06	**4:48**	2.6	10:24	**11:06**	a3.8
11	T	3:36	**4:18**	2.3	9:48	**10:36**	a3.5	5:00	**5:36**	a2.7	11:18	**11:54**	a3.9
12	F	4:24	**5:06**	a2.5	10:42	**11:24**	a3.7	5:54	**6:24**	a2.7	...	**12:06**	3.9
13	S	5:18	**5:54**	a2.6	11:36	...	3.9	6:48	**7:12**	a2.6	12:42	**1:00**	p3.8
14	S	6:06	**6:48**	a2.6	12:18	**12:24**	p3.9	7:42	**8:00**	a2.4	1:36	**1:54**	3.5
15	M	7:00	**7:36**	2.5	1:06	**1:18**	p3.8	8:42	**9:00**	2.2	2:24	**2:48**	a3.3
16	T	8:00	**8:30**	2.4	2:00	**2:12**	p3.6	9:48	**10:00**	a2.1	3:18	**3:48**	a3.0
17	W	9:06	**9:30**	2.3	2:54	**3:12**	p3.3	10:54	**11:00**	a2.0	4:12	**4:48**	a2.7
18	T	10:12	**10:24**	2.2	3:48	**4:06**	3.0	11:54	...	2.0	5:12	**5:48**	a2.4
19	F	11:12	**11:24**	a2.1	4:42	**5:06**	a2.8	12:01	**12:54**	p2.1	6:12	**6:48**	a2.4
20	S	...	**12:12**	2.1	5:36	**6:12**	a2.7	12:54	**1:48**	p2.2	7:12	**7:48**	a2.5
21	S	12:18	**1:12**	p2.2	6:36	**7:12**	a2.7	1:54	**2:42**	p2.3	8:06	**8:42**	a2.6
22	M	1:18	**2:12**	p2.3	7:36	**8:12**	a2.8	2:42	**3:24**	p2.4	8:54	**9:24**	a2.7
23	T	2:12	**3:00**	p2.4	8:30	**9:06**	a2.8	3:30	**4:12**	p2.3	9:42	**10:12**	a2.7
24	W	3:00	**3:54**	p2.5	9:18	**9:54**	a2.8	4:12	**4:48**	p2.2	10:24	**10:54**	a2.7
25	T	3:48	**4:36**	p2.4	10:06	**10:36**	a2.8	4:54	**5:24**	p2.0	11:06	**11:36**	a2.8
26	F	4:36	**5:18**	p2.3	10:48	**11:24**	a2.8	5:36	**6:00**	1.9	11:42	...	2.8
27	S	5:18	**6:00**	p2.1	11:36	...	2.8	6:12	**6:36**	1.9	12:12	**12:24**	p2.9
28	S	6:06	**6:42**	p1.9	12:06	**12:18**	p2.8	6:54	**7:12**	p1.9	12:48	**1:06**	2.8
29	M	6:48	**7:18**	1.8	12:48	**1:00**	p2.8	7:42	**7:48**	p1.9	1:30	**1:48**	2.8
30	T	7:30	**7:54**	p1.8	1:30	**1:36**	p2.7						
31	W	8:18	**8:36**	p1.8	2:12	**2:18**	p2.6						

See the Woods Hole Current Diagrams on pp. 59-65.

Mariners should exercise great caution when transiting Woods Hole Passage as velocities have been reported to exceed NOAA's predictions.

To hold longest fair current from Buzzards Bay headed East through Vineyard and Nantucket Sounds go through Woods Hole 2 1/2 hrs. after flood starts SE in Woods Hole. (Any earlier means adverse currents in the Sounds.)

2024 CURRENT TABLE
WOODS HOLE, MA, The Strait
41°31.16'N, 70°40.97'W

*Daylight Time starts Mar. 10 at 2 a.m.   Daylight Saving Time

		MARCH						APRIL			
		CURRENT TURNS TO						CURRENT TURNS TO			
D A Y O F M O N T H	D A Y O F W E E K	SOUTHEAST Flood Starts			NORTHWEST Ebb Starts		D A Y O F M O N T H	D A Y O F W E E K	SOUTHEAST Flood Starts			NORTHWEST Ebb Starts	
		a.m.	p.m.	Kts.	a.m.	p.m.	Kts.			a.m.	p.m.	Kts.	a.m.	p.m.	Kts.
1	F	8:24	8:36	p1.9	2:06	2:30	a2.8	1	M	10:42	10:54	p1.9	4:00	4:48	a2.9
2	S	9:18	9:24	p1.9	2:48	3:18	a2.8	2	T	11:42	11:54	p2.0	5:00	5:48	a2.9
3	S	10:18	10:24	p1.9	3:30	4:12	a2.7	3	W	...	12:42	1.9	6:00	6:48	a2.8
4	M	11:13	11:18	p1.9	4:24	5:12	a2.7	4	T	1:01	1:42	a2.1	7:06	7:48	a2.9
5	T	...	12:12	1.7	5:24	6:12	a2.7	5	F	1:54	2:36	2.2	8:06	8:48	a3.1
6	W	12:18	1:06	a2.0	6:24	7:12	a2.8	6	S	2:48	3:24	2.4	9:06	9:42	3.3
7	T	1:12	2:00	a2.1	7:24	8:12	a3.1	7	S	3:42	4:12	p2.6	10:00	10:30	3.5
8	F	2:06	2:48	2.3	8:24	9:00	a3.4	8	M	4:36	5:00	a2.7	10:48	11:18	3.6
9	S	3:00	3:36	2.5	9:18	9:54	a3.6	9	T	5:30	5:48	a2.7	11:42	...	3.6
10	S	*4:54	*5:24	2.7	*11:06	*11:42	a3.8	10	W	6:24	6:36	a2.7	12:06	12:36	a3.7
11	M	5:42	6:12	a2.8	...	12:01	3.8	11	T	7:12	7:24	a2.5	1:00	1:24	a3.6
12	T	6:36	7:00	a2.7	12:30	12:54	p3.8	12	F	8:06	8:18	a2.4	1:48	2:18	a3.4
13	W	7:30	7:48	a2.6	1:18	1:42	3.6	13	S	9:06	9:12	a2.2	2:36	3:12	a3.1
14	T	8:24	8:36	a2.4	2:12	2:36	a3.5	14	S	10:06	10:18	a2.1	3:30	4:06	a2.8
15	F	9:24	9:36	a2.2	3:00	3:30	a3.2	15	M	11:06	11:18	a2.0	4:24	5:06	a2.4
16	S	10:24	10:36	a2.1	3:54	4:30	a2.9	16	T	...	12:06	1.9	5:18	6:00	a2.2
17	S	11:30	11:42	a2.0	4:48	5:24	a2.6	17	W	12:18	1:00	p1.9	6:18	6:54	a2.1
18	M	...	12:30	2.0	5:48	6:24	a2.2	18	T	1:12	1:48	p1.9	7:12	7:48	2.2
19	T	12:42	1:30	p2.0	6:48	7:24	a2.2	19	F	2:00	2:36	p1.9	8:06	8:36	2.3
20	W	1:36	2:24	p2.1	7:42	8:18	a2.4	20	S	2:48	3:18	p1.9	8:54	9:24	p2.4
21	T	2:30	3:12	p2.1	8:36	9:12	a2.5	21	S	3:30	3:54	p1.9	9:42	10:06	p2.5
22	F	3:18	3:54	p2.2	9:30	9:54	a2.5	22	M	4:12	4:30	p1.8	10:24	10:42	p2.7
23	S	4:00	4:36	p2.1	10:12	10:36	a2.6	23	T	4:54	5:06	p2.0	11:00	11:18	p2.9
24	S	4:42	5:12	p2.0	10:54	11:18	p2.7	24	W	5:36	5:42	p2.1	11:42	11:54	p3.0
25	M	5:24	5:48	p2.0	11:36	...	2.7	25	T	6:12	6:18	p2.1	...	12:24	2.8
26	T	6:06	6:18	2.0	12:01	12:12	2.8	26	F	6:54	7:00	p2.1	12:30	1:06	a3.2
27	W	6:42	6:54	p2.1	12:36	12:54	2.9	27	S	7:36	7:42	p2.1	1:12	1:54	a3.3
28	T	7:24	7:30	2.0	1:12	1:36	a3.0	28	S	8:18	8:30	2.0	1:54	2:42	a3.3
29	F	8:06	8:12	p2.0	1:48	2:18	a3.0	29	M	9:12	9:24	p2.0	2:42	3:36	a3.3
30	S	8:48	8:54	p1.9	2:24	3:06	a3.1	30	T	10:12	10:30	2.0	3:36	4:30	a3.2
31	S	9:42	9:48	p1.9	3:12	3:54	a3.0								

See the Woods Hole Current Diagrams on pp. 59-65.

Mariners should exercise great caution when transiting Woods Hole Passage as velocities have been reported to exceed NOAA's predictions.

CAUTION: Going *from* Buzzards Bay *into* Vineyard Sound, whether through Woods Hole, Robinsons Hole, or Quicks Hole, *Red* Buoys must be kept on the LEFT or PORT hand, *Green* Buoys kept on the RIGHT or STARBOARD hand. You are considered to be proceeding seaward and should thus follow the rules for LEAVING a harbor.

See pp. 22-29 for Current Change at other points.

53

2024 CURRENT TABLE
WOODS HOLE, MA, The Strait
41°31.16'N, 70°40.97'W

Daylight Saving Time	Daylight Saving Time

DAY OF MONTH	DAY OF WEEK	CURRENT TURNS TO						DAY OF MONTH	DAY OF WEEK	CURRENT TURNS TO					
		SOUTHEAST Flood Starts			NORTHWEST Ebb Starts					SOUTHEAST Flood Starts			NORTHWEST Ebb Starts		
		a.m.	**p.m.**	Kts.	a.m.	**p.m.**	Kts.			a.m.	**p.m.**	Kts.	a.m.	**p.m.**	Kts.
		MAY								JUNE					
1	W	11:18	**11:36**	p2.1	4:36	**5:24**	a3.1	1	S	12:18	**12:42**	p2.3	6:18	**7:00**	a3.0
2	T	...	**12:18**	2.1	5:36	**6:24**	a3.0	2	S	1:18	**1:36**	p2.3	7:18	**7:54**	p3.1
3	F	12:36	**1:12**	2.2	6:42	**7:24**	a3.0	3	M	2:18	**2:30**	2.3	8:24	**8:48**	p3.2
4	S	1:37	**2:06**	2.3	7:42	**8:24**	3.1	4	T	3:13	**3:24**	a2.4	9:18	**9:42**	p3.3
5	S	2:36	**2:54**	2.4	8:42	**9:18**	p3.3	5	W	4:06	**4:12**	a2.6	10:18	**10:36**	p3.4
6	M	3:30	**3:48**	2.5	9:36	**10:06**	p3.5	6	T	5:00	**5:06**	a2.6	11:06	**11:24**	p3.3
7	T	4:24	**4:36**	a2.6	10:30	**10:54**	p3.6	7	F	5:54	**5:54**	a2.6	...	**12:01**	2.9
8	W	5:18	**5:24**	a2.7	11:24	**11:48**	p3.5	8	S	6:42	**6:48**	a2.5	12:12	**12:54**	a3.2
9	T	6:06	**6:12**	a2.6	...	**12:18**	3.2	9	S	7:30	**7:36**	a2.4	1:06	**1:42**	a3.1
10	F	7:00	**7:06**	a2.5	12:36	**1:12**	a3.4	10	M	8:24	**8:30**	a2.3	1:54	**2:30**	a2.9
11	S	7:48	**7:54**	a2.4	1:24	**2:00**	a3.2	11	T	9:12	**9:24**	a2.1	2:42	**3:18**	a2.7
12	S	8:42	**8:54**	a2.3	2:18	**2:54**	a3.0	12	W	10:06	**10:18**	a1.9	3:30	**4:06**	a2.5
13	M	9:42	**9:48**	a2.1	3:06	**3:42**	a2.7	13	T	10:54	**11:12**	a1.8	4:18	**4:54**	a2.3
14	T	10:36	**10:48**	a2.0	4:00	**4:36**	a2.4	14	F	11:42	...	1.6	5:06	**5:42**	a2.2
15	W	11:36	**11:48**	a1.9	4:48	**5:30**	a2.2	15	S	12:06	**12:24**	p1.6	5:54	**6:30**	2.0
16	T	...	**12:24**	1.8	5:42	**6:18**	a2.0	16	S	12:54	**1:06**	p1.6	6:48	**7:12**	p2.1
17	F	12:42	**1:12**	p1.7	6:36	**7:12**	2.0	17	M	1:42	**1:48**	p1.7	7:36	**8:00**	p2.3
18	S	1:30	**1:54**	p1.7	7:30	**8:00**	p2.1	18	T	2:30	**2:30**	p1.8	8:30	**8:42**	p2.5
19	S	2:18	**2:30**	p1.6	8:18	**8:42**	p2.3	19	W	3:12	**3:12**	p1.9	9:18	**9:30**	p2.7
20	M	3:00	**3:12**	p1.7	9:06	**9:24**	p2.5	20	T	3:54	**3:54**	p2.0	10:06	**10:06**	p3.0
21	T	3:42	**3:48**	p1.8	9:48	**10:06**	p2.7	21	F	4:36	**4:36**	p2.1	10:48	**10:54**	p3.2
22	W	4:24	**4:30**	p2.0	10:30	**10:42**	p2.9	22	S	5:24	**5:24**	p2.2	11:36	**11:36**	p3.5
23	T	5:06	**5:06**	p2.1	11:12	**11:18**	p3.2	23	S	6:06	**6:12**	p2.3	...	**12:24**	3.0
24	F	5:48	**5:48**	p2.2	...	**12:01**	2.8	24	M	6:54	**7:00**	p2.4	12:24	**1:12**	a3.6
25	S	6:30	**6:30**	p2.2	12:01	**12:48**	a3.3	25	T	7:36	**7:48**	p2.4	1:18	**2:00**	a3.7
26	S	7:12	**7:18**	p2.2	12:48	**1:30**	a3.5	26	W	8:30	**8:48**	p2.4	2:06	**2:54**	a3.7
27	M	8:00	**8:06**	p2.2	1:36	**2:24**	a3.5	27	T	9:24	**9:48**	2.3	3:00	**3:42**	a3.7
28	T	8:54	**9:06**	p2.2	2:24	**3:12**	a3.5	28	F	10:18	**10:54**	a2.4	4:00	**4:36**	a3.5
29	W	9:48	**10:12**	2.2	3:18	**4:06**	a3.4	29	S	11:18	...	2.3	4:54	**5:36**	a3.3
30	T	10:48	**11:18**	2.2	4:18	**5:06**	a3.3	30	S	12:01	**12:12**	2.2	5:54	**6:30**	a3.0
31	F	11:48	...	2.2	5:18	**6:00**	a3.2								

See the Woods Hole Current Diagrams on pp. 59-65.

Mariners should exercise great caution when transiting Woods Hole Passage as velocities have been reported to exceed NOAA's predictions.

To hold longest fair current from Buzzards Bay headed East through Vineyard and Nantucket Sounds go through Woods Hole 2 1/2 hrs. after flood starts SE in Woods Hole. (Any earlier means adverse currents in the Sounds.)

2024 CURRENT TABLE
WOODS HOLE, MA, The Strait
41°31.16'N, 70°40.97'W

Daylight Saving Time | Daylight Saving Time

		JULY						AUGUST			
		CURRENT TURNS TO						CURRENT TURNS TO			
		SOUTHEAST Flood Starts			NORTHWEST Ebb Starts			SOUTHEAST Flood Starts			NORTHWEST Ebb Starts
DAY OF MONTH	DAY OF WEEK	a.m.	**p.m.**	Kts.	a.m.	**p.m.**	Kts.	DAY OF MONTH	DAY OF WEEK	a.m.	**p.m.**	Kts.	a.m.	**p.m.**	Kts.

DAY OF MONTH	DAY OF WEEK	a.m.	p.m.	Kts.	a.m.	p.m.	Kts.	DAY OF MONTH	DAY OF WEEK	a.m.	p.m.	Kts.	a.m.	p.m.	Kts.
1	M	1:00	1:12	p2.2	7:00	7:30	p2.9	1	T	2:42	2:48	a2.3	8:42	9:00	p2.8
2	T	2:00	2:06	a2.2	8:00	8:30	p3.0	2	F	3:36	3:42	a2.4	9:42	9:54	p2.9
3	W	3:00	3:00	a2.3	9:00	9:24	p3.1	3	S	4:30	4:30	a2.6	10:30	10:42	p2.9
4	T	3:55	3:54	a2.5	10:00	10:12	p3.1	4	S	5:19	5:18	a2.6	11:18	11:30	p2.9
5	F	4:48	4:48	a2.6	10:48	11:06	p3.1	5	M	6:00	6:06	a2.5	...	12:06	2.7
6	S	5:36	5:36	a2.6	11:42	11:54	p3.0	6	T	6:42	6:48	a2.3	12:18	12:48	a2.9
7	S	6:24	6:30	a2.5	...	12:30	2.7	7	W	7:24	7:30	a2.1	1:00	1:30	a2.9
8	M	7:12	7:12	a2.4	12:42	1:18	a3.0	8	T	8:00	8:18	a1.9	1:42	2:12	a2.8
9	T	7:54	8:00	a2.2	1:30	2:00	a2.9	9	F	8:42	9:00	a1.8	2:24	2:54	a2.7
10	W	8:36	8:48	a2.0	2:12	2:48	a2.8	10	S	9:18	9:54	a1.7	3:06	3:36	a2.6
11	T	9:24	9:42	a1.8	3:00	3:30	a2.6	11	S	10:06	10:42	a1.7	3:48	4:12	2.4
12	F	10:06	10:30	a1.7	3:42	4:18	a2.5	12	M	10:48	11:36	a1.7	4:36	5:00	2.3
13	S	10:54	11:24	a1.7	4:24	5:00	a2.3	13	T	11:42	...	1.7	5:24	5:42	p2.3
14	S	11:36	...	1.7	5:12	5:42	a2.2	14	W	12:30	12:30	p1.7	6:24	6:36	p2.3
15	M	12:18	12:24	p1.7	6:06	6:30	p2.2	15	T	1:18	1:24	p1.8	7:18	7:30	p2.5
16	T	1:06	1:06	p1.7	7:00	7:18	p2.3	16	F	2:12	2:12	p1.9	8:18	8:24	p2.8
17	W	1:54	1:54	p1.8	7:54	8:06	p2.5	17	S	3:00	3:06	p2.1	9:12	9:18	p3.1
18	T	2:42	2:42	p1.9	8:48	8:54	p2.7	18	S	3:48	3:54	p2.3	10:00	10:12	p3.4
19	F	3:30	3:30	p2.0	9:36	9:42	p3.0	19	M	4:36	4:42	p2.5	10:48	11:00	p3.7
20	S	4:12	4:12	p2.2	10:24	10:30	p3.3	20	T	5:24	5:36	p2.7	11:36	11:48	p3.9
21	S	5:00	5:00	p2.4	11:12	11:18	p3.6	21	W	6:06	6:24	p2.7	...	12:24	3.6
22	M	5:42	5:48	p2.5	...	12:01	3.2	22	T	6:54	7:18	p2.7	12:42	1:18	a3.9
23	T	6:30	6:42	p2.6	12:06	12:48	a3.8	23	F	7:42	8:12	a2.6	1:30	2:06	a3.9
24	W	7:18	7:36	p2.6	1:00	1:42	a3.9	24	S	8:30	9:12	a2.4	2:24	2:54	a3.7
25	T	8:06	8:30	2.5	1:48	2:30	a3.9	25	S	9:24	10:12	a2.3	3:18	3:48	a3.4
26	F	8:54	9:30	a2.5	2:42	3:18	a3.8	26	M	10:24	11:18	2.1	4:18	4:42	a3.0
27	S	9:48	10:36	a2.4	3:36	4:12	a3.5	27	T	11:30	...	1.9	5:18	5:42	2.6
28	S	10:48	11:42	a2.3	4:36	5:06	a3.2	28	W	12:24	12:30	a2.0	6:18	6:42	p2.4
29	M	11:48	...	2.1	5:36	6:06	2.8	29	T	1:24	1:30	a2.1	7:24	7:42	p2.5
30	T	12:42	12:48	2.0	6:42	7:06	p2.7	30	F	2:24	2:30	a2.2	8:24	8:42	p2.7
31	W	1:42	1:48	a2.1	7:42	8:06	p2.7	31	S	3:18	3:18	a2.4	9:18	9:36	p2.8

See the Woods Hole Current Diagrams on pp. 59-65.

Mariners should exercise great caution when transiting Woods Hole Passage as velocities have been reported to exceed NOAA's predictions.

CAUTION: Going *from* Buzzards Bay *into* Vineyard Sound, whether through Woods Hole, Robinsons Hole, or Quicks Hole, *Red* Buoys must be kept on the LEFT or PORT hand, *Green* Buoys kept on the RIGHT or STARBOARD hand. You are considered to be proceeding seaward and should thus follow the rules for LEAVING a harbor.

See pp. 22-29 for Current Change at other points.

2024 CURRENT TABLE
WOODS HOLE, MA, The Strait
41°31.16'N, 70°40.97'W

Daylight Saving Time							Daylight Saving Time					
SEPTEMBER							**OCTOBER**					
DAY OF MONTH	DAY OF WEEK	CURRENT TURNS TO							CURRENT TURNS TO			
		SOUTHEAST Flood Starts			NORTHWEST Ebb Starts		DAY OF MONTH	DAY OF WEEK	SOUTHEAST Flood Starts			NORTHWEST Ebb Starts
		a.m.	**p.m.**	Kts.	a.m.	**p.m.**	Kts.			a.m.	**p.m.**	Kts.	a.m.	**p.m.**	Kts.

D	W	a.m.	p.m.	Kts.	a.m.	p.m.	Kts.	D	W	a.m.	p.m.	Kts.	a.m.	p.m.	Kts.
1	S	4:06	**4:06**	a2.5	10:06	**10:24**	p2.8	1	T	4:18	**4:30**	a2.2	10:24	**10:36**	2.6
2	M	4:48	**4:54**	a2.5	10:54	**11:06**	p2.8	2	W	4:54	**5:12**	a2.1	11:00	**11:18**	2.7
3	T	5:30	**5:36**	a2.4	11:36	**11:48**	p2.8	3	T	5:30	**5:48**	a2.0	11:42	...	2.8
4	W	6:13	**6:18**	a2.2	...	**12:18**	2.7	4	F	6:07	**6:30**	a2.0	12:01	**12:18**	p2.9
5	T	6:48	**7:00**	a2.0	12:30	**12:54**	2.8	5	S	6:42	**7:12**	a2.0	12:42	**1:00**	p2.9
6	F	7:24	**7:42**	a1.9	1:12	**1:36**	2.8	6	S	7:18	**7:54**	a1.9	1:24	**1:36**	p2.9
7	S	8:00	**8:24**	a1.9	1:54	**2:12**	2.8	7	M	7:54	**8:36**	a1.9	2:06	**2:12**	p2.9
8	S	8:36	**9:12**	a1.8	2:36	**2:54**	2.7	8	T	8:42	**9:24**	a1.8	2:48	**2:54**	p2.9
9	M	9:18	**10:00**	a1.8	3:18	**3:30**	p2.6	9	W	9:30	**10:18**	a1.8	3:36	**3:36**	p2.8
10	T	10:06	**11:00**	a1.7	4:06	**4:12**	p2.6	10	T	10:30	**11:18**	a1.8	4:30	**4:30**	p2.8
11	W	11:00	**11:54**	a1.7	4:54	**5:00**	p2.5	11	F	11:30	...	1.9	5:24	**5:30**	p2.7
12	T	...	**12:01**	1.8	5:48	**6:00**	p2.5	12	S	12:18	**12:30**	p2.0	6:24	**6:30**	p2.8
13	F	12:48	**12:54**	p1.8	6:48	**7:00**	p2.6	13	S	1:12	**1:30**	p2.1	7:18	**7:36**	p3.0
14	S	1:42	**1:48**	p2.0	7:48	**8:00**	p2.9	14	M	2:06	**2:24**	p2.3	8:18	**8:36**	p3.2
15	S	2:36	**2:42**	p2.2	8:42	**8:54**	p3.2	15	T	2:54	**3:18**	p2.5	9:12	**9:30**	p3.4
16	M	3:24	**3:36**	p2.4	9:36	**9:48**	p3.5	16	W	3:42	**4:12**	p2.6	10:00	**10:24**	p3.6
17	T	4:12	**4:24**	p2.6	10:24	**10:42**	p3.7	17	T	4:30	**5:00**	p2.7	10:48	**11:12**	a3.7
18	W	4:54	**5:18**	p2.8	11:12	**11:30**	p3.8	18	F	5:18	**5:54**	p2.7	11:42	...	3.8
19	T	5:42	**6:06**	p2.8	...	**12:01**	3.7	19	S	6:06	**6:48**	p2.6	12:06	**12:30**	p3.7
20	F	6:30	**7:00**	p2.7	12:24	**12:54**	3.8	20	S	6:54	**7:42**	p2.4	1:00	**1:18**	p3.6
21	S	7:18	**7:54**	2.5	1:18	**1:42**	3.7	21	M	7:48	**8:36**	p2.3	1:54	**2:12**	p3.3
22	S	8:06	**8:54**	2.3	2:12	**2:30**	3.5	22	T	8:42	**9:36**	p2.2	2:48	**3:06**	p3.0
23	M	9:00	**9:54**	p2.2	3:06	**3:24**	p3.2	23	W	9:48	**10:42**	p2.1	3:42	**4:00**	p2.7
24	T	10:06	**11:00**	p2.1	4:00	**4:24**	2.8	24	T	10:54	**11:42**	p2.1	4:36	**4:54**	p2.4
25	W	11:12	...	1.7	5:00	**5:18**	p2.5	25	F	11:54	...	1.7	5:36	**5:54**	2.1
26	T	12:06	**12:12**	a2.1	6:00	**6:18**	2.2	26	S	12:36	**12:48**	a2.0	6:30	**6:48**	p2.2
27	F	1:06	**1:12**	a2.1	7:00	**7:18**	p2.4	27	S	1:30	**1:42**	a2.0	7:24	**7:42**	p2.3
28	S	2:00	**2:06**	a2.1	7:54	**8:18**	p2.5	28	M	2:12	**2:30**	a2.0	8:18	**8:36**	2.4
29	S	2:48	**3:00**	a2.2	8:48	**9:06**	p2.6	29	T	3:00	**3:18**	a2.0	9:06	**9:24**	a2.5
30	M	3:36	**3:42**	a2.3	9:36	**9:54**	p2.6	30	W	3:36	**4:00**	a1.9	9:48	**10:06**	a2.5
								31	T	4:12	**4:42**	a1.9	10:24	**10:48**	a2.6

See the Woods Hole Current Diagrams on pp. 59-65.

Mariners should exercise great caution when transiting Woods Hole Passage as velocities have been reported to exceed NOAA's predictions.

CAUTION: Going *from* Buzzards Bay *into* Vineyard Sound, whether through Woods Hole, Robinsons Hole, or Quicks Hole, *Red* Buoys must be kept on the LEFT or PORT hand, *Green* Buoys kept on the RIGHT or STARBOARD hand. You are considered to be proceeding seaward and should thus follow the rules for LEAVING a harbor.

2024 CURRENT TABLE
WOODS HOLE, MA, The Strait
41°31.16'N, 70°40.97'W

Standard Time starts Nov. 3 at 2 a.m.　　　　　　　Standard Time

DAY OF MONTH	DAY OF WEEK	SOUTHEAST Flood Starts a.m.	p.m.	Kts.	NORTHWEST Ebb Starts a.m.	p.m.	Kts.	DAY OF MONTH	DAY OF WEEK	SOUTHEAST Flood Starts a.m.	p.m.	Kts.	NORTHWEST Ebb Starts a.m.	p.m.	Kts.
		NOVEMBER								**DECEMBER**					
1	F	4:54	**5:24**	1.9	11:06	**11:30**	a2.8	1	S	3:54	**4:36**	1.9	10:06	**10:48**	a2.9
2	S	5:30	**6:00**	1.9	11:42	**...**	2.9	2	M	4:36	**5:12**	2.0	10:48	**11:30**	a3.1
3	S	*5:06	***5:42**	a2.0	-A-	***11:54**	2.7	3	T	5:18	**5:54**	a2.1	11:30	**...**	3.3
4	M	5:43	**6:24**	a2.0	...	**12:01**	3.1	4	W	6:01	**6:42**	a2.1	12:12	**12:12**	p3.4
5	T	6:24	**7:06**	a2.0	12:36	**12:36**	p3.1	5	T	6:48	**7:30**	2.1	1:00	**1:00**	p3.4
6	W	7:12	**7:54**	a1.9	1:24	**1:24**	p3.1	6	F	7:42	**8:18**	2.1	1:48	**1:54**	p3.4
7	T	8:06	**8:48**	1.9	2:12	**2:12**	p3.1	7	S	8:36	**9:18**	2.2	2:42	**2:48**	p3.4
8	F	9:06	**9:48**	a2.0	3:06	**3:06**	p3.1	8	S	9:42	**10:12**	2.2	3:36	**3:42**	p3.3
9	S	10:06	**10:48**	2.0	4:00	**4:06**	p3.0	9	M	10:48	**11:12**	p2.3	4:30	**4:42**	p3.1
10	S	11:06	**11:42**	2.1	4:54	**5:06**	p3.0	10	T	11:48	**...**	2.2	5:24	**5:48**	3.0
11	M	...	**12:06**	2.2	5:54	**6:12**	p3.0	11	W	12:06	**12:48**	a2.3	6:24	**6:48**	a3.1
12	T	12:36	**1:06**	p2.3	6:48	**7:12**	p3.2	12	T	1:00	**1:42**	2.3	7:18	**7:48**	a3.2
13	W	1:24	**2:00**	p2.4	7:42	**8:06**	3.3	13	F	1:48	**2:42**	p2.4	8:12	**8:48**	a3.3
14	T	2:18	**2:54**	p2.5	8:36	**9:06**	a3.5	14	S	2:42	**3:36**	p2.6	9:06	**9:42**	a3.4
15	F	3:06	**3:48**	p2.6	9:30	**10:00**	a3.6	15	S	3:36	**4:30**	p2.7	10:00	**10:36**	a3.4
16	S	3:54	**4:42**	p2.7	10:18	**10:54**	a3.6	16	M	4:30	**5:18**	p2.6	10:48	**11:30**	a3.3
17	S	4:48	**5:30**	p2.6	11:06	**11:42**	a3.6	17	T	5:24	**6:12**	p2.6	11:42	**...**	3.2
18	M	5:36	**6:24**	p2.5	...	**12:01**	3.4	18	W	6:12	**7:00**	p2.4	12:18	**12:30**	p3.1
19	T	6:30	**7:18**	p2.4	12:36	**12:48**	p3.2	19	T	7:06	**7:48**	p2.3	1:06	**1:18**	p2.9
20	W	7:24	**8:12**	p2.3	1:30	**1:42**	p2.9	20	F	8:00	**8:42**	p2.1	2:00	**2:06**	p2.7
21	T	8:24	**9:12**	p2.2	2:24	**2:36**	p2.6	21	S	8:54	**9:30**	p1.9	2:48	**3:00**	p2.5
22	F	9:24	**10:12**	p2.0	3:12	**3:30**	p2.4	22	S	9:48	**10:18**	p1.8	3:36	**3:48**	p2.3
23	S	10:24	**11:00**	p1.9	4:06	**4:24**	2.2	23	M	10:42	**11:06**	p1.6	4:24	**4:36**	2.1
24	S	11:18	**11:48**	p1.8	5:00	**5:12**	2.0	24	T	11:36	**11:48**	p1.6	5:12	**5:30**	a2.0
25	M	...	**12:12**	1.5	5:48	**6:06**	2.1	25	W	...	**12:24**	1.4	5:54	**6:18**	a2.0
26	T	12:30	**1:00**	a1.7	6:36	**7:00**	a2.2	26	T	12:30	**1:12**	a1.6	6:42	**7:12**	a2.1
27	W	1:12	**1:48**	a1.7	7:24	**7:48**	a2.3	27	F	1:18	**2:00**	a1.6	7:30	**8:00**	a2.3
28	T	1:54	**2:30**	1.6	8:12	**8:36**	a2.4	28	S	2:00	**2:42**	a1.7	8:12	**8:48**	a2.5
29	F	2:36	**3:12**	a1.7	8:48	**9:18**	a2.6	29	S	2:42	**3:24**	a1.8	8:54	**9:36**	a2.7
30	S	3:12	**3:54**	1.8	9:30	**10:00**	a2.8	30	M	3:24	**4:06**	1.9	9:36	**10:18**	a3.0
								31	T	4:06	**4:48**	a2.1	10:18	**11:06**	a3.2

A at 12:12 a.m. (2.7) and *11:18 a.m. (3.0)

See the Woods Hole Current Diagrams on pp. 59-65.

Mariners should exercise great caution when transiting Woods Hole Passage as velocities have been reported to exceed NOAA's predictions.

CAUTION: Going *from* Buzzards Bay *into* Vineyard Sound, whether through Woods Hole, Robinsons Hole, or Quicks Hole, *Red* Buoys must be kept on the LEFT or PORT hand, *Green* Buoys kept on the RIGHT or STARBOARD hand. You are considered to be proceeding seaward and should thus follow the rules for LEAVING a harbor.

See pp. 22-29 for Current Change at other points.

Coping with Currents

See also p. 21, Piloting in a Cross Current

When going directly with or against a current, our piloting problems are simple. (See Smarter Boating, p. 36.) There is no change in course, and our speed over the bottom is easily figured. However, we tend to guess a bit when the current is at some other angle. Where these currents are strong, as between New York and Nantucket, it will be vital to figure the factors carefully, especially in haze or fog.

The Table below tells 1) how many degrees to change your course; 2) by what percent your speed is decreased, with the current off the Bow; 3) or by what percent it is increased, with the current off the Stern.

First: Estimate your boat's speed through the water. Then refer to the appropriate TIDAL CURRENT CHART (see pp. 72-83 or pp. 98-103) and estimate the current's speed. Put these two in the form of a ratio, for example: boat speed is 8 kts, current 2 kts; ratio is 4 to 1.

Second: Using the same CURRENT CHART, estimate the relative direction of the current to the nearest 15°. Example: your desired course is 60°, the current is from the East, or a relative angle of 30° on your starboard bow.

Third: Enter the Tables under Ratio of 4.0; drop down to the 30° block of numbers (indicated in the left margin). The top figure in the block shows you must change your course 7°, always toward the current, and in this example, to 67°. The middle figure, 22%, is the amount by which your speed over the bottom will be decreased if the current is off your bow, i.e. from 8 kts down to 6.25 kts. Had the figure been 30% off your stern, instead of your bow, you would apply the third figure, 21%, adding it to your 8 kts, making your true speed about 9.7 kts.

RATIOS OF BOAT SPEED TO CURRENT SPEED

Relative Angle of Current		2	2½	3	3½	4	5	6	7	8	10	12	15	20
0° from	°	0	0	0	0	0	0	0	0	0	0	0	0	0
Bow	−%	50	40	33	29	25	20	17	14	12	10	8.3	6.7	5.0
Stern	+%	50	40	33	29	25	20	17	14	12	10	8.3	6.7	5.0
15° from	°	7.0	6.0	5.0	4.0	3.5	3.0	2.5	2.0	1.5	1.5	1.0	1.0	0.5
Bow	−%	49	39	33	28	24	20	16	14	12	10	8.0	6.4	4.8
Stern	+%	48	38	32	27	24	19	16	14	12	10	8.0	6.4	4.8
30° from	°	14	11	9.5	8.0	7.0	5.5	4.5	4.0	3.0	2.5	2.0	2.0	1.0
Bow	−%	46	36	30	26	22	18	15	13	11	8.8	7.3	5.9	4.3
Stern	+%	40	33	28	24	21	17	14	12	11	8.6	7.1	5.7	4.3
45° from	°	20	16	13	11	10	8.0	7.0	5.5	5.0	4.0	3.0	2.5	1.5
Bow	−%	42	32	26	22	19	15	12	11	9.2	7.4	6.1	4.9	3.6
Stern	+%	29	24	21	18	16	13	11	10	8.4	6.8	5.7	4.5	3.4
60° from	°	25	20	16	14	12	9.5	8.0	7.0	6.0	4.5	3.5	3.0	2.0
Bow	−%	34	26	21	18	15	11	9.3	7.8	6.7	5.4	4.4	3.5	2.6
Stern	+%	16	14	13	11	10	8.6	7.3	6.4	5.7	4.6	3.8	3.1	2.4
75° from	°	29	23	18	16	14	10	9.0	7.5	6.5	5.0	4.0	3.5	2.5
Bow	−%	25	18	14	11	9.1	6.8	5.5	4.5	3.8	3.0	2.5	1.9	1.4
Stern	+%	0.8	2.5	3.7	3.8	3.6	3.6	3.1	2.9	2.6	2.2	1.9	1.5	1.2
90°	°	30	24	19	17	14	11	9.5	8.0	7.0	5.5	4.5	3.5	2.5
Abeam	−%	13	8.6	5.4	4.1	3.0	1.8	1.4	1.0	0.7	0.4	0.3	0.2	0.1

Note: In general, while rounding a headland where head current is strong, hug the shore as far as safety will permit or go well out. (Current is usually apt to be strongest between these two points.)

Woods Hole and Surrounds

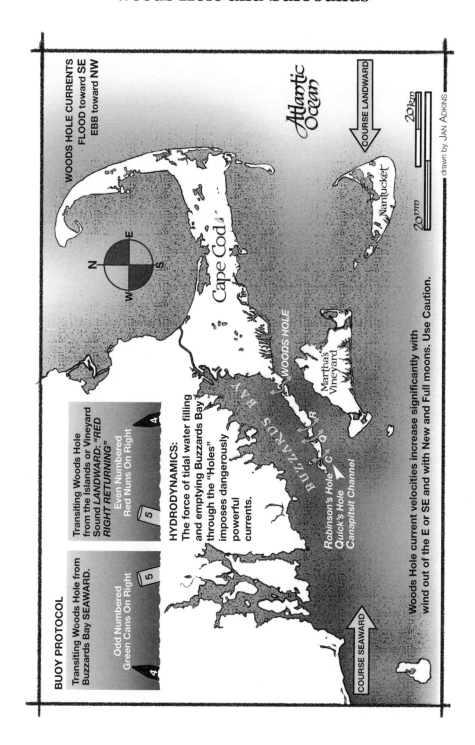

WOODS HOLE CURRENTS
FLOOD toward SE
EBB toward NW

Atlantic Ocean

COURSE LANDWARD

20 km

20 nm

drawn by JAN ADKINS

Cape Cod

N E S W

WOODS HOLE

Martha's Vineyard

Nantucket

BUZZARDS BAY

Robinson's Hole
Quick's Hole
Canapitsit Channel

BUOY PROTOCOL

Transiting Woods Hole from Buzzards Bay SEAWARD.

Odd Numbered
Green Cans On Right

Transiting Woods Hole from the Islands or Vineyard Sound LANDWARD: "RED RIGHT RETURNING"

Even Numbered
Red Nuns On Right

HYDRODYNAMICS:

The force of tidal water filling and emptying Buzzards Bay through the "Holes" imposes dangerously powerful currents.

COURSE SEAWARD

Woods Hole current velocities increase significantly with wind out of the E or SE and with New and Full moons. Use Caution.

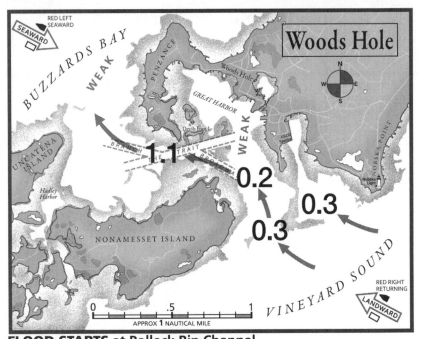

FLOOD STARTS at Pollock Rip Channel
4 hours AFTER HIGH WATER at Boston

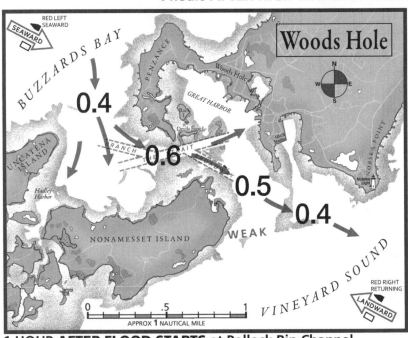

1 HOUR AFTER FLOOD STARTS at Pollock Rip Channel
5 hours AFTER HIGH WATER at Boston

Woods Hole velocities increase significantly with wind out of the E or SE and with New and Full Moons. Use Caution. Velocities shown are at Spring Tides. See note at bottom of Boston Tables: Rule-of-Thumb for Current Velocities.

Adapted from Buzzards Bay, Vineyard, and Nantucket Sounds chart on pp. 72–83.

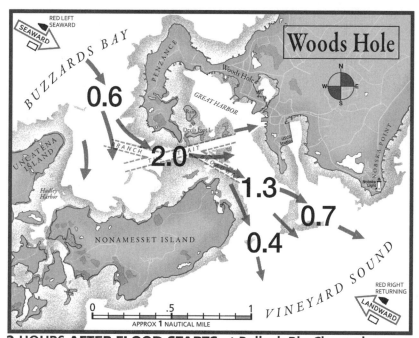

2 HOURS AFTER FLOOD STARTS at Pollock Rip Channel
LOW WATER at Boston

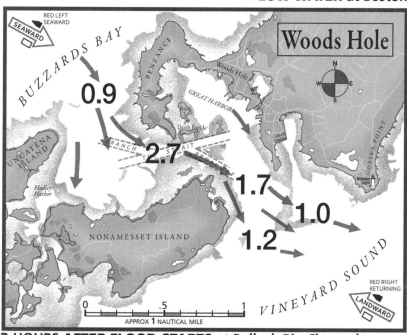

3 HOURS AFTER FLOOD STARTS at Pollock Rip Channel
1 HOUR AFTER LOW WATER at Boston

Woods Hole velocities increase significantly with wind out of the E or SE and with New and Full Moons. Use Caution. Velocities shown are at Spring Tides. See note at bottom of Boston Tables: Rule-of-Thumb for Current Velocities.

Adapted from Buzzards Bay, Vineyard, and Nantucket Sounds chart on pp. 72–83.

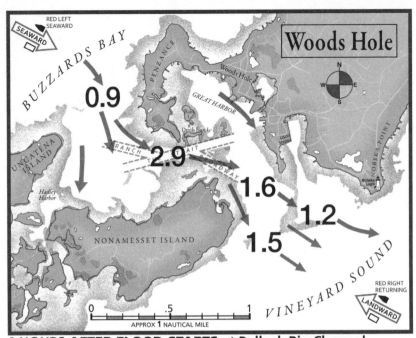

4 HOURS AFTER FLOOD STARTS at Pollock Rip Channel
2 HOURS AFTER LOW WATER at Boston

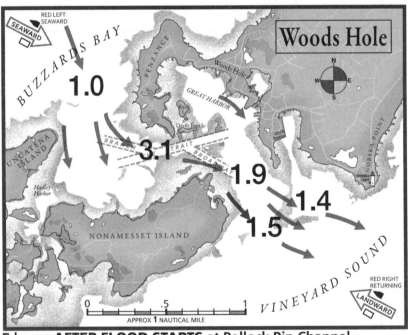

5 hours AFTER FLOOD STARTS at Pollock Rip Channel
3 hours AFTER LOW WATER at Boston

Woods Hole velocities increase significantly with wind out of the E or SE and with New and Full Moons. Use Caution. Velocities shown are at Spring Tides. See note at bottom of Boston Tables: Rule-of-Thumb for Current Velocities.

Adapted from Buzzards Bay, Vineyard, and Nantucket Sounds chart on pp. 72–83.

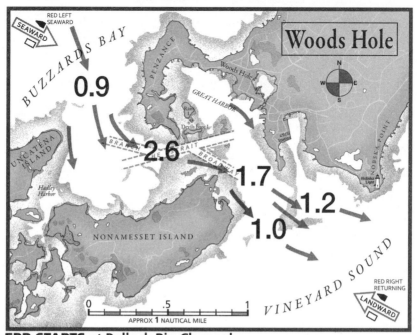

EBB STARTS at Pollock Rip Channel
4 hours AFTER LOW WATER at Boston

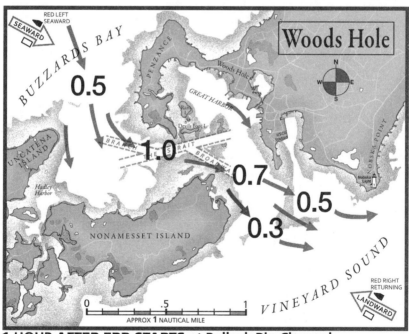

1 HOUR AFTER EBB STARTS at Pollock Rip Channel
5 hours AFTER LOW WATER at Boston

Woods Hole velocities increase significantly with wind out of the E or SE and with New and Full Moons. Use Caution. Velocities shown are at Spring Tides. See note at bottom of Boston Tables: Rule-of-Thumb for Current Velocities.

Adapted from Buzzards Bay, Vineyard, and Nantucket Sounds chart on pp. 72–83.

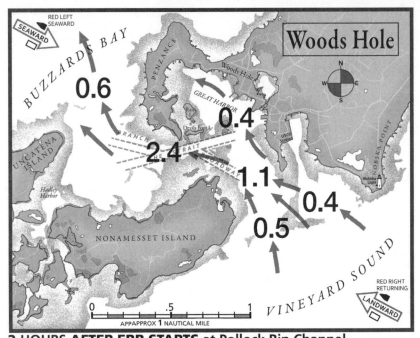

2 HOURS AFTER EBB STARTS at Pollock Rip Channel
HIGH WATER at Boston

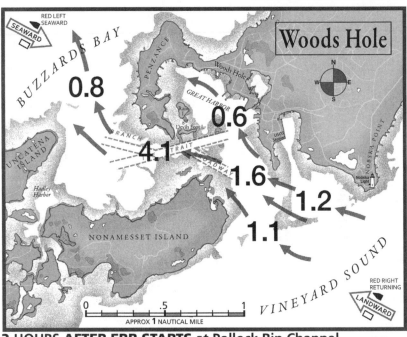

3 HOURS AFTER EBB STARTS at Pollock Rip Channel
1 HOUR AFTER HIGH WATER at Boston

Woods Hole velocities increase significantly with wind out of the E or SE and with New and Full Moons. Use Caution. Velocities shown are at Spring Tides. See note at bottom of Boston Tables: Rule-of-Thumb for Current Velocities.

Adapted from Buzzards Bay, Vineyard, and Nantucket Sounds chart on pp. 72–83.

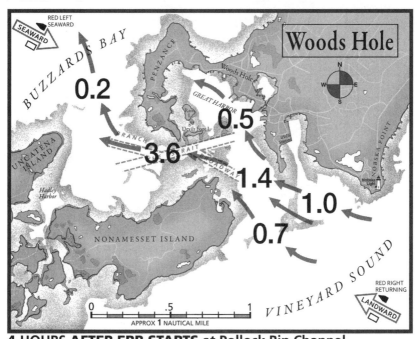

4 HOURS AFTER EBB STARTS at Pollock Rip Channel
2 HOURS AFTER HIGH WATER at Boston

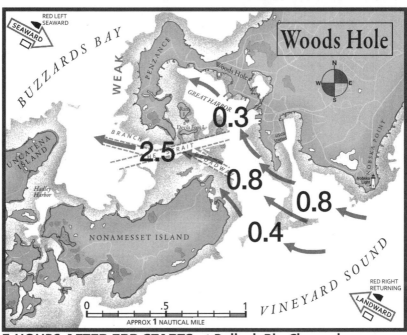

5 HOURS AFTER EBB STARTS at Pollock Rip Channel
3 HOURS AFTER HIGH WATER at Boston

Woods Hole velocities increase significantly with wind out of the E or SE and with New and Full Moons. Use Caution. Velocities shown are at Spring Tides. See note at bottom of Boston Tables: Rule-of-Thumb for Current Velocities.

Adapted from Buzzards Bay, Vineyard, and Nantucket Sounds chart on pp. 72–83.

2024 CURRENT TABLE
POLLOCK RIP CHANNEL, MA
41°33'N, 69°59'W SE of Monomoy Pt. at Butler Hole

Standard Time	Standard Time

JANUARY

D A Y O F M O N T H	D A Y O F W E E K	CURRENT TURNS TO					
		NORTHEAST Flood Starts			SOUTHWEST Ebb Starts		
		a.m.	p.m.	Kts.	a.m.	p.m.	Kts.
1	M	6:42	6:48	p1.9	12:54	1:06	1.5
2	T	7:30	7:36	p1.8	1:42	1:54	1.5
3	W	8:18	8:30	p1.7	2:24	2:48	a1.5
4	T	9:07	9:18	p1.7	3:18	3:42	a1.5
5	F	10:00	10:18	1.6	4:06	4:36	a1.5
6	S	10:48	11:12	a1.7	4:54	5:30	a1.5
7	S	11:42	...	1.7	5:48	6:24	a1.5
8	M	12:06	12:30	p1.8	6:36	7:18	a1.5
9	T	1:00	1:18	p2.0	7:24	8:06	a1.6
10	W	1:48	2:00	p2.1	8:06	8:54	a1.7
11	T	2:36	2:48	p2.2	8:54	9:36	a1.9
12	F	3:24	3:36	p2.3	9:36	10:24	a2.0
13	S	4:06	4:18	p2.4	10:24	11:12	a2.0
14	S	4:54	5:12	p2.4	11:12	...	2.1
15	M	5:48	6:00	p2.3	12:01	12:06	p2.1
16	T	6:36	6:54	p2.2	12:48	1:00	p2.0
17	W	7:30	7:54	p2.1	1:42	2:00	a1.9
18	T	8:30	8:54	1.9	2:36	3:06	a1.8
19	F	9:30	10:00	a1.9	3:36	4:12	a1.7
20	S	10:36	11:12	a1.9	4:36	5:18	a1.6
21	S	11:36	...	2.0	5:36	6:24	a1.6
22	M	12:18	12:36	p2.0	6:36	7:24	a1.6
23	T	1:18	1:30	p2.1	7:30	8:18	a1.6
24	W	2:12	2:24	p2.2	8:18	9:06	a1.6
25	T	2:54	3:06	p2.2	9:06	9:48	a1.7
26	F	3:36	3:48	p2.1	9:48	10:30	a1.7
27	S	4:18	4:24	p2.1	10:30	11:06	a1.7
28	S	4:54	5:00	p2.1	11:06	11:42	a1.7
29	M	5:30	5:36	p2.0	11:48	...	1.7
30	T	6:06	6:18	p1.9	12:18	12:30	p1.7
31	W	6:48	7:00	p1.8	1:00	1:18	1.6

FEBRUARY

D A Y O F M O N T H	D A Y O F W E E K	CURRENT TURNS TO					
		NORTHEAST Flood Starts			SOUTHWEST Ebb Starts		
		a.m.	p.m.	Kts.	a.m.	p.m.	Kts.
1	T	7:30	7:42	1.7	1:42	2:06	a1.6
2	F	8:18	8:36	1.6	2:30	3:00	a1.5
3	S	9:06	9:30	a1.6	3:18	3:54	a1.5
4	S	10:01	10:30	a1.6	4:12	4:54	a1.4
5	M	11:00	11:30	a1.7	5:06	5:54	a1.4
6	T	11:54		1.8	6:00	6:48	a1.5
7	W	12:30	12:48	p1.9	6:54	7:42	a1.6
8	T	1:24	1:42	p2.1	7:42	8:30	1.7
9	F	2:18	2:30	p2.3	8:36	9:18	a1.9
10	S	3:00	3:18	p2.4	9:18	10:00	a2.1
11	S	3:48	4:06	p2.5	10:06	10:48	a2.2
12	M	4:36	4:54	p2.5	10:54	11:30	a2.2
13	T	5:24	5:42	p2.4	11:48	...	2.2
14	W	6:12	6:36	2.2	12:18	12:42	a2.1
15	T	7:06	7:30	a2.1	1:12	1:36	a1.9
16	F	8:00	8:30	a2.0	2:06	2:42	a1.8
17	S	9:00	9:42	a1.9	3:06	3:48	a1.6
18	S	10:12	10:48	a1.8	4:12	5:00	a1.5
19	M	11:18	...	1.9	5:12	6:06	a1.4
20	T	12:01	12:18	p2.0	6:18	7:06	a1.5
21	W	1:00	1:18	p2.1	7:12	8:00	1.5
22	T	1:54	2:06	p2.2	8:06	8:42	1.6
23	F	2:36	2:48	p2.2	8:48	9:24	a1.7
24	S	3:12	3:24	p2.2	9:30	10:00	1.7
25	S	3:48	4:00	p2.1	10:06	10:36	1.7
26	M	4:24	4:30	p2.1	10:42	11:06	a1.8
27	T	4:54	5:06	p2.0	11:18	11:42	a1.8
28	W	5:30	5:42	1.9	...	12:01	1.7
29	T	6:06	6:24	1.8	12:18	12:42	1.7

The Kts. (knots) columns show the **maximum** predicted velocities of the stronger one of the Flood Currents and the stronger one of the Ebb Currents for each day.

The letter "a" means the velocity shown should occur **after** the **a.m.** Current Change. The letter "p" means the velocity shown should occur **after** the **p.m.** Current Change (even if next morning). No "a" or "p" means a.m. and p.m. velocities are the same for that day.

Avg. Max. Velocity: Flood 2.0 Kts., Ebb 1.8 Kts.

Max. Flood 3 hrs. 20 min. after Flood Starts, ±15 min.

Max. Ebb 2 hrs. 45 min. after Ebb Starts, ±15 min.

Gay Head (1 1/2 mi. NW of): avg. max velocity, Flood 2.0 kts., Ebb 2.0 kts. Time of Flood and Ebb 1 hr. 35 min. after Pollock Rip. Cross Rip: avg. max. velocity, Flood 1.3 kts., Ebb 0.9 kts. Time of Flood and Ebb 1 hr. 50 min. after Pollock Rip. Use POLLOCK RIP tables with current charts on pp. 72-83. See pp. 22-29 for Current Change at other points.

2024 CURRENT TABLE
POLLOCK RIP CHANNEL, MA
41°33'N, 69°59'W SE of Monomoy Pt. at Butler Hole

*Daylight Time starts March 10 at 2 a.m.   **Daylight Saving Time**

MARCH						APRIL					
DAY OF MONTH	DAY OF WEEK	CURRENT TURNS TO				DAY OF MONTH	DAY OF WEEK	CURRENT TURNS TO			
		NORTHEAST Flood Starts		SOUTHWEST Ebb Starts				NORTHEAST Flood Starts		SOUTHWEST Ebb Starts	
		a.m. **p.m.** Kts.		a.m. **p.m.** Kts.				a.m. **p.m.** Kts.		a.m. **p.m.** Kts.	
1	F	6:42 **7:06** a1.8		1:00 **1:30** a1.7		1	M	8:48 **9:30** a1.7		3:00 **3:48** a1.5	
2	S	7:30 **7:54** a1.7		1:48 **2:18** a1.6		2	T	9:48 **10:36** a1.7		4:00 **4:54** a1.4	
3	S	8:24 **8:54** a1.6		2:36 **3:18** a1.5		3	W	10:54 **11:42** a1.7		5:06 **5:54** a1.4	
4	M	9:19 **10:00** a1.6		3:30 **4:24** a1.4		4	T	... **12:01** 1.9		6:06 **6:54** 1.5	
5	T	10:24 **11:06** a1.6		4:30 **5:24** a1.4		5	F	12:42 **1:00** p2.0		7:06 **7:48** p1.7	
6	W	11:24 **...** 1.8		5:36 **6:24** 1.4		6	S	1:36 **1:54** p2.2		8:00 **8:36** 1.8	
7	T	12:06 **12:24** p2.0		6:30 **7:18** 1.6		7	S	2:30 **2:48** p2.3		8:54 **9:24** 2.0	
8	F	1:06 **1:18** p2.2		7:24 **8:06** 1.8		8	M	3:18 **3:36** p2.4		9:42 **10:12** 2.1	
9	S	1:54 **2:12** p2.3		8:12 **8:54** a2.0		9	T	4:00 **4:30** a2.4		10:30 **10:54** 2.1	
10	S	*3:42 ***4:00** p2.4		*10:00 ***10:36** 2.1		10	W	4:48 **5:18** a2.4		11:18 **11:42** 2.1	
11	M	4:24 **4:48** p2.5		10:48 **11:18** 2.2		11	T	5:36 **6:06** a2.4		... **12:12** 2.0	
12	T	5:12 **5:36** 2.4		11:36 **...** 2.2		12	F	6:18 **6:54** a2.3		12:30 **1:06** a2.0	
13	W	5:54 **6:24** a2.4		12:06 **12:30** p2.2		13	S	7:12 **7:48** a2.1		1:18 **2:00** a1.8	
14	T	6:42 **7:12** a2.3		12:54 **1:24** a2.1		14	S	8:06 **8:54** a1.9		2:12 **3:00** a1.6	
15	F	7:36 **8:12** a2.1		1:42 **2:18** a1.9		15	M	9:06 **10:00** a1.8		3:12 **4:06** a1.4	
16	S	8:30 **9:12** a2.0		2:36 **3:18** a1.7		16	T	10:12 **11:06** a1.8		4:18 **5:06** 1.3	
17	S	9:36 **10:18** a1.8		3:36 **4:30** a1.5		17	W	11:18 **...** 1.9		5:24 **6:06** p1.4	
18	M	10:42 **11:30** a1.8		4:42 **5:36** a1.4		18	T	12:06 **12:18** p1.9		6:24 **7:00** p1.5	
19	T	11:48 **...** 1.9		5:48 **6:42** 1.3		19	F	1:00 **1:12** p2.0		7:18 **7:48** p1.6	
20	W	12:36 **12:54** p2.0		6:54 **7:42** 1.4		20	S	1:48 **2:00** p2.0		8:06 **8:30** p1.6	
21	T	1:36 **1:48** p2.1		7:48 **8:30** 1.5		21	S	2:30 **2:42** p2.0		8:54 **9:12** p1.7	
22	F	2:24 **2:36** p2.1		8:36 **9:12** 1.6		22	M	3:06 **3:24** 2.0		9:30 **9:48** 1.7	
23	S	3:06 **3:18** p2.1		9:24 **9:48** 1.7		23	T	3:42 **4:00** a2.0		10:12 **10:24** p1.8	
24	S	3:42 **3:54** p2.1		10:00 **10:24** 1.7		24	W	4:12 **4:30** a2.0		10:48 **11:00** p1.8	
25	M	4:18 **4:30** p2.1		10:36 **11:00** p1.8		25	T	4:48 **5:12** a2.0		11:24 **11:36** p1.8	
26	T	4:48 **5:00** 2.0		11:12 **11:30** 1.8		26	F	5:24 **5:48** a2.0		... **12:06** 1.7	
27	W	5:18 **5:36** a2.0		11:54 **...** 1.8		27	S	6:00 **6:30** a2.0		12:12 **12:48** a1.7	
28	T	5:54 **6:12** a2.0		12:06 **12:30** a1.8		28	S	6:42 **7:18** a1.9		12:54 **1:36** a1.7	
29	F	6:30 **6:54** a1.9		12:42 **1:12** 1.7		29	M	7:30 **8:12** a1.9		1:42 **2:30** a1.6	
30	S	7:06 **7:36** a1.9		1:24 **2:00** a1.7		30	T	8:24 **9:12** a1.8		2:36 **3:30** a1.5	
31	S	7:54 **8:30** a1.8		2:12 **2:54** a1.6							

The Kts. (knots) columns show the **maximum** predicted velocities of the stronger one of the Flood Currents and the stronger one of the Ebb Currents for each day.

The letter "a" means the velocity shown should occur **after** the **a.m.** Current Change. The letter "p" means the velocity shown should occur **after** the **p.m.** Current Change (even if next morning). No "a" or "p" means a.m. and p.m. velocities are the same for that day.

Avg. Max. Velocity: Flood 2.0 Kts., Ebb 1.8 Kts.

Max. Flood 3 hrs. 20 min. after Flood Starts, ±15 min.

Max. Ebb 2 hrs. 45 min. after Ebb Starts, ±15 min.

Gay Head (1 1/2 mi. NW of): avg. max velocity, Flood 2.0 kts., Ebb 2.0 kts. Time of Flood and Ebb 1 hr. 35 min. after Pollock Rip. Cross Rip: avg. max. velocity, Flood 1.3 kts., Ebb 0.9 kts. Time of Flood and Ebb 1 hr. 50 min. after Pollock Rip. Use POLLOCK RIP tables with current charts on pp. 72-83. See pp. 22-29 for Current Change at other points.

POLLOCK RIP CHANNEL, MA
41°33'N, 69°59'W SE of Monomoy Pt. at Butler Hole

Daylight Saving Time	Daylight Saving Time

MAY	JUNE

D A Y O F M O N T H	D A Y O F W E E K	CURRENT TURNS TO						D A Y O F M O N T H	D A Y O F W E E K	CURRENT TURNS TO					
		NORTHEAST Flood Starts			SOUTHWEST Ebb Starts					NORTHEAST Flood Starts			SOUTHWEST Ebb Starts		
		a.m.	p.m.	Kts.	a.m.	p.m.	Kts.			a.m.	p.m.	Kts.	a.m.	p.m.	Kts.
1	W	9:24	10:12	a1.8	3:36	4:30	a1.5	1	S	11:12	11:48	a2.0	5:18	5:54	1.7
2	T	10:30	11:18	a1.9	4:42	5:30	1.5	2	S	...	12:12	2.0	6:18	6:48	p1.8
3	F	11:36	...	1.9	5:42	6:24	1.6	3	M	12:48	1:12	2.0	7:18	7:42	p1.8
4	S	12:19	12:36	p2.1	6:42	7:18	p1.8	4	T	1:43	2:12	a2.1	8:18	8:36	p1.9
5	S	1:12	1:36	p2.1	7:42	8:12	p1.9	5	W	2:30	3:06	a2.2	9:12	9:24	p1.9
6	M	2:06	2:30	p2.2	8:36	9:00	p2.0	6	T	3:24	3:54	a2.3	10:06	10:12	p1.8
7	T	2:54	3:18	a2.3	9:24	9:42	2.0	7	F	4:12	4:48	a2.2	10:54	11:00	p1.8
8	W	3:42	4:12	a2.3	10:18	10:30	2.0	8	S	5:00	5:36	a2.2	11:48	11:48	p1.7
9	T	4:24	5:00	a2.3	11:06	11:18	1.9	9	S	5:42	6:24	a2.1	...	12:36	1.6
10	F	5:12	5:48	a2.3	...	12:01	1.8	10	M	6:30	7:12	a2.1	12:36	1:24	a1.7
11	S	6:00	6:42	a2.2	12:06	12:48	a1.8	11	T	7:18	8:00	a2.0	1:30	2:12	a1.6
12	S	6:48	7:30	a2.1	12:54	1:42	a1.7	12	W	8:12	8:54	a1.9	2:18	3:00	a1.5
13	M	7:42	8:30	a2.0	1:48	2:42	a1.6	13	T	9:00	9:48	a1.9	3:12	3:54	p1.5
14	T	8:42	9:30	a1.9	2:48	3:36	1.4	14	F	9:54	10:36	a1.8	4:06	4:42	p1.5
15	W	9:42	10:30	a1.8	3:48	4:30	1.4	15	S	10:48	11:30	a1.8	5:06	5:30	p1.5
16	T	10:42	11:24	a1.8	4:48	5:24	p1.4	16	S	11:42	...	1.8	6:00	6:18	p1.5
17	F	11:36	...	1.9	5:48	6:18	p1.5	17	M	12:18	12:36	1.7	6:54	7:06	p1.6
18	S	12:18	12:30	p1.9	6:42	7:06	p1.6	18	T	1:06	1:24	a1.8	7:42	7:54	p1.6
19	S	1:06	1:18	p1.9	7:30	7:48	p1.6	19	W	1:48	2:12	a1.9	8:30	8:36	p1.6
20	M	1:48	2:06	1.9	8:18	8:30	p1.7	20	T	2:30	2:54	a1.9	9:12	9:18	p1.7
21	T	2:30	2:48	a2.0	9:00	9:12	p1.7	21	F	3:12	3:42	a2.0	10:00	10:00	p1.7
22	W	3:06	3:24	a2.0	9:42	9:48	p1.7	22	S	3:54	4:24	a2.0	10:42	10:42	p1.8
23	T	3:42	4:06	a2.0	10:24	10:30	p1.7	23	S	4:36	5:06	a2.1	11:24	11:24	p1.8
24	F	4:18	4:42	a2.0	11:06	11:06	p1.7	24	M	5:18	5:54	a2.2	...	12:12	1.7
25	S	4:54	5:24	a2.0	11:48	11:48	p1.8	25	T	6:06	6:42	a2.2	12:12	1:00	a1.9
26	S	5:36	6:12	a2.1	...	12:30	1.6	26	W	6:54	7:30	a2.2	1:00	1:48	a1.9
27	M	6:18	7:00	a2.1	12:30	1:18	a1.7	27	T	7:48	8:24	a2.2	1:54	2:36	a1.9
28	T	7:12	7:54	a2.0	1:18	2:12	a1.7	28	F	8:42	9:24	a2.1	2:54	3:30	1.8
29	W	8:06	8:48	a2.0	2:18	3:06	a1.7	29	S	9:42	10:24	a2.0	3:54	4:30	1.7
30	T	9:06	9:48	a2.0	3:12	4:00	a1.7	30	S	10:48	11:24	1.9	4:54	5:24	1.7
31	F	10:06	10:48	a2.0	4:18	5:00	1.6								

The Kts. (knots) columns show the **maximum** predicted velocities of the stronger one of the Flood Currents and the stronger one of the Ebb Currents for each day.

The letter "a" means the velocity shown should occur **after** the **a.m.** Current Change. The letter "p" means the velocity shown should occur **after** the **p.m.** Current Change (even if next morning). No "a" or "p" means a.m. and p.m. velocities are the same for that day.

Avg. Max. Velocity: Flood 2.0 Kts., Ebb 1.8 Kts.

Max. Flood 3 hrs. 20 min. after Flood Starts, ±15 min.

Max. Ebb 2 hrs. 45 min. after Ebb Starts, ±15 min.

Gay Head (1 1/2 mi. NW of): avg. max velocity, Flood 2.0 kts., Ebb 2.0 kts. Time of Flood and Ebb 1 hr. 35 min. after Pollock Rip. Cross Rip: avg. max. velocity, Flood 1.3 kts., Ebb 0.9 kts. Time of Flood and Ebb 1 hr. 50 min. after Pollock Rip. Use POLLOCK RIP tables with current charts on pp. 72-83. See pp. 22-29 for Current Change at other points.

2024 CURRENT TABLE
POLLOCK RIP CHANNEL, MA
41°33'N, 69°59'W SE of Monomoy Pt. at Butler Hole

Daylight Saving Time   **Daylight Saving Time**

JULY								AUGUST							
DAY OF MONTH	DAY OF WEEK	CURRENT TURNS TO						DAY OF MONTH	DAY OF WEEK	CURRENT TURNS TO					
		NORTHEAST Flood Starts			SOUTHWEST Ebb Starts					NORTHEAST Flood Starts			SOUTHWEST Ebb Starts		
		a.m.	**p.m.**	Kts.	a.m.	**p.m.**	Kts.			a.m.	**p.m.**	Kts.	a.m.	**p.m.**	Kts.
1	M	11:48	...	1.9	6:00	**6:24**	p1.7	1	T	1:06	**1:48**	a2.0	7:54	**8:00**	p1.6
2	T	12:24	**12:54**	a2.0	7:06	**7:18**	p1.7	2	F	2:06	**2:42**	a2.1	8:48	**8:54**	p1.7
3	W	1:24	**1:54**	a2.1	8:06	**8:18**	p1.7	3	S	3:00	**3:36**	a2.2	9:42	**9:42**	p1.7
4	T	2:19	**2:54**	a2.1	9:00	**9:06**	p1.7	4	S	3:49	**4:18**	a2.2	10:30	**10:30**	p1.7
5	F	3:12	**3:48**	a2.2	9:54	**10:00**	p1.7	5	M	4:30	**5:00**	a2.2	11:12	**11:12**	p1.7
6	S	4:00	**4:36**	a2.2	10:42	**10:48**	p1.7	6	T	5:06	**5:36**	a2.1	11:48	**11:54**	p1.7
7	S	4:42	**5:18**	a2.2	11:30	**11:30**	p1.7	7	W	5:48	**6:12**	a2.1	...	**12:24**	1.6
8	M	5:30	**6:06**	a2.1	...	**12:12**	1.6	8	T	6:24	**6:48**	a2.0	12:30	**1:06**	a1.7
9	T	6:12	**6:48**	a2.1	12:18	**1:00**	a1.7	9	F	7:00	**7:30**	a1.9	1:12	**1:42**	a1.7
10	W	6:54	**7:30**	a2.0	1:00	**1:42**	1.6	10	S	7:42	**8:12**	a1.8	2:00	**2:24**	1.6
11	T	7:36	**8:12**	a1.9	1:48	**2:24**	a1.6	11	S	8:30	**9:00**	a1.7	2:48	**3:12**	1.5
12	F	8:24	**9:00**	a1.9	2:36	**3:06**	1.5	12	M	9:18	**9:48**	1.6	3:42	**4:00**	p1.5
13	S	9:12	**9:48**	a1.8	3:30	**3:54**	1.5	13	T	10:12	**10:42**	p1.6	4:36	**4:54**	p1.4
14	S	10:00	**10:36**	a1.7	4:18	**4:42**	p1.5	14	W	11:12	**11:36**	p1.6	5:36	**5:48**	p1.4
15	M	10:54	**11:30**	1.6	5:18	**5:36**	p1.5	15	T	...	**12:12**	1.4	6:36	**6:42**	p1.4
16	T	11:54	...	1.5	6:12	**6:24**	p1.5	16	F	12:36	**1:12**	a1.7	7:30	**7:36**	p1.5
17	W	12:18	**12:48**	a1.7	7:06	**7:18**	p1.5	17	S	1:30	**2:06**	a1.9	8:24	**8:24**	p1.6
18	T	1:12	**1:42**	a1.8	8:00	**8:06**	p1.5	18	S	2:18	**2:54**	a2.0	9:06	**9:12**	p1.8
19	F	2:00	**2:30**	a1.9	8:48	**8:48**	p1.6	19	M	3:06	**3:42**	a2.2	9:54	**10:00**	p2.0
20	S	2:42	**3:18**	a2.0	9:36	**9:36**	p1.7	20	T	3:54	**4:24**	a2.3	10:36	**10:42**	p2.1
21	S	3:30	**4:06**	a2.1	10:18	**10:18**	p1.9	21	W	4:42	**5:06**	a2.4	11:18	**11:30**	p2.2
22	M	4:12	**4:48**	a2.2	11:06	**11:06**	p2.0	22	T	5:24	**5:54**	a2.4	...	**12:06**	2.1
23	T	5:00	**5:30**	a2.3	11:48	**11:54**	p2.0	23	F	6:12	**6:42**	a2.4	12:18	**12:54**	a2.2
24	W	5:48	**6:18**	a2.3	...	**12:30**	1.9	24	S	7:06	**7:30**	2.2	1:12	**1:42**	a2.1
25	T	6:36	**7:06**	a2.3	12:42	**1:18**	a2.1	25	S	8:00	**8:30**	2.0	2:06	**2:36**	a1.9
26	F	7:24	**8:00**	a2.3	1:36	**2:12**	a2.0	26	M	9:00	**9:30**	p1.9	3:12	**3:36**	1.7
27	S	8:24	**8:54**	a2.1	2:30	**3:06**	1.9	27	T	10:06	**10:36**	p1.9	4:18	**4:36**	1.5
28	S	9:24	**9:54**	a2.0	3:30	**4:00**	1.8	28	W	11:18	**11:42**	p1.9	5:24	**5:42**	p1.5
29	M	10:24	**11:00**	p1.9	4:36	**5:00**	p1.7	29	T	...	**12:30**	1.6	6:36	**6:48**	p1.5
30	T	11:30	...	1.7	5:42	**6:00**	p1.6	30	F	12:48	**1:36**	a2.0	7:36	**7:48**	p1.6
31	W	12:01	**12:42**	a1.9	6:48	**7:00**	p1.6	31	S	1:48	**2:30**	a2.1	8:36	**8:42**	p1.6

The Kts. (knots) columns show the **maximum** predicted velocities of the stronger one of the Flood Currents and the stronger one of the Ebb Currents for each day.

The letter "a" means the velocity shown should occur **after** the **a.m.** Current Change. The letter "p" means the velocity shown should occur **after** the **p.m.** Current Change (even if next morning). No "a" or "p" means a.m. and p.m. velocities are the same for that day.

Avg. Max. Velocity: Flood 2.0 Kts., Ebb 1.8 Kts.

Max. Flood 3 hrs. 20 min. after Flood Starts, ±15 min.

Max. Ebb 2 hrs. 45 min. after Ebb Starts, ±15 min.

Gay Head (1 1/2 mi. NW of): avg. max velocity, Flood 2.0 kts., Ebb 2.0 kts. Time of Flood and Ebb 1 hr. 35 min. after Pollock Rip. Cross Rip: avg. max. velocity, Flood 1.3 kts., Ebb 0.9 kts. Time of Flood and Ebb 1 hr. 50 min. after Pollock Rip. Use POLLOCK RIP tables with current charts on pp. 72-83. See pp. 22-29 for Current Change at other points.

2024 CURRENT TABLE
POLLOCK RIP CHANNEL, MA
41°33'N, 69°59'W SE of Monomoy Pt. at Butler Hole

Daylight Saving Time	Daylight Saving Time

SEPTEMBER / OCTOBER

DAY OF MONTH	DAY OF WEEK	CURRENT TURNS TO						DAY OF MONTH	DAY OF WEEK	CURRENT TURNS TO					
		NORTHEAST Flood Starts			SOUTHWEST Ebb Starts					NORTHEAST Flood Starts			SOUTHWEST Ebb Starts		
		a.m.	p.m.	Kts.	a.m.	p.m.	Kts.			a.m.	p.m.	Kts.	a.m.	p.m.	Kts.
1	S	2:42	3:18	a2.2	9:24	9:30	p1.7	1	T	3:00	3:24	a2.2	9:30	9:42	1.7
2	M	3:24	3:54	a2.2	10:06	10:12	1.7	2	W	3:36	4:00	a2.1	10:06	10:24	1.7
3	T	4:06	4:30	a2.2	10:42	10:48	1.7	3	T	4:12	4:30	a2.1	10:42	11:00	1.7
4	W	4:43	5:06	a2.1	11:18	11:24	1.7	4	F	4:49	5:06	2.0	11:18	11:36	a1.8
5	T	5:18	5:36	a2.0	11:48	...	1.7	5	S	5:24	5:36	1.9	11:48	...	1.7
6	F	5:54	6:12	a2.0	12:06	12:24	1.7	6	S	5:54	6:12	p1.9	12:12	12:24	1.7
7	S	6:30	6:48	a1.9	12:42	1:00	1.7	7	M	6:36	6:48	p1.8	12:54	1:06	1.6
8	S	7:06	7:30	1.8	1:24	1:42	1.6	8	T	7:18	7:36	p1.8	1:42	1:54	1.5
9	M	7:48	8:12	p1.7	2:12	2:30	1.5	9	W	8:12	8:24	p1.7	2:36	2:42	1.4
10	T	8:42	9:00	p1.6	3:06	3:18	1.4	10	T	9:12	9:24	p1.6	3:30	3:42	p1.4
11	W	9:36	10:00	p1.6	4:00	4:12	1.3	11	F	10:12	10:30	p1.7	4:30	4:42	1.3
12	T	10:42	11:00	p1.6	5:00	5:12	p1.3	12	S	11:18	11:30	p1.8	5:30	5:42	p1.4
13	F	11:48	...	1.4	6:00	6:12	p1.4	13	S	...	12:18	1.6	6:30	6:42	p1.6
14	S	12:01	12:48	a1.7	7:00	7:06	p1.5	14	M	12:30	1:12	a2.0	7:24	7:36	p1.8
15	S	1:00	1:42	a1.9	7:54	8:00	p1.7	15	T	1:30	2:00	a2.1	8:12	8:30	p1.9
16	M	1:54	2:30	a2.1	8:42	8:48	p1.9	16	W	2:18	2:48	2.2	8:54	9:18	p2.1
17	T	2:42	3:12	a2.3	9:24	9:36	p2.1	17	T	3:12	3:36	p2.4	9:42	10:06	2.1
18	W	3:30	4:00	a2.4	10:12	10:24	p2.2	18	F	4:00	4:18	p2.4	10:24	10:54	a2.2
19	T	4:18	4:42	2.4	10:54	11:12	p2.2	19	S	4:48	5:06	p2.4	11:12	11:42	2.1
20	F	5:06	5:30	2.4	11:36	...	2.2	20	S	5:36	5:54	p2.3	...	12:01	2.0
21	S	5:54	6:12	2.3	12:01	12:24	a2.2	21	M	6:30	6:42	p2.2	12:36	12:48	1.9
22	S	6:48	7:06	p2.2	12:54	1:12	2.0	22	T	7:24	7:42	p2.0	1:36	1:48	1.7
23	M	7:42	8:00	p2.0	1:48	2:06	1.8	23	W	8:24	8:42	p1.9	2:36	2:48	1.5
24	T	8:42	9:06	p1.9	2:54	3:12	1.6	24	T	9:30	9:48	p1.9	3:36	3:54	1.4
25	W	9:48	10:12	p1.9	4:00	4:18	1.4	25	F	10:42	10:54	p1.9	4:42	5:00	1.4
26	T	11:06	11:24	p1.9	5:06	5:24	p1.4	26	S	11:42	...	1.6	5:42	6:00	1.4
27	F	...	12:12	1.6	6:12	6:30	1.4	27	S	12:01	12:42	a2.0	6:42	7:00	1.5
28	S	12:30	1:12	a2.0	7:12	7:30	1.5	28	M	12:54	1:30	a2.0	7:30	7:48	1.6
29	S	1:24	2:06	a2.1	8:06	8:18	1.6	29	T	1:42	2:12	a2.1	8:12	8:36	a1.7
30	M	2:18	2:48	a2.2	8:54	9:06	1.7	30	W	2:24	2:54	a2.1	8:54	9:18	1.7
								31	T	3:06	3:24	2.0	9:30	9:54	1.7

The Kts. (knots) columns show the **maximum** predicted velocities of the stronger one of the Flood Currents and the stronger one of the Ebb Currents for each day.

The letter "a" means the velocity shown should occur **after** the **a.m.** Current Change. The letter "p" means the velocity shown should occur **after** the **p.m.** Current Change (even if next morning). No "a" or "p" means a.m. and p.m. velocities are the same for that day.

Avg. Max. Velocity: Flood 2.0 Kts., Ebb 1.8 Kts.

Max. Flood 3 hrs. 20 min. after Flood Starts, ±15 min.

Max. Ebb 2 hrs. 45 min. after Ebb Starts, ±15 min.

Gay Head (1 1/2 mi. NW of): avg. max velocity, Flood 2.0 kts., Ebb 2.0 kts. Time of Flood and Ebb 1 hr. 35 min. after Pollock Rip. Cross Rip: avg. max. velocity, Flood 1.3 kts., Ebb 0.9 kts. Time of Flood and Ebb 1 hr. 50 min. after Pollock Rip. Use POLLOCK RIP tables with current charts on pp. 72-83. See pp. 22-29 for Current Change at other points.

2024 CURRENT TABLE
POLLOCK RIP CHANNEL, MA
41°33'N, 69°59'W SE of Monomoy Pt. at Butler Hole

Standard Time starts Nov. 3 at 2 a.m.   **Standard Time**

NOVEMBER

DAY OF MONTH	DAY OF WEEK	NORTHEAST Flood Starts a.m.	p.m.	Kts.	SOUTHWEST Ebb Starts a.m.	p.m.	Kts.
1	F	3:42	**4:00**	p2.0	10:06	**10:36**	a1.7
2	S	4:18	**4:30**	p2.0	10:42	**11:12**	a1.7
3	S	*3:54	*4:06	p2.0	*10:18	*10:54	a1.7
4	M	4:31	**4:42**	p2.0	10:54	**11:36**	a1.7
5	T	5:12	**5:24**	p1.9	11:36	...	1.6
6	W	6:00	**6:06**	p1.9	12:18	**12:24**	p1.6
7	T	6:48	**7:00**	p1.8	1:12	**1:12**	p1.5
8	F	7:48	**7:54**	p1.8	2:06	**2:12**	p1.5
9	S	8:48	**9:00**	p1.8	3:00	**3:12**	p1.5
10	S	9:48	**10:00**	p1.9	4:00	**4:18**	1.5
11	M	10:48	**11:06**	p2.0	4:54	**5:18**	1.6
12	T	11:42	...	1.9	5:48	**6:12**	p1.8
13	W	12:01	**12:36**	2.1	6:42	**7:06**	1.9
14	T	1:00	**1:24**	p2.3	7:30	**8:00**	a2.0
15	F	1:48	**2:12**	p2.4	8:18	**8:48**	2.0
16	S	2:42	**3:00**	p2.4	9:00	**9:42**	a2.1
17	S	3:30	**3:48**	p2.4	9:48	**10:30**	a2.0
18	M	4:24	**4:36**	p2.3	10:36	**11:24**	a1.9
19	T	5:12	**5:24**	p2.2	11:30	...	1.8
20	W	6:06	**6:18**	p2.1	12:18	**12:24**	p1.7
21	T	7:06	**7:18**	p2.0	1:12	**1:24**	1.5
22	F	8:06	**8:18**	p1.9	2:12	**2:24**	1.4
23	S	9:06	**9:18**	p1.9	3:12	**3:24**	1.4
24	S	10:06	**10:18**	p1.9	4:06	**4:24**	1.4
25	M	11:00	**11:12**	p1.9	5:00	**5:24**	a1.5
26	T	11:48	...	1.8	5:48	**6:12**	a1.6
27	W	12:01	**12:30**	1.9	6:30	**7:00**	a1.6
28	T	12:48	**1:12**	p2.0	7:18	**7:48**	a1.7
29	F	1:30	**1:54**	p2.0	7:54	**8:30**	a1.7
30	S	2:12	**2:30**	p2.0	8:36	**9:12**	a1.7

DECEMBER

DAY OF MONTH	DAY OF WEEK	NORTHEAST Flood Starts a.m.	p.m.	Kts.	SOUTHWEST Ebb Starts a.m.	p.m.	Kts.
1	S	2:54	**3:06**	p2.0	9:12	**9:48**	a1.7
2	M	3:30	**3:42**	p2.0	9:48	**10:30**	a1.7
3	T	4:12	**4:18**	p2.0	10:30	**11:12**	a1.7
4	W	4:55	**5:00**	p2.0	11:12	...	1.7
5	T	5:36	**5:48**	p2.0	12:01	**12:01**	p1.7
6	F	6:30	**6:36**	p2.0	12:48	**12:48**	p1.7
7	S	7:24	**7:30**	p2.0	1:36	**1:48**	1.6
8	S	8:18	**8:30**	p1.9	2:30	**2:42**	1.6
9	M	9:18	**9:36**	p1.9	3:24	**3:48**	1.6
10	T	10:18	**10:36**	p1.9	4:24	**4:48**	a1.7
11	W	11:12	**11:36**	1.9	5:18	**5:48**	1.7
12	T	...	**12:12**	2.1	6:12	**6:48**	a1.8
13	F	12:36	**1:00**	p2.2	7:06	**7:42**	a1.9
14	S	1:36	**1:54**	p2.3	7:54	**8:36**	a1.9
15	S	2:30	**2:42**	p2.3	8:48	**9:30**	a1.9
16	M	3:18	**3:36**	p2.3	9:36	**10:24**	a1.9
17	T	4:12	**4:24**	p2.3	10:24	**11:12**	a1.8
18	W	5:00	**5:12**	p2.2	11:12	...	1.8
19	T	5:48	**6:00**	p2.1	12:01	**12:06**	p1.7
20	F	6:42	**6:48**	p2.0	12:48	**12:54**	1.6
21	S	7:30	**7:42**	p1.9	1:36	**1:48**	1.5
22	S	8:24	**8:36**	p1.8	2:30	**2:48**	a1.5
23	M	9:18	**9:30**	p1.8	3:18	**3:42**	a1.5
24	T	10:06	**10:24**	1.7	4:12	**4:42**	a1.5
25	W	11:00	**11:18**	1.7	5:00	**5:36**	a1.5
26	T	11:48	...	1.8	5:48	**6:24**	a1.5
27	F	12:12	**12:36**	p1.8	6:36	**7:18**	a1.5
28	S	1:00	**1:18**	p1.9	7:24	**8:06**	a1.6
29	S	1:48	**2:00**	p2.0	8:06	**8:48**	a1.6
30	M	2:30	**2:42**	p2.0	8:48	**9:30**	a1.7
31	T	3:12	**3:18**	p2.1	9:30	**10:12**	1.7

The Kts. (knots) columns show the **maximum** predicted velocities of the stronger one of the Flood Currents and the stronger one of the Ebb Currents for each day.

The letter "a" means the velocity shown should occur **after** the **a.m.** Current Change. The letter "p" means the velocity shown should occur **after** the **p.m.** Current Change (even if next morning). No "a" or "p" means a.m. and p.m. velocities are the same for that day.

Avg. Max. Velocity: Flood 2.0 Kts., Ebb 1.8 Kts.

Max. Flood 3 hrs. 20 min. after Flood Starts, ±15 min.

Max. Ebb 2 hrs. 45 min. after Ebb Starts, ±15 min.

Gay Head (1 1/2 mi. NW of): avg. max velocity, Flood 2.0 kts., Ebb 2.0 kts. Time of Flood and Ebb 1 hr. 35 min. after Pollock Rip. Cross Rip: avg. max. velocity, Flood 1.3 kts., Ebb 0.9 kts. Time of Flood and Ebb 1 hr. 50 min. after Pollock Rip. Use POLLOCK RIP tables with current charts on pp. 72-83. See pp. 22-29 for Current Change at other points.

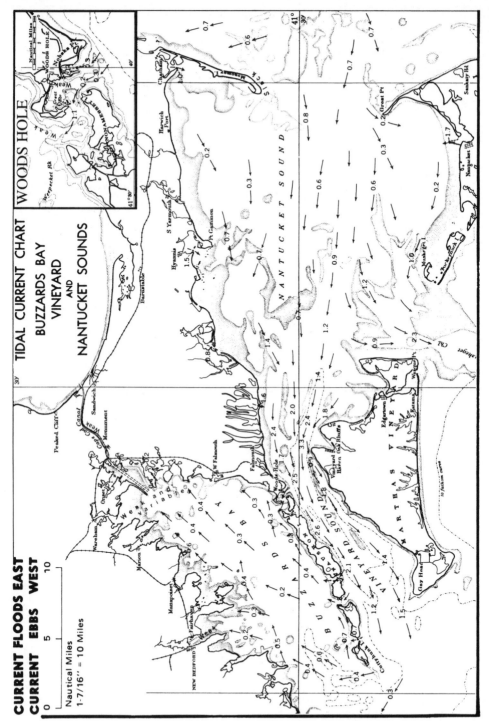

CURRENT FLOODS EAST
CURRENT EBBS WEST

TIDAL CURRENT CHART
BUZZARDS BAY
VINEYARD
AND
NANTUCKET SOUNDS

WOODS HOLE

Nautical Miles
1-7/16'' = 10 Miles

0   5   10

FLOOD STARTS AT POLLOCK RIP CHANNEL
OR: 4 HOURS **AFTER** HIGH WATER AT BOSTON

Velocities shown are at Spring Tides. See note at bottom of Boston Tables: Rule-of-Thumb for Current Velocities. See pp. 60–65 for an enlarged version of Woods Hole inset.
Pollock Rip Ch. is SE of Monomoy Pt.

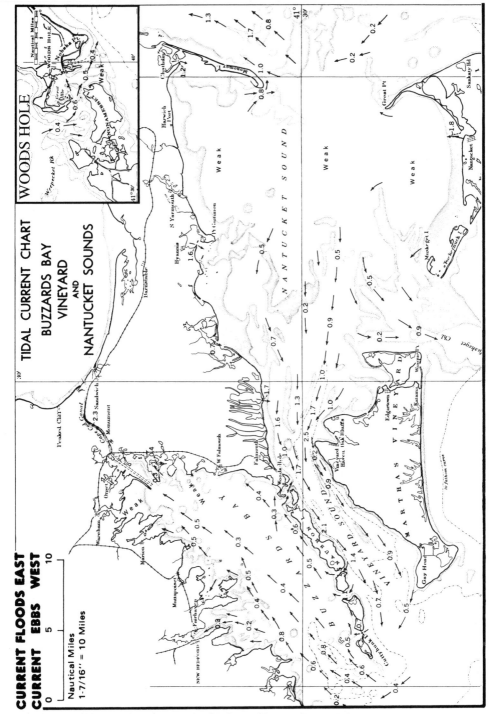

1 HOUR **AFTER** FLOOD STARTS AT POLLOCK RIP CHANNEL
OR: 5 HOURS **AFTER** HIGH WATER AT BOSTON

Velocities shown are at Spring Tides. See note at bottom of Boston Tables: Rule-of-Thumb for Current Velocities. See pp. 60–65 for an enlarged version of Woods Hole inset.
Pollock Rip Ch. is SE of Monomoy Pt.

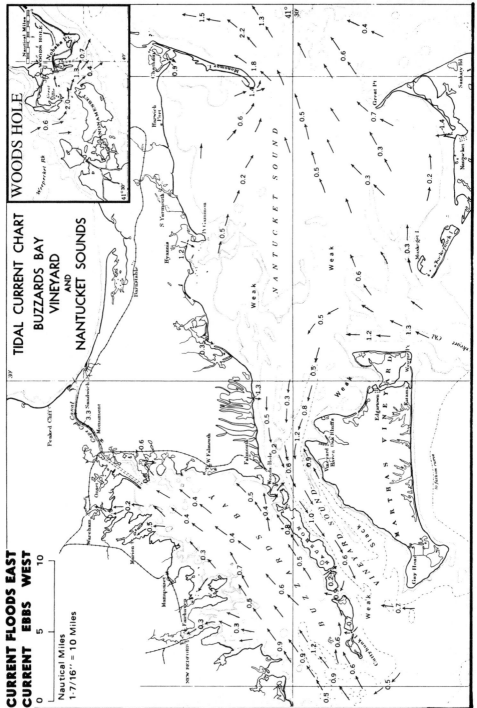

2 HOURS **AFTER** FLOOD STARTS AT POLLOCK RIP CHANNEL
OR: LOW WATER AT BOSTON

Velocities shown are at Spring Tides. See note at bottom of Boston Tables: Rule-of-Thumb for Current Velocities. See pp. 60–65 for an enlarged version of Woods Hole inset.
Pollock Rip Ch. is SE of Monomoy Pt.

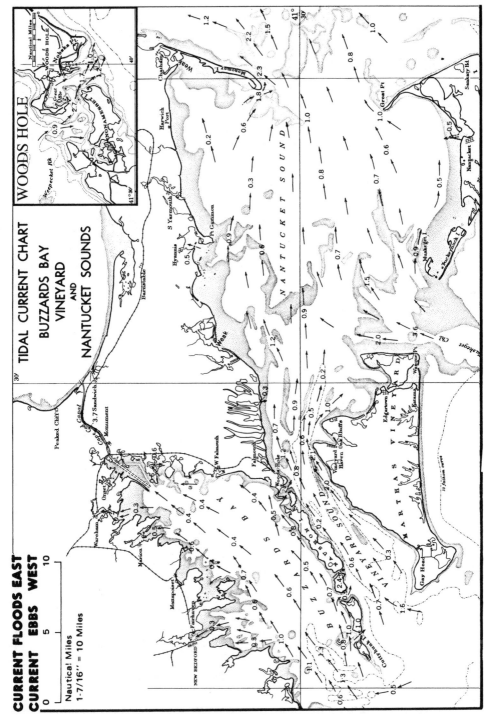

TIDAL CURRENT CHART
BUZZARDS BAY
VINEYARD
AND
NANTUCKET SOUNDS

WOODS HOLE

CURRENT FLOODS EAST
CURRENT EBBS WEST

Nautical Miles
1-7/16" = 10 Miles

N A N T U C K E T   S O U N D

B U Z Z A R D S   B A Y

V I N E Y A R D   S O U N D

M A R T H A ' S   V I N E Y A R D

NEW BEDFORD

3 HOURS **AFTER** FLOOD STARTS AT POLLOCK RIP CHANNEL
OR: 1 HOUR **AFTER** LOW WATER AT BOSTON

Velocities shown are at Spring Tides. See note at bottom of Boston Tables: Rule-of-
Thumb for Current Velocities. See pp. 60–65 for an enlarged version of Woods Hole inset.
Pollock Rip Ch. is SE of Monomoy Pt.

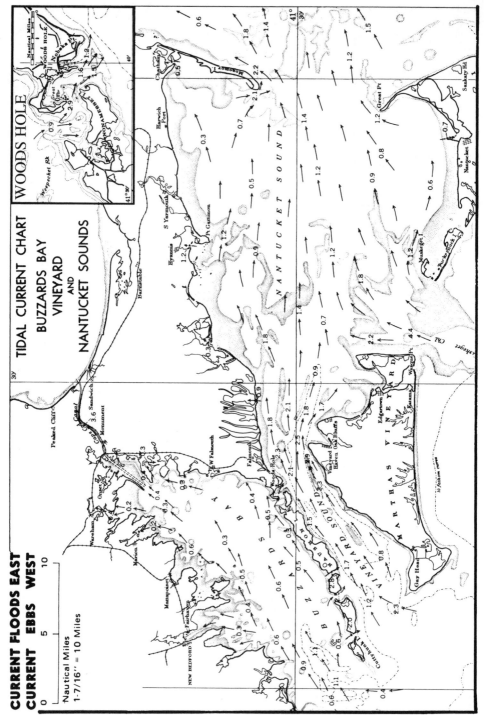

4 HOURS **AFTER** FLOOD STARTS AT POLLOCK RIP CHANNEL
OR: 2 HOURS **AFTER** LOW WATER AT BOSTON

Velocities shown are at Spring Tides. See note at bottom of Boston Tables: Rule-of-Thumb for Current Velocities. See pp. 60–65 for an enlarged version of Woods Hole inset.

Pollock Rip Ch. is SE of Monomoy Pt.

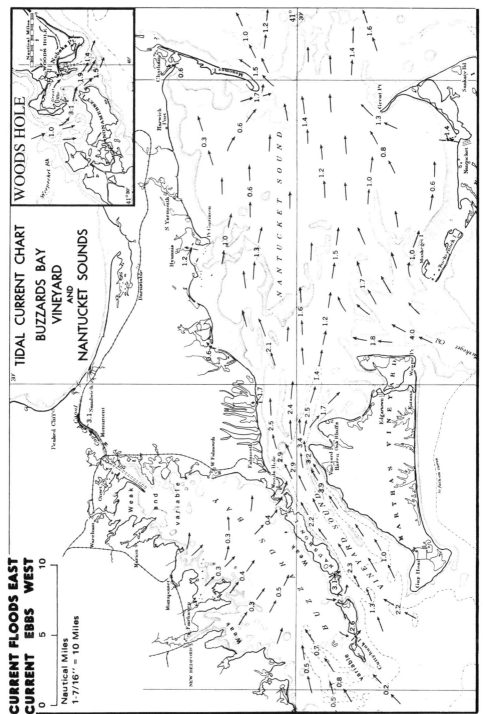

5 HOURS **AFTER** FLOOD STARTS AT POLLOCK RIP CHANNEL
OR: 3 HOURS **AFTER** LOW WATER AT BOSTON

Velocities shown are at Spring Tides. See note at bottom of Boston Tables: Rule-of-Thumb for Current Velocities. See pp. 60–65 for an enlarged version of Woods Hole inset.
Pollock Rip Ch. is SE of Monomoy Pt.

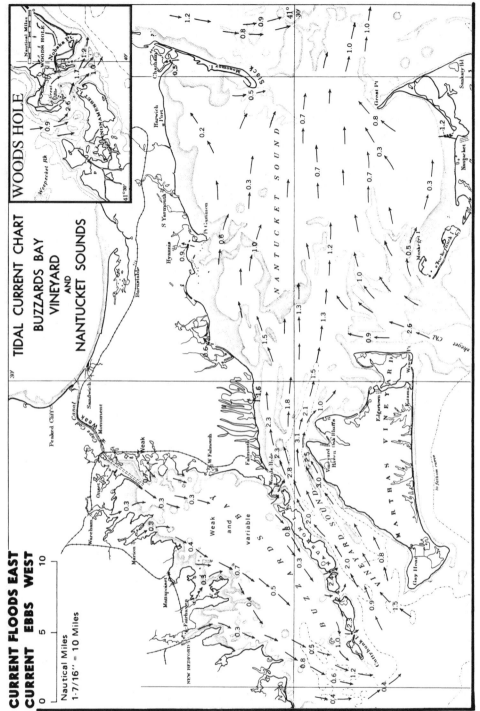

EBB STARTS AT POLLOCK RIP CHANNEL
OR: 4 HOURS **AFTER** LOW WATER AT BOSTON

Velocities shown are at Spring Tides. See note at bottom of Boston Tables: Rule-of-
Thumb for Current Velocities. See pp. 60–65 for an enlarged version of Woods Hole inset.
Pollock Rip Ch. is SE of Monomoy Pt.

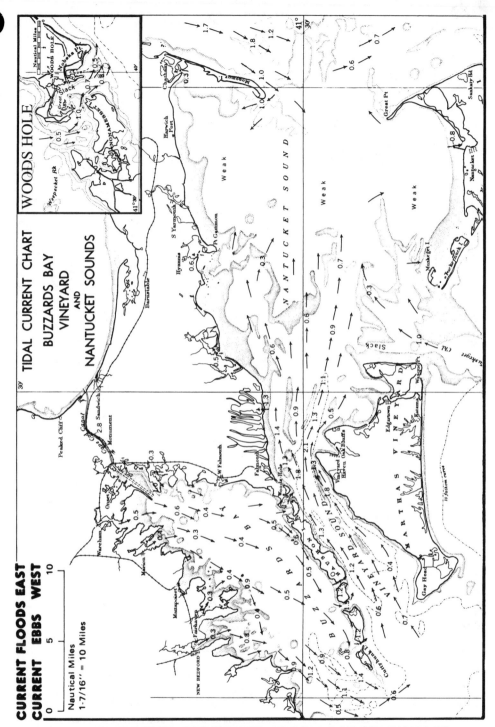

1 HOUR **AFTER** EBB STARTS AT POLLOCK RIP CHANNEL
OR: 5 HOURS **AFTER** LOW WATER AT BOSTON

Velocities shown are at Spring Tides. See note at bottom of Boston Tables: Rule-of-Thumb for Current Velocities. See pp. 60–65 for an enlarged version of Woods Hole inset.
Pollock Rip Ch. is SE of Monomoy Pt.

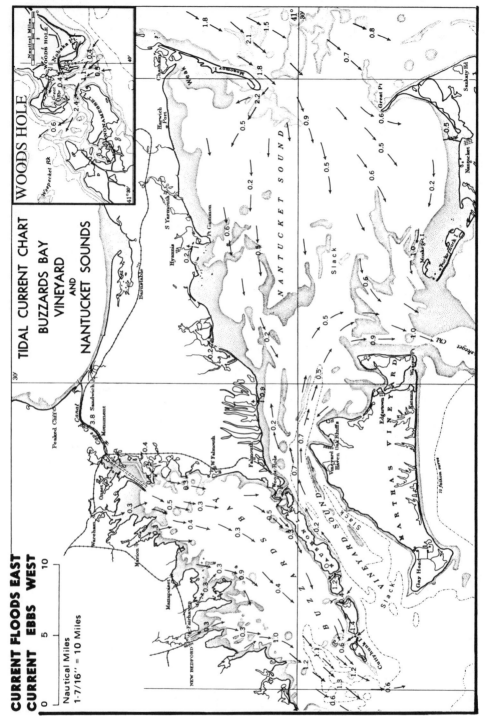

TIDAL CURRENT CHART
BUZZARDS BAY
VINEYARD
AND
NANTUCKET SOUNDS

WOODS HOLE

CURRENT FLOODS EAST
CURRENT EBBS WEST

Nautical Miles
1-7/16'' = 10 Miles

2 HOURS **AFTER** EBB STARTS AT POLLOCK RIP CHANNEL
OR: HIGH WATER AT BOSTON

Velocities shown are at Spring Tides. See note at bottom of Boston Tables: Rule-of-Thumb for Current Velocities. See pp. 60–65 for an enlarged version of Woods Hole inset.
Pollock Rip Ch. is SE of Monomoy Pt.

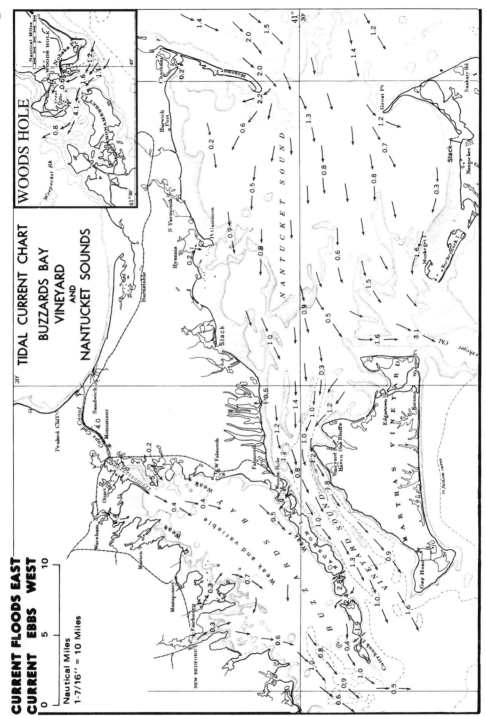

3 HOURS **AFTER** EBB STARTS AT POLLOCK RIP CHANNEL
OR: 1 HOUR **AFTER** HIGH WATER AT BOSTON

Velocities shown are at Spring Tides. See note at bottom of Boston Tables: Rule-of-Thumb for Current Velocities. See pp. 60–65 for an enlarged version of Woods Hole inset.
Pollock Rip Ch. is SE of Monomoy Pt.

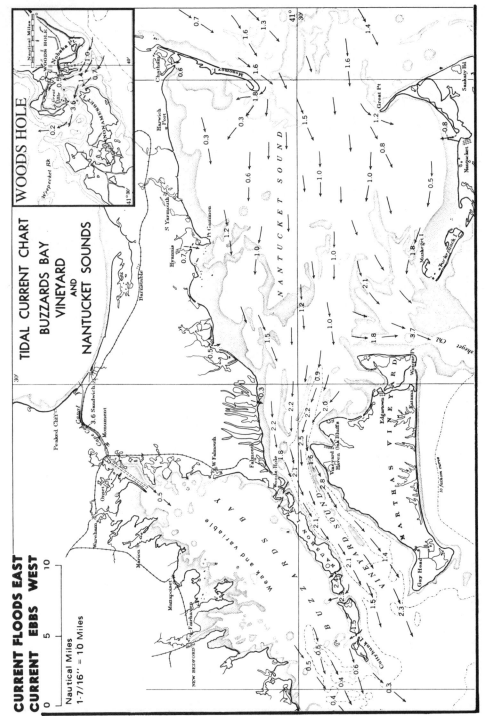

4 HOURS **AFTER** EBB STARTS AT POLLOCK RIP CHANNEL
OR: 2 HOURS **AFTER** HIGH WATER AT BOSTON

Velocities shown are at Spring Tides. See note at bottom of Boston Tables: Rule-of-Thumb for Current Velocities. See pp. 60–65 for an enlarged version of Woods Hole inset.

Pollock Rip Ch. is SE of Monomoy Pt.

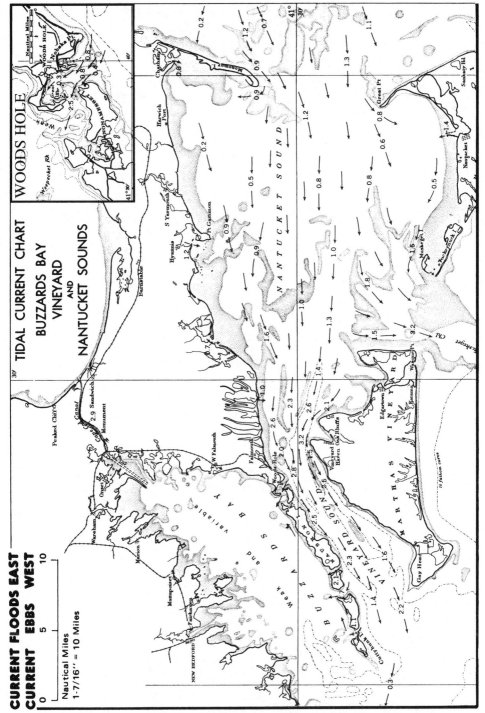

5 HOURS **AFTER** EBB STARTS AT POLLOCK RIP CHANNEL
OR: 3 HOURS **AFTER** HIGH WATER AT BOSTON

Velocities shown are at Spring Tides. See note at bottom of Boston Tables: Rule-of-Thumb for Current Velocities. See pp. 60–65 for an enlarged version of Woods Hole inset.
Pollock Rip Ch. is SE of Monomoy Pt.

2024 HIGH & LOW WATER
NEWPORT, RI
41°30.3'N, 71°19.6'W

		Standard Time								Standard Time				
DAY OF MONTH	**DAY OF WEEK**	**JANUARY**						**DAY OF MONTH**	**DAY OF WEEK**	**FEBRUARY**				
		HIGH		**LOW**						**HIGH**		**LOW**		
		a.m.	Ht.	p.m.	Ht.	a.m.	p.m.			a.m.	Ht.	p.m.	Ht.	a.m.	p.m.
1	M	11:14	2.9	**11:47**	2.8	4:10	**4:44**	1	T	11:49	2.5	...	...	5:08	**5:09**
2	T	11:53	2.7	...	...	4:57	**5:24**	2	F	12:20	2.8	**12:35**	2.4	6:01	**5:55**
3	W	12:29	2.8	**12:34**	2.5	5:54	**6:10**	3	S	1:06	2.8	**1:27**	2.3	7:11	**6:54**
4	T	1:12	2.8	**1:18**	2.4	7:04	**7:02**	4	S	2:00	2.9	**2:27**	2.3	8:36	**8:02**
5	F	1:56	2.9	**2:08**	2.3	8:20	**7:57**	5	M	3:04	3.0	**3:36**	2.4	9:48	**9:12**
6	S	2:47	3.0	**3:07**	2.4	9:25	**8:53**	6	T	4:14	3.2	**4:43**	2.7	10:44	**10:15**
7	S	3:46	3.1	**4:11**	2.5	10:17	**9:46**	7	W	5:16	3.6	**5:41**	3.1	11:32	**11:12**
8	M	4:44	3.4	**5:10**	2.7	11:05	**10:37**	8	T	6:10	4.0	**6:33**	3.5	...	**12:20**
9	T	5:38	3.7	**6:02**	3.0	11:51	**11:26**	9	F	7:00	4.3	**7:23**	3.9	12:06	**1:05**
10	W	6:28	4.0	**6:52**	3.3	...	**12:39**	10	S	7:48	4.4	**8:12**	4.1	1:01	**1:49**
11	T	7:16	4.2	**7:41**	3.5	12:16	**1:27**	11	S	8:37	4.4	**9:02**	4.3	1:55	**2:30**
12	F	8:05	4.3	**8:30**	3.7	1:09	**2:13**	12	M	9:26	4.2	**9:53**	4.3	2:47	**3:09**
13	S	8:55	4.3	**9:21**	3.8	2:01	**2:55**	13	T	10:17	3.9	**10:46**	4.2	3:37	**3:47**
14	S	9:45	4.2	**10:14**	3.9	2:53	**3:36**	14	W	11:10	3.6	**11:41**	4.0	4:29	**4:27**
15	M	10:38	4.0	**11:09**	3.9	3:45	**4:17**	15	T	...	...	**12:06**	3.2	5:30	**5:12**
16	T	11:33	3.7	...	...	4:40	**5:01**	16	F	12:38	3.7	**1:03**	3.0	7:16	**6:07**
17	W	12:06	3.8	**12:28**	3.4	5:50	**5:51**	17	S	1:38	3.4	**2:03**	2.7	8:56	**7:17**
18	T	1:03	3.7	**1:25**	3.1	7:41	**6:50**	18	S	2:44	3.2	**3:10**	2.6	10:04	**8:45**
19	F	2:02	3.6	**2:26**	2.9	9:11	**7:56**	19	M	3:56	3.1	**4:18**	2.7	10:57	**10:01**
20	S	3:06	3.5	**3:32**	2.8	10:16	**9:02**	20	T	5:01	3.2	**5:16**	2.9	11:40	**10:50**
21	S	4:13	3.5	**4:37**	2.8	11:09	**10:00**	21	W	5:52	3.3	**6:05**	3.1	-B-	**12:15**
22	M	5:14	3.5	**5:33**	3.0	11:55	**10:49**	22	T	6:35	3.4	**6:47**	3.2	...	**12:42**
23	T	6:06	3.6	**6:23**	3.1	-A-	**12:36**	23	F	7:12	3.4	**7:26**	3.3	12:10	**1:07**
24	W	6:52	3.6	**7:07**	3.2	...	**1:10**	24	S	7:47	3.4	**8:02**	3.4	12:50	**1:33**
25	T	7:33	3.6	**7:49**	3.3	12:18	**1:40**	25	S	8:19	3.4	**8:36**	3.4	1:30	**2:00**
26	F	8:12	3.6	**8:29**	3.3	1:02	**2:07**	26	M	8:50	3.3	**9:09**	3.4	2:09	**2:28**
27	S	8:48	3.5	**9:07**	3.2	1:46	**2:35**	27	T	9:21	3.1	**9:42**	3.3	2:46	**2:55**
28	S	9:22	3.3	**9:44**	3.1	2:27	**3:03**	28	W	9:55	2.9	**10:16**	3.2	3:21	**3:23**
29	M	9:56	3.1	**10:22**	3.0	3:07	**3:32**	29	T	10:33	2.7	**10:55**	3.1	3:56	**3:53**
30	T	10:31	2.9	**10:59**	3.0	3:45	**4:01**								
31	W	11:08	2.7	**11:38**	2.9	4:25	**4:33**								

A also at 11:34 p.m. **B** also at 11:30 p.m.

Dates when Ht. of **Low** Water is below Mean Lower Low with Ht. of lowest given for each period and Date of lowest in ( ):

9th–16th: -0.7' (13th)   6th–14th: -0.9' (11th)
27th–28th: -0.2'   25th–27th: -0.2'

Average Rise and Fall 3.5 ft.

When a high tide exceeds avg. ht., the *following* low tide will be lower than avg.

2024 HIGH & LOW WATER
NEWPORT, RI
41°30.3'N, 71°19.6'W

Daylight Time starts March 10 at 2 a.m.   **Daylight Saving Time**

DAY OF MONTH	DAY OF WEEK	MARCH HIGH a.m.	Ht.	p.m.	Ht.	LOW a.m.	p.m.	DAY OF MONTH	DAY OF WEEK	APRIL HIGH a.m.	Ht.	p.m.	Ht.	LOW a.m.	p.m.
1	F	11:16	2.5	**11:39**	3.0	4:32	**4:27**	1	M	1:07	3.2	**1:43**	2.6	6:45	**6:43**
2	S	...	...	**12:05**	2.4	5:16	**5:10**	2	T	2:08	3.2	**2:43**	2.7	8:11	**8:02**
3	S	12:30	3.0	**1:00**	2.4	6:15	**6:09**	3	W	3:13	3.2	**3:49**	2.9	9:50	**9:33**
4	M	1:29	3.0	**2:01**	2.4	7:44	**7:25**	4	T	4:23	3.4	**4:56**	3.3	10:51	**10:51**
5	T	2:34	3.0	**3:09**	2.6	9:20	**8:47**	5	F	5:29	3.7	**5:57**	3.8	11:36	**11:53**
6	W	3:47	3.3	**4:19**	2.9	10:21	**10:00**	6	S	6:26	3.9	**6:52**	4.2	...	**12:18**
7	T	4:53	3.6	**5:19**	3.4	11:09	**11:02**	7	S	7:18	4.1	**7:42**	4.6	12:48	**12:58**
8	F	5:49	4.0	**6:13**	3.9	11:52	**11:58**	8	M	8:07	4.2	**8:31**	4.9	1:42	**1:40**
9	S	6:40	4.3	**7:03**	4.3	...	**12:35**	9	T	8:56	4.2	**9:19**	4.9	2:35	**2:22**
10	S	*8:29	4.4	***8:52**	4.6	12:52	***2:16**	10	W	9:45	4.0	**10:08**	4.7	3:25	**3:05**
11	M	9:17	4.3	**9:41**	4.7	2:46	**2:57**	11	T	10:35	3.8	**10:59**	4.4	4:11	**3:48**
12	T	10:05	4.2	**10:30**	4.6	3:37	**3:37**	12	F	11:28	3.5	**11:53**	4.0	4:55	**4:31**
13	W	10:55	3.9	**11:22**	4.3	4:25	**4:16**	13	S	...	...	**12:23**	3.3	5:42	**5:16**
14	T	11:48	3.5	...	...	5:12	**4:57**	14	S	12:51	3.6	**1:20**	3.1	6:50	**6:09**
15	F	12:16	4.0	**12:44**	3.2	6:05	**5:41**	15	M	1:50	3.2	**2:18**	2.9	8:51	**7:19**
16	S	1:14	3.6	**1:42**	3.0	7:38	**6:34**	16	T	2:51	3.0	**3:18**	2.9	9:59	**9:12**
17	S	2:14	3.3	**2:42**	2.8	9:32	**7:45**	17	W	3:55	2.9	**4:20**	2.9	10:44	**10:30**
18	M	3:20	3.0	**3:46**	2.7	10:40	**9:42**	18	T	4:58	2.8	**5:19**	3.1	11:16	**11:14**
19	T	4:32	2.9	**4:53**	2.8	11:31	**11:00**	19	F	5:50	2.9	**6:08**	3.3	11:41	**11:52**
20	W	5:38	3.0	**5:52**	2.9	-A-	**12:07**	20	S	6:31	3.0	**6:48**	3.5	...	**12:06**
21	T	6:28	3.1	**6:40**	3.2	...	**12:35**	21	S	7:07	3.1	**7:24**	3.6	12:30	**12:34**
22	F	7:09	3.2	**7:21**	3.3	12:18	**12:58**	22	M	7:41	3.2	**7:57**	3.8	1:08	**1:05**
23	S	7:44	3.3	**7:58**	3.5	12:54	**1:22**	23	T	8:14	3.2	**8:29**	3.8	1:48	**1:38**
24	S	8:16	3.3	**8:31**	3.6	1:32	**1:50**	24	W	8:48	3.2	**9:02**	3.8	2:26	**2:12**
25	M	8:47	3.3	**9:03**	3.7	2:11	**2:19**	25	T	9:25	3.2	**9:38**	3.8	3:04	**2:46**
26	T	9:18	3.2	**9:34**	3.6	2:49	**2:49**	26	F	10:05	3.1	**10:18**	3.7	3:39	**3:22**
27	W	9:51	3.1	**10:07**	3.5	3:25	**3:19**	27	S	10:49	3.0	**11:04**	3.6	4:14	**3:59**
28	T	10:27	3.0	**10:42**	3.4	3:58	**3:50**	28	S	11:38	2.9	**11:56**	3.5	4:51	**4:41**
29	F	11:07	2.8	**11:23**	3.3	4:31	**4:22**	29	M	...	...	**12:33**	2.9	5:35	**5:29**
30	S	11:54	2.7	...	...	5:06	**4:58**	30	T	12:53	3.4	**1:30**	3.0	6:32	**6:31**
31	S	12:12	3.2	**12:46**	2.6	5:48	**5:43**								

A also at 11:42 p.m.

Dates when Ht. of **Low** Water is below Mean Lower Low with Ht. of lowest given for each period and Date of lowest in ( ):

    7th–14th: -0.9' (11th)   5th–11th: -0.7' (8th, 9th)
    25th–27th: -0.2'

Average Rise and Fall 3.5 ft.

When a high tide exceeds avg. ht., the *following* low tide will be lower than avg.

2024 HIGH & LOW WATER
NEWPORT, RI
41°30.3'N, 71°19.6'W

		Daylight Saving Time							Daylight Saving Time				
D A Y O F M O N T H	**D A Y O F W E E K**	**MAY**				**D A Y O F M O N T H**	**D A Y O F W E E K**	**JUNE**					
		HIGH		**LOW**				**HIGH**		**LOW**			
		a.m.	Ht.	p.m.	Ht.	a.m.	p.m.			a.m.	Ht.	p.m.	Ht.	a.m.	p.m.
1	W	1:53	3.4	2:28	3.1	7:50	7:52	1	S	3:33	3.5	4:10	4.0	9:28	10:42
2	T	2:54	3.5	3:29	3.4	9:12	9:27	2	S	4:36	3.5	5:12	4.3	10:18	11:41
3	F	3:57	3.5	4:33	3.7	10:11	10:46	3	M	5:39	3.5	6:10	4.5	11:06	...
4	S	5:03	3.6	5:34	4.1	10:58	11:46	4	T	6:37	3.6	7:03	4.7	12:33	-A-
5	S	6:02	3.8	6:30	4.5	11:40	...	5	W	7:29	3.7	7:54	4.7	1:23	12:37
6	M	6:56	3.9	7:21	4.8	12:39	12:22	6	T	8:19	3.8	8:43	4.6	2:14	1:25
7	T	7:47	4.0	8:11	4.9	1:31	1:06	7	F	9:08	3.7	9:32	4.4	3:03	2:14
8	W	8:37	4.0	8:59	4.8	2:23	1:50	8	S	9:57	3.7	10:20	4.1	3:45	3:03
9	T	9:26	3.9	9:49	4.6	3:12	2:37	9	S	10:46	3.5	11:08	3.8	4:23	3:51
10	F	10:16	3.7	10:39	4.3	3:57	3:23	10	M	11:37	3.4	11:57	3.5	4:58	4:37
11	S	11:07	3.5	11:31	3.9	4:39	4:09	11	T	...	...	12:27	3.3	5:36	5:25
12	S	...	...	12:01	3.3	5:22	4:56	12	W	12:45	3.3	1:17	3.2	6:19	6:20
13	M	12:26	3.5	12:56	3.2	6:12	5:47	13	T	1:31	3.0	2:04	3.2	7:07	7:27
14	T	1:21	3.2	1:51	3.1	7:28	6:51	14	F	2:14	2.9	2:50	3.2	7:59	8:43
15	W	2:14	3.0	2:44	3.0	8:44	8:18	15	S	2:57	2.7	3:36	3.2	8:48	9:49
16	T	3:06	2.8	3:38	3.1	9:31	9:40	16	S	3:44	2.6	4:25	3.3	9:35	10:43
17	F	3:59	2.8	4:33	3.2	10:07	10:35	17	M	4:38	2.6	5:15	3.4	10:19	11:30
18	S	4:53	2.7	5:23	3.3	10:40	11:20	18	T	5:34	2.7	6:02	3.6	11:02	...
19	S	5:41	2.8	6:07	3.5	11:13	11:59	19	W	6:24	2.9	6:46	3.8	12:13	-B-
20	M	6:23	2.9	6:45	3.7	11:47	...	20	T	7:10	3.0	7:30	4.0	12:56	12:28
21	T	7:02	3.0	7:21	3.8	12:41	12:23	21	F	7:55	3.2	8:14	4.1	1:41	1:12
22	W	7:41	3.1	7:57	3.9	1:22	1:00	22	S	8:40	3.4	8:59	4.2	2:26	1:59
23	T	8:20	3.2	8:36	4.0	2:03	1:38	23	S	9:28	3.5	9:47	4.2	3:11	2:48
24	F	9:02	3.2	9:17	4.0	2:44	2:19	24	M	10:17	3.6	10:36	4.2	3:53	3:37
25	S	9:46	3.2	10:02	4.0	3:24	3:02	25	T	11:08	3.7	11:29	4.1	4:34	4:27
26	S	10:33	3.2	10:50	3.9	4:03	3:45	26	W	...	...	12:02	3.8	5:16	5:20
27	M	11:24	3.2	11:44	3.8	4:44	4:32	27	T	12:23	4.0	12:58	3.9	6:01	6:23
28	T	...	...	12:19	3.3	5:28	5:23	28	F	1:18	3.8	1:53	4.0	6:52	7:47
29	W	12:40	3.8	1:16	3.4	6:21	6:26	29	S	2:13	3.6	2:49	4.1	7:48	9:27
30	T	1:36	3.7	2:12	3.6	7:24	7:49	30	S	3:11	3.4	3:48	4.2	8:47	10:41
31	F	2:33	3.6	3:10	3.8	8:30	9:27								

A also at 11:52 a.m. **B** also at 11:45 a.m.

Dates when Ht. of **Low** Water is below Mean Lower Low with Ht. of lowest given for each period and Date of lowest in ( ):

5th–9th: -0.4' (7th, 8th)

Average Rise and Fall 3.5 ft.

When a high tide exceeds avg. ht., the *following* low tide will be lower than avg.

2024 HIGH & LOW WATER
NEWPORT, RI
41°30.3'N, 71°19.6'W

Daylight Saving Time **Daylight Saving Time**

D A Y O F M O N T H	D A Y O F W E E K	JULY HIGH a.m.	Ht.	p.m.	Ht.	LOW a.m.	p.m.	D A Y O F M O N T H	D A Y O F W E E K	AUGUST HIGH a.m.	Ht.	p.m.	Ht.	LOW a.m.	p.m.
1	M	4:14	3.3	4:51	4.2	9:44	11:40	1	T	6:04	3.3	6:38	4.0	12:30	-B-
2	T	5:18	3.3	5:53	4.3	10:39	...	2	F	6:58	3.5	7:28	4.1	1:15	12:12
3	W	6:19	3.4	6:49	4.3	12:32	-A-	3	S	7:46	3.6	8:13	4.1	1:55	12:58
4	T	7:14	3.5	7:41	4.4	1:21	12:19	4	S	8:32	3.7	8:54	4.0	2:28	1:44
5	F	8:03	3.6	8:29	4.3	2:09	1:08	5	M	9:13	3.8	9:33	3.9	2:55	2:29
6	S	8:51	3.7	9:15	4.2	2:52	1:57	6	T	9:54	3.7	10:10	3.7	3:22	3:13
7	S	9:37	3.7	9:59	4.0	3:28	2:46	7	W	10:34	3.7	10:46	3.5	3:49	3:54
8	M	10:22	3.6	10:41	3.8	3:58	3:33	8	T	11:12	3.6	11:22	3.3	4:18	4:34
9	T	11:07	3.5	11:23	3.5	4:27	4:17	9	F	11:51	3.5	11:59	3.0	4:48	5:15
10	W	11:53	3.4	...	...	4:58	5:01	10	S	...	...	12:30	3.3	5:21	5:59
11	T	12:04	3.3	12:37	3.3	5:31	5:47	11	S	12:39	2.9	1:09	3.3	5:56	6:50
12	F	12:44	3.1	1:19	3.3	6:08	6:41	12	M	1:22	2.7	1:52	3.2	6:39	7:57
13	S	1:24	2.9	1:59	3.2	6:50	7:46	13	T	2:10	2.6	2:40	3.2	7:34	9:18
14	S	2:04	2.7	2:40	3.2	7:38	8:57	14	W	3:04	2.6	3:38	3.3	8:39	10:29
15	M	2:49	2.6	3:26	3.2	8:31	10:03	15	T	4:08	2.7	4:45	3.5	9:47	11:23
16	T	3:43	2.6	4:21	3.3	9:27	10:58	16	F	5:16	2.9	5:48	3.8	10:50	...
17	W	4:46	2.7	5:20	3.5	10:21	11:46	17	S	6:15	3.3	6:43	4.1	12:09	-C-
18	T	5:47	2.8	6:15	3.7	11:14	...	18	S	7:08	3.7	7:33	4.4	12:53	12:40
19	F	6:41	3.1	7:06	4.0	12:32	12:04	19	M	7:57	4.1	8:21	4.6	1:37	1:33
20	S	7:31	3.4	7:54	4.2	1:19	12:54	20	T	8:46	4.4	9:09	4.7	2:20	2:27
21	S	8:19	3.7	8:41	4.4	2:05	1:45	21	W	9:35	4.6	9:58	4.6	3:01	3:21
22	M	9:08	3.9	9:29	4.5	2:51	2:38	22	T	10:25	4.7	10:48	4.3	3:41	4:12
23	T	9:57	4.1	10:19	4.5	3:33	3:30	23	F	11:18	4.7	11:41	4.1	4:21	5:04
24	W	10:48	4.2	11:09	4.3	4:12	4:22	24	S	...	...	12:12	4.5	5:01	6:02
25	T	11:41	4.3	...	...	4:51	5:15	25	S	12:37	3.8	1:10	4.3	5:46	7:33
26	F	12:03	4.1	12:36	4.3	5:32	6:16	26	M	1:35	3.5	2:09	4.1	6:38	9:22
27	S	12:57	3.8	1:31	4.2	6:18	7:43	27	T	2:34	3.3	3:11	3.9	7:45	10:35
28	S	1:53	3.5	2:28	4.2	7:11	9:27	28	W	3:38	3.2	4:20	3.7	9:10	11:32
29	M	2:52	3.3	3:28	4.1	8:12	10:41	29	T	4:45	3.2	5:28	3.7	10:35	...
30	T	3:55	3.2	4:35	4.0	9:19	11:39	30	F	5:48	3.3	6:24	3.8	12:18	-D-
31	W	5:01	3.2	5:40	4.0	10:25	...	31	S	6:41	3.5	7:11	3.9	12:55	12:11

A also at 11:30 a.m. **B** also at 11:22 a.m. **C** also at 11:46 a.m. **D** also at 11:30 a.m.

Dates when Ht. of **Low** Water is below Mean Lower Low with Ht. of lowest given for each period and Date of lowest in ( ):

22nd–25th: -0.2' 19th–24th: -0.4' (21st, 22nd)

Average Rise and Fall 3.5 ft.

When a high tide exceeds avg. ht., the *following* low tide will be lower than avg.

2024 HIGH & LOW WATER
NEWPORT, RI
41°30.3'N, 71°19.6'W

Daylight Saving Time   Daylight Saving Time

Day of Month	Day of Week	SEPTEMBER HIGH a.m.	Ht.	HIGH p.m.	Ht.	LOW a.m.	LOW p.m.	Day of Month	Day of Week	OCTOBER HIGH a.m.	Ht.	HIGH p.m.	Ht.	LOW a.m.	LOW p.m.
1	S	7:26	3.7	7:52	3.9	1:24	12:50	1	T	7:41	3.9	7:58	3.6	1:01	1:11
2	M	8:08	3.8	8:28	3.9	1:47	1:30	2	W	8:16	4.0	8:31	3.6	1:26	1:49
3	T	8:46	3.9	9:03	3.8	2:11	2:11	3	T	8:49	4.0	9:03	3.5	1:56	2:28
4	W	9:24	3.9	9:36	3.7	2:38	2:51	4	F	9:22	3.9	9:36	3.3	2:28	3:06
5	T	9:57	3.8	10:09	3.5	3:08	3:30	5	S	9:53	3.8	10:11	3.2	3:00	3:43
6	F	10:31	3.7	10:43	3.2	3:38	4:08	6	S	10:27	3.7	10:50	3.0	3:33	4:17
7	S	11:05	3.6	11:20	3.0	4:08	4:44	7	M	11:06	3.5	11:34	2.9	4:06	4:52
8	S	11:42	3.4	...	...	4:40	5:22	8	T	11:52	3.4	...	...	4:42	5:32
9	M	12:02	2.9	12:25	3.3	5:14	6:04	9	W	12:25	2.8	12:46	3.3	5:24	6:25
10	T	12:50	2.7	1:13	3.2	5:54	7:02	10	T	1:21	2.8	1:44	3.3	6:18	7:47
11	W	1:42	2.7	2:07	3.2	6:48	8:29	11	F	2:19	2.9	2:45	3.4	7:32	9:27
12	T	2:38	2.7	3:08	3.3	8:00	10:01	12	S	3:20	3.1	3:49	3.5	9:02	10:24
13	F	3:41	2.9	4:16	3.5	9:21	10:58	13	S	4:24	3.4	4:54	3.8	10:21	11:08
14	S	4:49	3.1	5:22	3.8	10:33	11:42	14	M	5:26	3.8	5:53	4.0	11:23	11:48
15	S	5:50	3.6	6:19	4.1	11:34	...	15	T	6:21	4.3	6:47	4.2	...	12:17
16	M	6:45	4.0	7:10	4.4	12:22	12:28	16	W	7:13	4.8	7:37	4.4	12:27	1:09
17	T	7:35	4.5	7:59	4.6	1:03	1:21	17	T	8:02	5.1	8:26	4.4	1:09	2:02
18	W	8:24	4.8	8:47	4.6	1:44	2:15	18	F	8:51	5.2	9:16	4.3	1:52	2:54
19	T	9:12	5.0	9:36	4.5	2:25	3:08	19	S	9:41	5.0	10:07	4.1	2:37	3:45
20	F	10:02	5.0	10:27	4.3	3:08	3:59	20	S	10:33	4.8	11:00	3.8	3:22	4:34
21	S	10:54	4.8	11:20	4.0	3:50	4:49	21	M	11:28	4.4	11:57	3.6	4:08	5:26
22	S	11:49	4.6	...	...	4:33	5:45	22	T	...	...	12:27	4.0	4:56	6:45
23	M	12:17	3.7	12:48	4.2	5:18	7:17	23	W	12:56	3.4	1:28	3.7	5:49	8:38
24	T	1:16	3.4	1:50	3.9	6:12	9:08	24	T	1:56	3.2	2:30	3.4	7:00	9:45
25	W	2:17	3.3	2:53	3.6	7:23	10:18	25	F	2:57	3.2	3:31	3.2	9:15	10:34
26	T	3:20	3.2	4:01	3.5	9:29	11:11	26	S	3:58	3.2	4:32	3.2	10:26	11:08
27	F	4:26	3.2	5:07	3.5	10:47	11:51	27	S	4:57	3.3	5:27	3.2	11:07	11:31
28	S	5:27	3.4	6:02	3.5	11:30	...	28	M	5:49	3.5	6:12	3.2	11:41	11:52
29	S	6:18	3.5	6:46	3.6	12:20	12:03	29	T	6:32	3.7	6:50	3.3	...	12:14
30	M	7:02	3.7	7:24	3.6	12:40	12:36	30	W	7:10	3.8	7:25	3.3	12:16	12:50
								31	T	7:44	3.9	7:59	3.3	12:46	1:27

Dates when Ht. of **Low** Water is below Mean Lower Low with Ht. of lowest given for each period and Date of lowest in ( ):

17th–21st: -0.5' (19th, 20th)   15th–20th: -0.6' (18th)

Average Rise and Fall 3.5 ft.

When a high tide exceeds avg. ht., the *following* low tide will be lower than avg.

2024 HIGH & LOW WATER
NEWPORT, RI
41°30.3'N, 71°19.6'W

*Standard Time starts Nov. 3 at 2 a.m. **Standard Time**

DAY OF MONTH	DAY OF WEEK	NOVEMBER HIGH a.m.	Ht.	p.m.	Ht.	LOW a.m.	p.m.	DAY OF MONTH	DAY OF WEEK	DECEMBER HIGH a.m.	Ht.	p.m.	Ht.	LOW a.m.	p.m.
1	F	8:16	3.9	8:33	3.3	1:18	2:06	1	S	7:22	3.8	7:44	3.1	12:24	1:27
2	S	8:48	3.9	9:08	3.2	1:52	2:45	2	M	8:00	3.8	8:25	3.1	1:04	2:06
3	S	*8:22	3.8	*8:46	3.1	*1:28	*2:21	3	T	8:42	3.7	9:09	3.1	1:44	2:44
4	M	9:01	3.7	9:27	3.0	2:04	2:57	4	W	9:28	3.7	9:57	3.0	2:26	3:22
5	T	9:42	3.6	10:14	2.9	2:41	3:33	5	T	10:16	3.6	10:49	3.0	3:09	4:01
6	W	10:32	3.5	11:07	2.9	3:21	4:14	6	F	11:09	3.5	11:44	3.1	3:55	4:47
7	T	11:27	3.4	...	...	4:05	5:04	7	S	...	...	12:05	3.5	4:50	5:41
8	F	12:03	2.9	12:25	3.4	5:00	6:13	8	S	12:40	3.3	1:01	3.4	6:00	6:44
9	S	1:00	3.0	1:23	3.4	6:14	7:36	9	M	1:36	3.5	1:59	3.3	7:33	7:48
10	S	1:59	3.3	2:24	3.5	7:47	8:39	10	T	2:35	3.7	3:01	3.3	9:04	8:46
11	M	3:00	3.6	3:27	3.6	9:11	9:27	11	W	3:38	4.0	4:05	3.3	10:10	9:38
12	T	4:01	4.0	4:28	3.7	10:15	10:12	12	T	4:39	4.2	5:05	3.4	11:05	10:28
13	W	4:59	4.4	5:25	3.9	11:08	10:55	13	F	5:35	4.5	6:01	3.6	11:56	11:16
14	T	5:52	4.8	6:17	4.0	11:59	11:39	14	S	6:28	4.6	6:52	3.7	...	12:48
15	F	6:43	4.9	7:08	4.0	...	12:51	15	S	7:19	4.6	7:43	3.7	12:05	1:39
16	S	7:33	5.0	7:58	4.0	12:24	1:44	16	M	8:09	4.4	8:32	3.7	12:54	2:26
17	S	8:23	4.8	8:49	3.9	1:12	2:34	17	T	8:58	4.2	9:22	3.6	1:45	3:06
18	M	9:14	4.5	9:41	3.7	2:00	3:21	18	W	9:47	3.9	10:12	3.4	2:33	3:42
19	T	10:08	4.1	10:36	3.5	2:49	4:07	19	T	10:36	3.6	11:04	3.2	3:19	4:18
20	W	11:04	3.8	11:33	3.3	3:37	5:00	20	F	11:26	3.3	11:56	3.1	4:06	4:56
21	T	...	...	12:01	3.5	4:28	6:23	21	S	...	...	12:14	3.0	4:56	5:41
22	F	12:30	3.2	12:56	3.2	5:29	7:40	22	S	12:46	3.0	1:00	2.7	5:58	6:33
23	S	1:25	3.1	1:49	3.0	6:59	8:28	23	M	1:34	3.0	1:45	2.5	7:17	7:27
24	S	2:21	3.1	2:42	2.8	8:33	9:02	24	T	2:23	2.9	2:34	2.4	8:33	8:18
25	M	3:16	3.2	3:37	2.8	9:28	9:30	25	W	3:16	3.0	3:30	2.3	9:32	9:07
26	T	4:09	3.3	4:27	2.8	10:10	10:01	26	T	4:09	3.0	4:26	2.4	10:20	9:53
27	W	4:56	3.4	5:12	2.8	10:49	10:34	27	F	4:57	3.2	5:15	2.6	11:04	10:37
28	T	5:35	3.5	5:51	2.9	11:27	11:09	28	S	5:40	3.3	5:59	2.7	11:46	11:20
29	F	6:11	3.7	6:28	3.0	-A-	12:06	29	S	6:21	3.5	6:41	2.9	...	12:28
30	S	6:46	3.7	7:06	3.1	...	12:46	30	M	7:01	3.7	7:23	3.1	12:02	1:11
								31	T	7:42	3.8	8:04	3.2	12:46	1:53

A also at 11:46 p.m.

Dates when Ht. of **Low** Water is below Mean Lower Low with Ht. of lowest given for each period and Date of lowest in ( ):

12th–18th: -0.5' (14th, 16th)   11th–17th: -0.4' (13th, 15th, 16th)
31st: -0.2'

Average Rise and Fall 3.5 ft.

When a high tide exceeds avg. ht., the *following* low tide will be lower than avg.

Narragansett Bay Currents

This current diagram shows current **directions** and **average maximum velocities** when the tides have a normal (3.5 ft.) range at Newport. (pp. 84-89).

Average maximum Ebb currents occur about 3 hours *after* High Water at Newport and are shown by light arrows.

Average maximum Flood currents occur about 2 1/2 hours *before* High Water at Newport and are shown by black arrows.

When height of High Water at Newport is 3.0 ft., subtract 30% from velocities shown. When height is 4.0 ft., add 20%; when 4.5 ft., add 40%; when 5.0 ft., add 60%.

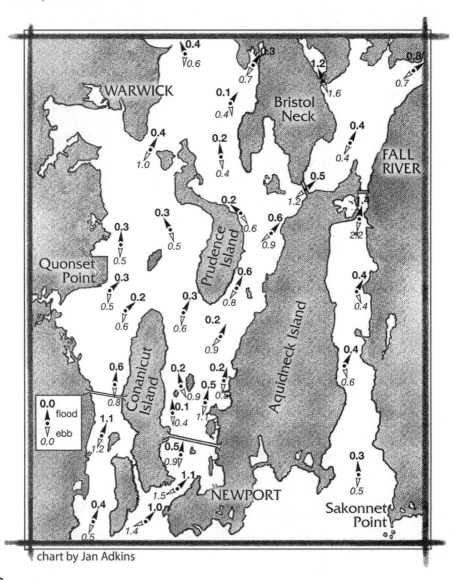

chart by Jan Adkins

Holding a Fair Current Between Eastern Long Island and Nantucket

There is a curious phenomenon which can be used to advantage by every vessel, and particularly the slower cruiser or auxiliary, in making the passage *either* way between eastern Long Island Sound, on the west, and Buzzards Bay, Vineyard and Nantucket Sounds on the east.

Note in the very simplified diagram below, that in Long Island Sound, the Ebb Current flows to the *east*, and in Buzzards Bay, Vineyard and Nantucket Sounds the Ebb Current flows to the *west*. (Off Newport, these opposed Ebb Currents merge and flow *south*.) The reverse is also true: the Flood Current flows *west* through Long Island Sound and *east* through Buzzards Bay, Vineyard and Nantucket Sounds. (Half arrow indicates Ebb Current, whole arrow indicates Flood Current.)

In making a *complete* passage through the area of the diagram, simply ride the favoring Ebb Current toward Newport from either direction and, pick up the favoring Flood Current in leaving the Newport area.

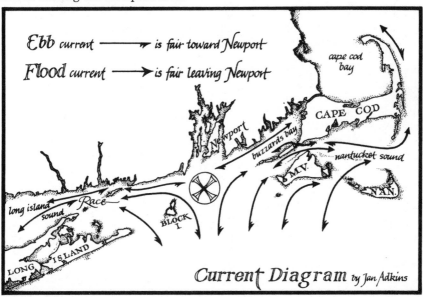

Current Diagram by Jan Adkins

Arrive at "X" at the times shown for "Current Turns to Northwest at The Race," tables pp. 92-97.

The E-W currents between Pt. Judith and Cuttyhunk are only 1/2 to 1 kt., while those to the West of Pt. Judith and to the East of Cuttyhunk are much greater. Bearing this in mind, those making *only a partial trip* through the area may find it better even to buck a slight head current in the Pt. Judith-Cuttyhunk area so as to pick up the maximum hours of strong favoring currents beyond those points.

For example, if headed for the Cape Cod Canal, refer to the Tidal Current Chart Buzzards Bay, Vineyard & Nantucket Sound, pp. 72-83 and arrive just N. of Cuttyhunk as Flood Starts at Pollock Rip, pp. 66-71 to ensure the most favorable currents. If headed for Nantucket, refer to the same Charts and arrive just S. of Cuttyhunk at 3 hours after Flood Starts at Pollock Rip, pp. 66-71. If headed into Long Island Sound, refer to the Tidal Current Chart Long Island Sound and Block Island Sound, pp. 98-103 and arrive at Pt. Judith when Flood Current turns West at The Race, p. 101.

2024 CURRENT TABLE
THE RACE, LONG ISLAND SOUND
41°13.69'N, 72°03.75'W 0.2 nm E.N.E. of Valiant Rock

Standard Time	Standard Time

		JANUARY						FEBRUARY				
DAY OF MONTH	**DAY OF WEEK**	CURRENT TURNS TO					**DAY OF MONTH**	**DAY OF WEEK**	CURRENT TURNS TO			
		NORTHWEST Flood Starts			SOUTHEAST Ebb Starts				NORTHWEST Flood Starts			SOUTHEAST Ebb Starts
		a.m.	**p.m.**	Kts.	a.m.	**p.m.**	Kts.			a.m.	**p.m.**	Kts.	a.m.	**p.m.**	Kts.

DAY OF MONTH	DAY OF WEEK	a.m.	p.m.	Kts.	a.m.	p.m.	Kts.	DAY OF MONTH	DAY OF WEEK	a.m.	p.m.	Kts.	a.m.	p.m.	Kts.
1	M	9:30	**9:42**	p2.7	2:54	**3:00**	a3.5	1	T	10:24	**10:18**	p2.7	3:30	**3:48**	a3.6
2	T	10:18	**10:24**	p2.6	3:30	**3:42**	a3.4	2	F	11:12	**11:12**	p2.6	4:12	**4:42**	a3.6
3	W	11:12	**11:06**	p2.5	4:12	**4:30**	a3.4	3	S	...	**12:06**	2.2	5:00	**5:36**	a3.5
4	T	11:59	**11:54**	p2.5	5:00	**5:24**	a3.4	4	S	12:07	**1:06**	a2.6	6:00	**6:36**	a3.6
5	F	...	**12:54**	2.1	5:48	**6:18**	a3.5	5	M	1:06	**2:00**	a2.7	7:00	**7:42**	a3.8
6	S	12:48	**1:42**	a2.6	6:36	**7:18**	a3.6	6	T	2:00	**2:54**	a3.0	8:00	**8:42**	a4.1
7	S	1:36	**2:36**	a2.7	7:30	**8:12**	a3.9	7	W	3:00	**3:48**	a3.3	8:54	**9:36**	a4.5
8	M	2:30	**3:24**	a3.0	8:24	**9:06**	a4.2	8	T	3:54	**4:36**	3.7	9:48	**10:30**	a4.9
9	T	3:24	**4:12**	a3.3	9:18	**10:00**	a4.5	9	F	4:48	**5:24**	p4.1	10:42	**11:18**	a5.2
10	W	4:12	**5:00**	a3.6	10:12	**10:48**	a4.8	10	S	5:36	**6:12**	p4.3	11:36	...	5.3
11	T	5:06	**5:48**	3.8	11:00	**11:42**	a5.1	11	S	6:30	**7:00**	p4.4	12:06	**12:24**	p5.3
12	F	5:54	**6:36**	4.0	11:54	...	5.2	12	M	7:24	**7:48**	p4.3	1:00	**1:18**	a5.3
13	S	6:48	**7:24**	4.1	12:30	**12:42**	p5.2	13	T	8:18	**8:36**	p4.1	1:48	**2:12**	a5.3
14	S	7:42	**8:12**	p4.1	1:18	**1:36**	p5.0	14	W	9:18	**9:30**	p3.8	2:42	**3:06**	a5.0
15	M	8:36	**9:00**	p3.9	2:12	**2:30**	a4.9	15	T	10:18	**10:30**	p3.4	3:36	**4:06**	a4.7
16	T	9:36	**9:54**	p3.7	3:06	**3:24**	a4.8	16	F	11:24	**11:36**	p3.1	4:30	**5:12**	a4.3
17	W	10:42	**10:54**	p3.5	4:00	**4:24**	a4.6	17	S	...	**12:30**	2.6	5:36	**6:18**	a4.1
18	T	11:48	**11:54**	p3.3	5:00	**5:30**	a4.5	18	S	12:42	**1:36**	a2.9	6:36	**7:24**	a3.9
19	F	...	**12:54**	2.8	6:00	**6:36**	a4.3	19	M	1:42	**2:36**	a2.8	7:42	**8:24**	a3.9
20	S	1:00	**1:54**	a3.2	7:00	**7:42**	a4.3	20	T	2:42	**3:30**	2.9	8:42	**9:18**	a4.0
21	S	2:00	**2:54**	a3.1	8:00	**8:42**	a4.3	21	W	3:36	**4:18**	3.0	9:30	**10:00**	a4.0
22	M	3:00	**3:48**	a3.2	8:54	**9:36**	a4.4	22	T	4:24	**5:00**	3.1	10:18	**10:42**	a4.0
23	T	3:54	**4:36**	a3.2	9:48	**10:24**	a4.4	23	F	5:12	**5:36**	p3.2	10:54	**11:18**	4.0
24	W	4:42	**5:24**	3.2	10:36	**11:12**	a4.3	24	S	5:48	**6:06**	p3.2	11:36	**11:54**	p4.1
25	T	5:30	**6:00**	p3.3	11:18	**11:48**	a4.2	25	S	6:30	**6:42**	p3.2	...	**12:06**	3.8
26	F	6:12	**6:36**	p3.2	11:54	...	4.1	26	M	7:06	**7:12**	p3.2	12:24	**12:42**	a4.1
27	S	6:54	**7:12**	p3.2	12:24	**12:36**	p4.0	27	T	7:42	**7:42**	p3.1	1:00	**1:18**	a4.1
28	S	7:30	**7:48**	p3.1	1:00	**1:12**	a3.9	28	W	8:18	**8:18**	p3.0	1:30	**1:54**	a4.1
29	M	8:12	**8:18**	p3.0	1:36	**1:48**	a3.8	29	T	9:00	**9:00**	p2.9	2:12	**2:36**	a4.0
30	T	8:54	**8:54**	p2.9	2:12	**2:24**	a3.8								
31	W	9:36	**9:36**	p2.8	2:48	**3:06**	a3.7								

The Kts. (knots) columns show the **maximum** predicted velocities of the stronger one of the Flood Currents and the stronger one of the Ebb Currents for each day.
The letter "a" means the velocity shown should occur **after** the **a.m.** Current Change. The letter "p" means the velocity shown should occur **after** the **p.m.** Current Change (even if next morning). No "a" or "p" means a.m. and p.m. velocities are the same for that day.
Avg. Max. Velocity: Flood 3.3 Kts., Ebb 4.2 Kts.
Max. Flood 2 hrs. 45 min. after Flood Starts, ±15 min.
Max. Ebb 3 hrs. 25 min. after Ebb Starts, ±15 min.
Use THE RACE tables with current charts pp. 98-103

See pp. 22-29 for Current Change at other points.

2024 CURRENT TABLE
THE RACE, LONG ISLAND SOUND
41°13.69'N, 72°03.75'W 0.2 nm E.N.E. of Valiant Rock

Daylight Time starts March 10 at 2 a.m.   **Daylight Saving Time**

		MARCH					APRIL		
		CURRENT TURNS TO					CURRENT TURNS TO		
DAY OF MONTH	DAY OF WEEK	NORTHWEST Flood Starts	SOUTHEAST Ebb Starts		DAY OF MONTH	DAY OF WEEK	NORTHWEST Flood Starts	SOUTHEAST Ebb Starts	
		a.m. **p.m.** Kts.	a.m. **p.m.** Kts.				a.m. **p.m.** Kts.	a.m. **p.m.** Kts.	
1	F	9:42 **9:42** p2.8	2:48 **3:18** a3.9		1	M	... **12:01** 2.5	5:06 **5:42** a3.7	
2	S	10:36 **10:36** p2.7	3:36 **4:06** a3.7		2	T	12:12 **1:00** a2.7	6:06 **6:48** a3.7	
3	S	11:30 **11:36** p2.7	4:30 **5:06** a3.6		3	W	1:18 **2:00** 2.8	7:06 **7:48** 3.8	
4	M	... **12:30** 2.3	5:30 **6:06** a3.6		4	T	2:25 **3:00** p3.2	8:12 **8:54** p4.3	
5	T	12:36 **1:30** a2.8	6:30 **7:12** a3.8		5	F	3:18 **3:48** p3.6	9:12 **9:48** p4.8	
6	W	1:36 **2:24** a3.0	7:36 **8:12** a4.1		6	S	4:18 **4:42** p4.0	10:12 **10:42** p5.2	
7	T	2:36 **3:18** 3.4	8:36 **9:12** 4.5		7	S	5:12 **5:30** p4.3	11:06 **11:30** p5.5	
8	F	3:36 **4:06** p3.9	9:30 **10:06** p5.0		8	M	6:06 **6:18** p4.5	... **12:01** 5.0	
9	S	4:30 **4:54** p4.3	10:24 **10:54** p5.3		9	T	6:54 **7:06** p4.4	12:18 **12:48** a5.7	
10	S	*6:18 ***6:42** p4.5	... ***12:18** 5.3		10	W	7:48 **8:00** p4.2	1:06 **1:42** a5.6	
11	M	7:12 **7:30** p4.5	12:42 **1:06** a5.6		11	T	8:42 **8:48** 3.8	2:00 **2:30** a5.3	
12	T	8:06 **8:18** p4.4	1:30 **2:00** a5.6		12	F	9:36 **9:48** 3.4	2:48 **3:24** a4.9	
13	W	9:00 **9:12** p4.0	2:24 **2:54** a5.4		13	S	10:30 **10:48** a3.0	3:42 **4:24** a4.4	
14	T	9:54 **10:06** p3.6	3:12 **3:48** a5.1		14	S	11:36 **11:48** a2.7	4:36 **5:24** a3.9	
15	F	10:54 **11:06** p3.2	4:06 **4:48** a4.6		15	M	... **12:36** 2.5	5:42 **6:24** a3.5	
16	S	... **12:01** 2.7	5:06 **5:48** a4.1		16	T	12:54 **1:36** 2.4	6:42 **7:24** a3.3	
17	S	12:12 **1:06** a2.8	6:06 **6:54** a3.8		17	W	2:00 **2:30** p2.5	7:42 **8:18** p3.3	
18	M	1:18 **2:12** a2.6	7:12 **8:00** a3.6		18	T	3:00 **3:18** p2.6	8:42 **9:06** p3.5	
19	T	2:24 **3:12** p2.6	8:18 **8:54** a3.5		19	F	3:48 **4:06** p2.7	9:30 **9:48** p3.7	
20	W	3:24 **4:00** p2.7	9:18 **9:48** a3.6		20	S	4:30 **4:42** p2.9	10:18 **10:30** p3.9	
21	T	4:18 **4:42** p2.9	10:06 **10:30** 3.7		21	S	5:12 **5:18** p3.0	10:54 **11:06** p4.1	
22	F	5:00 **5:24** p3.0	10:48 **11:12** p3.9		22	M	5:54 **5:54** p3.1	11:36 **11:42** p4.3	
23	S	5:42 **6:00** p3.1	11:30 **11:42** p4.1		23	T	6:30 **6:30** p3.2	... **12:12** 3.5	
24	S	6:24 **6:30** p3.2	... **12:06** 3.7		24	W	7:06 **7:06** p3.3	12:12 **12:48** a4.4	
25	M	7:00 **7:06** p3.2	12:18 **12:42** a4.2		25	T	7:42 **7:42** p3.3	12:48 **1:24** a4.4	
26	T	7:36 **7:36** p3.2	12:48 **1:12** a4.3		26	F	8:18 **8:24** p3.2	1:30 **2:06** a4.4	
27	W	8:12 **8:12** p3.2	1:24 **1:48** a4.3		27	S	9:00 **9:06** p3.1	2:12 **2:48** a4.4	
28	T	8:48 **8:48** p3.1	2:00 **2:30** a4.3		28	S	9:48 **10:00** p3.0	3:00 **3:36** a4.2	
29	F	9:24 **9:30** p3.0	2:36 **3:06** a4.2		29	M	10:42 **10:54** p2.9	3:48 **4:30** a4.1	
30	S	10:12 **10:18** p2.9	3:18 **3:54** a4.0		30	T	11:36 **...** 2.8	4:42 **5:30** a3.9	
31	S	11:06 **11:12** p2.8	4:06 **4:48** a3.9						

The Kts. (knots) columns show the **maximum** predicted velocities of the stronger one of the Flood Currents and the stronger one of the Ebb Currents for each day.

The letter "a" means the velocity shown should occur **after** the **a.m.** Current Change. The letter "p" means the velocity shown should occur **after** the **p.m.** Current Change (even if next morning). No "a" or "p" means a.m. and p.m. velocities are the same for that day.

Avg. Max. Velocity: Flood 3.3 Kts., Ebb 4.2 Kts.

Max. Flood 2 hrs. 45 min. after Flood Starts, ±15 min.

Max. Ebb 3 hrs. 25 min. after Ebb Starts, ±15 min.

Use THE RACE tables with current charts pp. 98-103

See pp. 22-29 for Current Change at other points.

2024 CURRENT TABLE
THE RACE, LONG ISLAND SOUND
41°13.69'N, 72°03.75'W 0.2 nm E.N.E. of Valiant Rock

Daylight Saving Time	Daylight Saving Time

		MAY							JUNE					
D A Y O F M O N T H	**D A Y O F W E E K**	CURRENT TURNS TO						**D A Y O F M O N T H**	**D A Y O F W E E K**	CURRENT TURNS TO				
		NORTHWEST Flood Starts			SOUTHEAST Ebb Starts					NORTHWEST Flood Starts			SOUTHEAST Ebb Starts		
		a.m.	**p.m.**	Kts.	a.m.	**p.m.**	Kts.			a.m.	**p.m.**	Kts.	a.m.	**p.m.**	Kts.
1	W	12:01	**12:36**	2.9	5:48	**6:30**	a3.9	1	S	1:48	**2:00**	p3.5	7:36	**8:06**	p4.6
2	T	1:00	**1:36**	p3.1	6:48	**7:30**	p4.1	2	S	2:54	**3:00**	p3.7	8:36	**9:06**	p4.9
3	F	2:06	**2:30**	p3.4	7:54	**8:30**	p4.5	3	M	3:48	**3:54**	p3.8	9:42	**10:00**	p5.1
4	S	3:07	**3:24**	p3.7	8:54	**9:24**	p4.9	4	T	4:43	**4:48**	p3.9	10:36	**10:48**	p5.2
5	S	4:00	**4:18**	p4.0	9:54	**10:18**	p5.3	5	W	5:36	**5:42**	p3.9	11:30	**11:42**	p5.2
6	M	5:00	**5:06**	p4.2	10:48	**11:06**	p5.5	6	T	6:30	**6:30**	p3.9	...	**12:18**	4.3
7	T	5:48	**6:00**	p4.3	11:42	...	4.6	7	F	7:18	**7:24**	p3.7	12:30	**1:06**	a5.1
8	W	6:42	**6:48**	p4.2	12:01	**12:36**	a5.5	8	S	8:06	**8:12**	a3.5	1:18	**1:54**	a4.8
9	T	7:30	**7:42**	3.9	12:48	**1:24**	a5.4	9	S	8:54	**9:06**	a3.3	2:06	**2:42**	a4.5
10	F	8:24	**8:30**	3.6	1:36	**2:18**	a5.1	10	M	9:36	**10:00**	a3.1	2:54	**3:30**	a4.1
11	S	9:12	**9:24**	a3.3	2:24	**3:06**	a4.7	11	T	10:24	**10:48**	a2.9	3:36	**4:18**	a3.7
12	S	10:06	**10:24**	a3.0	3:18	**4:00**	a4.3	12	W	11:12	**11:48**	a2.7	4:24	**5:06**	a3.4
13	M	11:00	**11:24**	a2.7	4:12	**4:54**	a3.8	13	T	...	**12:01**	2.5	5:12	**5:48**	p3.2
14	T	11:54	...	2.5	5:06	**5:48**	a3.4	14	F	12:42	**12:48**	p2.4	6:06	**6:36**	p3.2
15	W	12:24	**12:48**	p2.4	6:00	**6:42**	3.1	15	S	1:36	**1:36**	p2.4	7:00	**7:24**	p3.3
16	T	1:24	**1:42**	p2.4	7:00	**7:30**	p3.2	16	S	2:24	**2:24**	p2.4	7:54	**8:12**	p3.5
17	F	2:18	**2:30**	p2.4	7:54	**8:18**	p3.4	17	M	3:12	**3:06**	p2.5	8:48	**8:54**	p3.7
18	S	3:12	**3:12**	p2.5	8:48	**9:00**	p3.6	18	T	4:00	**3:54**	p2.7	9:36	**9:42**	p4.0
19	S	3:54	**3:54**	p2.7	9:36	**9:42**	p3.8	19	W	4:42	**4:42**	p2.9	10:24	**10:30**	p4.2
20	M	4:36	**4:36**	p2.8	10:18	**10:24**	p4.1	20	T	5:24	**5:24**	p3.2	11:12	**11:12**	p4.5
21	T	5:18	**5:18**	p3.0	11:00	**11:00**	p4.3	21	F	6:12	**6:12**	p3.4	11:54	...	3.8
22	W	6:00	**5:54**	p3.2	11:42	**11:42**	p4.4	22	S	6:54	**6:54**	p3.6	12:01	**12:42**	a4.7
23	T	6:36	**6:36**	p3.3	...	**12:24**	3.6	23	S	7:36	**7:42**	p3.7	12:48	**1:24**	a4.8
24	F	7:18	**7:18**	p3.4	12:24	**1:06**	a4.5	24	M	8:18	**8:36**	3.6	1:36	**2:12**	a4.8
25	S	8:00	**8:00**	p3.4	1:06	**1:48**	a4.6	25	T	9:06	**9:24**	a3.7	2:24	**3:06**	a4.8
26	S	8:42	**8:48**	p3.3	1:54	**2:30**	a4.6	26	W	9:54	**10:24**	a3.6	3:18	**3:54**	a4.6
27	M	9:30	**9:42**	3.2	2:42	**3:24**	a4.5	27	T	10:48	**11:24**	a3.6	4:12	**4:48**	p4.5
28	T	10:18	**10:42**	a3.2	3:30	**4:12**	a4.4	28	F	11:42	...	3.5	5:12	**5:48**	p4.4
29	W	11:12	**11:42**	a3.2	4:30	**5:12**	a4.2	29	S	12:30	**12:42**	p3.5	6:12	**6:42**	p4.5
30	T	...	**12:06**	3.3	5:30	**6:06**	p4.1	30	S	1:36	**1:42**	p3.4	7:18	**7:42**	p4.5
31	F	12:48	**1:06**	p3.4	6:30	**7:06**	p4.3								

The Kts. (knots) columns show the **maximum** predicted velocities of the stronger one of the Flood Currents and the stronger one of the Ebb Currents for each day.

The letter "a" means the velocity shown should occur **after** the **a.m.** Current Change. The letter "p" means the velocity shown should occur **after** the **p.m.** Current Change (even if next morning). No "a" or "p" means a.m. and p.m. velocities are the same for that day.

Avg. Max. Velocity: Flood 3.3 Kts., Ebb 4.2 Kts.

Max. Flood 2 hrs. 45 min. after Flood Starts, ±15 min.

Max. Ebb 3 hrs. 25 min. after Ebb Starts, ±15 min.

Use THE RACE tables with current charts pp. 98-103

See pp. 22-29 for Current Change at other points.

THE RACE, LONG ISLAND SOUND
41°13.69'N, 72°03.75'W 0.2 nm E.N.E. of Valiant Rock

Daylight Saving Time	Daylight Saving Time
JULY	**AUGUST**

DAY OF MONTH	DAY OF WEEK	CURRENT TURNS TO						DAY OF MONTH	DAY OF WEEK	CURRENT TURNS TO					
		NORTHWEST Flood Starts			SOUTHEAST Ebb Starts					NORTHWEST Flood Starts			SOUTHEAST Ebb Starts		
		a.m.	**p.m.**	Kts.	a.m.	**p.m.**	Kts.			a.m.	**p.m.**	Kts.	a.m.	**p.m.**	Kts.
1	M	2:36	**2:42**	p3.4	8:24	**8:42**	p4.6	1	T	4:24	**4:24**	p3.3	10:12	**10:24**	p4.5
2	T	3:36	**3:36**	p3.5	9:24	**9:42**	p4.8	2	F	5:12	**5:18**	p3.4	11:00	**11:12**	p4.5
3	W	4:36	**4:36**	p3.6	10:24	**10:36**	p4.8	3	S	6:00	**6:06**	3.4	11:48	**...**	4.0
4	T	5:25	**5:30**	p3.6	11:18	**11:30**	p4.8	4	S	6:43	**6:54**	a3.4	12:01	**12:30**	a4.4
5	F	6:18	**6:18**	p3.6	...	**12:06**	4.1	5	M	7:24	**7:36**	a3.4	12:42	**1:12**	a4.3
6	S	7:00	**7:12**	3.5	12:18	**12:54**	a4.7	6	T	8:00	**8:18**	a3.4	1:24	**1:48**	4.1
7	S	7:48	**7:54**	a3.4	1:00	**1:36**	a4.6	7	W	8:30	**9:00**	a3.2	2:00	**2:24**	p4.0
8	M	8:24	**8:42**	a3.3	1:42	**2:18**	a4.3	8	T	9:06	**9:42**	a3.1	2:36	**3:00**	p3.9
9	T	9:06	**9:30**	a3.2	2:24	**3:00**	a4.0	9	F	9:42	**10:24**	a2.9	3:12	**3:36**	p3.7
10	W	9:48	**10:18**	a3.0	3:06	**3:36**	3.7	10	S	10:24	**11:06**	a2.7	3:48	**4:12**	p3.6
11	T	10:24	**11:06**	a2.8	3:48	**4:18**	p3.5	11	S	11:06	**11:54**	a2.6	4:36	**4:54**	p3.5
12	F	11:06	**11:54**	a2.6	4:30	**5:00**	p3.4	12	M	11:54	**...**	2.5	5:24	**5:42**	p3.4
13	S	11:54	**...**	2.5	5:18	**5:42**	p3.3	13	T	12:48	**12:48**	p2.4	6:18	**6:36**	p3.4
14	S	12:42	**12:42**	p2.4	6:06	**6:30**	p3.3	14	W	1:42	**1:42**	p2.5	7:18	**7:36**	p3.5
15	M	1:36	**1:30**	p2.4	7:00	**7:18**	p3.4	15	T	2:42	**2:42**	p2.7	8:18	**8:36**	p3.8
16	T	2:30	**2:24**	p2.5	8:00	**8:12**	p3.6	16	F	3:36	**3:36**	p3.0	9:18	**9:30**	p4.2
17	W	3:18	**3:18**	p2.7	8:54	**9:06**	p3.8	17	S	4:24	**4:30**	p3.4	10:12	**10:24**	p4.6
18	T	4:06	**4:06**	p2.9	9:48	**10:00**	p4.2	18	S	5:12	**5:24**	p3.8	11:06	**11:18**	p4.9
19	F	4:54	**4:54**	p3.3	10:42	**10:48**	p4.5	19	M	6:00	**6:12**	p4.0	11:54	**...**	4.8
20	S	5:42	**5:48**	p3.6	11:30	**11:42**	p4.8	20	T	6:42	**7:06**	4.2	12:06	**12:42**	p5.2
21	S	6:24	**6:36**	p3.8	...	**12:18**	4.4	21	W	7:30	**7:54**	a4.4	1:00	**1:30**	p5.3
22	M	7:12	**7:24**	p4.0	12:30	**1:06**	a5.0	22	T	8:18	**8:48**	a4.4	1:48	**2:18**	p5.4
23	T	7:54	**8:18**	4.0	1:18	**1:54**	a5.1	23	F	9:06	**9:48**	a4.2	2:42	**3:06**	p5.2
24	W	8:42	**9:12**	a4.1	2:06	**2:42**	a5.0	24	S	10:00	**10:48**	a3.9	3:36	**4:00**	p4.9
25	T	9:30	**10:06**	a4.0	3:00	**3:36**	p4.9	25	S	10:54	**11:48**	a3.6	4:36	**5:00**	p4.5
26	F	10:24	**11:06**	a3.9	3:54	**4:24**	p4.8	26	M	...	**12:01**	3.2	5:36	**6:00**	p4.2
27	S	11:18	**...**	3.6	4:54	**5:24**	p4.6	27	T	1:00	**1:06**	p3.0	6:42	**7:06**	p4.0
28	S	12:12	**12:18**	p3.4	5:54	**6:24**	p4.4	28	W	2:06	**2:12**	p2.9	7:48	**8:12**	p4.0
29	M	1:18	**1:24**	p3.2	7:00	**7:24**	p4.3	29	T	3:06	**3:18**	p3.0	8:54	**9:12**	p4.0
30	T	2:24	**2:24**	p3.2	8:06	**8:30**	p4.3	30	F	4:06	**4:12**	p3.1	9:54	**10:12**	p4.1
31	W	3:24	**3:30**	p3.2	9:12	**9:30**	p4.4	31	S	4:54	**5:06**	p3.2	10:42	**11:00**	p4.1

The Kts. (knots) columns show the **maximum** predicted velocities of the stronger one of the Flood Currents and the stronger one of the Ebb Currents for each day.

The letter "a" means the velocity shown should occur **after** the **a.m.** Current Change. The letter "p" means the velocity shown should occur **after** the **p.m.** Current Change (even if next morning). No "a" or "p" means a.m. and p.m. velocities are the same for that day.

Avg. Max. Velocity: Flood 3.3 Kts., Ebb 4.2 Kts.

Max. Flood 2 hrs. 45 min. after Flood Starts, ±15 min.

Max. Ebb 3 hrs. 25 min. after Ebb Starts, ±15 min.

Use THE RACE tables with current charts pp. 98-103

See pp. 22-29 for Current Change at other points.

2024 CURRENT TABLE
THE RACE, LONG ISLAND SOUND
41°13.69'N, 72°03.75'W 0.2 nm E.N.E. of Valiant Rock

Daylight Saving Time

Daylight Saving Time

DAY OF MONTH	DAY OF WEEK	NORTHWEST Flood Starts a.m.	**p.m.**	Kts.	SOUTHEAST Ebb Starts a.m.	**p.m.**	Kts.	DAY OF MONTH	DAY OF WEEK	NORTHWEST Flood Starts a.m.	**p.m.**	Kts.	SOUTHEAST Ebb Starts a.m.	**p.m.**	Kts.
		SEPTEMBER								**OCTOBER**					
1	S	5:36	**5:54**	a3.3	11:24	**11:42**	p4.1	1	T	5:42	**6:12**	a3.2	11:30	**11:54**	a4.2
2	M	6:18	**6:36**	a3.3	...	**12:06**	4.2	2	W	6:18	**6:48**	a3.2	...	**12:06**	4.2
3	T	6:54	**7:12**	a3.4	12:18	**12:42**	p4.2	3	T	6:54	**7:24**	a3.2	12:30	**12:36**	p4.3
4	W	7:25	**7:48**	a3.3	12:54	**1:12**	p4.2	4	F	7:25	**8:00**	a3.2	1:06	**1:12**	p4.3
5	T	8:00	**8:30**	a3.2	1:30	**1:48**	p4.2	5	S	8:00	**8:36**	a3.1	1:36	**1:42**	p4.2
6	F	8:30	**9:06**	a3.1	2:06	**2:18**	p4.1	6	S	8:36	**9:12**	a3.0	2:12	**2:18**	p4.1
7	S	9:06	**9:42**	a3.0	2:42	**2:54**	p3.9	7	M	9:12	**9:54**	a2.9	2:54	**3:00**	p3.9
8	S	9:42	**10:24**	a2.8	3:18	**3:30**	p3.8	8	T	10:00	**10:42**	a2.8	3:36	**3:48**	p3.8
9	M	10:24	**11:12**	a2.7	4:00	**4:12**	p3.6	9	W	10:48	**11:36**	a2.6	4:24	**4:36**	p3.6
10	T	11:18	...	2.5	4:48	**5:06**	p3.5	10	T	11:48	...	2.6	5:18	**5:36**	p3.6
11	W	12:06	**12:12**	p2.5	5:42	**6:00**	p3.4	11	F	12:30	**12:48**	p2.7	6:18	**6:36**	p3.6
12	T	1:06	**1:12**	p2.6	6:42	**7:00**	p3.5	12	S	1:30	**1:54**	p2.8	7:18	**7:42**	p3.9
13	F	2:06	**2:18**	p2.8	7:48	**8:06**	p3.8	13	S	2:24	**2:54**	p3.1	8:18	**8:42**	p4.2
14	S	3:00	**3:12**	p3.1	8:48	**9:06**	p4.2	14	M	3:18	**3:48**	p3.5	9:18	**9:42**	a4.6
15	S	3:54	**4:12**	p3.5	9:42	**10:06**	p4.6	15	T	4:12	**4:42**	3.8	10:12	**10:36**	a5.1
16	M	4:42	**5:00**	p3.9	10:36	**11:00**	p4.9	16	W	5:00	**5:36**	a4.2	11:00	**11:30**	a5.5
17	T	5:30	**5:54**	p4.2	11:24	**11:48**	a5.2	17	T	5:48	**6:30**	a4.4	11:48	...	5.7
18	W	6:18	**6:48**	a4.4	...	**12:18**	5.5	18	F	6:42	**7:18**	a4.5	12:24	**12:42**	p5.7
19	T	7:06	**7:36**	a4.5	12:42	**1:06**	p5.7	19	S	7:30	**8:12**	a4.4	1:12	**1:30**	p5.5
20	F	7:54	**8:30**	a4.5	1:30	**1:54**	p5.6	20	S	8:24	**9:06**	a4.1	2:06	**2:24**	p5.2
21	S	8:42	**9:24**	a4.2	2:24	**2:42**	p5.3	21	M	9:18	**10:06**	a3.7	3:00	**3:18**	p4.8
22	S	9:36	**10:24**	a3.8	3:18	**3:36**	p4.9	22	T	10:18	**11:06**	a3.2	4:00	**4:12**	p4.3
23	M	10:36	**11:30**	a3.4	4:18	**4:36**	p4.4	23	W	11:24	...	2.9	4:54	**5:12**	p3.8
24	T	11:42	...	3.0	5:18	**5:36**	p4.0	24	T	12:06	**12:30**	a2.7	6:00	**6:18**	p3.5
25	W	12:36	**12:48**	p2.8	6:24	**6:42**	p3.7	25	F	1:06	**1:36**	a2.6	7:00	**7:18**	p3.4
26	T	1:42	**1:54**	p2.7	7:30	**7:48**	p3.7	26	S	2:06	**2:36**	a2.6	7:54	**8:18**	a3.4
27	F	2:42	**3:00**	2.7	8:30	**8:54**	p3.7	27	S	3:00	**3:30**	a2.7	8:48	**9:12**	a3.6
28	S	3:36	**3:54**	2.8	9:24	**9:48**	p3.8	28	M	3:42	**4:18**	a2.8	9:36	**10:00**	a3.8
29	S	4:24	**4:42**	3.0	10:12	**10:36**	a3.9	29	T	4:24	**5:00**	a2.9	10:12	**10:48**	a4.0
30	M	5:06	**5:30**	a3.1	10:54	**11:18**	a4.1	30	W	5:06	**5:42**	a3.0	10:54	**11:24**	a4.1
								31	T	5:42	**6:18**	a3.0	11:24	...	4.2

The Kts. (knots) columns show the **maximum** predicted velocities of the stronger one of the Flood Currents and the stronger one of the Ebb Currents for each day.

The letter "a" means the velocity shown should occur **after** the **a.m.** Current Change. The letter "p" means the velocity shown should occur **after** the **p.m.** Current Change (even if next morning). No "a" or "p" means a.m. and p.m. velocities are the same for that day.

Avg. Max. Velocity: Flood 3.3 Kts., Ebb 4.2 Kts.

Max. Flood 2 hrs. 45 min. after Flood Starts, ±15 min.

Max. Ebb 3 hrs. 25 min. after Ebb Starts, ±15 min.

Use THE RACE tables with current charts pp. 98-103

See pp. 22-29 for Current Change at other points.

2024 CURRENT TABLE
THE RACE, LONG ISLAND SOUND
41°13.69'N, 72°03.75'W 0.2 nm E.N.E. of Valiant Rock

*Standard Time starts Nov. 3 at 2 a.m.   **Standard Time**

		NOVEMBER						DECEMBER			
		CURRENT TURNS TO						CURRENT TURNS TO			
		NORTHWEST Flood Starts			SOUTHEAST Ebb Starts			NORTHWEST Flood Starts			SOUTHEAST Ebb Starts
DAY OF MONTH	DAY OF WEEK	a.m.	**p.m.**	Kts.	a.m.	**p.m.**	Kts.	DAY OF MONTH	DAY OF WEEK	a.m.	**p.m.**	Kts.	a.m.	**p.m.**	Kts.
1	F	6:18	**6:54**	a3.1	12:01	**12:01**	p4.3	1	S	5:24	**6:06**	a3.1	11:06	**11:48**	a4.3
2	S	6:54	**7:30**	a3.1	12:36	**12:36**	p4.3	2	M	6:06	**6:42**	a3.2	11:48	...	4.4
3	S	*6:30	***7:06**	a3.1	12:54	***12:12**	p4.3	3	T	6:48	**7:24**	3.2	12:30	**12:30**	p4.4
4	M	7:07	**7:48**	a3.1	12:54	**12:54**	p4.2	4	W	7:31	**8:06**	3.2	1:12	**1:18**	p4.4
5	T	7:48	**8:30**	a3.0	1:30	**1:36**	p4.1	5	T	8:18	**8:54**	3.2	2:00	**2:06**	p4.3
6	W	8:36	**9:18**	a2.9	2:18	**2:24**	p4.0	6	F	9:12	**9:42**	p3.2	2:48	**3:00**	p4.2
7	T	9:30	**10:06**	2.8	3:06	**3:18**	p3.9	7	S	10:12	**10:36**	p3.3	3:42	**3:54**	4.0
8	F	10:30	**11:00**	p2.9	4:00	**4:12**	p3.8	8	S	11:12	**11:30**	p3.3	4:36	**4:54**	a4.1
9	S	11:30	...	2.8	4:54	**5:12**	p3.8	9	M	...	**12:18**	2.9	5:30	**5:54**	a4.3
10	S	12:01	**12:36**	a3.0	5:54	**6:18**	a4.0	10	T	12:24	**1:18**	a3.4	6:30	**7:00**	a4.5
11	M	12:54	**1:36**	a3.3	6:54	**7:18**	a4.3	11	W	1:24	**2:18**	a3.6	7:30	**8:06**	a4.8
12	T	1:48	**2:30**	a3.6	7:54	**8:24**	a4.8	12	T	2:18	**3:12**	a3.7	8:24	**9:06**	a5.0
13	W	2:42	**3:30**	a3.9	8:48	**9:18**	a5.1	13	F	3:18	**4:06**	a3.9	9:18	**10:00**	a5.2
14	T	3:36	**4:18**	a4.1	9:36	**10:12**	a5.4	14	S	4:12	**5:00**	a4.0	10:12	**10:54**	a5.3
15	F	4:30	**5:12**	a4.3	10:30	**11:06**	a5.6	15	S	5:06	**5:54**	a4.0	11:06	**11:42**	a5.2
16	S	5:18	**6:06**	a4.3	11:18	...	5.5	16	M	6:00	**6:42**	a3.9	11:54	...	5.1
17	S	6:12	**6:54**	a4.1	12:01	**12:12**	p5.3	17	T	6:48	**7:30**	a3.7	12:36	**12:42**	p4.8
18	M	7:06	**7:48**	a3.9	12:48	**1:00**	p5.0	18	W	7:42	**8:18**	3.4	1:24	**1:30**	p4.5
19	T	8:00	**8:42**	a3.5	1:42	**1:54**	p4.6	19	T	8:36	**9:06**	p3.2	2:12	**2:24**	p4.1
20	W	9:00	**9:36**	a3.1	2:36	**2:48**	p4.2	20	F	9:30	**9:54**	p2.9	3:00	**3:12**	a3.8
21	T	10:00	**10:30**	p2.8	3:30	**3:42**	p3.7	21	S	10:24	**10:42**	p2.7	3:48	**4:00**	a3.6
22	F	11:00	**11:30**	p2.7	4:24	**4:42**	a3.4	22	S	11:24	**11:30**	p2.5	4:36	**4:54**	a3.4
23	S	...	**12:01**	2.2	5:18	**5:42**	a3.3	23	M	...	**12:18**	2.0	5:18	**5:48**	a3.3
24	S	12:18	**1:00**	a2.6	6:12	**6:36**	a3.4	24	T	12:18	**1:12**	a2.4	6:06	**6:42**	a3.3
25	M	1:12	**1:54**	a2.5	7:00	**7:30**	a3.5	25	W	1:06	**2:00**	a2.3	6:54	**7:36**	a3.4
26	T	2:00	**2:42**	a2.5	7:48	**8:24**	a3.6	26	T	1:54	**2:48**	a2.4	7:42	**8:24**	a3.5
27	W	2:42	**3:24**	a2.6	8:30	**9:06**	a3.8	27	F	2:42	**3:30**	a2.5	8:30	**9:12**	a3.7
28	T	3:24	**4:06**	a2.7	9:12	**9:48**	a3.9	28	S	3:30	**4:12**	a2.7	9:12	**10:00**	a3.9
29	F	4:06	**4:48**	2.8	9:48	**10:30**	a4.1	29	S	4:12	**4:54**	2.9	10:00	**10:42**	a4.2
30	S	4:42	**5:24**	a3.0	10:30	**11:12**	a4.2	30	M	4:54	**5:36**	a3.2	10:42	**11:24**	a4.4
								31	T	5:42	**6:18**	3.4	11:30	...	4.6

The Kts. (knots) columns show the **maximum** predicted velocities of the stronger one of the Flood Currents and the stronger one of the Ebb Currents for each day.

The letter "a" means the velocity shown should occur **after** the **a.m.** Current Change. The letter "p" means the velocity shown should occur **after** the **p.m.** Current Change (even if next morning). No "a" or "p" means a.m. and p.m. velocities are the same for that day.

Avg. Max. Velocity: Flood 3.3 Kts., Ebb 4.2 Kts.

Max. Flood 2 hrs. 45 min. after Flood Starts, ±15 min.

Max. Ebb 3 hrs. 25 min. after Ebb Starts, ±15 min.

Use THE RACE tables with current charts pp. 98-103

See pp. 22-29 for Current Change at other points.

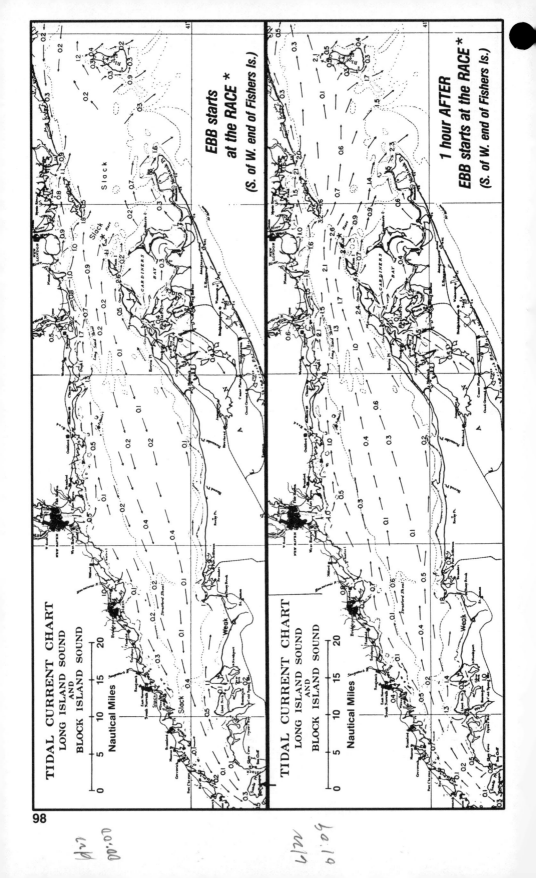

TIDAL CURRENT CHART
LONG ISLAND SOUND
AND
BLOCK ISLAND SOUND

Nautical Miles

EBB starts
*at the RACE ***
(S. of W. end of Fishers Is.)

TIDAL CURRENT CHART
LONG ISLAND SOUND
AND
BLOCK ISLAND SOUND

Nautical Miles

1 hour AFTER
*EBB starts at the RACE ***
(S. of W. end of Fishers Is.)

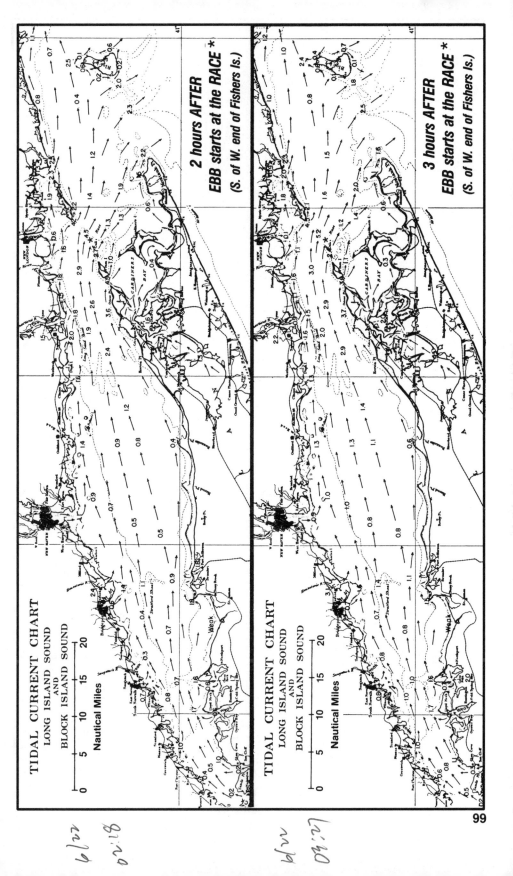

TIDAL CURRENT CHART
LONG ISLAND SOUND
AND
BLOCK ISLAND SOUND

Nautical Miles

2 hours AFTER
EBB starts at the RACE *
(S. of W. end of Fishers Is.)

3 hours AFTER
EBB starts at the RACE *
(S. of W. end of Fishers Is.)

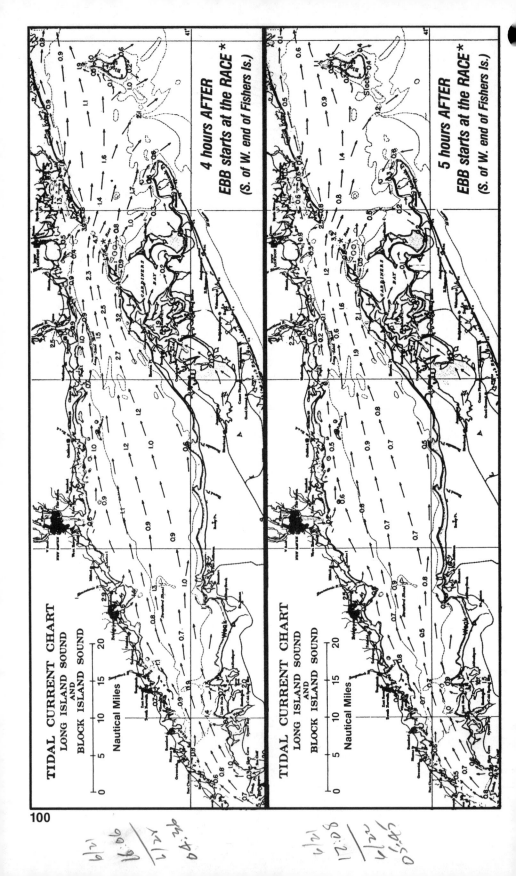

TIDAL CURRENT CHART
LONG ISLAND SOUND
AND
BLOCK ISLAND SOUND

Nautical Miles

4 hours AFTER
EBB starts at the RACE*
(S. of W. end of Fishers Is.)

5 hours AFTER
EBB starts at the RACE*
(S. of W. end of Fishers Is.)

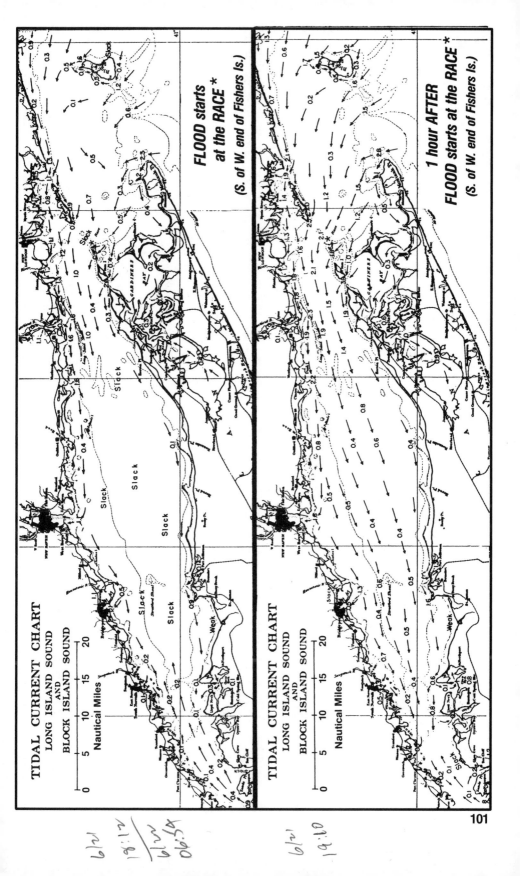

TIDAL CURRENT CHART
LONG ISLAND SOUND
AND
BLOCK ISLAND SOUND

Nautical Miles

*FLOOD starts
at the RACE **
(S. of W. end of Fishers Is.)

TIDAL CURRENT CHART
LONG ISLAND SOUND
AND
BLOCK ISLAND SOUND

Nautical Miles

*1 hour AFTER
FLOOD starts at the RACE **
(S. of W. end of Fishers Is.)

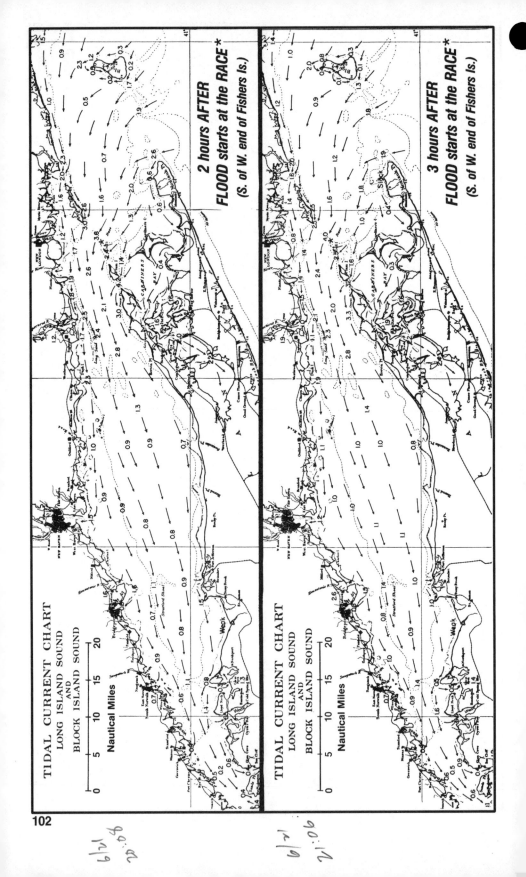

TIDAL CURRENT CHART
LONG ISLAND SOUND
AND
BLOCK ISLAND SOUND

Nautical Miles

2 hours AFTER
FLOOD starts at the RACE
(S. of W. end of Fishers Is.)

3 hours AFTER
FLOOD starts at the RACE
(S. of W. end of Fishers Is.)

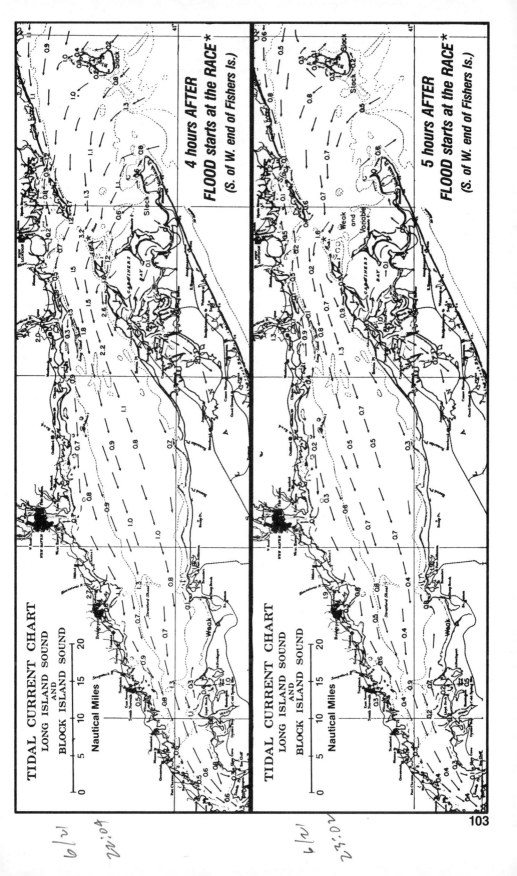

TIDAL CURRENT CHART
LONG ISLAND SOUND
AND
BLOCK ISLAND SOUND

Nautical Miles

4 hours AFTER
FLOOD starts at the RACE*
(S. of W. end of Fishers Is.)

TIDAL CURRENT CHART
LONG ISLAND SOUND
AND
BLOCK ISLAND SOUND

Nautical Miles

5 hours AFTER
FLOOD starts at the RACE*
(S. of W. end of Fishers Is.)

2024 HIGH & LOW WATER
BRIDGEPORT, CT
41°10.4'N, 73°10.9'W

		Standard Time								Standard Time			
DAY OF MONTH	DAY OF WEEK	**JANUARY**				DAY OF MONTH	DAY OF WEEK	**FEBRUARY**					
		HIGH		LOW				HIGH			LOW		
		a.m.	Ht.	p.m.	Ht.	a.m.	p.m.		a.m.	Ht.	p.m.	Ht.	a.m.	p.m.
1	M	2:31	6.0	2:44	6.0	8:39	9:04	1	T	3:14	6.2	3:39	5.6	9:36	9:45
2	T	3:16	6.0	3:32	5.8	9:29	9:49	2	F	3:59	6.1	4:30	5.4	10:28	10:35
3	W	4:02	6.0	4:23	5.5	10:21	10:36	3	S	4:49	6.1	5:27	5.2	11:24	11:32
4	T	4:52	6.0	5:17	5.4	11:16	11:26	4	S	5:47	6.1	6:27	5.3	...	12:24
5	F	5:42	6.1	6:13	5.3	...	12:11	5	M	6:46	6.3	7:27	5.5	12:31	1:24
6	S	6:34	6.3	7:10	5.4	12:18	1:06	6	T	7:46	6.6	8:24	5.8	1:31	2:21
7	S	7:26	6.5	8:03	5.6	1:10	1:59	7	W	8:42	7.0	9:16	6.2	2:28	3:15
8	M	8:16	6.8	8:53	5.8	2:03	2:50	8	T	9:35	7.4	10:06	6.6	3:23	4:05
9	T	9:06	7.1	9:41	6.1	2:54	3:40	9	F	10:26	7.7	10:55	7.0	4:16	4:54
10	W	9:54	7.3	10:29	6.3	3:44	4:28	10	S	11:16	7.8	11:44	7.3	5:08	5:41
11	T	10:43	7.6	11:16	6.6	4:34	5:16	11	S	...	...	12:06	7.8	5:59	6:28
12	F	11:32	7.7	...	...	5:24	6:03	12	M	12:33	7.5	12:57	7.6	6:51	7:15
13	S	12:05	6.8	12:23	7.7	6:15	6:51	13	T	1:24	7.6	1:49	7.2	7:45	8:05
14	S	12:56	6.9	1:15	7.5	7:08	7:40	14	W	2:15	7.5	2:43	6.8	8:41	8:56
15	M	1:48	7.1	2:08	7.2	8:03	8:31	15	T	3:09	7.3	3:39	6.3	9:40	9:52
16	T	2:41	7.1	3:04	6.8	9:02	9:24	16	F	4:06	7.0	4:40	6.0	10:42	10:52
17	W	3:36	7.1	4:02	6.4	10:03	10:20	17	S	5:07	6.7	5:45	5.7	11:46	11:56
18	T	4:34	7.0	5:04	6.1	11:06	11:18	18	S	6:13	6.4	6:52	5.6	...	12:50
19	F	5:35	6.9	6:08	5.8	...	12:10	19	M	7:18	6.4	7:54	5.7	1:00	1:52
20	S	6:36	6.8	7:12	5.8	12:19	1:13	20	T	8:18	6.4	8:48	5.9	2:01	2:47
21	S	7:37	6.8	8:12	5.8	1:19	2:12	21	W	9:09	6.5	9:35	6.1	2:55	3:35
22	M	8:33	6.8	9:06	5.9	2:17	3:06	22	T	9:54	6.6	10:17	6.3	3:43	4:25
23	T	9:24	6.8	9:54	6.1	3:10	3:55	23	F	10:34	6.7	10:55	6.4	4:25	4:54
24	W	10:10	6.8	10:38	6.2	3:59	4:39	24	S	11:12	6.7	11:32	6.5	5:05	5:29
25	T	10:52	6.8	11:19	6.2	4:43	5:19	25	S	11:48	6.6	...	...	5:42	6:02
26	F	11:32	6.7	11:58	6.2	5:25	5:57	26	M	12:07	6.6	12:24	6.5	6:19	6:35
27	S	...	...	12:11	6.6	6:04	6:33	27	T	12:41	6.6	1:01	6.4	6:55	7:09
28	S	12:37	6.3	12:50	6.5	6:44	7:08	28	W	1:16	6.6	1:39	6.2	7:33	7:44
29	M	1:15	6.3	1:29	6.3	7:23	7:44	29	T	1:53	6.5	2:19	6.0	8:13	8:22
30	T	1:54	6.2	2:10	6.1	8:05	8:21								
31	W	2:33	6.2	2:52	5.8	8:48	9:01								

Dates when Ht. of **Low** Water is below Mean Lower Low with Ht. of lowest given for each period and Date of lowest in ( ):

9th–17th: -0.9' (12th–14th)   7th–15th: -1.2' (11th)
24th–25th: -0.2'

Average Rise and Fall 6.8 ft.

When a high tide exceeds avg. ht., the *following* low tide will be lower than avg.

2024 HIGH & LOW WATER
BRIDGEPORT, CT
41°10.4'N, 73°10.9'W

*Daylight Time starts March 10 at 2 a.m.   Daylight Saving Time

DAY OF MONTH	DAY OF WEEK	MARCH HIGH a.m.	Ht.	p.m.	Ht.	LOW a.m.	p.m.	DAY OF MONTH	DAY OF WEEK	APRIL HIGH a.m.	Ht.	p.m.	Ht.	LOW a.m.	p.m.
1	F	2:32	6.4	3:03	5.8	8:57	9:05	1	M	4:39	6.5	5:23	5.8	11:17	11:32
2	S	3:16	6.3	3:52	5.6	9:47	9:56	2	T	5:42	6.4	6:26	5.9	...	12:20
3	S	4:07	6.2	4:49	5.4	10:45	10:55	3	W	6:50	6.6	7:30	6.1	12:39	1:25
4	M	5:09	6.2	5:52	5.4	11:48	...	4	T	7:57	6.8	8:31	6.6	1:46	2:25
5	T	6:14	6.3	6:56	5.7	12:01	12:52	5	F	8:58	7.1	9:27	7.1	2:48	3:21
6	W	7:20	6.7	7:57	6.1	1:06	1:53	6	S	9:54	7.4	10:19	7.7	3:47	4:12
7	T	8:20	7.1	8:52	6.6	2:07	2:49	7	S	10:46	7.6	11:08	8.1	4:41	5:01
8	F	9:15	7.4	9:43	7.1	3:05	3:40	8	M	11:37	7.7	11:56	8.3	5:33	5:49
9	S	10:07	7.7	10:32	7.6	3:59	4:29	9	T	...	...	12:26	7.6	6:24	6:36
10	S	*11:57	7.8	...	...	*5:51	*6:15	10	W	12:43	8.3	1:16	7.4	7:13	7:24
11	M	12:20	7.9	12:46	7.8	6:42	7:02	11	T	1:32	8.1	2:07	7.1	8:04	8:13
12	T	1:09	8.0	1:36	7.6	7:33	7:49	12	F	2:22	7.8	2:59	6.8	8:55	9:05
13	W	1:58	8.0	2:28	7.2	8:25	8:38	13	S	3:15	7.3	3:54	6.5	9:49	10:01
14	T	2:48	7.8	3:21	6.8	9:18	9:30	14	S	4:11	6.8	4:51	6.2	10:47	11:02
15	F	3:41	7.4	4:17	6.4	10:15	10:26	15	M	5:12	6.4	5:52	6.0	11:47	...
16	S	4:38	6.9	5:16	6.0	11:15	11:27	16	T	6:16	6.2	6:54	6.0	12:06	12:47
17	S	5:40	6.5	6:21	5.8	...	12:18	17	W	7:20	6.1	7:53	6.1	1:09	1:45
18	M	6:47	6.2	7:26	5.7	12:33	1:23	18	T	8:20	6.1	8:46	6.4	2:08	2:37
19	T	7:54	6.1	8:28	5.9	1:38	2:24	19	F	9:12	6.2	9:33	6.6	3:02	3:24
20	W	8:55	6.2	9:22	6.1	2:39	3:18	20	S	9:58	6.4	10:13	6.9	3:49	4:06
21	T	9:46	6.4	10:08	6.4	3:33	4:05	21	S	10:39	6.5	10:51	7.1	4:32	4:44
22	F	10:30	6.5	10:49	6.6	4:20	4:45	22	M	11:17	6.6	11:26	7.2	5:12	5:21
23	S	11:10	6.6	11:26	6.8	5:02	5:22	23	T	11:55	6.6	...	...	5:50	5:56
24	S	11:46	6.7	...	...	5:40	5:56	24	W	12:01	7.2	12:32	6.6	6:27	6:32
25	M	12:01	6.9	12:22	6.6	6:17	6:30	25	T	12:36	7.2	1:10	6.5	7:04	7:09
26	T	12:34	7.0	12:58	6.6	6:53	7:03	26	F	1:12	7.2	1:49	6.4	7:42	7:48
27	W	1:08	7.0	1:34	6.5	7:29	7:37	27	S	1:52	7.1	2:31	6.3	8:23	8:30
28	T	1:42	6.9	2:12	6.3	8:05	8:12	28	S	2:36	7.0	3:17	6.3	9:09	9:19
29	F	2:18	6.8	2:52	6.2	8:45	8:51	29	M	3:26	6.9	4:08	6.2	10:00	10:15
30	S	2:59	6.7	3:36	6.0	9:28	9:36	30	T	4:22	6.8	5:05	6.3	10:57	11:17
31	S	3:45	6.6	4:26	5.9	10:18	10:30								

Dates when Ht. of **Low** Water is below Mean Lower Low with Ht. of lowest given for each period and Date of lowest in ( ):

7th–15th: -1.2' (11th, 12th)   6th–12th: -1.1' (9th)

Average Rise and Fall 6.8 ft.

When a high tide exceeds avg. ht., the *following* low tide will be lower than avg.

2024 HIGH & LOW WATER
BRIDGEPORT, CT
41°10.4'N, 73°10.9'W

		Daylight Saving Time							Daylight Saving Time				

DAY OF MONTH	DAY OF WEEK	MAY						DAY OF MONTH	DAY OF WEEK	JUNE					
		HIGH				LOW				HIGH				LOW	
		a.m.	Ht.	p.m.	Ht.	a.m.	p.m.			a.m.	Ht.	p.m.	Ht.	a.m.	p.m.
1	W	5:24	6.7	6:05	6.4	11:58	...	1	S	7:12	6.8	7:43	7.6	1:12	1:29
2	T	6:29	6.8	7:07	6.7	12:23	12:58	2	S	8:14	6.8	8:39	7.8	2:13	2:25
3	F	7:34	6.9	8:07	7.1	1:28	1:57	3	M	9:12	6.9	9:33	8.1	3:12	3:19
4	S	8:36	7.0	9:03	7.6	2:31	2:52	4	T	10:09	6.9	10:24	8.2	4:07	4:12
5	S	9:32	7.2	9:55	8.0	3:29	3:44	5	W	11:00	7.0	11:13	8.1	4:59	5:03
6	M	10:26	7.3	10:44	8.3	4:24	4:35	6	T	11:50	7.0	...	...	5:49	5:54
7	T	11:17	7.4	11:32	8.4	5:16	5:24	7	F	12:02	8.0	12:39	6.9	6:37	6:43
8	W	...	...	12:07	7.3	6:06	6:13	8	S	12:50	7.7	1:28	6.8	7:24	7:32
9	T	12:20	8.3	12:57	7.2	6:55	7:01	9	S	1:39	7.4	2:16	6.7	8:11	8:21
10	F	1:09	8.0	1:47	7.0	7:44	7:51	10	M	2:27	7.1	3:05	6.6	8:57	9:11
11	S	1:59	7.6	2:38	6.8	8:33	8:43	11	T	3:17	6.8	3:53	6.6	9:44	10:02
12	S	2:51	7.2	3:30	6.5	9:24	9:37	12	W	4:07	6.5	4:42	6.5	10:31	10:55
13	M	3:45	6.8	4:24	6.4	10:17	10:34	13	T	4:58	6.2	5:31	6.5	11:18	11:50
14	T	4:41	6.5	5:19	6.3	11:11	11:33	14	F	5:51	6.0	6:21	6.6	...	12:07
15	W	5:39	6.2	6:15	6.3	...	12:05	15	S	6:46	5.9	7:11	6.7	12:44	12:55
16	T	6:38	6.0	7:10	6.4	12:32	12:58	16	S	7:41	5.8	8:01	6.8	1:38	1:44
17	F	7:35	6.0	8:02	6.6	1:29	1:48	17	M	8:35	5.9	8:48	6.9	2:29	2:33
18	S	8:29	6.0	8:49	6.8	2:22	2:36	18	T	9:24	6.0	9:33	7.1	3:18	3:20
19	S	9:18	6.1	9:32	7.0	3:12	3:20	19	W	10:11	6.2	10:17	7.2	4:05	4:07
20	M	10:03	6.2	10:12	7.2	3:57	4:02	20	T	10:55	6.3	11:00	7.4	4:50	4:53
21	T	10:45	6.3	10:51	7.3	4:40	4:43	21	F	11:39	6.5	11:44	7.5	5:34	5:38
22	W	11:26	6.4	11:29	7.3	5:20	5:23	22	S	...	...	12:22	6.6	6:18	6:24
23	T	...	...	12:05	6.5	6:00	6:04	23	S	12:30	7.6	1:08	6.7	7:03	7:11
24	F	12:08	7.4	12:46	6.5	6:40	6:45	24	M	1:17	7.6	1:55	6.9	7:49	8:01
25	S	12:49	7.4	1:28	6.5	7:22	7:28	25	T	2:07	7.6	2:44	7.1	8:36	8:54
26	S	1:33	7.3	2:13	6.6	8:06	8:15	26	W	2:59	7.5	3:35	7.2	9:26	9:50
27	M	2:21	7.3	3:01	6.6	8:54	9:07	27	T	3:53	7.3	4:28	7.4	10:17	10:50
28	T	3:13	7.2	3:53	6.7	9:45	10:04	28	F	4:49	7.1	5:24	7.5	11:11	11:51
29	W	4:08	7.1	4:48	6.8	10:39	11:05	29	S	5:49	6.8	6:21	7.6	...	12:06
30	T	5:07	7.0	5:45	7.0	11:35	...	30	S	6:51	6.6	7:20	7.7	12:54	1:03
31	F	6:09	6.8	6:44	7.2	12:08	12:32								

Dates when Ht. of **Low** Water is below Mean Lower Low with Ht. of lowest given for each period and Date of lowest in ( ):

5th–10th: -0.8' (7th, 8th)   4th–7th: -0.4' (5th, 6th)

Average Rise and Fall 6.8 ft.

When a high tide exceeds avg. ht., the *following* low tide will be lower than avg.

2024 HIGH & LOW WATER
BRIDGEPORT, CT
41°10.4'N, 73°10.9'W

Daylight Saving Time   **Daylight Saving Time**

DAY OF MONTH	DAY OF WEEK	JULY HIGH a.m.	Ht.	JULY HIGH p.m.	Ht.	JULY LOW a.m.	JULY LOW p.m.	DAY OF MONTH	DAY OF WEEK	AUGUST HIGH a.m.	Ht.	AUGUST HIGH p.m.	Ht.	AUGUST LOW a.m.	AUGUST LOW p.m.
1	M	7:54	6.5	8:18	7.8	1:56	2:01	1	T	9:39	6.5	9:57	7.4	3:38	3:43
2	T	8:55	6.5	9:15	7.8	2:55	2:59	2	F	10:32	6.6	10:47	7.4	4:30	4:36
3	W	9:52	6.6	10:08	7.8	3:52	3:55	3	S	11:19	6.8	11:33	7.4	5:18	5:25
4	T	10:46	6.7	10:59	7.7	4:45	4:48	4	S	...	...	12:02	6.9	6:01	6:09
5	F	11:35	6.8	11:47	7.6	5:34	5:39	5	M	12:15	7.3	12:43	6.9	6:40	6:51
6	S	...	...	12:22	6.8	6:21	6:26	6	T	12:56	7.2	1:23	7.0	7:18	7:32
7	S	12:33	7.5	1:07	6.8	7:04	7:12	7	W	1:36	7.0	2:01	7.0	7:54	8:12
8	M	1:18	7.3	1:51	6.8	7:46	7:57	8	T	2:16	6.8	2:40	7.0	8:30	8:53
9	T	2:03	7.1	2:35	6.8	8:27	8:42	9	F	2:57	6.6	3:19	6.9	9:06	9:36
10	W	2:47	6.8	3:18	6.8	9:08	9:28	10	S	3:39	6.4	3:59	6.9	9:45	10:22
11	T	3:31	6.6	4:01	6.7	9:48	10:16	11	S	4:25	6.1	4:42	6.8	10:28	11:12
12	F	4:17	6.3	4:45	6.7	10:31	11:05	12	M	5:14	5.9	5:30	6.7	11:16	...
13	S	5:06	6.1	5:31	6.7	11:16	11:57	13	T	6:09	5.8	6:24	6.6	12:06	12:10
14	S	5:58	5.9	6:20	6.7	...	12:03	14	W	7:08	5.7	7:23	6.7	1:03	1:09
15	M	6:53	5.7	7:11	6.7	12:51	12:55	15	T	8:07	5.9	8:22	6.9	2:02	2:08
16	T	7:50	5.7	8:03	6.8	1:45	1:48	16	F	9:03	6.1	9:19	7.2	2:58	3:06
17	W	8:45	5.8	8:55	7.0	2:39	2:42	17	S	9:55	6.5	10:11	7.6	3:52	4:01
18	T	9:36	6.1	9:46	7.2	3:31	3:34	18	S	10:45	6.9	11:01	7.9	4:42	4:53
19	F	10:25	6.3	10:35	7.5	4:21	4:25	19	M	11:32	7.4	11:50	8.1	5:29	5:44
20	S	11:12	6.6	11:23	7.7	5:08	5:15	20	T	...	...	12:19	7.8	6:15	6:35
21	S	11:58	6.9	...	...	5:55	6:04	21	W	12:39	8.1	1:07	8.1	7:01	7:26
22	M	12:11	7.9	12:45	7.2	6:41	6:54	22	T	1:29	8.0	1:56	8.2	7:47	8:19
23	T	1:00	7.9	1:33	7.4	7:27	7:45	23	F	2:21	7.8	2:47	8.2	8:35	9:13
24	W	1:50	7.9	2:22	7.6	8:14	8:38	24	S	3:14	7.4	3:39	8.1	9:26	10:11
25	T	2:41	7.7	3:13	7.8	9:02	9:33	25	S	4:10	7.0	4:35	7.9	10:21	11:12
26	F	3:34	7.4	4:05	7.8	9:52	10:32	26	M	5:10	6.6	5:35	7.5	11:20	...
27	S	4:30	7.1	5:00	7.8	10:45	11:32	27	T	6:14	6.4	6:40	7.3	12:15	12:24
28	S	5:29	6.7	5:58	7.7	11:42	...	28	W	7:21	6.3	7:46	7.1	1:20	1:29
29	M	6:32	6.4	6:59	7.5	12:35	12:42	29	T	8:26	6.3	8:49	7.1	2:23	2:32
30	T	7:37	6.3	8:01	7.4	1:38	1:44	30	F	9:24	6.5	9:44	7.2	3:20	3:30
31	W	8:41	6.3	9:01	7.4	2:40	2:45	31	S	10:14	6.7	10:32	7.2	4:11	4:22

Dates when Ht. of **Low** Water is below Mean Lower Low with Ht. of lowest given for each period and Date of lowest in ( ):

22nd–25th: -0.4' (24th)   20th–23rd: -0.5' (21st, 22nd)

Average Rise and Fall 6.8 ft.

When a high tide exceeds avg. ht., the *following* low tide will be lower than avg.

2024 HIGH & LOW WATER
BRIDGEPORT, CT
41°10.4'N, 73°10.9'W

Daylight Saving Time   **Daylight Saving Time**

DAY OF MONTH	DAY OF WEEK	SEPTEMBER HIGH a.m.	Ht.	p.m.	Ht.	LOW a.m.	p.m.	DAY OF MONTH	DAY OF WEEK	OCTOBER HIGH a.m.	Ht.	p.m.	Ht.	LOW a.m.	p.m.
1	S	10:58	6.9	11:14	7.3	4:56	5:07	1	T	11:09	7.3	11:28	7.0	5:03	5:24
2	M	11:38	7.1	11:53	7.2	5:35	5:49	2	W	11:44	7.4	...	...	5:38	6:02
3	T	...	...	12:15	7.2	6:11	6:27	3	T	12:04	7.0	12:18	7.4	6:12	6:38
4	W	12:32	7.1	12:51	7.2	6:45	7:05	4	F	12:42	6.8	12:51	7.4	6:45	7:13
5	T	1:08	7.0	1:26	7.2	7:19	7:42	5	S	1:17	6.7	1:26	7.3	7:19	7:50
6	F	1:46	6.8	2:01	7.2	7:52	8:20	6	S	1:55	6.5	2:02	7.1	7:54	8:29
7	S	2:24	6.6	2:38	7.1	8:27	9:00	7	M	2:35	6.3	2:41	7.0	8:32	9:11
8	S	3:05	6.4	3:16	7.0	9:05	9:43	8	T	3:19	6.2	3:26	6.8	9:16	10:00
9	M	3:48	6.2	3:59	6.8	9:47	10:31	9	W	4:07	6.0	4:18	6.7	10:07	10:56
10	T	4:37	6.0	4:49	6.7	10:36	11:26	10	T	5:02	5.9	5:17	6.7	11:08	11:57
11	W	5:31	5.8	5:46	6.6	11:34	...	11	F	6:03	6.0	6:22	6.7	...	12:13
12	T	6:32	5.8	6:50	6.7	12:27	12:37	12	S	7:05	6.3	7:27	6.9	12:59	1:19
13	F	7:34	6.0	7:54	6.9	1:29	1:41	13	S	8:05	6.7	8:28	7.2	1:57	2:21
14	S	8:33	6.4	8:53	7.3	2:28	2:42	14	M	9:00	7.3	9:24	7.5	2:52	3:18
15	S	9:27	6.9	9:48	7.7	3:22	3:39	15	T	9:51	7.8	10:16	7.8	3:43	4:13
16	M	10:18	7.4	10:39	8.0	4:13	4:33	16	W	10:40	8.3	11:07	7.9	4:31	5:05
17	T	11:06	7.9	11:28	8.1	5:00	5:24	17	T	11:27	8.7	11:57	7.8	5:19	5:56
18	W	11:53	8.4	...	...	5:47	6:15	18	F	...	...	12:15	8.8	6:06	6:46
19	T	12:18	8.1	12:40	8.6	6:33	7:06	19	S	12:47	7.7	1:04	8.6	6:54	7:37
20	F	1:08	7.9	1:29	8.6	7:20	7:58	20	S	1:39	7.4	1:55	8.3	7:44	8:30
21	S	1:59	7.7	2:20	8.4	8:08	8:52	21	M	2:32	7.1	2:49	7.8	8:38	9:26
22	S	2:53	7.3	3:14	8.1	9:01	9:48	22	T	3:29	6.7	3:47	7.4	9:35	10:25
23	M	3:50	6.9	4:11	7.7	9:57	10:49	23	W	4:28	6.4	4:48	6.9	10:37	11:26
24	T	4:50	6.6	5:13	7.2	10:59	11:53	24	T	5:31	6.3	5:53	6.6	11:43	...
25	W	5:55	6.3	6:19	6.9	...	12:06	25	F	6:34	6.3	6:58	6.4	12:28	12:48
26	T	7:02	6.3	7:27	6.8	12:58	1:12	26	S	7:35	6.4	7:59	6.4	1:26	1:49
27	F	8:05	6.4	8:30	6.8	2:00	2:15	27	S	8:29	6.6	8:52	6.5	2:19	2:44
28	S	9:02	6.6	9:23	6.9	2:55	3:12	28	M	9:16	6.9	9:39	6.6	3:06	3:33
29	S	9:49	6.9	10:09	7.0	3:43	4:01	29	T	9:58	7.1	10:21	6.6	3:48	4:16
30	M	10:31	7.1	10:50	7.0	4:25	4:45	30	W	10:35	7.3	11:00	6.7	4:27	4:56
								31	T	11:11	7.4	11:37	6.6	5:03	5:34

Dates when Ht. of **Low** Water is below Mean Lower Low with Ht. of lowest given for each period and Date of lowest in ( ):

17th–21st: -0.6' (18th–20th)   15th–20th: -0.8' (17th, 18th)

Average Rise and Fall 6.8 ft.

When a high tide exceeds avg. ht., the *following* low tide will be lower than avg.

2024 HIGH & LOW WATER
BRIDGEPORT, CT
41°10.4'N, 73°10.9'W

*Standard Time starts Nov. 3 at 2 a.m.　　　　　　**Standard Time**

DAY OF MONTH	DAY OF WEEK	NOVEMBER HIGH				NOVEMBER LOW		DAY OF MONTH	DAY OF WEEK	DECEMBER HIGH				DECEMBER LOW	
		a.m.	Ht.	**p.m.**	Ht.	a.m.	**p.m.**			a.m.	Ht.	**p.m.**	Ht.	a.m.	**p.m.**
1	F	11:45	7.4	...	...	5:39	**6:11**	1	S	10:54	7.1	**11:28**	6.2	4:47	**5:24**
2	S	12:14	6.6	**12:20**	7.3	6:14	**6:47**	2	M	11:32	7.1	...	...	5:27	**6:04**
3	S	12:52	6.5	-A-	...	*5:50	*6:25	3	T	12:08	6.2	**12:14**	7.0	6:08	**6:46**
4	M	12:31	6.3	**12:34**	7.1	6:28	**7:05**	4	W	12:52	6.2	**12:58**	7.0	6:51	**7:30**
5	T	1:11	6.2	**1:16**	6.9	7:09	**7:48**	5	T	1:36	6.2	**1:46**	6.9	7:39	**8:18**
6	W	1:56	6.1	**2:03**	6.8	7:55	**8:37**	6	F	2:25	6.2	**2:39**	6.8	8:32	**9:10**
7	T	2:45	6.1	**2:56**	6.7	8:48	**9:32**	7	S	3:18	6.3	**3:35**	6.7	9:31	**10:04**
8	F	3:39	6.1	**3:55**	6.7	9:48	**10:30**	8	S	4:14	6.5	**4:35**	6.5	10:34	**11:00**
9	S	4:38	6.2	**4:58**	6.7	10:53	**11:30**	9	M	5:12	6.8	**5:38**	6.4	11:38	**11:57**
10	S	5:39	6.5	**6:02**	6.8	11:58	...	10	T	6:11	7.1	**6:40**	6.4	...	**12:41**
11	M	6:38	7.0	**7:03**	6.9	12:27	**1:00**	11	W	7:09	7.4	**7:41**	6.5	12:53	**1:41**
12	T	7:34	7.5	**8:01**	7.1	1:22	**1:59**	12	T	8:04	7.7	**8:37**	6.6	1:49	**2:38**
13	W	8:26	8.0	**8:55**	7.2	2:14	**2:54**	13	F	8:57	7.9	**9:31**	6.7	2:43	**3:32**
14	T	9:16	8.3	**9:47**	7.3	3:05	**3:47**	14	S	9:48	8.0	**10:22**	6.8	3:36	**4:24**
15	F	10:05	8.5	**10:38**	7.3	3:54	**4:38**	15	S	10:38	7.9	**11:12**	6.7	4:27	**5:13**
16	S	10:54	8.5	**11:28**	7.2	4:44	**5:28**	16	M	11:27	7.7	...	...	5:17	**6:02**
17	S	11:43	8.3	...	...	5:33	**6:19**	17	T	12:02	6.6	**12:17**	7.4	6:07	**6:49**
18	M	12:20	7.0	**12:34**	7.9	6:24	**7:10**	18	W	12:52	6.5	**1:06**	7.1	6:57	**7:37**
19	T	1:12	6.8	**1:28**	7.5	7:17	**8:02**	19	T	1:41	6.4	**1:56**	6.8	7:48	**8:25**
20	W	2:06	6.5	**2:23**	7.0	8:13	**8:57**	20	F	2:31	6.2	**2:47**	6.4	8:40	**9:13**
21	T	3:02	6.3	**3:20**	6.6	9:11	**9:53**	21	S	3:22	6.2	**3:39**	6.1	9:35	**10:02**
22	F	3:59	6.2	**4:19**	6.3	10:12	**10:48**	22	S	4:13	6.1	**4:32**	5.8	10:31	**10:51**
23	S	4:57	6.2	**5:18**	6.1	11:13	**11:42**	23	M	5:04	6.1	**5:28**	5.6	11:27	**11:41**
24	S	5:54	6.3	**6:17**	6.0	...	**12:12**	24	T	5:57	6.2	**6:25**	5.4	...	**12:22**
25	M	6:47	6.4	**7:12**	5.9	12:33	**1:07**	25	W	6:48	6.2	**7:20**	5.5	12:31	**1:15**
26	T	7:35	6.6	**8:02**	6.0	1:21	**1:57**	26	T	7:37	6.4	**8:11**	5.6	1:21	**2:05**
27	W	8:19	6.8	**8:48**	6.1	2:06	**2:43**	27	F	8:23	6.5	**8:58**	5.7	2:09	**2:52**
28	T	9:00	7.0	**9:30**	6.2	2:48	**3:26**	28	S	9:07	6.7	**9:41**	5.8	2:55	**3:37**
29	F	9:38	7.1	**10:10**	6.2	3:29	**4:06**	29	S	9:49	6.8	**10:23**	6.0	3:40	**4:20**
30	S	10:16	7.1	**10:49**	6.2	4:08	**4:45**	30	M	10:31	6.9	**11:04**	6.1	4:23	**5:02**
								31	T	11:13	7.1	...	...	5:06	**5:44**

A also at *11:56 a.m. (7.2)

Dates when Ht. of **Low** Water is below Mean Lower Low with Ht. of lowest given for each period and Date of lowest in ( ):

13th–18th: -0.9' (15th, 16th)　　　　　11th–17th: -0.8' (14th, 15th)
　　　　　　　　　　　　　　　　　　　30th–31st: -0.3'

Average Rise and Fall 6.8 ft.

When a high tide exceeds avg. ht., the *following* low tide will be lower than avg.

2024 HIGH & LOW WATER
KINGS POINT, NY
40°48.7'N, 73°45.9'W

		Standard Time							Standard Time				
D A Y O F M O N T H	**D A Y O F W E E K**	**JANUARY**					**D A Y O F M O N T H**	**D A Y O F W E E K**	**FEBRUARY**				
		HIGH		LOW					HIGH		LOW		
		a.m.	Ht.	p.m.	Ht.	a.m.	p.m.			a.m.	Ht.	p.m.	Ht.	a.m.	p.m.
1	M	2:32	6.6	2:26	6.4	8:21	8:44	1	T	2:51	6.8	3:12	6.1	9:13	9:25
2	T	3:07	6.6	3:10	6.2	9:08	9:25	2	F	3:34	6.8	4:02	5.9	10:04	10:15
3	W	3:46	6.6	3:58	5.9	10:01	10:11	3	S	4:23	6.7	4:57	5.7	11:00	11:09
4	T	4:30	6.6	4:51	5.8	10:57	11:01	4	S	5:18	6.7	5:59	5.7	...	12:04
5	F	5:17	6.6	5:51	5.7	11:59	11:54	5	M	6:19	6.8	7:14	5.8	12:09	1:31
6	S	6:10	6.7	7:03	5.8	...	1:17	6	T	7:28	7.1	8:28	6.2	1:16	2:51
7	S	7:08	6.9	8:10	6.0	12:52	2:25	7	W	8:34	7.6	9:23	6.7	2:27	3:47
8	M	8:04	7.3	8:59	6.3	1:52	3:18	8	T	9:31	8.1	10:12	7.2	3:33	4:36
9	T	8:55	7.7	9:42	6.6	2:50	4:06	9	F	10:24	8.4	11:00	7.6	4:31	5:23
10	W	9:44	8.1	10:27	6.9	3:44	4:53	10	S	11:16	8.6	11:49	8.0	5:26	6:07
11	T	10:33	8.4	11:14	7.2	4:37	5:40	11	S	...	...	12:07	8.6	6:19	6:49
12	F	11:24	8.5	...	...	5:30	6:24	12	M	12:37	8.3	12:58	8.3	7:11	7:32
13	S	12:03	7.4	12:16	8.5	6:22	7:09	13	T	1:26	8.4	1:50	7.9	8:07	8:18
14	S	12:54	7.7	1:08	8.3	7:16	7:55	14	W	2:18	8.2	2:48	7.4	9:09	9:12
15	M	1:46	7.8	2:04	7.9	8:15	8:45	15	T	3:14	7.9	3:52	6.9	10:17	10:17
16	T	2:42	7.8	3:04	7.4	9:25	9:43	16	F	4:18	7.5	5:04	6.4	11:26	11:32
17	W	3:43	7.8	4:11	7.0	10:39	10:46	17	S	5:32	7.1	6:19	6.2	...	12:32
18	T	4:48	7.6	5:24	6.6	11:49	11:55	18	S	6:48	6.9	7:29	6.2	12:45	1:36
19	F	5:57	7.5	6:39	6.4	...	12:55	19	M	7:56	6.9	8:29	6.4	1:51	2:34
20	S	7:08	7.4	7:48	6.4	1:04	1:57	20	T	8:53	7.0	9:20	6.7	2:49	3:27
21	S	8:11	7.4	8:46	6.6	2:07	2:54	21	W	9:42	7.2	10:06	6.9	3:41	4:14
22	M	9:06	7.4	9:37	6.7	3:05	3:47	22	T	10:26	7.3	10:48	7.1	4:27	4:57
23	T	9:55	7.5	10:24	6.9	3:57	4:35	23	F	11:06	7.3	11:26	7.2	5:09	5:36
24	W	10:40	7.5	11:08	6.9	4:45	5:21	24	S	11:41	7.2	11:58	7.2	5:47	6:09
25	T	11:22	7.4	11:49	6.9	5:28	6:02	25	S	...	...	12:10	7.1	6:18	6:31
26	F	11:59	7.3	...	...	6:07	6:37	26	M	12:23	7.2	12:29	7.0	6:37	6:37
27	S	12:25	6.9	12:30	7.1	6:38	7:05	27	T	12:38	7.3	12:49	6.8	6:52	6:56
28	S	12:56	6.9	12:54	6.9	6:58	7:16	28	W	1:00	7.3	1:18	6.7	7:20	7:28
29	M	1:19	6.9	1:17	6.7	7:17	7:31	29	T	1:32	7.3	1:55	6.6	7:55	8:06
30	T	1:42	6.9	1:49	6.5	7:49	8:02								
31	W	2:13	6.9	2:28	6.3	8:28	8:41								

Dates when Ht. of **Low** Water is below Mean Lower Low with Ht. of lowest given for each period and Date of lowest in ( ):

9th–27th: -1.3' (13th)

7th–16th: -1.6' (11th)
20th–25th: -0.4' (22nd, 23rd)

Average Rise and Fall 7.1 ft.

When a high tide exceeds avg. ht., the *following* low tide will be lower than avg.

2024 HIGH & LOW WATER
KINGS POINT, NY
40°48.7'N, 73°45.9'W

*Daylight Time starts March 10 at 2 a.m.   **Daylight Saving Time**

D A Y O F M O N T H	D A Y O F W E E K	MARCH						D A Y O F M O N T H	D A Y O F W E E K	APRIL					
		HIGH				LOW				HIGH				LOW	
		a.m.	Ht.	p.m.	Ht.	a.m.	p.m.			a.m.	Ht.	p.m.	Ht.	a.m.	p.m.
1	F	2:10	7.2	2:38	6.4	8:38	8:50	1	M	4:19	7.4	4:58	6.4	10:58	11:13
2	S	2:55	7.1	3:27	6.2	9:26	9:40	2	T	5:18	7.3	6:01	6.3	...	12:05
3	S	3:45	7.0	4:22	6.0	10:22	10:36	3	W	6:25	7.2	7:16	6.5	12:20	1:29
4	M	4:43	6.9	5:24	5.9	11:27	11:39	4	T	7:44	7.4	8:39	7.1	1:41	2:56
5	T	5:46	7.0	6:38	6.0	...	12:53	5	F	9:04	7.8	9:42	7.8	3:13	3:54
6	W	7:02	7.2	8:02	6.4	12:52	2:25	6	S	10:06	8.1	10:32	8.4	4:18	4:45
7	T	8:19	7.7	9:03	7.1	2:16	3:23	7	S	10:58	8.4	11:19	8.9	5:14	5:32
8	F	9:20	8.1	9:54	7.8	3:27	4:13	8	M	11:49	8.5	...	...	6:07	6:17
9	S	10:13	8.5	10:41	8.3	4:25	4:59	9	T	12:05	9.2	12:38	8.4	6:57	7:01
10	S	...	...	*12:04	8.6	*6:19	*6:42	10	W	12:52	9.2	1:28	8.2	7:46	7:45
11	M	12:28	8.7	12:54	8.6	7:10	7:25	11	T	1:38	8.9	2:19	7.9	8:35	8:30
12	T	1:15	8.9	1:43	8.3	8:00	8:07	12	F	2:26	8.5	3:13	7.4	9:29	9:21
13	W	2:02	8.8	2:35	7.9	8:51	8:52	13	S	3:19	7.9	4:14	7.0	10:30	10:30
14	T	2:51	8.5	3:30	7.4	9:49	9:44	14	S	4:23	7.3	5:21	6.7	11:34	11:47
15	F	3:45	8.0	4:33	6.9	10:54	10:52	15	M	5:40	6.8	6:27	6.5	...	12:37
16	S	4:50	7.4	5:44	6.5	...	12:01	16	T	6:54	6.6	7:32	6.6	12:56	1:37
17	S	6:07	6.9	6:56	6.3	12:11	1:07	17	W	8:02	6.6	8:31	6.8	1:59	2:33
18	M	7:25	6.7	8:04	6.3	1:23	2:10	18	T	9:00	6.7	9:22	7.1	2:56	3:24
19	T	8:34	6.7	9:05	6.5	2:29	3:08	19	F	9:49	6.9	10:07	7.4	3:47	4:09
20	W	9:32	6.9	9:56	6.8	3:27	4:00	20	S	10:33	7.0	10:46	7.6	4:33	4:49
21	T	10:20	7.1	10:40	7.1	4:17	4:46	21	S	11:12	7.1	11:19	7.8	5:15	5:25
22	F	11:03	7.2	11:20	7.4	5:03	5:27	22	M	11:47	7.1	11:45	7.8	5:52	5:53
23	S	11:42	7.3	11:56	7.5	5:45	6:04	23	T	...	...	12:16	7.1	6:24	6:09
24	S	...	...	12:17	7.2	6:22	6:34	24	W	12:01	7.8	12:35	7.1	6:47	6:28
25	M	12:25	7.6	12:45	7.1	6:53	6:52	25	T	12:21	7.9	12:57	7.1	7:05	6:59
26	T	12:43	7.6	1:03	7.0	7:13	7:01	26	F	12:54	8.0	1:29	7.1	7:34	7:36
27	W	12:58	7.6	1:22	7.0	7:27	7:26	27	S	1:33	8.0	2:09	7.0	8:11	8:18
28	T	1:24	7.7	1:52	6.9	7:54	8:00	28	S	2:17	7.9	2:54	7.0	8:55	9:05
29	F	1:59	7.7	2:29	6.9	8:29	8:39	29	M	3:06	7.9	3:45	6.9	9:45	9:58
30	S	2:40	7.6	3:12	6.7	9:11	9:23	30	T	4:01	7.7	4:43	6.8	10:45	11:01
31	S	3:26	7.5	4:02	6.5	10:01	10:15								

Dates when Ht. of **Low** Water is below Mean Lower Low with Ht. of lowest given for each period and Date of lowest in ( ):

7th–15th: -1.6' (11th)   5th–12th: -1.5' (9th)
25th: -0.2'

Average Rise and Fall 7.1 ft.

When a high tide exceeds avg. ht., the *following* low tide will be lower than avg.

2024 HIGH & LOW WATER
KINGS POINT, NY
40°48.7'N, 73°45.9'W

		Daylight Saving Time							Daylight Saving Time				
D A Y O F M O N T H	**D A Y O F W E E K**	**MAY**					**D A Y O F M O N T H**	**D A Y O F W E E K**	**JUNE**				
		HIGH		**LOW**					**HIGH**		**LOW**		
		a.m.	Ht.	p.m.	Ht.	a.m.	p.m.			a.m.	Ht.	p.m.	Ht.	a.m.	p.m.
1	W	5:02	7.6	5:47	7.0	11:52	...	1	S	7:14	7.4	7:54	8.2	1:43	1:52
2	T	6:10	7.5	7:00	7.2	12:13	1:08	2	S	8:32	7.4	8:57	8.6	2:53	2:57
3	F	7:28	7.5	8:16	7.8	1:44	2:23	3	M	9:36	7.6	9:52	8.8	3:53	3:55
4	S	8:49	7.7	9:19	8.3	3:05	3:24	4	T	10:32	7.8	10:42	8.9	4:48	4:50
5	S	9:50	7.9	10:10	8.9	4:07	4:17	5	W	11:23	7.8	11:31	8.9	5:41	5:42
6	M	10:43	8.1	10:58	9.2	5:02	5:07	6	T	...	...	12:13	7.8	6:31	6:33
7	T	11:34	8.2	11:44	9.2	5:54	5:56	7	F	12:19	8.7	1:03	7.8	7:19	7:21
8	W	...	...	12:24	8.1	6:44	6:43	8	S	1:07	8.4	1:51	7.6	8:05	8:06
9	T	12:31	9.1	1:14	8.0	7:32	7:30	9	S	1:53	8.0	2:39	7.4	8:51	8:50
10	F	1:18	8.7	2:05	7.7	8:20	8:16	10	M	2:40	7.7	3:28	7.3	9:37	9:37
11	S	2:07	8.3	2:57	7.4	9:10	9:06	11	T	3:29	7.3	4:18	7.1	10:23	10:32
12	S	2:58	7.8	3:53	7.2	10:05	10:07	12	W	4:21	7.0	5:07	7.1	11:08	11:30
13	M	3:58	7.3	4:53	6.9	11:03	11:16	13	T	5:17	6.7	5:56	7.0	11:50	...
14	T	5:06	6.9	5:52	6.8	...	12:01	14	F	6:15	6.4	6:45	7.1	12:27	12:27
15	W	6:13	6.6	6:50	6.8	12:20	12:54	15	S	7:16	6.3	7:36	7.1	1:25	1:03
16	T	7:17	6.5	7:47	6.9	1:20	1:47	16	S	8:18	6.2	8:26	7.2	2:20	1:49
17	F	8:17	6.5	8:39	7.2	2:17	2:36	17	M	9:11	6.3	9:08	7.4	3:12	2:40
18	S	9:10	6.6	9:25	7.4	3:09	3:22	18	T	9:57	6.5	9:41	7.6	3:59	3:26
19	S	9:56	6.7	10:04	7.6	3:57	4:02	19	W	10:35	6.7	10:12	7.8	4:41	4:09
20	M	10:37	6.8	10:36	7.7	4:39	4:37	20	T	11:08	6.8	10:47	8.0	5:21	4:51
21	T	11:13	6.9	10:58	7.8	5:18	5:03	21	F	11:39	7.0	11:28	8.2	5:59	5:35
22	W	11:43	7.0	11:20	7.9	5:53	5:27	22	S	...	...	12:15	7.2	6:37	6:21
23	T	-A-	...	12:06	7.0	6:22	5:59	23	S	12:13	8.4	12:57	7.3	7:16	7:08
24	F	...	...	12:35	7.1	6:49	6:37	24	M	1:01	8.5	1:43	7.5	7:57	7:57
25	S	12:30	8.2	1:11	7.2	7:22	7:19	25	T	1:51	8.5	2:32	7.7	8:41	8:50
26	S	1:14	8.2	1:54	7.2	8:02	8:04	26	W	2:44	8.4	3:25	7.9	9:29	9:50
27	M	2:02	8.2	2:42	7.2	8:47	8:54	27	T	3:40	8.1	4:21	8.1	10:22	11:02
28	T	2:53	8.1	3:35	7.3	9:38	9:51	28	F	4:41	7.8	5:21	8.2	11:19	...
29	W	3:49	8.0	4:33	7.4	10:36	10:58	29	S	5:48	7.5	6:25	8.3	12:19	12:20
30	T	4:51	7.8	5:36	7.6	11:38	...	30	S	7:02	7.2	7:34	8.3	1:32	1:29
31	F	5:58	7.5	6:43	7.9	12:18	12:44								

A also at 11:51 p.m. (8.1)

Dates when Ht. of **Low** Water is below Mean Lower Low with Ht. of lowest given for each period and Date of lowest in ( ):

5th–11th: -1.2' (8th)

3rd–8th: -0.8' (5th, 6th)
23rd–26th: -0.3' (25th)

Average Rise and Fall 7.1 ft.

When a high tide exceeds avg. ht., the *following* low tide will be lower than avg.

2024 HIGH & LOW WATER
KINGS POINT, NY
40°48.7'N, 73°45.9'W

		Daylight Saving Time								**Daylight Saving Time**					

DAY OF MONTH	DAY OF WEEK	JULY				DAY OF MONTH	DAY OF WEEK	AUGUST					
		HIGH		LOW				HIGH		LOW			
		a.m.	Ht.	**p.m.**	Ht.	a.m.	**p.m.**			a.m.	Ht.	**p.m.**	Ht.	a.m.	**p.m.**

DAY OF MONTH	DAY OF WEEK	a.m.	Ht.	**p.m.**	Ht.	a.m.	**p.m.**	DAY OF MONTH	DAY OF WEEK	a.m.	Ht.	**p.m.**	Ht.	a.m.	**p.m.**
1	M	8:19	7.2	**8:42**	8.4	2:39	**2:39**	1	T	10:11	7.3	**10:29**	8.1	4:20	**4:31**
2	T	9:25	7.3	**9:41**	8.5	3:39	**3:43**	2	F	11:01	7.5	**11:18**	8.1	5:11	**5:23**
3	W	10:21	7.4	**10:35**	8.5	4:35	**4:40**	3	S	11:48	7.6	**...**	...	5:59	**6:10**
4	T	11:14	7.6	**11:25**	8.4	5:27	**5:34**	4	S	12:04	8.1	**12:31**	7.7	6:43	**6:54**
5	F	...	...	**12:02**	7.6	6:17	**6:24**	5	M	12:44	8.0	**1:11**	7.7	7:23	**7:32**
6	S	12:13	8.3	**12:50**	7.6	7:04	**7:10**	6	T	1:21	7.8	**1:46**	7.7	7:56	**8:04**
7	S	12:58	8.1	**1:34**	7.6	7:47	**7:52**	7	W	1:53	7.6	**2:15**	7.7	8:19	**8:25**
8	M	1:40	7.9	**2:16**	7.5	8:27	**8:29**	8	T	2:18	7.3	**2:38**	7.6	8:26	**8:45**
9	T	2:19	7.6	**2:55**	7.4	9:02	**9:02**	9	F	2:46	7.1	**3:04**	7.6	8:49	**9:19**
10	W	2:55	7.3	**3:32**	7.4	9:27	**9:31**	10	S	3:20	6.9	**3:38**	7.6	9:25	**10:00**
11	T	3:30	7.0	**4:05**	7.3	9:41	**10:08**	11	S	4:01	6.7	**4:18**	7.4	10:07	**10:47**
12	F	4:09	6.8	**4:38**	7.3	10:12	**10:53**	12	M	4:48	6.5	**5:04**	7.3	10:55	**11:40**
13	S	4:52	6.5	**5:15**	7.2	10:53	**11:44**	13	T	5:39	6.3	**5:55**	7.2	11:47	**...**
14	S	5:40	6.3	**5:58**	7.2	11:39	**...**	14	W	6:38	6.2	**6:53**	7.3	12:39	**12:44**
15	M	6:36	6.1	**6:46**	7.2	12:40	**12:29**	15	T	7:51	6.3	**7:59**	7.4	1:56	**1:48**
16	T	7:49	6.1	**7:42**	7.2	1:52	**1:25**	16	F	9:09	6.6	**9:07**	7.8	3:24	**2:59**
17	W	9:04	6.3	**8:41**	7.4	3:07	**2:26**	17	S	10:03	7.0	**10:05**	8.3	4:21	**4:06**
18	T	9:53	6.5	**9:35**	7.7	4:02	**3:27**	18	S	10:49	7.6	**10:56**	8.7	5:10	**5:05**
19	F	10:34	6.8	**10:23**	8.1	4:51	**4:24**	19	M	11:34	8.1	**11:47**	8.9	5:55	**5:59**
20	S	11:14	7.1	**11:11**	8.4	5:37	**5:18**	20	T	...	...	**12:20**	8.5	6:37	**6:52**
21	S	11:56	7.5	**...**	...	6:20	**6:10**	21	W	12:37	9.0	**1:07**	8.9	7:19	**7:43**
22	M	12:01	8.7	**12:42**	7.8	7:02	**7:01**	22	T	1:28	8.9	**1:55**	9.1	8:00	**8:36**
23	T	12:50	8.8	**1:29**	8.1	7:43	**7:52**	23	F	2:19	8.6	**2:44**	9.1	8:44	**9:35**
24	W	1:41	8.7	**2:17**	8.4	8:25	**8:46**	24	S	3:14	8.1	**3:38**	8.9	9:34	**10:42**
25	T	2:34	8.5	**3:08**	8.6	9:10	**9:47**	25	S	4:16	7.7	**4:39**	8.5	10:34	**11:52**
26	F	3:29	8.1	**4:02**	8.6	9:59	**10:57**	26	M	5:27	7.3	**5:50**	8.1	11:50	**...**
27	S	4:30	7.7	**5:01**	8.5	10:56	**...**	27	T	6:43	7.0	**7:09**	7.8	1:00	**1:08**
28	S	5:37	7.3	**6:06**	8.3	12:08	**12:01**	28	W	7:56	7.0	**8:23**	7.7	2:05	**2:19**
29	M	6:53	7.1	**7:19**	8.1	1:17	**1:16**	29	T	9:01	7.1	**9:25**	7.8	3:06	**3:21**
30	T	8:09	7.0	**8:32**	8.0	2:23	**2:29**	30	F	9:56	7.4	**10:17**	7.9	4:01	**4:16**
31	W	9:15	7.1	**9:35**	8.1	3:24	**3:34**	31	S	10:44	7.6	**11:04**	8.0	4:50	**5:06**

Dates when Ht. of **Low** Water is below Mean Lower Low with Ht. of lowest given for each period and Date of lowest in ( ):

    3rd–6th: -0.4' (4th, 5th)   19th–23rd: -0.8' (21st)
    21st–26th: -0.6' (23rd, 24th)

Average Rise and Fall 7.1 ft.

When a high tide exceeds avg. ht., the *following* low tide will be lower than avg.

2024 HIGH & LOW WATER
KINGS POINT, NY
40°48.7'N, 73°45.9'W

		Daylight Saving Time						Daylight Saving Time				

DAY OF MONTH	DAY OF WEEK	SEPTEMBER				DAY OF MONTH	DAY OF WEEK	OCTOBER				
		HIGH		LOW				HIGH		LOW		
		a.m.	Ht.	p.m.	Ht.	a.m.	p.m.			a.m.	Ht.	p.m.	Ht.	a.m.	p.m.

DAY OF MONTH	DAY OF WEEK	a.m.	Ht.	p.m.	Ht.	a.m.	p.m.	DAY OF MONTH	DAY OF WEEK	a.m.	Ht.	p.m.	Ht.	a.m.	p.m.
1	S	11:27	7.8	11:45	8.0	5:36	5:51	1	T	11:37	8.2	11:58	7.7	5:44	6:06
2	M	...	...	12:07	8.0	6:17	6:32	2	W	...	...	12:08	8.2	6:17	6:40
3	T	12:24	7.9	12:42	8.0	6:52	7:08	3	T	12:30	7.6	12:31	8.1	6:40	7:06
4	W	12:58	7.7	1:11	8.0	7:20	7:36	4	F	12:55	7.4	12:45	8.1	6:46	7:19
5	T	1:23	7.5	1:30	7.9	7:31	7:50	5	S	1:11	7.3	1:08	8.0	7:07	7:40
6	F	1:43	7.3	1:49	7.9	7:42	8:10	6	S	1:37	7.2	1:41	8.0	7:40	8:12
7	S	2:08	7.2	2:18	7.9	8:11	8:42	7	M	2:12	7.1	2:20	7.9	8:18	8:52
8	S	2:42	7.0	2:54	7.8	8:48	9:21	8	T	2:53	6.9	3:04	7.7	9:02	9:39
9	M	3:23	6.9	3:36	7.6	9:31	10:08	9	W	3:41	6.8	3:55	7.6	9:52	10:35
10	T	4:10	6.7	4:24	7.5	10:20	11:02	10	T	4:35	6.6	4:52	7.5	10:49	11:39
11	W	5:03	6.5	5:19	7.4	11:14	...	11	F	5:37	6.6	5:55	7.5	11:53	...
12	T	6:02	6.4	6:20	7.4	12:03	12:15	12	S	6:46	6.8	7:06	7.6	12:51	1:06
13	F	7:12	6.5	7:29	7.6	1:17	1:23	13	S	8:03	7.3	8:24	7.9	2:13	2:32
14	S	8:33	6.9	8:44	7.9	2:49	2:41	14	M	9:08	8.0	9:29	8.3	3:16	3:43
15	S	9:35	7.5	9:47	8.4	3:50	3:54	15	T	9:59	8.7	10:23	8.6	4:07	4:41
16	M	10:24	8.2	10:40	8.8	4:39	4:53	16	W	10:45	9.3	11:14	8.7	4:53	5:34
17	T	11:09	8.8	11:30	9.0	5:24	5:47	17	T	11:31	9.6	...	...	5:39	6:25
18	W	11:55	9.3	...	...	6:07	6:39	18	F	12:04	8.7	12:18	9.7	6:24	7:16
19	T	12:20	9.0	12:42	9.5	6:50	7:30	19	S	12:54	8.5	1:06	9.5	7:11	8:07
20	F	1:11	8.8	1:29	9.5	7:34	8:22	20	S	1:47	8.2	1:56	9.1	7:59	9:02
21	S	2:03	8.5	2:19	9.3	8:19	9:19	21	M	2:43	7.8	2:51	8.5	8:52	10:04
22	S	2:58	8.0	3:13	8.8	9:10	10:24	22	T	3:46	7.4	3:57	7.9	10:01	11:11
23	M	4:02	7.6	4:17	8.3	10:16	11:33	23	W	4:57	7.1	5:16	7.4	11:23	...
24	T	5:15	7.2	5:36	7.8	11:40	...	24	T	6:06	7.0	6:31	7.2	12:15	12:33
25	W	6:28	7.0	6:55	7.5	12:40	12:55	25	F	7:11	7.0	7:38	7.1	1:15	1:37
26	T	7:38	7.0	8:06	7.4	1:43	2:02	26	S	8:10	7.2	8:37	7.1	2:11	2:35
27	F	8:40	7.2	9:06	7.5	2:42	3:02	27	S	9:03	7.5	9:28	7.2	3:03	3:28
28	S	9:33	7.5	9:57	7.7	3:36	3:55	28	M	9:48	7.8	10:13	7.3	3:49	4:15
29	S	10:19	7.8	10:41	7.8	4:23	4:43	29	T	10:28	8.0	10:53	7.4	4:30	4:58
30	M	11:00	8.0	11:21	7.8	5:06	5:26	30	W	11:03	8.1	11:30	7.3	5:07	5:37
								31	T	11:32	8.1	...	...	5:38	6:12

Dates when Ht. of **Low** Water is below Mean Lower Low with Ht. of lowest given for each period and Date of lowest in ( ):

    17th–21st: -0.9' (19th)   15th–20th: -1.1' (17th, 18th)

Average Rise and Fall 7.1 ft.

When a high tide exceeds avg. ht., the *following* low tide will be lower than avg.

2024 HIGH & LOW WATER
KINGS POINT, NY
40°48.7'N, 73°45.9'W

*Standard Time starts Nov. 3 at 2 a.m.   Standard Time

DAY OF MONTH	DAY OF WEEK	NOVEMBER						DAY OF MONTH	DAY OF WEEK	DECEMBER					
		HIGH				LOW				HIGH				LOW	
		a.m.	Ht.	p.m.	Ht.	a.m.	p.m.			a.m.	Ht.	p.m.	Ht.	a.m.	p.m.
1	F	12:02	7.2	-A-	...	5:58	6:39	1	S	10:40	7.8	11:23	6.8	4:45	5:39
2	S	12:26	7.2	12:08	8.0	6:11	6:55	2	M	11:13	7.8	11:53	6.8	5:19	6:06
3	S	12:44	7.1	-B-	...	*5:39	*6:17	3	T	11:53	7.8	...	...	5:58	6:40
4	M	12:13	7.0	12:13	7.9	6:15	6:51	4	W	12:32	6.8	12:37	7.9	6:40	7:21
5	T	12:48	6.9	12:54	7.9	6:56	7:32	5	T	1:15	6.8	1:25	7.8	7:26	8:07
6	W	1:31	6.9	1:41	7.8	7:40	8:20	6	F	2:04	6.9	2:18	7.7	8:18	9:00
7	T	2:20	6.8	2:33	7.7	8:32	9:16	7	S	2:59	7.0	3:15	7.5	9:19	9:57
8	F	3:15	6.8	3:32	7.5	9:31	10:19	8	S	3:58	7.2	4:18	7.2	10:29	10:58
9	S	4:17	6.9	4:36	7.4	10:39	11:26	9	M	5:01	7.5	5:27	7.1	11:53	...
10	S	5:24	7.2	5:46	7.4	11:58	...	10	T	6:08	7.8	6:45	7.0	12:02	1:15
11	M	6:35	7.7	7:03	7.6	12:36	1:25	11	W	7:17	8.2	7:58	7.2	1:11	2:20
12	T	7:41	8.3	8:12	7.8	1:41	2:32	12	T	8:18	8.5	8:58	7.4	2:16	3:18
13	W	8:36	8.9	9:08	8.1	2:37	3:29	13	F	9:12	8.8	9:51	7.5	3:14	4:12
14	T	9:25	9.3	10:00	8.2	3:28	4:22	14	S	10:02	8.8	10:43	7.6	4:09	5:04
15	F	10:12	9.4	10:50	8.2	4:18	5:14	15	S	10:52	8.7	11:34	7.6	5:02	5:54
16	S	11:00	9.4	11:42	8.1	5:07	6:04	16	M	11:42	8.4	...	...	5:53	6:42
17	S	11:49	9.1	...	...	5:57	6:54	17	T	12:24	7.4	12:31	8.1	6:41	7:29
18	M	12:34	7.8	12:40	8.6	6:47	7:46	18	W	1:14	7.3	1:20	7.7	7:29	8:16
19	T	1:29	7.5	1:34	8.1	7:40	8:42	19	T	2:04	7.1	2:10	7.3	8:18	9:05
20	W	2:28	7.2	2:36	7.6	8:43	9:42	20	F	2:56	6.9	3:04	6.8	9:15	9:54
21	T	3:31	7.0	3:46	7.1	9:55	10:41	21	S	3:49	6.8	4:02	6.5	10:16	10:42
22	F	4:34	6.9	4:54	6.8	11:02	11:37	22	S	4:41	6.7	5:02	6.1	11:15	11:29
23	S	5:33	6.9	5:57	6.6	...	12:03	23	M	5:33	6.7	6:04	5.9	...	12:13
24	S	6:30	7.0	6:57	6.5	12:30	1:00	24	T	6:27	6.7	7:05	5.9	12:17	1:10
25	M	7:23	7.2	7:52	6.6	1:20	1:53	25	W	7:21	6.8	8:01	5.9	1:07	2:02
26	T	8:10	7.4	8:40	6.7	2:07	2:42	26	T	8:09	6.9	8:49	6.1	1:57	2:51
27	W	8:52	7.6	9:23	6.7	2:49	3:26	27	F	8:50	7.0	9:32	6.2	2:41	3:35
28	T	9:28	7.7	10:01	6.8	3:27	4:07	28	S	9:22	7.2	10:08	6.4	3:19	4:16
29	F	9:57	7.7	10:35	6.8	3:59	4:43	29	S	9:49	7.3	10:38	6.5	3:51	4:53
30	S	10:16	7.7	11:01	6.8	4:21	5:15	30	M	10:19	7.5	11:05	6.6	4:26	5:27
								31	T	10:57	7.7	...	...	5:05	5:59

A also at 11:51 a.m. (8.1)   **B** also at *11:36 a.m. (8.0)

Dates when Ht. of **Low** Water is below Mean Lower Low with Ht. of lowest given for each period and Date of lowest in ( ):

13th–18th: -1.2' (15th)   11th–18th: -1.2' (14th)
                                           30th–31st: -0.5'

Average Rise and Fall 7.1 ft.

When a high tide exceeds avg. ht., the *following* low tide will be lower than avg.

2024 CURRENT TABLE
HELL GATE, NY (EAST RIVER)
40°46.7'N, 73°56.3'W Off Mill Rock

Standard Time	Standard Time
JANUARY	**FEBRUARY**

DAY OF MONTH	DAY OF WEEK	CURRENT TURNS TO						DAY OF MONTH	DAY OF WEEK	CURRENT TURNS TO					
		NORTHEAST Flood Starts			SOUTHWEST Ebb Starts					NORTHEAST Flood Starts			SOUTHWEST Ebb Starts		
		a.m.	**p.m.**	Kts.	a.m.	**p.m.**	Kts.			a.m.	**p.m.**	Kts.	a.m.	**p.m.**	Kts.
1	M	7:54	**8:24**	a2.4	1:24	**1:54**	a3.5	1	T	8:36	**9:00**	2.5	2:06	**2:30**	3.5
2	T	8:36	**9:06**	a2.3	2:06	**2:36**	a3.3	2	F	9:24	**9:48**	p2.6	2:48	**3:12**	a3.5
3	W	9:24	**9:54**	a2.3	2:48	**3:18**	a3.2	3	S	10:18	**10:42**	p2.7	3:36	**4:00**	3.4
4	T	10:13	**10:36**	2.3	3:36	**4:00**	3.1	4	S	11:13	**11:36**	p2.8	4:30	**5:00**	3.5
5	F	11:00	**11:24**	p2.5	4:18	**4:42**	3.2	5	M	...	**12:12**	2.8	5:24	**5:54**	3.6
6	S	11:48	...	2.6	5:12	**5:36**	p3.4	6	T	12:30	**1:06**	3.0	6:24	**6:54**	p3.9
7	S	12:12	**12:36**	2.8	6:00	**6:24**	p3.7	7	W	1:18	**1:54**	3.3	7:18	**7:48**	4.2
8	M	12:54	**1:24**	p3.1	6:48	**7:18**	p4.0	8	T	2:12	**2:48**	3.6	8:12	**8:42**	4.5
9	T	1:42	**2:18**	3.3	7:42	**8:06**	p4.3	9	F	3:06	**3:42**	3.8	9:06	**9:30**	4.7
10	W	2:30	**3:06**	3.6	8:30	**9:00**	4.5	10	S	3:54	**4:30**	a4.0	9:54	**10:24**	4.8
11	T	3:24	**3:54**	a3.8	9:18	**9:48**	4.6	11	S	4:48	**5:18**	a4.1	10:48	**11:12**	a4.9
12	F	4:12	**4:48**	a3.9	10:12	**10:36**	4.7	12	M	5:36	**6:06**	a4.1	11:36	...	4.8
13	S	5:00	**5:36**	a4.0	11:00	**11:30**	4.7	13	T	6:30	**7:00**	a3.9	12:01	**12:30**	a4.8
14	S	5:54	**6:30**	a3.9	11:54	...	4.7	14	W	7:24	**7:48**	a3.6	12:54	**1:24**	a4.7
15	M	6:48	**7:24**	a3.8	12:24	**12:54**	a4.7	15	T	8:18	**8:42**	a3.2	1:48	**2:18**	a4.4
16	T	7:42	**8:18**	a3.6	1:18	**1:48**	a4.6	16	F	9:24	**9:42**	a3.0	2:42	**3:18**	a4.1
17	W	8:42	**9:12**	a3.3	2:12	**2:42**	a4.4	17	S	10:30	**10:48**	2.8	3:42	**4:18**	a3.8
18	T	9:42	**10:12**	a3.2	3:06	**3:42**	a4.1	18	S	11:36	**11:54**	2.8	4:42	**5:24**	a3.6
19	F	10:48	**11:12**	a3.1	4:06	**4:42**	a3.9	19	M	...	**12:36**	2.9	5:48	**6:24**	a3.8
20	S	11:54	...	3.1	5:06	**5:42**	a3.9	20	T	12:54	**1:36**	p3.1	6:48	**7:18**	a4.0
21	S	12:12	**12:54**	p3.2	6:06	**6:42**	a4.0	21	W	1:48	**2:24**	p3.3	7:48	**8:06**	4.1
22	M	1:12	**1:48**	p3.3	7:06	**7:36**	a4.2	22	T	2:42	**3:12**	a3.4	8:36	**8:54**	p4.2
23	T	2:06	**2:42**	p3.4	8:00	**8:30**	a4.3	23	F	3:24	**3:54**	a3.4	9:24	**9:36**	p4.2
24	W	3:00	**3:30**	3.4	8:54	**9:18**	4.2	24	S	4:06	**4:30**	a3.3	10:00	**10:12**	p4.1
25	T	3:48	**4:18**	a3.4	9:42	**10:00**	p4.2	25	S	4:42	**5:06**	a3.1	10:42	**10:54**	p4.0
26	F	4:30	**5:00**	a3.3	10:30	**10:48**	p4.1	26	M	5:18	**5:42**	a3.0	11:12	**11:30**	p3.9
27	S	5:18	**5:42**	a3.1	11:12	**11:24**	p4.0	27	T	5:54	**6:18**	a3.0	11:48	...	3.8
28	S	5:54	**6:24**	a2.9	11:54	...	3.6	28	W	6:30	**6:54**	a3.0	12:06	**12:24**	3.9
29	M	6:36	**7:00**	a2.8	12:06	**12:36**	a3.8	29	T	7:12	**7:30**	p3.0	12:42	**1:06**	3.9
30	T	7:12	**7:36**	a2.7	12:48	**1:12**	a3.7								
31	W	7:54	**8:18**	a2.6	1:24	**1:48**	a3.6								

The Kts. (knots) columns show the **maximum** predicted velocities of the stronger one of the Flood Currents and the stronger one of the Ebb Currents for each day.

The letter "a" means the velocity shown should occur **after** the **a.m.** Current Change. The letter "p" means the velocity shown should occur **after** the **p.m.** Current Change (even if next morning). No "a" or "p" means a.m. and p.m. velocities are the same for that day.

Avg. Max. Velocity: Flood 3.4 Kts., Ebb 4.6 Kts.

Max. Flood 3 hrs. after Flood Starts, ±10 min.

Max. Ebb 3 hrs. after Ebb Starts, ±10 min.

At **City Island** the Current turns 2 hours before Hell Gate. At **Throg's Neck** the Current turns 1 hour before Hell Gate. At **Whitestone Pt.** the Current turns 25 min. before Hell Gate. At **College Pt.** the Current turns 30 min. before Hell Gate.

2024 CURRENT TABLE
HELL GATE, NY (EAST RIVER)

40°46.7'N, 73°56.3'W Off Mill Rock

*Daylight Time starts March 10 at 2 a.m.　　　　　　　**Daylight Saving Time**

		MARCH									APRIL					
D A Y O F M O N T H	D A Y O F W E E K	CURRENT TURNS TO						D A Y O F M O N T H	D A Y O F W E E K	CURRENT TURNS TO					
		NORTHEAST Flood Starts			SOUTHWEST Ebb Starts					NORTHEAST Flood Starts			SOUTHWEST Ebb Starts		
		a.m.	p.m.	Kts.	a.m.	p.m.	Kts.			a.m.	p.m.	Kts.	a.m.	p.m.	Kts.
1	F	7:54	8:12	p2.9	1:24	1:48	a3.9	1	M	10:18	10:36	p2.9	3:30	4:00	a3.9
2	S	8:48	9:06	p2.8	2:12	2:30	a3.8	2	T	11:24	11:42	p2.9	4:30	5:06	a3.7
3	S	9:42	10:00	p2.8	3:00	3:30	a3.7	3	W	...	12:24	2.8	5:36	6:12	a3.7
4	M	10:49	11:06	p2.9	3:54	4:30	a3.6	4	T	12:43	1:24	a3.1	6:42	7:12	3.9
5	T	11:48	...	2.7	4:54	5:36	3.6	5	F	1:42	2:18	p3.4	7:42	8:12	p4.3
6	W	12:06	12:42	3.0	6:00	6:36	3.8	6	S	2:36	3:12	3.7	8:36	9:00	p4.7
7	T	1:00	1:42	3.3	7:00	7:30	4.2	7	S	3:30	4:00	4.0	9:30	9:54	4.9
8	F	1:54	2:30	p3.7	7:54	8:24	4.6	8	M	4:18	4:48	a4.2	10:18	10:42	5.0
9	S	2:48	3:24	3.9	8:48	9:12	4.8	9	T	5:12	5:36	a4.1	11:06	11:30	4.9
10	S	*4:36	*5:12	a4.1	*10:36	*11:00	4.9	10	W	6:00	6:18	a4.0	11:54	...	4.7
11	M	5:30	5:54	a4.2	11:30	11:48	4.9	11	T	6:54	7:12	a3.7	12:18	12:48	a4.8
12	T	6:18	6:42	a4.1	...	12:18	4.8	12	F	7:48	8:00	a3.3	1:12	1:42	a4.5
13	W	7:12	7:30	a3.8	12:42	1:12	a4.9	13	S	8:42	9:00	a2.9	2:06	2:36	a4.1
14	T	8:06	8:24	a3.5	1:30	2:00	a4.7	14	S	9:48	10:00	2.6	3:00	3:36	a3.7
15	F	9:00	9:18	3.0	2:24	3:00	a4.4	15	M	10:54	11:06	p2.6	4:00	4:30	a3.4
16	S	10:06	10:18	a2.8	3:18	3:54	a3.9	16	T	...	12:01	2.5	5:06	5:30	3.2
17	S	11:12	11:30	2.6	4:18	4:54	a3.5	17	W	12:12	12:54	a2.7	6:06	6:24	p3.4
18	M	...	12:18	2.6	5:24	6:00	a3.4	18	T	1:06	1:48	a2.8	7:06	7:18	p3.6
19	T	12:36	1:24	p2.8	6:30	7:00	3.5	19	F	2:00	2:30	a2.9	7:54	8:06	p3.8
20	W	1:36	2:12	2.9	7:30	7:54	p3.8	20	S	2:42	3:06	a3.0	8:36	8:48	3.8
21	T	2:30	3:00	3.1	8:24	8:42	p4.0	21	S	3:18	3:42	a3.0	9:12	9:30	p3.9
22	F	3:12	3:42	a3.2	9:12	9:24	p4.1	22	M	3:54	4:18	3.0	9:48	10:06	3.9
23	S	3:54	4:24	a3.3	9:54	10:06	p4.1	23	T	4:30	4:48	p3.2	10:18	10:36	4.0
24	S	4:30	4:54	a3.2	10:24	10:42	p4.0	24	W	5:06	5:24	p3.4	10:54	11:12	4.2
25	M	5:06	5:30	3.1	11:00	11:18	p4.0	25	T	5:42	6:00	p3.5	11:30	11:54	4.3
26	T	5:42	6:00	3.2	11:30	11:48	4.0	26	F	6:24	6:42	p3.6	...	12:12	4.3
27	W	6:18	6:36	p3.3	...	12:06	4.1	27	S	7:12	7:24	p3.5	12:36	1:00	4.3
28	T	6:54	7:12	p3.4	12:30	12:42	p4.2	28	S	8:00	8:12	p3.4	1:24	1:48	a4.3
29	F	7:36	7:54	p3.3	1:06	1:24	p4.2	29	M	8:54	9:12	p3.2	2:18	2:42	a4.2
30	S	8:24	8:42	p3.2	1:48	2:12	4.1	30	T	9:54	10:12	p3.0	3:12	3:42	a4.0
31	S	9:18	9:30	p3.0	2:36	3:06	a4.0								

The Kts. (knots) columns show the **maximum** predicted velocities of the stronger one of the Flood Currents and the stronger one of the Ebb Currents for each day.

The letter "a" means the velocity shown should occur **after** the **a.m.** Current Change. The letter "p" means the velocity shown should occur **after** the **p.m.** Current Change (even if next morning). No "a" or "p" means a.m. and p.m. velocities are the same for that day.

Avg. Max. Velocity: Flood 3.4 Kts., Ebb 4.6 Kts.

Max. Flood 3 hrs. after Flood Starts, ±10 min.

Max. Ebb 3 hrs. after Ebb Starts, ±10 min.

See pp. 22-29 for Current Change at other points.

2024 CURRENT TABLE
HELL GATE, NY (EAST RIVER)
40°46.7'N, 73°56.3'W Off Mill Rock

Daylight Saving Time **Daylight Saving Time**

		MAY									JUNE					
		CURRENT TURNS TO									CURRENT TURNS TO						
DAY OF MONTH	DAY OF WEEK	NORTHEAST Flood Starts			SOUTHWEST Ebb Starts			DAY OF MONTH	DAY OF WEEK	NORTHEAST Flood Starts			SOUTHWEST Ebb Starts		
		a.m.	p.m.	Kts.	a.m.	p.m.	Kts.			a.m.	p.m.	Kts.	a.m.	p.m.	Kts.
1	W	11:00	11:18	p3.1	4:12	4:48	a3.9	1	S	12:01	12:36	a3.3	5:54	6:24	4.0
2	T	...	12:06	2.9	5:18	5:48	3.8	2	S	1:00	1:30	a3.4	6:54	7:24	p4.3
3	F	12:18	1:00	a3.2	6:18	6:48	4.0	3	M	1:54	2:24	a3.6	7:54	8:18	p4.5
4	S	1:19	1:54	3.4	7:18	7:48	4.3	4	T	2:49	3:12	3.7	8:48	9:12	p4.7
5	S	2:12	2:48	3.7	8:18	8:42	p4.7	5	W	3:48	4:06	3.8	9:42	10:00	p4.7
6	M	3:06	3:36	3.9	9:06	9:30	p4.9	6	T	4:36	4:54	a3.8	10:30	10:54	p4.6
7	T	4:00	4:24	4.0	10:00	10:18	p4.9	7	F	5:30	5:42	3.6	11:18	11:42	p4.4
8	W	4:54	5:12	a4.0	10:48	11:06	p4.8	8	S	6:24	6:36	a3.4	...	12:12	4.2
9	T	5:42	6:00	a3.8	11:36	...	4.5	9	S	7:12	7:30	3.1	12:36	1:00	4.1
10	F	6:36	6:48	a3.5	12:01	12:30	a4.6	10	M	8:06	8:24	p2.9	1:30	1:54	p3.9
11	S	7:30	7:42	3.1	12:54	1:24	a4.3	11	T	9:00	9:12	p2.7	2:24	2:42	p3.7
12	S	8:24	8:42	2.8	1:48	2:18	a3.9	12	W	9:48	10:06	p2.5	3:18	3:30	p3.4
13	M	9:24	9:42	p2.7	2:48	3:12	a3.6	13	T	10:42	11:00	p2.4	4:06	4:18	p3.2
14	T	10:24	10:42	p2.6	3:42	4:06	3.3	14	F	11:36	11:48	p2.3	4:54	5:06	p3.0
15	W	11:24	11:42	p2.6	4:42	4:54	p3.2	15	S	...	12:18	2.1	5:36	5:54	p3.0
16	T	...	12:18	2.4	5:36	5:48	p3.2	16	S	12:36	1:00	a2.3	6:24	6:42	p3.1
17	F	12:30	1:06	a2.6	6:24	6:42	p3.3	17	M	1:18	1:42	p2.4	7:06	7:24	p3.3
18	S	1:18	1:48	a2.6	7:12	7:24	p3.4	18	T	2:00	2:18	p2.7	7:48	8:06	p3.6
19	S	2:00	2:24	2.6	7:54	8:06	3.5	19	W	2:42	3:00	p3.0	8:30	8:48	p3.9
20	M	2:36	3:00	2.7	8:30	8:48	p3.7	20	T	3:24	3:36	p3.3	9:12	9:30	p4.2
21	T	3:18	3:36	p3.0	9:06	9:24	p3.9	21	F	4:06	4:24	p3.6	9:54	10:18	p4.4
22	W	3:54	4:12	p3.3	9:42	10:06	4.1	22	S	4:54	5:06	p3.7	10:42	11:06	p4.5
23	T	4:36	4:48	p3.5	10:24	10:42	4.3	23	S	5:42	5:54	p3.8	11:30	11:54	4.5
24	F	5:18	5:30	p3.7	11:00	11:24	4.4	24	M	6:30	6:48	p3.8	...	12:18	4.6
25	S	6:00	6:18	p3.7	11:48	...	4.4	25	T	7:18	7:36	p3.7	12:48	1:12	4.6
26	S	6:48	7:06	p3.7	12:12	12:36	4.4	26	W	8:12	8:30	p3.6	1:42	2:06	a4.6
27	M	7:36	7:54	p3.5	1:00	1:30	4.4	27	T	9:12	9:30	p3.4	2:36	3:00	a4.5
28	T	8:36	8:54	p3.4	2:00	2:24	a4.4	28	F	10:06	10:30	p3.3	3:30	4:00	a4.3
29	W	9:30	9:48	p3.2	2:54	3:24	a4.2	29	S	11:06	11:36	p3.3	4:30	4:54	4.0
30	T	10:36	10:54	p3.2	3:54	4:24	a4.1	30	S	...	12:06	3.1	5:30	5:54	p4.0
31	F	11:36	...	3.0	4:54	5:24	a4.0								

The Kts. (knots) columns show the **maximum** predicted velocities of the stronger one of the Flood Currents and the stronger one of the Ebb Currents for each day.

The letter "a" means the velocity shown should occur **after** the a.m. Current Change. The letter "p" means the velocity shown should occur **after** the p.m. Current Change (even if next morning). No "a" or "p" means a.m. and p.m. velocities are the same for that day.

Avg. Max. Velocity: Flood 3.4 Kts., Ebb 4.6 Kts.

Max. Flood 3 hrs. after Flood Starts, ±10 min.

Max. Ebb 3 hrs. after Ebb Starts, ±10 min.

At **City Island** the Current turns 2 hours before Hell Gate. At **Throg's Neck** the Current turns 1 hour before Hell Gate. At **Whitestone Pt.** the Current turns 25 min. before Hell Gate. At **College Pt.** the Current turns 30 min. before Hell Gate.

2024 CURRENT TABLE
HELL GATE, NY (EAST RIVER)
40°46.7'N, 73°56.3'W Off Mill Rock

Daylight Saving Time **Daylight Saving Time**

JULY | AUGUST

D A Y O F M O N T H	D A Y O F W E E K	CURRENT TURNS TO					D A Y O F M O N T H	D A Y O F W E E K	CURRENT TURNS TO				
		NORTHEAST Flood Starts			SOUTHWEST Ebb Starts				NORTHEAST Flood Starts			SOUTHWEST Ebb Starts	
		a.m.	p.m.	Kts.	a.m.	p.m.	Kts.			a.m.	p.m.	Kts.	a.m.	p.m.	Kts.
1	M	12:36	1:06	3.2	6:30	6:54	p4.1	1	T	2:24	2:36	p3.3	8:12	8:36	p4.3
2	T	1:36	2:00	3.3	7:30	7:54	p4.3	2	F	3:18	3:30	p3.5	9:06	9:30	p4.4
3	W	2:36	2:54	a3.5	8:30	8:48	p4.5	3	S	4:12	4:24	3.6	9:54	10:24	4.3
4	T	3:31	3:48	3.6	9:24	9:48	p4.5	4	S	5:01	5:12	p3.6	10:42	11:12	a4.4
5	F	4:24	4:42	3.6	10:12	10:36	p4.4	5	M	5:42	6:00	p3.5	11:30	...	4.4
6	S	5:18	5:30	3.5	11:06	11:30	4.3	6	T	6:24	6:42	3.2	12:01	12:12	p4.2
7	S	6:06	6:18	3.4	11:54	...	4.3	7	W	7:06	7:24	3.0	12:42	12:54	p4.0
8	M	6:54	7:06	3.2	12:18	12:36	p4.2	8	T	7:48	8:00	2.7	1:24	1:36	p3.8
9	T	7:42	7:54	2.9	1:12	1:24	p4.0	9	F	8:24	8:42	2.5	2:00	2:18	p3.6
10	W	8:24	8:42	p2.7	2:00	2:12	p3.8	10	S	9:06	9:24	2.4	2:36	2:54	p3.5
11	T	9:12	9:24	2.4	2:42	2:54	p3.5	11	S	9:42	10:12	2.3	3:18	3:36	3.3
12	F	9:54	10:12	p2.3	3:24	3:36	p3.3	12	M	10:30	11:00	a2.3	3:54	4:18	3.2
13	S	10:36	11:00	p2.2	4:06	4:18	p3.1	13	T	11:18	11:54	a2.4	4:42	5:06	3.2
14	S	11:24	11:48	p2.2	4:48	5:06	p3.0	14	W	...	12:12	2.5	5:36	6:00	p3.3
15	M	...	12:12	2.2	5:30	5:54	3.0	15	T	12:48	1:06	p2.7	6:30	7:00	p3.5
16	T	12:36	12:54	p2.4	6:18	6:42	p3.2	16	F	1:42	2:00	p3.0	7:30	7:54	p3.9
17	W	1:24	1:42	p2.7	7:06	7:30	p3.5	17	S	2:36	2:48	p3.4	8:24	8:48	p4.3
18	T	2:06	2:24	p3.0	7:54	8:18	p3.9	18	S	3:24	3:42	p3.7	9:18	9:42	p4.6
19	F	2:54	3:12	p3.3	8:48	9:06	p4.2	19	M	4:12	4:30	p4.0	10:06	10:30	p4.8
20	S	3:42	4:00	p3.6	9:36	9:54	p4.5	20	T	5:06	5:18	p4.1	10:54	11:18	p4.9
21	S	4:36	4:48	p3.8	10:24	10:48	p4.6	21	W	5:54	6:12	p4.2	11:42	...	4.9
22	M	5:24	5:36	p4.0	11:12	11:36	4.7	22	T	6:36	7:00	4.0	12:06	12:36	a5.0
23	T	6:12	6:30	p4.0	...	12:06	4.7	23	F	7:30	7:54	a3.9	1:00	1:24	a4.9
24	W	7:00	7:18	p3.9	12:30	12:54	4.8	24	S	8:18	8:48	a3.6	1:54	2:18	4.6
25	T	7:54	8:12	p3.8	1:24	1:48	a4.8	25	S	9:12	9:48	a3.3	2:48	3:12	4.3
26	F	8:42	9:06	3.5	2:18	2:42	4.6	26	M	10:06	10:54	a3.0	3:42	4:06	p3.9
27	S	9:36	10:06	a3.3	3:12	3:36	4.3	27	T	11:12	...	2.8	4:48	5:12	p3.6
28	S	10:36	11:12	3.1	4:06	4:30	4.0	28	W	12:06	12:18	2.8	5:48	6:18	p3.7
29	M	11:36	...	3.0	5:06	5:30	p3.9	29	T	1:12	1:24	2.9	6:54	7:18	p3.9
30	T	12:18	12:42	a3.0	6:12	6:36	p3.9	30	F	2:06	2:24	p3.2	7:54	8:24	p4.2
31	W	1:24	1:42	3.1	7:12	7:36	p4.1	31	S	3:00	3:18	p3.5	8:48	9:18	p4.3

The Kts. (knots) columns show the **maximum** predicted velocities of the stronger one of the Flood Currents and the stronger one of the Ebb Currents for each day.

The letter "a" means the velocity shown should occur **after** the **a.m.** Current Change. The letter "p" means the velocity shown should occur **after** the **p.m.** Current Change (even if next morning). No "a" or "p" means a.m. and p.m. velocities are the same for that day.

Avg. Max. Velocity: Flood 3.4 Kts., Ebb 4.6 Kts.

Max. Flood 3 hrs. after Flood Starts, ±10 min.

Max. Ebb 3 hrs. after Ebb Starts, ±10 min.

See pp. 22-29 for Current Change at other points.

2024 CURRENT TABLE
HELL GATE, NY (EAST RIVER)
40°46.7'N, 73°56.3'W Off Mill Rock

Daylight Saving Time | **Daylight Saving Time**

SEPTEMBER | OCTOBER

DAY OF MONTH	DAY OF WEEK	NORTHEAST Flood Starts a.m.	p.m.	Kts.	SOUTHWEST Ebb Starts a.m.	p.m.	Kts.	DAY OF MONTH	DAY OF WEEK	NORTHEAST Flood Starts a.m.	p.m.	Kts.	SOUTHWEST Ebb Starts a.m.	p.m.	Kts.
1	S	3:54	4:06	p3.6	9:36	10:06	a4.4	1	T	4:06	4:18	p3.4	9:48	10:12	a4.3
2	M	4:36	4:48	p3.6	10:18	10:48	a4.4	2	W	4:42	4:54	3.2	10:30	10:48	a4.1
3	T	5:18	5:30	3.4	11:00	11:24	a4.3	3	T	5:18	5:30	3.1	11:06	11:24	a4.0
4	W	5:55	6:06	3.2	11:42	...	4.1	4	F	5:55	6:06	a3.1	11:42	11:54	3.9
5	T	6:30	6:48	3.0	12:06	12:18	p4.0	5	S	6:24	6:42	a3.1	...	12:18	3.9
6	F	7:06	7:24	a2.9	12:36	12:54	3.8	6	S	7:00	7:24	a3.1	12:30	12:54	3.9
7	S	7:42	8:00	a2.8	1:12	1:36	3.7	7	M	7:36	8:06	a3.1	1:12	1:36	3.9
8	S	8:18	8:42	a2.8	1:48	2:12	3.7	8	T	8:24	8:54	a3.0	1:54	2:18	a3.9
9	M	9:00	9:30	a2.7	2:30	2:54	3.6	9	W	9:12	9:48	a2.9	2:42	3:06	a3.8
10	T	9:42	10:24	a2.6	3:12	3:36	3.5	10	T	10:06	10:54	a2.8	3:36	4:06	3.6
11	W	10:36	11:24	a2.6	4:06	4:30	3.4	11	F	11:12	...	2.8	4:36	5:06	p3.6
12	T	11:36	...	2.7	5:00	5:30	p3.4	12	S	12:01	12:12	p3.0	5:42	6:12	p3.7
13	F	12:24	12:42	p2.8	6:06	6:30	p3.6	13	S	12:54	1:12	p3.2	6:42	7:12	p4.1
14	S	1:18	1:36	p3.1	7:06	7:30	p4.0	14	M	1:54	2:06	p3.6	7:42	8:06	p4.5
15	S	2:12	2:30	p3.5	8:06	8:30	p4.4	15	T	2:42	3:00	p3.9	8:36	9:00	p4.8
16	M	3:06	3:18	p3.8	8:54	9:18	p4.8	16	W	3:30	3:48	p4.1	9:24	9:48	p5.0
17	T	3:54	4:12	p4.1	9:48	10:12	p5.0	17	T	4:18	4:42	p4.2	10:12	10:36	5.0
18	W	4:42	5:00	p4.2	10:36	11:00	p5.0	18	F	5:06	5:30	a4.1	11:00	11:30	a5.0
19	T	5:30	5:48	p4.2	11:24	11:48	5.0	19	S	5:54	6:24	a4.0	11:48	...	4.9
20	F	6:18	6:42	a4.1	...	12:12	5.0	20	S	6:42	7:18	a3.8	12:18	12:42	4.6
21	S	7:00	7:36	a3.9	12:36	1:00	4.8	21	M	7:30	8:12	a3.4	1:12	1:36	4.3
22	S	7:54	8:30	a3.6	1:30	1:54	4.5	22	T	8:30	9:18	a3.0	2:06	2:36	a4.0
23	M	8:48	9:30	a3.2	2:30	2:48	4.1	23	W	9:30	10:18	a2.8	3:06	3:36	3.6
24	T	9:48	10:36	a2.8	3:24	3:48	3.7	24	T	10:36	11:24	a2.7	4:06	4:36	3.4
25	W	10:54	11:48	2.7	4:24	4:54	p3.5	25	F	11:42	...	2.8	5:00	5:42	3.4
26	T	...	12:01	2.7	5:30	6:00	p3.5	26	S	12:30	12:42	p2.9	6:00	6:42	p3.6
27	F	12:54	1:06	p2.9	6:30	7:06	p3.8	27	S	1:24	1:36	p3.1	7:00	7:36	p3.8
28	S	1:48	2:06	p3.2	7:30	8:00	p4.0	28	M	2:12	2:24	p3.2	7:48	8:18	3.9
29	S	2:42	2:54	p3.4	8:18	8:54	4.2	29	T	2:54	3:06	p3.2	8:36	9:00	a4.0
30	M	3:24	3:36	p3.5	9:06	9:36	a4.3	30	W	3:30	3:42	p3.1	9:18	9:36	a4.0
								31	T	4:06	4:18	3.0	9:54	10:12	3.9

The Kts. (knots) columns show the **maximum** predicted velocities of the stronger one of the Flood Currents and the stronger one of the Ebb Currents for each day.

The letter "a" means the velocity shown should occur **after** the **a.m.** Current Change. The letter "p" means the velocity shown should occur **after** the **p.m.** Current Change (even if next morning). No "a" or "p" means a.m. and p.m. velocities are the same for that day.

Avg. Max. Velocity: Flood 3.4 Kts., Ebb 4.6 Kts.

Max. Flood 3 hrs. after Flood Starts, ±10 min.

Max. Ebb 3 hrs. after Ebb Starts, ±10 min.

At **City Island** the Current turns 2 hours before Hell Gate. At **Throg's Neck** the Current turns 1 hour before Hell Gate. At **Whitestone Pt.** the Current turns 25 min. before Hell Gate. At **College Pt.** the Current turns 30 min. before Hell Gate.

2024 CURRENT TABLE
HELL GATE, NY (EAST RIVER)

40°46.7'N, 73°56.3'W Off Mill Rock

*Standard Time starts Nov. 3 at 2 a.m.   Standard Time

DAY OF MONTH	DAY OF WEEK	NORTHEAST Flood Starts			SOUTHWEST Ebb Starts			DAY OF MONTH	DAY OF WEEK	NORTHEAST Flood Starts			SOUTHWEST Ebb Starts		
		a.m.	p.m.	Kts.	a.m.	p.m.	Kts.			a.m.	p.m.	Kts.	a.m.	p.m.	Kts.
1	F	4:36	4:54	3.0	10:30	10:42	3.9	1	S	3:36	4:00	a3.2	9:30	9:48	p4.1
2	S	5:12	5:30	3.1	11:06	11:18	p4.0	2	M	4:18	4:42	a3.4	10:12	10:30	p4.2
3	S	*4:48	*5:12	a3.3	*10:42	*10:54	p4.1	3	T	5:00	5:30	a3.5	10:54	11:18	p4.3
4	M	5:25	5:54	a3.3	11:18	11:36	p4.1	4	W	5:43	6:18	a3.6	11:42	...	4.3
5	T	6:06	6:36	a3.3	...	12:01	4.1	5	T	6:30	7:06	a3.5	12:06	12:30	a4.4
6	W	6:54	7:30	a3.3	12:24	12:54	4.1	6	F	7:24	8:06	a3.4	1:00	1:30	4.3
7	T	7:48	8:24	a3.1	1:18	1:48	a4.1	7	S	8:18	9:00	a3.3	1:54	2:24	4.2
8	F	8:42	9:30	a3.0	2:18	2:42	3.9	8	S	9:18	10:00	a3.3	2:54	3:24	4.1
9	S	9:48	10:30	a3.1	3:12	3:42	3.8	9	M	10:24	11:00	a3.3	3:48	4:24	4.0
10	S	10:48	11:30	a3.2	4:18	4:48	p3.9	10	T	11:24	...	3.4	4:48	5:24	p4.1
11	M	11:48	...	3.4	5:18	5:48	p4.1	11	W	12:01	12:24	p3.4	5:48	6:18	p4.2
12	T	12:24	12:42	p3.6	6:18	6:42	p4.4	12	T	12:54	1:18	p3.6	6:48	7:18	a4.4
13	W	1:18	1:36	p3.8	7:12	7:36	p4.7	13	F	1:42	2:18	p3.7	7:42	8:12	a4.6
14	T	2:06	2:30	p4.0	8:00	8:30	4.8	14	S	2:36	3:12	3.7	8:30	9:06	a4.7
15	F	2:54	3:24	4.0	8:54	9:18	a4.9	15	S	3:24	4:06	3.7	9:24	9:54	a4.6
16	S	3:42	4:18	a3.9	9:42	10:12	a4.8	16	M	4:18	4:54	a3.6	10:18	10:48	a4.5
17	S	4:30	5:12	a3.8	10:30	11:00	a4.7	17	T	5:12	5:48	a3.5	11:12	11:36	4.3
18	M	5:24	6:06	a3.6	11:24	11:54	a4.4	18	W	6:06	6:42	a3.3	...	12:06	4.1
19	T	6:18	7:00	a3.3	...	12:24	4.2	19	T	7:00	7:36	a3.1	12:30	1:00	a4.2
20	W	7:12	8:00	a3.0	12:48	1:18	a4.0	20	F	7:48	8:30	a3.0	1:18	1:54	a4.0
21	T	8:12	8:54	a2.9	1:48	2:18	a3.8	21	S	8:42	9:18	a2.8	2:12	2:48	a3.7
22	F	9:12	10:00	a2.8	2:42	3:18	a3.6	22	S	9:36	10:12	a2.7	3:00	3:36	a3.5
23	S	10:12	10:54	a2.8	3:36	4:12	a3.5	23	M	10:30	11:00	a2.5	3:48	4:24	a3.2
24	S	11:12	11:48	a2.8	4:30	5:06	a3.4	24	T	11:18	11:48	a2.3	4:36	5:06	a3.1
25	M	...	12:01	2.8	5:24	5:54	a3.5	25	W	...	12:06	2.3	5:24	5:54	a3.1
26	T	12:36	12:48	p2.7	6:12	6:36	3.5	26	T	12:30	12:48	2.3	6:12	6:36	p3.2
27	W	1:12	1:30	p2.7	6:54	7:18	3.6	27	F	1:06	1:30	p2.5	6:54	7:18	p3.4
28	T	1:48	2:06	2.7	7:36	7:54	3.6	28	S	1:48	2:12	2.7	7:36	8:00	p3.7
29	F	2:24	2:42	2.8	8:12	8:30	p3.8	29	S	2:24	2:54	3.0	8:18	8:42	p4.0
30	S	3:00	3:24	3.0	8:54	9:06	p4.0	30	M	3:06	3:36	a3.3	9:00	9:24	p4.2
								31	T	3:54	4:18	a3.5	9:48	10:12	p4.6

The Kts. (knots) columns show the **maximum** predicted velocities of the stronger one of the Flood Currents and the stronger one of the Ebb Currents for each day.

The letter "a" means the velocity shown should occur **after** the **a.m.** Current Change. The letter "p" means the velocity shown should occur **after** the **p.m.** Current Change (even if next morning). No "a" or "p" means a.m. and p.m. velocities are the same for that day.

Avg. Max. Velocity: Flood 3.4 Kts., Ebb 4.6 Kts.

Max. Flood 3 hrs. after Flood Starts, ±10 min.

Max. Ebb 3 hrs. after Ebb Starts, ±10 min.

See pp. 22-29 for Current Change at other points.

2024 CURRENT TABLE
THE NARROWS
40°36.36'N, 74°02.29'W

Standard Time   Standard Time

JANUARY

Day of Month	Day of Week	NORTH Flood Starts			SOUTH Ebb Starts		
		a.m.	p.m.	Kts.	a.m.	p.m.	Kts.
1	M	7:30	8:30	a1.2	1:06	1:12	p1.8
2	T	8:24	9:12	a1.1	1:54	2:00	p1.7
3	W	9:24	10:00	p1.1	2:42	2:48	p1.7
4	T	10:25	10:48	p1.2	3:36	3:42	p1.7
5	F	11:18	11:36	p1.3	4:24	4:36	p1.7
6	S	...	12:18	0.8	5:18	5:30	p1.8
7	S	12:24	1:18	a1.4	6:12	6:24	p1.8
8	M	1:12	2:12	a1.4	7:00	7:18	p1.7
9	T	2:00	3:12	a1.4	7:48	8:06	p1.7
10	W	2:48	4:06	a1.4	8:36	8:54	1.6
11	T	3:42	5:00	a1.5	9:18	9:42	1.6
12	F	4:36	5:42	a1.5	10:06	10:30	p1.7
13	S	5:30	6:30	a1.5	11:00	11:18	p1.7
14	S	6:24	7:06	a1.4	11:48	...	1.7
15	M	7:18	7:48	a1.4	12:12	12:42	1.7
16	T	8:18	8:36	p1.4	1:06	1:36	a1.8
17	W	9:18	9:24	p1.4	2:00	2:30	1.7
18	T	10:18	10:18	p1.5	3:00	3:24	p1.7
19	F	11:24	11:12	p1.5	4:00	4:24	p1.8
20	S	...	12:24	1.1	5:06	5:24	p1.9
21	S	12:06	1:30	a1.6	6:06	6:18	p2.0
22	M	1:00	2:24	a1.6	7:00	7:18	p2.0
23	T	1:48	3:18	a1.6	7:54	8:06	p2.0
24	W	2:36	4:06	a1.5	8:36	8:54	p1.9
25	T	3:24	4:48	a1.5	9:18	9:42	1.7
26	F	4:12	5:24	a1.3	10:00	10:30	1.7
27	S	5:00	6:00	a1.3	10:42	11:12	a1.7
28	S	5:42	6:30	a1.2	11:18	11:48	a1.8
29	M	6:24	7:06	1.2	11:54	...	1.8
30	T	7:06	7:42	1.3	12:30	12:36	p1.9
31	W	7:54	8:24	p1.4	1:06	1:12	p1.9

FEBRUARY

Day of Month	Day of Week	NORTH Flood Starts			SOUTH Ebb Starts		
		a.m.	p.m.	Kts.	a.m.	p.m.	Kts.
1	T	8:48	9:12	p1.5	1:54	2:00	p1.9
2	F	9:42	10:00	p1.5	2:42	2:54	p1.9
3	S	10:42	10:54	p1.5	3:36	3:48	p1.8
4	S	11:43	11:48	p1.5	4:30	4:54	p1.8
5	M	...	12:48	0.8	5:30	5:54	p1.7
6	T	12:42	1:48	a1.4	6:30	6:54	p1.7
7	W	1:36	2:48	a1.4	7:24	7:48	p1.7
8	T	2:30	3:42	a1.4	8:12	8:36	1.6
9	F	3:24	4:30	a1.4	9:00	9:24	1.6
10	S	4:24	5:18	a1.4	9:48	10:06	p1.7
11	S	5:18	5:54	a1.3	10:42	10:54	p1.7
12	M	6:06	6:30	a1.3	11:30	11:42	p1.7
13	T	7:00	7:12	p1.3	...	12:12	1.7
14	W	7:54	7:54	p1.3	12:36	1:06	1.7
15	T	8:54	8:48	p1.3	1:30	1:54	1.7
16	F	10:00	9:42	p1.3	2:30	2:54	p1.7
17	S	11:06	10:42	p1.3	3:30	3:54	p1.7
18	S	-A-	12:12	1.0	4:36	5:00	p1.8
19	M	...	1:18	1.2	5:42	6:06	p1.9
20	T	12:42	2:12	a1.5	6:42	7:06	p2.0
21	W	1:36	3:00	a1.5	7:36	8:00	1.9
22	T	2:30	3:42	1.5	8:24	8:48	1.9
23	F	3:18	4:18	a1.5	9:00	9:30	a1.9
24	S	4:00	4:54	a1.4	9:42	10:06	a1.8
25	S	4:42	5:24	1.2	10:18	10:42	a1.8
26	M	5:24	5:48	p1.3	10:54	11:18	a1.8
27	T	6:00	6:24	p1.4	11:24	11:54	a1.9
28	W	6:42	7:00	p1.6	...	12:01	2.0
29	T	7:24	7:42	p1.7	12:30	12:36	p2.1

A also at 11:42 p.m. (1.4)

The Kts. (knots) columns show the **maximum** predicted velocities of the stronger one of the Flood Currents and the stronger one of the Ebb Currents for each day.

The letter "a" means the velocity shown should occur **after** the **a.m.** Current Change. The letter "p" means the velocity shown should occur **after** the **p.m.** Current Change (even if next morning). No "a" or "p" means a.m. and p.m. velocities are the same for that day.

Avg. Max. Velocity: Flood 1.4 Kts., Ebb 1.9 Kts.

Max. Flood 2 hrs. 45 min. after Flood Starts, ±30 min.

Max. Ebb 3 hrs. 25 min. after Ebb Starts, ±25 min.

At **The Battery, Desbrosses St., & Chelsea Dock** Current turns 1 1/2 hrs. after the Narrows. At **42nd St.** and the **George Washington Bridge**, the Current turns 1 3/4 hrs. after the Narrows. See pp. 22-29 for Current Change at other points.

2024 CURRENT TABLE
THE NARROWS
40°36.36'N, 74°02.29'W

*Daylight Time starts March 10 at 2 a.m.   Daylight Saving Time

MARCH								APRIL							
DAY OF MONTH	DAY OF WEEK	CURRENT TURNS TO						DAY OF MONTH	DAY OF WEEK	CURRENT TURNS TO					
		NORTH Flood Starts			SOUTH Ebb Starts					NORTH Flood Starts			SOUTH Ebb Starts		
		a.m.	p.m.	Kts.	a.m.	p.m.	Kts.			a.m.	p.m.	Kts.	a.m.	p.m.	Kts.
1	F	8:12	8:30	p1.8	1:12	1:24	p2.1	1	M	10:48	10:54	p1.7	3:24	4:00	a1.9
2	S	9:12	9:24	p1.7	2:00	2:18	p2.0	2	T	11:54	11:54	p1.5	4:30	5:06	a1.8
3	S	10:12	10:18	p1.6	2:54	3:18	p1.8	3	W	...	12:54	1.2	5:30	6:12	a1.8
4	M	11:19	11:18	p1.5	3:54	4:24	1.7	4	T	1:01	1:48	a1.4	6:36	7:12	1.8
5	T	...	12:18	1.0	4:54	5:30	p1.7	5	F	2:00	2:42	1.4	7:36	8:06	1.8
6	W	12:18	1:18	a1.4	6:00	6:36	1.7	6	S	3:00	3:30	1.4	8:30	8:54	1.8
7	T	1:18	2:18	a1.4	7:00	7:30	1.7	7	S	3:54	4:12	p1.4	9:18	9:36	1.8
8	F	2:12	3:06	a1.4	7:54	8:18	1.7	8	M	4:48	4:54	p1.4	10:00	10:18	p1.8
9	S	3:12	3:54	a1.4	8:42	9:00	p1.7	9	T	5:42	5:30	p1.4	10:42	11:06	1.7
10	S	*5:06	*5:36	1.3	*10:30	*10:42	p1.7	10	W	6:36	6:12	p1.3	11:24	11:48	a1.8
11	M	6:00	6:12	p1.3	11:12	11:30	p1.8	11	T	7:18	6:54	p1.3	...	12:12	1.8
12	T	6:54	6:54	p1.3	...	12:01	1.7	12	F	8:06	7:42	p1.3	12:36	1:00	p1.7
13	W	7:42	7:30	p1.3	12:18	12:42	1.7	13	S	9:06	8:36	p1.2	1:30	1:54	p1.6
14	T	8:30	8:18	p1.3	1:06	1:30	1.7	14	S	10:12	9:42	p1.1	2:24	3:00	p1.5
15	F	9:30	9:12	p1.3	2:00	2:24	p1.7	15	M	11:18	10:48	p1.0	3:30	4:12	p1.4
16	S	10:36	10:12	p1.2	3:00	3:24	p1.6	16	T	-A-	12:24	1.0	4:36	5:24	1.5
17	S	11:48	11:18	p1.2	4:00	4:30	p1.6	17	W	...	1:24	1.2	5:48	6:30	a1.8
18	M	...	12:54	1.0	5:12	5:42	p1.7	18	T	1:00	2:12	p1.4	6:48	7:30	a2.0
19	T	12:18	2:00	a1.3	6:18	6:54	p1.8	19	F	2:00	2:54	p1.5	7:48	8:24	a2.1
20	W	1:24	2:48	1.4	7:18	7:54	1.9	20	S	2:54	3:30	p1.5	8:30	9:06	a2.1
21	T	2:18	3:30	1.5	8:12	8:42	2.0	21	S	3:42	4:00	p1.5	9:12	9:42	a2.0
22	F	3:12	4:12	p1.6	9:00	9:30	a2.1	22	M	4:24	4:30	p1.4	9:48	10:12	a1.9
23	S	4:00	4:42	p1.5	9:42	10:06	a2.0	23	T	5:06	5:00	p1.4	10:18	10:42	a1.8
24	S	4:48	5:12	p1.4	10:18	10:42	a1.9	24	W	5:48	5:36	p1.6	10:48	11:18	a1.8
25	M	5:24	5:42	p1.4	10:48	11:18	a1.8	25	T	6:24	6:12	p1.8	11:18	11:54	a1.9
26	T	6:06	6:12	p1.5	11:18	11:48	a1.9	26	F	7:06	6:54	p1.9	...	12:01	2.0
27	W	6:42	6:48	p1.7	11:48	...	2.0	27	S	7:48	7:42	p1.9	12:36	12:48	p2.0
28	T	7:18	7:24	p1.8	12:24	12:24	p2.1	28	S	8:36	8:36	p1.9	1:18	1:42	2.0
29	F	8:00	8:06	p1.9	1:00	1:06	p2.1	29	M	9:30	9:30	p1.8	2:12	2:42	a2.0
30	S	8:54	9:00	p1.9	1:42	2:00	p2.1	30	T	10:30	10:36	p1.6	3:06	3:42	a2.0
31	S	9:48	9:54	p1.8	2:30	2:54	p2.0								

A also at 11:54 p.m. (1.1)

The Kts. (knots) columns show the **maximum** predicted velocities of the stronger one of the Flood Currents and the stronger one of the Ebb Currents for each day.

The letter "a" means the velocity shown should occur **after** the a.m. Current Change. The letter "p" means the velocity shown should occur **after** the p.m. Current Change (even if next morning). No "a" or "p" means a.m. and p.m. velocities are the same for that day.

Avg. Max. Velocity: Flood 1.4 Kts., Ebb 1.9 Kts.
Max. Flood 2 hrs. 45 min. after Flood Starts, ±30 min.
Max. Ebb 3 hrs. 25 min. after Ebb Starts, ±25 min.

See pp. 22-29 for Current Change at other points.

2024 CURRENT TABLE
THE NARROWS

40°36.36'N, 74°02.29'W

Daylight Saving Time   Daylight Saving Time

MAY   JUNE

DAY OF MONTH	DAY OF WEEK	NORTH Flood Starts a.m.	**p.m.**	Kts.	SOUTH Ebb Starts a.m.	**p.m.**	Kts.	DAY OF MONTH	DAY OF WEEK	NORTH Flood Starts a.m.	**p.m.**	Kts.	SOUTH Ebb Starts a.m.	**p.m.**	Kts.
1	W	11:30	**11:36**	p1.5	4:06	**4:48**	a1.9	1	S	12:24	**12:48**	p1.6	5:48	**6:24**	a1.9
2	T	...	**12:24**	1.4	5:12	**5:48**	1.8	2	S	1:24	**1:30**	p1.6	6:48	**7:18**	a1.9
3	F	12:42	**1:18**	p1.5	6:12	**6:48**	1.9	3	M	2:24	**2:18**	p1.6	7:36	**8:06**	a2.0
4	S	1:43	**2:06**	p1.5	7:12	**7:42**	1.9	4	T	3:25	**3:00**	p1.6	8:24	**8:54**	a2.0
5	S	2:42	**2:54**	p1.5	8:06	**8:30**	1.9	5	W	4:18	**3:48**	p1.5	9:12	**9:42**	a2.0
6	M	3:36	**3:30**	p1.5	8:54	**9:12**	a1.9	6	T	5:12	**4:30**	p1.4	9:54	**10:24**	a1.9
7	T	4:30	**4:12**	p1.5	9:36	**10:00**	a1.9	7	F	6:00	**5:18**	p1.3	10:42	**11:06**	a1.8
8	W	5:24	**4:54**	p1.4	10:12	**10:42**	a1.9	8	S	6:42	**6:06**	p1.2	11:30	**11:54**	a1.7
9	T	6:18	**5:42**	p1.3	11:00	**11:24**	a1.8	9	S	7:30	**6:54**	p1.2	...	**12:24**	1.6
10	F	7:00	**6:24**	p1.3	11:42	...	1.8	10	M	8:18	**7:48**	p1.1	12:42	**1:18**	a1.6
11	S	7:48	**7:18**	p1.2	12:12	**12:36**	p1.7	11	T	9:06	**8:42**	p1.1	1:30	**2:12**	a1.6
12	S	8:42	**8:12**	p1.1	1:06	**1:36**	p1.6	12	W	9:54	**9:42**	p1.0	2:24	**3:12**	a1.6
13	M	9:42	**9:12**	p1.0	2:00	**2:36**	a1.5	13	T	10:48	**10:42**	0.9	3:24	**4:12**	a1.7
14	T	10:42	**10:18**	p0.9	3:00	**3:48**	a1.5	14	F	11:36	**11:48**	a1.0	4:24	**5:12**	a1.7
15	W	11:42	**11:24**	1.0	4:00	**4:54**	a1.6	15	S	...	**12:24**	1.1	5:18	**6:06**	a1.8
16	T	...	**12:36**	1.1	5:06	**6:00**	a1.8	16	S	12:48	**1:06**	p1.1	6:18	**7:00**	a1.8
17	F	12:24	**1:24**	p1.3	6:12	**6:54**	a1.9	17	M	1:48	**1:48**	p1.2	7:06	**7:48**	a1.8
18	S	1:30	**2:00**	p1.3	7:06	**7:48**	a2.0	18	T	2:42	**2:30**	p1.3	7:48	**8:30**	a1.8
19	S	2:24	**2:42**	p1.4	7:54	**8:30**	a2.0	19	W	3:30	**3:12**	p1.3	8:30	**9:06**	a1.7
20	M	3:12	**3:12**	p1.4	8:36	**9:06**	a1.9	20	T	4:24	**3:54**	p1.4	9:12	**9:42**	a1.7
21	T	4:00	**3:48**	p1.4	9:12	**9:42**	a1.8	21	F	5:12	**4:42**	p1.5	9:54	**10:24**	a1.7
22	W	4:48	**4:24**	p1.4	9:42	**10:12**	a1.7	22	S	5:54	**5:30**	p1.6	10:36	**11:06**	1.7
23	T	5:30	**5:06**	p1.6	10:18	**10:48**	a1.8	23	S	6:36	**6:18**	p1.6	11:24	**11:54**	p1.8
24	F	6:12	**5:48**	p1.7	10:54	**11:30**	a1.8	24	M	7:24	**7:12**	p1.7	...	**12:18**	1.8
25	S	6:54	**6:36**	p1.8	11:42	...	1.9	25	T	8:06	**8:06**	p1.6	12:42	**1:12**	1.8
26	S	7:36	**7:24**	p1.8	12:12	**12:30**	p1.9	26	W	8:54	**9:00**	p1.5	1:36	**2:06**	1.9
27	M	8:24	**8:18**	p1.8	1:00	**1:30**	1.9	27	T	9:42	**10:00**	a1.5	2:30	**3:00**	1.9
28	T	9:12	**9:18**	p1.7	1:54	**2:24**	a2.0	28	F	10:30	**11:06**	a1.5	3:30	**4:00**	a1.9
29	W	10:06	**10:18**	p1.6	2:48	**3:24**	a1.9	29	S	11:24	...	1.6	4:24	**4:54**	a1.8
30	T	11:00	**11:24**	a1.5	3:48	**4:24**	a1.9	30	S	12:06	**12:12**	p1.6	5:24	**5:54**	a1.8
31	F	11:54	...	1.5	4:48	**5:24**	a1.9								

The Kts. (knots) columns show the **maximum** predicted velocities of the stronger one of the Flood Currents and the stronger one of the Ebb Currents for each day.

The letter "a" means the velocity shown should occur **after** the **a.m.** Current Change. The letter "p" means the velocity shown should occur **after** the **p.m.** Current Change (even if next morning). No "a" or "p" means a.m. and p.m. velocities are the same for that day.

Avg. Max. Velocity: Flood 1.4 Kts., Ebb 1.9 Kts.

Max. Flood 2 hrs. 45 min. after Flood Starts, ±30 min.

Max. Ebb 3 hrs. 25 min. after Ebb Starts, ±25 min.

At **The Battery, Desbrosses St., & Chelsea Dock** Current turns 1 1/2 hrs. after the Narrows. At **42nd St.** and the **George Washington Bridge**, the Current turns 1 3/4 hrs. after the Narrows. See pp. 22-29 for Current Change at other points.

2024 CURRENT TABLE
THE NARROWS
40°36.36'N, 74°02.29'W

	Daylight Saving Time								Daylight Saving Time					

		JULY								AUGUST				
DAY OF MONTH	DAY OF WEEK	CURRENT TURNS TO						DAY OF MONTH	DAY OF WEEK	CURRENT TURNS TO				
		NORTH Flood Starts			SOUTH Ebb Starts					NORTH Flood Starts			SOUTH Ebb Starts		
		a.m.	p.m.	Kts.	a.m.	p.m.	Kts.			a.m.	p.m.	Kts.	a.m.	p.m.	Kts.
1	M	1:12	1:00	p1.6	6:18	6:54	a1.9	1	T	3:00	2:24	p1.5	7:48	8:24	a2.0
2	T	2:12	1:54	p1.6	7:12	7:48	a2.0	2	F	3:48	3:18	p1.5	8:42	9:12	a2.0
3	W	3:06	2:42	p1.6	8:06	8:42	a2.0	3	S	4:36	4:06	p1.5	9:36	9:54	a1.9
4	T	4:07	3:30	p1.5	8:54	9:24	a2.0	4	S	5:25	4:54	p1.4	10:24	10:36	a1.8
5	F	4:54	4:18	p1.4	9:42	10:12	a1.9	5	M	6:00	5:42	1.3	11:06	11:18	p1.8
6	S	5:42	5:06	p1.3	10:30	10:54	a1.8	6	T	6:36	6:24	1.2	11:54	...	1.6
7	S	6:24	5:54	p1.2	11:18	11:36	a1.7	7	W	7:12	7:06	p1.2	12:01	12:36	a1.8
8	M	7:06	6:36	p1.2	...	12:12	1.6	8	T	7:48	7:48	p1.2	12:42	1:12	a1.9
9	T	7:42	7:24	p1.2	12:24	1:00	a1.7	9	F	8:24	8:36	a1.2	1:18	1:54	a1.9
10	W	8:24	8:12	p1.1	1:06	1:48	a1.8	10	S	9:06	9:24	a1.3	2:00	2:36	a1.9
11	T	9:06	9:06	p1.1	1:54	2:36	a1.8	11	S	9:48	10:24	a1.4	2:42	3:24	a1.9
12	F	9:54	10:06	1.0	2:42	3:24	a1.8	12	M	10:36	11:24	a1.4	3:30	4:12	a1.8
13	S	10:42	11:06	a1.1	3:30	4:18	a1.7	13	T	11:30	...	1.4	4:24	5:12	a1.7
14	S	11:30	...	1.1	4:24	5:12	a1.7	14	W	12:24	12:24	p1.4	5:24	6:06	a1.6
15	M	12:06	12:18	p1.2	5:18	6:06	a1.7	15	T	1:30	1:18	p1.4	6:30	7:06	a1.6
16	T	1:06	1:00	p1.3	6:12	6:54	a1.7	16	F	2:24	2:12	p1.3	7:30	8:00	1.6
17	W	2:06	1:48	p1.3	7:06	7:48	a1.7	17	S	3:24	3:06	p1.3	8:24	8:54	1.6
18	T	3:00	2:36	p1.3	8:00	8:30	a1.7	18	S	4:12	4:00	p1.4	9:18	9:42	1.6
19	F	3:54	3:30	p1.4	8:48	9:18	a1.6	19	M	5:00	5:00	p1.4	10:00	10:30	a1.7
20	S	4:42	4:18	p1.4	9:36	10:00	1.6	20	T	5:48	5:54	p1.4	10:48	11:18	1.7
21	S	5:36	5:12	p1.5	10:24	10:48	1.6	21	W	6:30	6:48	1.3	11:30	...	1.8
22	M	6:18	6:06	p1.5	11:12	11:36	1.7	22	T	7:06	7:36	a1.3	12:06	12:18	p1.8
23	T	7:00	7:00	p1.5	...	12:01	1.7	23	F	7:48	8:30	a1.4	12:54	1:06	p1.8
24	W	7:42	7:54	p1.5	12:24	12:48	p1.8	24	S	8:30	9:24	a1.4	1:42	2:00	1.7
25	T	8:24	8:48	1.4	1:18	1:36	1.8	25	S	9:18	10:30	a1.4	2:30	3:00	a1.7
26	F	9:06	9:48	a1.5	2:06	2:30	1.8	26	M	10:12	11:36	a1.4	3:24	4:00	a1.7
27	S	9:54	10:48	a1.5	3:00	3:30	a1.8	27	T	11:12	...	1.3	4:24	5:06	a1.7
28	S	10:48	11:54	a1.5	3:54	4:30	a1.8	28	W	12:42	12:12	p1.4	5:30	6:12	a1.7
29	M	11:42	...	1.5	4:54	5:30	a1.8	29	T	1:48	1:12	p1.4	6:36	7:12	a1.9
30	T	12:54	12:36	p1.5	5:54	6:30	a1.8	30	F	2:42	2:12	p1.5	7:36	8:06	a1.9
31	W	2:00	1:30	p1.5	6:48	7:30	a1.9	31	S	3:30	3:06	1.5	8:36	9:00	a2.0

The Kts. (knots) columns show the **maximum** predicted velocities of the stronger one of the Flood Currents and the stronger one of the Ebb Currents for each day.

The letter "a" means the velocity shown should occur **after** the **a.m.** Current Change. The letter "p" means the velocity shown should occur **after** the **p.m.** Current Change (even if next morning). No "a" or "p" means a.m. and p.m. velocities are the same for that day.

Avg. Max. Velocity: Flood 1.4 Kts., Ebb 1.9 Kts.

Max. Flood 2 hrs. 45 min. after Flood Starts, ±30 min.

Max. Ebb 3 hrs. 25 min. after Ebb Starts, ±25 min.

See pp. 22-29 for Current Change at other points.

2024 CURRENT TABLE
THE NARROWS
40°36.36'N, 74°02.29'W

Daylight Saving Time   **Daylight Saving Time**

SEPTEMBER   OCTOBER

DAY OF MONTH	DAY OF WEEK	NORTH Flood Starts a.m.	**p.m.**	Kts.	SOUTH Ebb Starts a.m.	**p.m.**	Kts.	DAY OF MONTH	DAY OF WEEK	NORTH Flood Starts a.m.	**p.m.**	Kts.	SOUTH Ebb Starts a.m.	**p.m.**	Kts.
1	S	4:12	**3:54**	1.5	9:24	**9:42**	1.9	1	T	4:18	**4:30**	a1.7	9:48	**10:00**	p2.0
2	M	4:54	**4:42**	a1.6	10:12	**10:24**	1.9	2	W	4:54	**5:12**	a1.6	10:30	**10:36**	p1.9
3	T	5:30	**5:24**	a1.5	10:48	**11:00**	p1.9	3	T	5:24	**5:54**	a1.4	11:00	**11:06**	p1.9
4	W	6:01	**6:06**	a1.4	11:30	**11:36**	p1.9	4	F	5:55	**6:30**	a1.4	11:36	**11:36**	p1.9
5	T	6:36	**6:48**	a1.3	...	**12:06**	1.7	5	S	6:30	**7:06**	a1.6	...	**12:06**	1.7
6	F	7:06	**7:24**	a1.4	12:12	**12:42**	a1.9	6	S	7:06	**7:48**	a1.7	12:12	**12:42**	a2.0
7	S	7:42	**8:06**	a1.5	12:42	**1:18**	a2.0	7	M	7:48	**8:30**	a1.8	12:48	**1:24**	a2.0
8	S	8:18	**8:54**	a1.6	1:18	**1:54**	a2.0	8	T	8:30	**9:24**	a1.8	1:30	**2:06**	a2.0
9	M	9:06	**9:48**	a1.7	2:00	**2:42**	a2.0	9	W	9:24	**10:24**	a1.8	2:30	**3:00**	1.9
10	T	9:54	**10:48**	a1.7	2:48	**3:30**	a1.9	10	T	10:24	**11:24**	a1.7	3:30	**4:00**	1.8
11	W	10:54	**11:54**	a1.6	3:48	**4:30**	a1.8	11	F	11:30	**...**	1.5	4:36	**5:00**	p1.8
12	T	11:54	**...**	1.5	5:00	**5:30**	a1.7	12	S	12:24	**12:30**	p1.4	5:42	**6:06**	p1.8
13	F	12:54	**12:54**	p1.4	6:06	**6:30**	p1.7	13	S	1:18	**1:30**	p1.4	6:48	**7:06**	p1.9
14	S	1:54	**1:54**	p1.4	7:12	**7:30**	1.7	14	M	2:12	**2:30**	1.4	7:42	**8:06**	p1.9
15	S	2:48	**2:48**	p1.3	8:06	**8:30**	1.7	15	T	3:00	**3:30**	a1.4	8:30	**8:54**	1.8
16	M	3:36	**3:48**	p1.4	8:54	**9:18**	1.7	16	W	3:48	**4:24**	a1.4	9:12	**9:42**	1.8
17	T	4:24	**4:42**	p1.4	9:36	**10:06**	a1.8	17	T	4:30	**5:18**	a1.4	9:54	**10:24**	a1.8
18	W	5:12	**5:36**	1.3	10:24	**10:54**	a1.8	18	F	5:06	**6:18**	a1.4	10:42	**11:06**	a1.8
19	T	5:48	**6:30**	a1.3	11:06	**11:36**	a1.8	19	S	5:48	**7:06**	a1.4	11:24	**11:48**	1.7
20	F	6:30	**7:24**	a1.4	11:54	**...**	1.8	20	S	6:30	**7:54**	a1.3	...	**12:12**	1.6
21	S	7:06	**8:12**	a1.4	12:18	**12:42**	1.7	21	M	7:18	**8:48**	a1.3	12:36	**1:06**	a1.7
22	S	7:54	**9:06**	a1.4	1:06	**1:30**	a1.7	22	T	8:12	**9:48**	a1.2	1:30	**2:00**	a1.6
23	M	8:42	**10:12**	a1.3	1:54	**2:30**	a1.7	23	W	9:12	**10:54**	a1.1	2:30	**3:00**	a1.5
24	T	9:42	**11:18**	a1.2	2:54	**3:30**	a1.6	24	T	10:18	**11:54**	1.0	3:42	**4:06**	a1.5
25	W	10:48	**...**	1.1	4:00	**4:36**	a1.6	25	F	11:30	**...**	1.1	4:54	**5:12**	p1.7
26	T	12:24	**-A-**	0.9	5:12	**5:42**	1.6	26	S	12:48	**12:36**	1.2	6:00	**6:18**	p1.9
27	F	1:24	**1:00**	p1.3	6:18	**6:48**	1.8	27	S	1:42	**1:36**	a1.4	7:06	**7:18**	p2.1
28	S	2:18	**2:00**	1.4	7:24	**7:48**	p2.0	28	M	2:24	**2:36**	a1.6	8:00	**8:12**	p2.2
29	S	3:00	**2:54**	a1.6	8:18	**8:36**	p2.1	29	T	3:06	**3:24**	a1.6	8:48	**8:54**	p2.1
30	M	3:42	**3:42**	a1.7	9:06	**9:18**	p2.1	30	W	3:42	**4:12**	a1.6	9:24	**9:30**	p2.0
								31	T	4:12	**4:54**	a1.5	10:00	**10:06**	p1.8

A also at 11:54 a.m. (1.2)

The Kts. (knots) columns show the **maximum** predicted velocities of the stronger one of the Flood Currents and the stronger one of the Ebb Currents for each day.

The letter "a" means the velocity shown should occur **after** the **a.m.** Current Change. The letter "p" means the velocity shown should occur **after** the **p.m.** Current Change (even if next morning). No "a" or "p" means a.m. and p.m. velocities are the same for that day.

Avg. Max. Velocity: Flood 1.4 Kts., Ebb 1.9 Kts.

Max. Flood 2 hrs. 45 min. after Flood Starts, ±30 min.

Max. Ebb 3 hrs. 25 min. after Ebb Starts, ±25 min.

At **The Battery, Desbrosses St., & Chelsea Dock** Current turns 1 1/2 hrs. after the Narrows. At **42nd St.** and the **George Washington Bridge**, the Current turns 1 3/4 hrs. after the Narrows. See pp. 22-29 for Current Change at other points.

2024 CURRENT TABLE
THE NARROWS
40°36.36'N, 74°02.29'W

*Standard Time starts Nov. 3 at 2 a.m. Standard Time

NOVEMBER								DECEMBER					
DAY OF MONTH	DAY OF WEEK	CURRENT TURNS TO						DAY OF MONTH	DAY OF WEEK	CURRENT TURNS TO			
		NORTH Flood Starts			SOUTH Ebb Starts					NORTH Flood Starts			SOUTH Ebb Starts
		a.m.	p.m.	Kts.	a.m.	p.m.	Kts.			a.m.	p.m.	Kts.	a.m.	p.m.	Kts.
1	F	4:48	5:36	a1.4	10:36	10:36	p1.8	1	S	3:48	5:00	a1.5	9:36	9:42	p1.7
2	S	5:18	6:12	a1.5	11:06	11:06	p1.8	2	M	4:30	5:36	a1.6	10:12	10:24	p1.8
3	S	*4:54	*5:48	a1.6	*10:42	*10:42	p1.9	3	T	5:12	6:18	a1.7	10:54	11:12	1.8
4	M	5:37	6:30	a1.8	11:18	11:24	p1.9	4	W	6:01	7:00	a1.8	11:36	...	1.9
5	T	6:18	7:12	a1.8	...	12:01	1.9	5	T	6:54	7:48	a1.8	12:01	12:24	p2.0
6	W	7:06	8:06	a1.9	12:18	12:42	2.0	6	F	7:48	8:36	a1.7	12:54	1:18	p2.0
7	T	8:06	9:00	a1.8	1:12	1:36	p2.0	7	S	8:48	9:30	a1.7	1:54	2:18	p2.0
8	F	9:06	10:00	a1.7	2:12	2:36	p2.0	8	S	9:48	10:24	p1.6	2:54	3:18	p2.0
9	S	10:06	10:54	a1.6	3:18	3:36	p1.9	9	M	10:54	11:18	p1.6	3:54	4:18	p1.9
10	S	11:12	11:48	1.5	4:18	4:42	p1.9	10	T	11:54	...	1.3	4:48	5:18	p2.0
11	M	...	12:12	1.4	5:18	5:42	p2.0	11	W	12:06	12:54	a1.6	5:48	6:12	p2.0
12	T	12:36	1:12	a1.6	6:12	6:36	1.9	12	T	12:54	1:54	a1.6	6:42	7:00	p2.0
13	W	1:24	2:12	a1.6	7:06	7:30	1.9	13	F	1:36	2:54	a1.6	7:30	7:48	p1.9
14	T	2:06	3:06	a1.5	7:48	8:12	p1.9	14	S	2:24	3:48	a1.5	8:18	8:30	p1.9
15	F	2:48	4:06	a1.5	8:36	8:54	1.8	15	S	3:06	4:42	a1.4	9:00	9:18	p1.8
16	S	3:30	5:00	a1.4	9:18	9:36	p1.8	16	M	3:54	5:30	a1.3	9:48	10:06	p1.7
17	S	4:18	5:48	a1.4	10:06	10:24	p1.7	17	T	4:48	6:12	a1.2	10:30	11:00	1.6
18	M	5:06	6:36	a1.3	10:48	11:12	p1.7	18	W	5:36	6:54	a1.2	11:18	11:54	1.6
19	T	5:54	7:24	a1.2	11:42	...	1.5	19	T	6:24	7:42	a1.1	...	12:12	1.6
20	W	6:48	8:18	a1.1	12:06	12:36	a1.6	20	F	7:18	8:30	a1.1	12:48	1:00	p1.6
21	T	7:48	9:12	a1.0	1:12	1:30	1.5	21	S	8:18	9:24	1.0	1:48	2:00	p1.7
22	F	8:54	10:12	p1.0	2:18	2:36	p1.5	22	S	9:24	10:12	p1.0	2:48	3:00	p1.7
23	S	10:00	11:06	p1.2	3:24	3:42	p1.7	23	M	10:24	11:00	p1.1	3:48	4:00	p1.8
24	S	11:06	11:54	p1.3	4:30	4:42	p1.9	24	T	11:30	11:48	p1.2	4:48	4:54	p1.9
25	M	...	12:06	1.1	5:30	5:42	p2.0	25	W	...	12:30	0.8	5:42	5:48	p1.9
26	T	12:42	1:06	a1.4	6:30	6:36	p2.1	26	T	12:30	1:30	a1.2	6:36	6:42	p1.8
27	W	1:18	2:00	a1.5	7:12	7:18	p2.0	27	F	1:12	2:24	a1.2	7:18	7:24	p1.7
28	T	2:00	2:54	a1.4	7:54	8:00	1.8	28	S	1:54	3:12	a1.3	8:00	8:00	p1.6
29	F	2:36	3:36	a1.4	8:30	8:30	p1.7	29	S	2:36	4:00	a1.3	8:36	8:36	p1.6
30	S	3:12	4:18	a1.4	9:06	9:06	p1.7	30	M	3:24	4:42	a1.4	9:12	9:18	p1.6
								31	T	4:06	5:18	a1.5	9:48	10:06	p1.7

The Kts. (knots) columns show the **maximum** predicted velocities of the stronger one of the Flood Currents and the stronger one of the Ebb Currents for each day.

The letter "a" means the velocity shown should occur **after** the a.m. Current Change. The letter "p" means the velocity shown should occur **after** the p.m. Current Change (even if next morning). No "a" or "p" means a.m. and p.m. velocities are the same for that day.

Avg. Max. Velocity: Flood 1.4 Kts., Ebb 1.9 Kts.

Max. Flood 2 hrs. 45 min. after Flood Starts, ±30 min.

Max. Ebb 3 hrs. 25 min. after Ebb Starts, ±25 min.

See pp. 22-29 for Current Change at other points.

2024 HIGH & LOW WATER
THE BATTERY, NY HARBOR
40°42'N, 74°00.8'W

Standard Time

JANUARY

Day of Month	Day of Week	HIGH a.m.	Ht.	HIGH p.m.	Ht.	LOW a.m.	LOW p.m.
1	M	11:40	4.0	...	...	5:19	6:05
2	T	12:32	3.8	12:23	3.8	6:06	6:47
3	W	1:14	3.8	1:05	3.6	7:05	7:35
4	T	1:56	3.8	1:48	3.5	8:13	8:27
5	F	2:38	3.9	2:38	3.3	9:17	9:19
6	S	3:26	4.1	3:40	3.3	10:14	10:10
7	S	4:21	4.3	4:47	3.4	11:07	11:00
8	M	5:14	4.7	5:43	3.6	11:57	11:50
9	T	6:03	5.0	6:32	3.8	...	12:48
10	W	6:49	5.3	7:18	4.1	12:41	1:37
11	T	7:36	5.5	8:06	4.2	1:33	2:26
12	F	8:24	5.6	8:56	4.4	2:25	3:13
13	S	9:15	5.5	9:50	4.5	3:15	3:58
14	S	10:09	5.3	10:47	4.6	4:05	4:43
15	M	11:06	5.1	11:44	4.7	4:57	5:31
16	T	...	...	12:03	4.8	5:54	6:23
17	W	12:41	4.7	12:59	4.4	7:00	7:21
18	T	1:35	4.7	1:55	4.1	8:09	8:22
19	F	2:31	4.6	2:55	3.8	9:17	9:22
20	S	3:32	4.5	4:02	3.7	10:19	10:19
21	S	4:35	4.5	5:07	3.7	11:16	11:13
22	M	5:33	4.6	6:03	3.8	...	12:08
23	T	6:23	4.7	6:52	3.9	12:04	12:57
24	W	7:08	4.8	7:36	4.0	12:53	1:43
25	T	7:49	4.8	8:18	4.1	1:39	2:26
26	F	8:28	4.7	8:59	4.1	2:22	3:05
27	S	9:06	4.6	9:40	4.1	3:02	3:41
28	S	9:43	4.4	10:21	4.0	3:40	4:15
29	M	10:19	4.2	11:01	4.0	4:15	4:46
30	T	10:54	4.0	11:40	3.9	4:50	5:14
31	W	11:30	3.8	...	...	5:25	5:41

Standard Time

FEBRUARY

Day of Month	Day of Week	HIGH a.m.	Ht.	HIGH p.m.	Ht.	LOW a.m.	LOW p.m.
1	T	12:17	3.9	12:09	3.6	6:08	6:13
2	F	12:53	3.9	12:53	3.4	7:09	6:58
3	S	1:33	4.0	1:44	3.2	8:26	8:08
4	S	2:24	4.1	2:47	3.2	9:36	9:24
5	M	3:27	4.2	4:05	3.2	10:37	10:29
6	T	4:38	4.5	5:16	3.5	11:32	11:28
7	W	5:40	4.9	6:12	3.9	...	12:24
8	T	6:33	5.3	7:02	4.3	12:23	1:15
9	F	7:23	5.5	7:50	4.6	1:18	2:03
10	S	8:11	5.6	8:39	4.9	2:11	2:50
11	S	9:01	5.6	9:30	5.1	3:03	3:35
12	M	9:52	5.4	10:23	5.1	3:52	4:19
13	T	10:46	5.1	11:18	5.0	4:43	5:04
14	W	11:42	4.7	...	...	5:36	5:53
15	T	12:13	4.9	12:39	4.3	6:37	6:48
16	F	1:08	4.7	1:36	4.0	7:45	7:51
17	S	2:04	4.5	2:36	3.7	8:54	8:56
18	S	3:05	4.3	3:42	3.5	9:59	9:59
19	M	4:12	4.2	4:50	3.5	10:57	10:56
20	T	5:16	4.3	5:47	3.7	11:48	11:47
21	W	6:08	4.4	6:34	3.9	...	12:35
22	T	6:51	4.6	7:16	4.1	12:34	1:18
23	F	7:30	4.7	7:55	4.3	1:19	1:58
24	S	8:06	4.7	8:32	4.4	2:01	2:35
25	S	8:41	4.6	9:07	4.4	2:41	3:09
26	M	9:13	4.4	9:41	4.4	3:18	3:40
27	T	9:44	4.2	10:13	4.3	3:52	4:08
28	W	10:14	4.0	10:43	4.3	4:25	4:33
29	T	10:46	3.8	11:15	4.2	4:57	4:56

Dates when Ht. of **Low** Water is below Mean Lower Low with Ht. of lowest given for each period and Date of lowest in ( ):

9th–18th: -1.0' (12th–14th)
23rd–28th: -0.4' (25th, 26th)

7th–15th: -1.3' (11th)
22nd–26th: -0.3' (24th, 25th)

Average Rise and Fall 4.5 ft.

When a high tide exceeds avg. ht., the *following* low tide will be lower than avg.

2024 HIGH & LOW WATER
THE BATTERY, NY HARBOR
40°42'N, 74°00.8'W

*Daylight Time starts March 10 at 2 a.m.　　　　**Daylight Saving Time**

D A Y O F M O N T H	D A Y O F W E E K	MARCH HIGH a.m.	Ht.	p.m.	Ht.	LOW a.m.	p.m.	D A Y O F M O N T H	D A Y O F W E E K	APRIL HIGH a.m.	Ht.	p.m.	Ht.	LOW a.m.	p.m.
1	F	11:26	3.6	**11:54**	4.2	5:32	**5:24**	1	M	1:12	4.5	**1:58**	3.6	8:14	**7:48**
2	S	...	...	**12:14**	3.5	6:21	**6:04**	2	T	2:17	4.5	**3:04**	3.7	9:34	**9:32**
3	S	12:42	4.2	**1:10**	3.3	7:39	**7:08**	3	W	3:27	4.6	**4:16**	3.9	10:40	**10:51**
4	M	1:41	4.2	**2:16**	3.3	9:01	**8:48**	4	T	4:45	4.7	**5:28**	4.3	11:38	**11:54**
5	T	2:49	4.3	**3:35**	3.4	10:08	**10:07**	5	F	5:54	4.9	**6:29**	4.8	...	**12:30**
6	W	4:09	4.6	**4:52**	3.8	11:06	**11:10**	6	S	6:53	5.2	**7:20**	5.3	12:51	**1:19**
7	T	5:19	4.9	**5:52**	4.3	11:58	...	7	S	7:44	5.4	**8:08**	5.7	1:46	**2:07**
8	F	6:15	5.3	**6:43**	4.8	12:08	**12:48**	8	M	8:33	5.5	**8:54**	6.0	2:39	**2:55**
9	S	7:05	5.5	**7:30**	5.2	1:03	**1:37**	9	T	9:21	5.4	**9:41**	6.0	3:31	**3:42**
10	S	*8:53	5.6	***9:18**	5.5	1:56	***3:23**	10	W	10:12	5.2	**10:30**	5.8	4:20	**4:27**
11	M	9:42	5.6	**10:06**	5.6	3:48	**4:09**	11	T	11:06	4.9	**11:21**	5.5	5:09	**5:12**
12	T	10:32	5.3	**10:56**	5.6	4:37	**4:53**	12	F	...	...	**12:03**	4.5	5:58	**5:58**
13	W	11:25	5.0	**11:49**	5.3	5:26	**5:37**	13	S	12:16	5.1	**1:02**	4.3	6:52	**6:50**
14	T	...	...	**12:22**	4.6	6:17	**6:24**	14	S	1:14	4.8	**2:00**	4.1	7:53	**7:52**
15	F	12:44	5.1	**1:20**	4.3	7:14	**7:17**	15	M	2:11	4.5	**2:57**	3.9	8:59	**9:02**
16	S	1:40	4.7	**2:18**	4.0	8:19	**8:21**	16	T	3:09	4.2	**3:54**	3.9	10:02	**10:09**
17	S	2:37	4.4	**3:17**	3.7	9:29	**9:31**	17	W	4:08	4.1	**4:53**	4.0	10:57	**11:07**
18	M	3:38	4.2	**4:21**	3.6	10:34	**10:37**	18	T	5:10	4.1	**5:48**	4.2	11:44	**11:58**
19	T	4:44	4.1	**5:26**	3.7	11:31	**11:35**	19	F	6:05	4.2	**6:36**	4.5	...	**12:26**
20	W	5:50	4.1	**6:23**	3.9	...	**12:21**	20	S	6:52	4.3	**7:16**	4.7	12:43	**1:05**
21	T	6:43	4.3	**7:09**	4.2	12:25	**1:05**	21	S	7:31	4.4	**7:52**	5.0	1:27	**1:43**
22	F	7:26	4.4	**7:49**	4.4	1:12	**1:45**	22	M	8:08	4.4	**8:25**	5.1	2:09	**2:19**
23	S	8:04	4.6	**8:26**	4.7	1:55	**2:23**	23	T	8:42	4.4	**8:56**	5.2	2:50	**2:55**
24	S	8:39	4.6	**9:00**	4.8	2:37	**2:59**	24	W	9:15	4.3	**9:24**	5.2	3:30	**3:30**
25	M	9:12	4.5	**9:32**	4.9	3:17	**3:33**	25	T	9:47	4.2	**9:52**	5.2	4:09	**4:03**
26	T	9:44	4.4	**10:01**	4.8	3:54	**4:05**	26	F	10:22	4.1	**10:24**	5.1	4:46	**4:35**
27	W	10:13	4.2	**10:28**	4.8	4:30	**4:34**	27	S	11:02	4.0	**11:05**	5.0	5:24	**5:08**
28	T	10:43	4.1	**10:55**	4.7	5:03	**5:00**	28	S	11:53	3.9	**11:58**	4.9	6:05	**5:46**
29	F	11:17	3.9	**11:30**	4.7	5:37	**5:25**	29	M	...	...	**12:54**	3.8	6:55	**6:36**
30	S	...	...	**12:01**	3.7	6:14	**5:57**	30	T	1:01	4.8	**1:56**	3.9	8:00	**7:52**
31	S	12:15	4.6	**12:55**	3.6	7:02	**6:40**								

Dates when Ht. of **Low** Water is below Mean Lower Low with Ht. of lowest given for each period and Date of lowest in ( ):

　　7th–14th: -1.2' (10th, 11th)　　　　　　5th–12th: -0.9' (8th–10th)

Average Rise and Fall 4.5 ft.

When a high tide exceeds avg. ht., the *following* low tide will be lower than avg.

2024 HIGH & LOW WATER
THE BATTERY, NY HARBOR
40°42'N, 74°00.8'W

Daylight Saving Time   **Daylight Saving Time**

DAY OF MONTH	DAY OF WEEK	MAY HIGH a.m.	Ht.	p.m.	Ht.	LOW a.m.	p.m.	DAY OF MONTH	DAY OF WEEK	JUNE HIGH a.m.	Ht.	p.m.	Ht.	LOW a.m.	p.m.
1	W	2:07	4.8	2:57	4.1	9:09	9:23	1	S	3:58	4.8	4:41	5.2	10:38	11:21
2	T	3:12	4.8	4:00	4.4	10:12	10:35	2	S	5:02	4.7	5:40	5.5	11:31	...
3	F	4:20	4.8	5:05	4.8	11:08	11:38	3	M	6:05	4.7	6:35	5.8	12:18	12:22
4	S	5:29	4.9	6:05	5.3	...	12:01	4	T	7:03	4.8	7:25	5.9	1:12	1:12
5	S	6:28	5.0	6:57	5.7	12:35	12:49	5	W	7:55	4.8	8:12	5.9	2:06	2:03
6	M	7:22	5.1	7:45	6.0	1:29	1:38	6	T	8:46	4.8	8:58	5.8	2:57	2:54
7	T	8:12	5.2	8:31	6.1	2:22	2:27	7	F	9:37	4.7	9:45	5.6	3:47	3:43
8	W	9:02	5.1	9:18	6.0	3:14	3:16	8	S	10:30	4.5	10:34	5.4	4:34	4:30
9	T	9:53	4.9	10:05	5.8	4:04	4:04	9	S	11:24	4.4	11:26	5.1	5:20	5:14
10	F	10:48	4.7	10:56	5.5	4:52	4:50	10	M	...	...	12:19	4.3	6:05	6:00
11	S	11:45	4.5	11:51	5.1	5:40	5:36	11	T	12:19	4.8	1:11	4.3	6:51	6:48
12	S	...	...	12:43	4.3	6:29	6:25	12	W	1:10	4.6	2:00	4.3	7:40	7:45
13	M	12:48	4.8	1:39	4.2	7:24	7:21	13	T	1:58	4.4	2:45	4.3	8:30	8:48
14	T	1:43	4.5	2:32	4.1	8:23	8:27	14	F	2:43	4.2	3:30	4.4	9:19	9:48
15	W	2:36	4.3	3:22	4.1	9:20	9:32	15	S	3:29	4.0	4:16	4.5	10:06	10:44
16	T	3:27	4.2	4:13	4.2	10:13	10:31	16	S	4:20	3.9	5:03	4.7	10:51	11:34
17	F	4:21	4.0	5:05	4.4	10:59	11:23	17	M	5:16	3.8	5:51	4.8	11:33	...
18	S	5:16	4.0	5:54	4.6	11:41	...	18	T	6:11	3.8	6:34	5.1	12:22	12:16
19	S	6:08	4.1	6:37	4.9	12:10	12:20	19	W	6:59	4.0	7:13	5.3	1:08	12:58
20	M	6:53	4.1	7:15	5.1	12:55	12:59	20	T	7:42	4.1	7:51	5.5	1:55	1:43
21	T	7:34	4.2	7:49	5.3	1:39	1:38	21	F	8:24	4.2	8:30	5.6	2:42	2:30
22	W	8:11	4.2	8:21	5.4	2:23	2:17	22	S	9:06	4.2	9:12	5.7	3:28	3:18
23	T	8:48	4.2	8:53	5.4	3:06	2:57	23	S	9:52	4.3	9:59	5.7	4:13	4:05
24	F	9:25	4.2	9:27	5.4	3:48	3:38	24	M	10:44	4.4	10:51	5.6	4:57	4:53
25	S	10:07	4.1	10:08	5.4	4:30	4:18	25	T	11:40	4.5	11:48	5.4	5:41	5:42
26	S	10:55	4.1	10:57	5.3	5:12	5:00	26	W	...	...	12:38	4.7	6:28	6:38
27	M	11:51	4.1	11:54	5.2	5:56	5:45	27	T	12:47	5.2	1:34	4.9	7:18	7:44
28	T	...	...	12:52	4.2	6:46	6:41	28	F	1:44	5.1	2:27	5.1	8:14	8:54
29	W	12:57	5.1	1:50	4.4	7:42	7:53	29	S	2:40	4.8	3:21	5.3	9:12	10:02
30	T	1:58	5.0	2:45	4.6	8:43	9:10	30	S	3:38	4.6	4:17	5.4	10:10	11:04
31	F	2:57	4.9	3:41	4.9	9:42	10:19								

Dates when Ht. of **Low** Water is below Mean Lower Low with Ht. of lowest given for each period and Date of lowest in ( ):

4th–11th: -0.7' (8th)   3rd–8th: -0.3' (5th–7th)
24th–25th: -0.2'

Average Rise and Fall 4.5 ft.

When a high tide exceeds avg. ht., the *following* low tide will be lower than avg.

2024 HIGH & LOW WATER
THE BATTERY, NY HARBOR
40°42'N, 74°00.8'W

Daylight Saving Time　　　　Daylight Saving Time

DAY OF MONTH	DAY OF WEEK	JULY HIGH a.m.	Ht.	JULY HIGH p.m.	Ht.	JULY LOW a.m.	JULY LOW p.m.	DAY OF MONTH	DAY OF WEEK	AUGUST HIGH a.m.	Ht.	AUGUST HIGH p.m.	Ht.	AUGUST LOW a.m.	AUGUST LOW p.m.
1	M	4:41	4.5	5:17	5.5	11:06	...	1	T	6:35	4.3	6:56	5.4	12:42	12:37
2	T	5:46	4.4	6:16	5.6	12:02	12:01	2	F	7:28	4.5	7:44	5.4	1:33	1:28
3	W	6:47	4.4	7:08	5.7	12:57	12:52	3	S	8:16	4.6	8:28	5.4	2:21	2:17
4	T	7:42	4.5	7:57	5.7	1:50	1:44	4	S	9:01	4.7	9:09	5.4	3:07	3:04
5	F	8:31	4.6	8:43	5.6	2:41	2:35	5	M	9:43	4.7	9:49	5.3	3:48	3:48
6	S	9:20	4.6	9:28	5.5	3:29	3:24	6	T	10:26	4.8	10:28	5.1	4:26	4:28
7	S	10:09	4.5	10:13	5.3	4:14	4:09	7	W	11:08	4.7	11:07	4.8	5:01	5:06
8	M	10:58	4.5	10:59	5.1	4:56	4:52	8	T	11:51	4.7	11:47	4.6	5:34	5:44
9	T	11:47	4.5	11:45	4.8	5:35	5:33	9	F	...	...	12:32	4.7	6:04	6:22
10	W	...	...	12:35	4.4	6:14	6:15	10	S	12:27	4.3	1:12	4.6	6:33	7:06
11	T	12:31	4.6	1:20	4.5	6:52	7:02	11	S	1:08	4.1	1:50	4.6	7:03	8:03
12	F	1:15	4.3	2:02	4.5	7:32	7:57	12	M	1:50	3.9	2:28	4.6	7:42	9:12
13	S	1:57	4.1	2:42	4.5	8:15	8:59	13	T	2:37	3.8	3:11	4.7	8:43	10:18
14	S	2:38	3.9	3:23	4.6	9:03	10:00	14	W	3:32	3.7	4:06	4.8	9:57	11:17
15	M	3:24	3.8	4:07	4.7	9:53	10:56	15	T	4:42	3.7	5:11	5.0	11:03	...
16	T	4:19	3.7	4:58	4.8	10:45	11:48	16	F	5:53	3.9	6:13	5.3	12:10	12:01
17	W	5:25	3.7	5:51	5.0	11:35	...	17	S	6:50	4.3	7:06	5.7	1:01	12:56
18	T	6:25	3.8	6:41	5.3	12:38	12:26	18	S	7:39	4.7	7:55	5.9	1:50	1:50
19	F	7:15	4.1	7:27	5.6	1:28	1:16	19	M	8:25	5.1	8:42	6.1	2:37	2:44
20	S	8:01	4.3	8:12	5.8	2:17	2:08	20	T	9:12	5.4	9:30	6.1	3:24	3:36
21	S	8:47	4.5	8:59	5.9	3:05	3:01	21	W	10:01	5.6	10:20	5.9	4:09	4:27
22	M	9:34	4.8	9:47	5.9	3:51	3:52	22	T	10:53	5.7	11:14	5.7	4:52	5:17
23	T	10:25	4.9	10:39	5.8	4:35	4:42	23	F	11:48	5.8	...	...	5:37	6:10
24	W	11:19	5.1	11:34	5.6	5:19	5:32	24	S	12:11	5.3	12:45	5.7	6:24	7:09
25	T	...	...	12:16	5.3	6:03	6:26	25	S	1:10	5.0	1:41	5.6	7:16	8:16
26	F	12:31	5.3	1:11	5.4	6:51	7:28	26	M	2:09	4.7	2:38	5.4	8:18	9:25
27	S	1:28	5.1	2:05	5.4	7:45	8:36	27	T	3:08	4.4	3:37	5.2	9:25	10:31
28	S	2:24	4.8	2:59	5.4	8:44	9:44	28	W	4:12	4.3	4:41	5.1	10:29	11:31
29	M	3:21	4.5	3:56	5.3	9:45	10:48	29	T	5:19	4.2	5:46	5.1	11:29	...
30	T	4:25	4.3	4:58	5.3	10:46	11:47	30	F	6:21	4.4	6:41	5.2	12:24	12:22
31	W	5:32	4.2	6:01	5.3	11:43	...	31	S	7:12	4.6	7:27	5.3	1:12	1:11

Dates when Ht. of **Low** Water is below Mean Lower Low with Ht. of lowest given for each period and Date of lowest in ( ):

22nd–26th: -0.5' (24th)　　　　19th–24th: -0.6' (21st, 22nd)

Average Rise and Fall 4.5 ft.

When a high tide exceeds avg. ht., the *following* low tide will be lower than avg.

2024 HIGH & LOW WATER
THE BATTERY, NY HARBOR
40°42'N, 74°00.8'W

Daylight Saving Time   **Daylight Saving Time**

DAY OF MONTH	DAY OF WEEK	SEPTEMBER						DAY OF MONTH	DAY OF WEEK	OCTOBER					
		HIGH			LOW					HIGH			LOW		
		a.m.	Ht.	p.m.	Ht.	a.m.	p.m.			a.m.	Ht.	p.m.	Ht.	a.m.	p.m.
1	S	7:56	4.8	8:08	5.3	1:56	1:58	1	T	8:07	5.2	8:18	5.1	2:03	2:17
2	M	8:35	4.9	8:45	5.3	2:38	2:42	2	W	8:42	5.3	8:52	5.0	2:40	2:58
3	T	9:13	5.1	9:21	5.2	3:16	3:24	3	T	9:15	5.3	9:24	4.8	3:14	3:37
4	W	9:51	5.1	9:56	5.0	3:52	4:03	4	F	9:47	5.3	9:56	4.6	3:47	4:15
5	T	10:26	5.1	10:29	4.8	4:25	4:40	5	S	10:14	5.2	10:27	4.4	4:17	4:50
6	F	11:01	5.0	11:03	4.5	4:54	5:15	6	S	10:42	5.1	11:00	4.2	4:45	5:25
7	S	11:35	4.9	11:38	4.3	5:21	5:49	7	M	11:14	5.0	11:41	4.0	5:10	6:02
8	S	...	...	12:10	4.8	5:45	6:26	8	T	11:57	4.9	...	...	5:39	6:47
9	M	12:18	4.1	12:48	4.8	6:11	7:14	9	W	12:37	3.8	12:53	4.8	6:18	7:54
10	T	1:06	3.9	1:34	4.7	6:47	8:27	10	T	1:41	3.8	1:57	4.8	7:15	9:11
11	W	2:01	3.8	2:26	4.8	7:43	9:43	11	F	2:45	3.9	3:02	4.9	8:56	10:16
12	T	3:02	3.8	3:27	4.9	9:18	10:47	12	S	3:51	4.1	4:11	5.0	10:20	11:12
13	F	4:12	3.9	4:38	5.1	10:39	11:42	13	S	4:58	4.5	5:20	5.2	11:25	...
14	S	5:25	4.2	5:47	5.3	11:42	...	14	M	5:59	5.0	6:20	5.5	12:02	12:21
15	S	6:25	4.6	6:44	5.7	12:32	12:38	15	T	6:51	5.5	7:12	5.7	12:50	1:16
16	M	7:15	5.2	7:34	6.0	1:20	1:33	16	W	7:38	6.0	8:01	5.8	1:37	2:09
17	T	8:02	5.6	8:22	6.1	2:07	2:26	17	T	8:25	6.3	8:49	5.7	2:24	3:02
18	W	8:48	6.0	9:09	6.0	2:54	3:19	18	F	9:11	6.4	9:39	5.5	3:12	3:53
19	T	9:35	6.2	9:59	5.8	3:40	4:10	19	S	10:00	6.3	10:33	5.2	3:59	4:44
20	F	10:25	6.2	10:52	5.5	4:25	5:01	20	S	10:53	6.0	11:32	4.9	4:46	5:35
21	S	11:19	6.0	11:51	5.2	5:10	5:52	21	M	11:51	5.6	...	...	5:34	6:29
22	S	...	...	12:17	5.8	5:57	6:49	22	T	12:35	4.6	12:53	5.3	6:27	7:30
23	M	12:53	4.8	1:17	5.5	6:50	7:54	23	W	1:38	4.4	1:54	5.0	7:28	8:37
24	T	1:55	4.6	2:17	5.2	7:53	9:04	24	T	2:37	4.3	2:52	4.8	8:39	9:41
25	W	2:55	4.4	3:17	5.0	9:04	10:10	25	F	3:35	4.2	3:50	4.6	9:47	10:38
26	T	3:57	4.3	4:20	4.9	10:12	11:09	26	S	4:33	4.3	4:49	4.5	10:47	11:27
27	F	5:01	4.3	5:23	4.8	11:12	...	27	S	5:28	4.5	5:44	4.5	11:39	...
28	S	6:00	4.5	6:18	4.9	12:01	12:04	28	M	6:17	4.7	6:31	4.6	12:09	12:25
29	S	6:48	4.7	7:03	5.0	12:44	12:51	29	T	6:58	5.0	7:12	4.6	12:48	1:09
30	M	7:30	5.0	7:42	5.1	1:25	1:35	30	W	7:36	5.2	7:49	4.6	1:25	1:51
								31	T	8:10	5.3	8:24	4.6	2:01	2:32

Dates when Ht. of **Low** Water is below Mean Lower Low with Ht. of lowest given for each period and Date of lowest in ( ):

    17th–21st: -0.6' (19th, 20th)   15th–20th: -0.6' (17th, 18th)

Average Rise and Fall 4.5 ft.

When a high tide exceeds avg. ht., the *following* low tide will be lower than avg.

2024 HIGH & LOW WATER
THE BATTERY, NY HARBOR
40°42'N, 74°00.8'W

*Standard Time starts Nov. 3 at 2 a.m.   Standard Time

D A Y O F M O N T H	D A Y O F W E E K	NOVEMBER HIGH a.m.	Ht.	HIGH p.m.	Ht.	LOW a.m.	LOW p.m.	D A Y O F M O N T H	D A Y O F W E E K	DECEMBER HIGH a.m.	Ht.	HIGH p.m.	Ht.	LOW a.m.	LOW p.m.
1	F	8:41	5.4	8:57	4.5	2:37	3:13	1	S	7:43	5.2	8:10	4.0	1:42	2:32
2	S	9:11	5.3	9:29	4.3	3:12	3:52	2	M	8:15	5.2	8:46	3.9	2:22	3:12
3	S	*8:38	5.2	*9:02	4.2	*2:46	*3:30	3	T	8:51	5.1	9:27	3.8	3:00	3:53
4	M	9:09	5.1	9:38	4.0	3:18	4:08	4	W	9:33	5.0	10:16	3.8	3:39	4:34
5	T	9:44	5.0	10:24	3.8	3:49	4:47	5	T	10:23	4.9	11:14	3.8	4:19	5:18
6	W	10:32	4.9	11:24	3.8	4:24	5:33	6	F	11:22	4.8	...	...	5:06	6:09
7	T	11:32	4.8	...	...	5:06	6:32	7	S	12:14	4.0	12:23	4.7	6:08	7:07
8	F	12:29	3.8	12:38	4.8	6:09	7:40	8	S	1:10	4.2	1:22	4.6	7:27	8:08
9	S	1:30	4.0	1:42	4.8	7:42	8:43	9	M	2:06	4.5	2:22	4.5	8:42	9:06
10	S	2:29	4.3	2:46	4.8	9:02	9:40	10	T	3:05	4.8	3:25	4.4	9:49	10:01
11	M	3:31	4.7	3:52	4.9	10:07	10:31	11	W	4:06	5.1	4:31	4.4	10:48	10:54
12	T	4:32	5.1	4:55	5.0	11:05	11:20	12	T	5:05	5.4	5:32	4.5	11:44	11:46
13	W	5:27	5.6	5:50	5.2	11:59	...	13	F	5:59	5.6	6:27	4.6	...	12:38
14	T	6:17	6.0	6:42	5.2	12:09	12:53	14	S	6:49	5.7	7:19	4.6	12:38	1:31
15	F	7:04	6.2	7:32	5.2	12:58	1:46	15	S	7:37	5.7	8:10	4.6	1:30	2:23
16	S	7:51	6.2	8:23	5.0	1:48	2:38	16	M	8:25	5.6	9:02	4.4	2:20	3:12
17	S	8:40	6.0	9:17	4.8	2:38	3:28	17	T	9:14	5.3	9:56	4.3	3:09	3:58
18	M	9:31	5.7	10:15	4.6	3:26	4:17	18	W	10:06	5.0	10:51	4.2	3:55	4:44
19	T	10:27	5.3	11:16	4.3	4:14	5:08	19	T	10:58	4.7	11:45	4.0	4:41	5:30
20	W	11:27	5.0	...	...	5:04	6:02	20	F	11:51	4.4	...	...	5:28	6:19
21	T	12:15	4.2	12:26	4.7	6:00	7:02	21	S	12:36	4.0	12:41	4.2	6:22	7:10
22	F	1:11	4.1	1:20	4.4	7:04	8:01	22	S	1:24	4.0	1:28	3.9	7:24	8:01
23	S	2:03	4.1	2:12	4.2	8:11	8:56	23	M	2:10	4.0	2:15	3.7	8:27	8:51
24	S	2:55	4.2	3:05	4.1	9:13	9:44	24	T	2:58	4.0	3:06	3.5	9:26	9:38
25	M	3:47	4.3	3:59	4.0	10:07	10:27	25	W	3:48	4.1	4:04	3.4	10:20	10:23
26	T	4:37	4.5	4:52	4.0	10:55	11:07	26	T	4:39	4.3	5:01	3.4	11:09	11:07
27	W	5:22	4.7	5:39	4.0	11:40	11:46	27	F	5:26	4.5	5:51	3.5	11:55	11:50
28	T	6:02	4.9	6:20	4.1	...	12:24	28	S	6:08	4.7	6:34	3.7	...	12:41
29	F	6:38	5.1	6:58	4.1	12:24	1:07	29	S	6:46	4.9	7:14	3.8	12:34	1:26
30	S	7:12	5.2	7:34	4.1	1:03	1:49	30	M	7:23	5.0	7:53	3.8	1:18	2:11
								31	T	8:01	5.1	8:30	3.9	2:03	2:54

Dates when Ht. of **Low** Water is below Mean Lower Low with Ht. of lowest given for each period and Date of lowest in ( ):

12th–18th: -0.6' (15th–17th)   10th–18th: -0.7' (14th–16th)
                                       30th–31st: -0.4'

Average Rise and Fall 4.5 ft.

When a high tide exceeds avg. ht., the *following* low tide will be lower than avg.

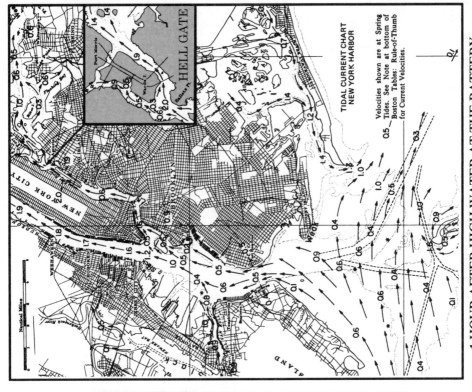

1 HOUR AFTER HIGH WATER AT THE BATTERY

NEW YORK BAY CURRENTS

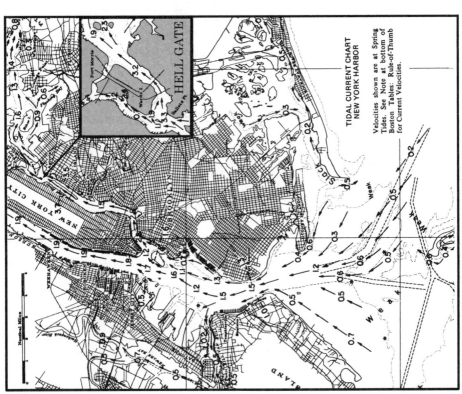

HIGH WATER AT THE BATTERY

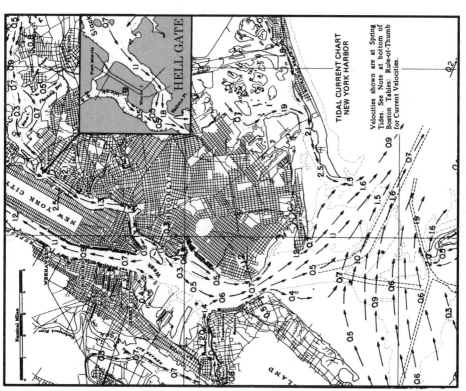

NEW YORK BAY CURRENTS

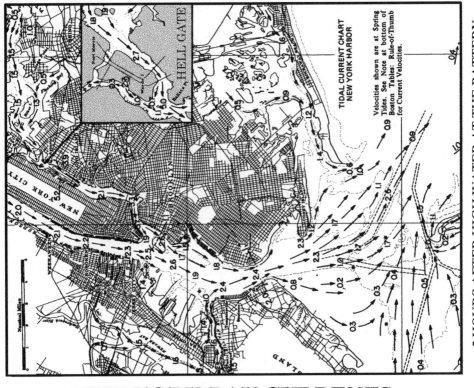

NEW YORK BAY CURRENTS

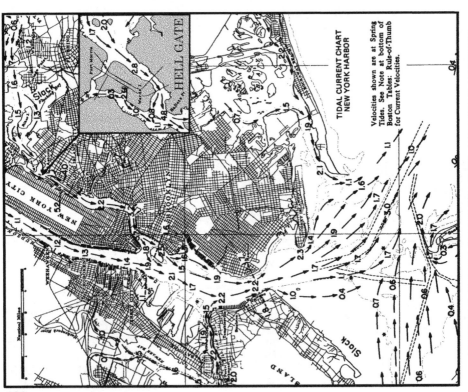

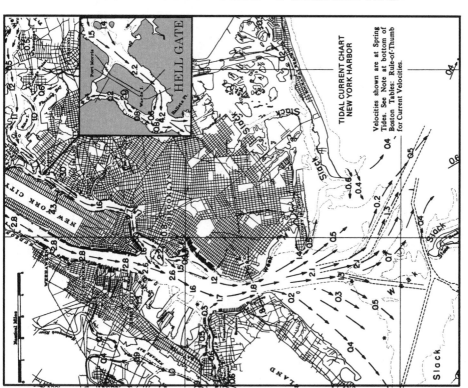

NEW YORK BAY CURRENTS

1 HOUR AFTER LOW WATER AT THE BATTERY

LOW WATER AT THE BATTERY

TIDAL CURRENT CHART
NEW YORK HARBOR

Velocities shown are at Spring
Tides. See Note at bottom of
Boston Tables: Rule-of-Thumb
for Current Velocities.

HELL GATE

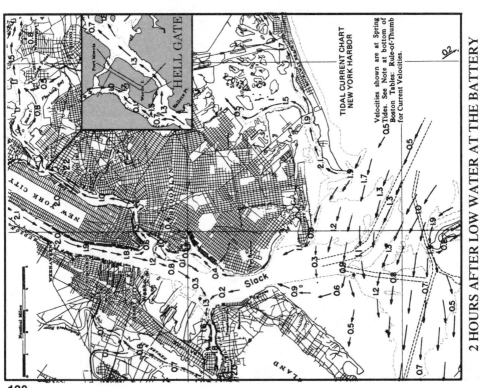

NEW YORK BAY CURRENTS

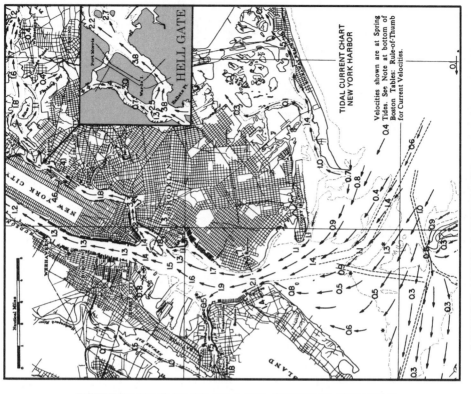

5 HOURS AFTER LOW WATER AT THE BATTERY

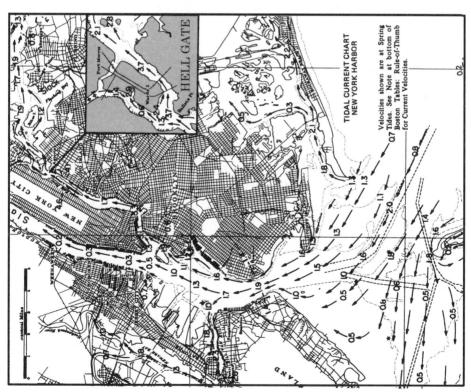

4 HOURS AFTER LOW WATER AT THE BATTERY

2024 HIGH & LOW WATER
SANDY HOOK, NJ
40°28.1'N, 74°00.6'W

		Standard Time							Standard Time				
DAY OF MONTH	**DAY OF WEEK**	**JANUARY**				**DAY OF MONTH**	**DAY OF WEEK**	**FEBRUARY**					
		HIGH		LOW				HIGH				LOW	
		a.m.	Ht.	p.m.	Ht.	a.m.	p.m.		a.m.	Ht.	p.m.	Ht.	a.m.	p.m.
1	M	11:08	4.1	**11:58**	3.8	4:50	**5:29**	1	T	11:46	3.6	...	...	5:43	**5:49**
2	T	11:52	3.9	...	...	5:36	**6:11**	2	F	12:29	4.0	**12:33**	3.4	6:39	**6:35**
3	W	12:42	3.8	**12:37**	3.7	6:31	**6:58**	3	S	1:13	4.0	**1:25**	3.3	7:50	**7:40**
4	T	1:26	3.9	**1:23**	3.6	7:36	**7:51**	4	S	2:05	4.1	**2:26**	3.2	9:01	**8:52**
5	F	2:09	4.0	**2:13**	3.5	8:41	**8:45**	5	M	3:06	4.3	**3:38**	3.3	10:04	**9:58**
6	S	2:58	4.2	**3:12**	3.4	9:41	**9:38**	6	T	4:13	4.6	**4:48**	3.6	11:01	**10:57**
7	S	3:53	4.4	**4:16**	3.5	10:35	**10:29**	7	W	5:16	5.0	**5:46**	3.9	11:54	**11:53**
8	M	4:48	4.7	**5:15**	3.7	11:26	**11:20**	8	T	6:10	5.3	**6:38**	4.3	...	**12:45**
9	T	5:40	5.1	**6:07**	3.9	...	**12:17**	9	F	7:00	5.6	**7:27**	4.7	12:48	**1:35**
10	W	6:28	5.4	**6:56**	4.1	12:11	**1:08**	10	S	7:49	5.7	**8:17**	5.0	1:43	**2:22**
11	T	7:16	5.6	**7:44**	4.3	1:03	**1:57**	11	S	8:38	5.7	**9:07**	5.1	2:35	**3:08**
12	F	8:04	5.7	**8:34**	4.5	1:56	**2:45**	12	M	9:28	5.5	**9:58**	5.2	3:25	**3:52**
13	S	8:54	5.7	**9:26**	4.6	2:47	**3:31**	13	T	10:20	5.1	**10:52**	5.1	4:15	**4:36**
14	S	9:46	5.5	**10:21**	4.7	3:38	**4:16**	14	W	11:15	4.7	**11:47**	4.9	5:07	**5:23**
15	M	10:40	5.2	**11:18**	4.7	4:29	**5:02**	15	T	...	...	**12:11**	4.3	6:05	**6:15**
16	T	11:36	4.9	...	...	5:24	**5:53**	16	F	12:41	4.8	**1:07**	4.0	7:12	**7:16**
17	W	12:14	4.8	**12:32**	4.5	6:27	**6:48**	17	S	1:36	4.5	**2:05**	3.7	8:23	**8:21**
18	T	1:09	4.7	**1:28**	4.2	7:37	**7:48**	18	S	2:35	4.3	**3:09**	3.5	9:29	**9:25**
19	F	2:04	4.7	**2:26**	3.9	8:46	**8:49**	19	M	3:39	4.2	**4:15**	3.5	10:28	**10:23**
20	S	3:02	4.6	**3:29**	3.7	9:50	**9:47**	20	T	4:42	4.3	**5:15**	3.7	11:19	**11:14**
21	S	4:03	4.6	**4:34**	3.7	10:47	**10:41**	21	W	5:36	4.4	**6:04**	3.9	...	**12:05**
22	M	5:03	4.6	**5:32**	3.8	11:39	**11:31**	22	T	6:21	4.6	**6:47**	4.1	12:02	**12:48**
23	T	5:54	4.7	**6:22**	3.9	...	**12:28**	23	F	7:01	4.7	**7:26**	4.3	12:47	**1:28**
24	W	6:39	4.8	**7:07**	4.0	12:20	**1:14**	24	S	7:37	4.7	**8:03**	4.4	1:29	**2:05**
25	T	7:21	4.8	**7:49**	4.1	1:06	**1:56**	25	S	8:12	4.6	**8:38**	4.4	2:10	**2:39**
26	F	8:00	4.8	**8:30**	4.1	1:50	**2:35**	26	M	8:45	4.5	**9:13**	4.4	2:48	**3:10**
27	S	8:37	4.7	**9:10**	4.1	2:31	**3:11**	27	T	9:18	4.3	**9:46**	4.4	3:23	**3:39**
28	S	9:14	4.5	**9:49**	4.1	3:10	**3:44**	28	W	9:50	4.1	**10:18**	4.3	3:57	**4:06**
29	M	9:49	4.3	**10:29**	4.0	3:46	**4:15**	29	T	10:24	3.9	**10:54**	4.3	4:31	**4:32**
30	T	10:26	4.1	**11:08**	4.0	4:22	**4:45**								
31	W	11:04	3.8	**11:48**	3.9	4:59	**5:15**								

Dates when Ht. of **Low** Water is below Mean Lower Low with Ht. of lowest given for each period and Date of lowest in ( ):

9th–18th: -1.1' (13th)
23rd–28th: -0.4' (26th)

7th–15th: -1.4' (11th)
23rd–26th: -0.3' (24th, 25th)

Average Rise and Fall 4.7 ft.

When a high tide exceeds avg. ht., the *following* low tide will be lower than avg.

2024 HIGH & LOW WATER
SANDY HOOK, NJ
40°28.1'N, 74°00.6'W

*Daylight Time starts March 10 at 2 a.m. **Daylight Saving Time**

DAY OF MONTH	DAY OF WEEK	MARCH HIGH a.m.	Ht.	p.m.	Ht.	LOW a.m.	p.m.	DAY OF MONTH	DAY OF WEEK	APRIL HIGH a.m.	Ht.	p.m.	Ht.	LOW a.m.	p.m.
1	F	11:06	3.7	11:36	4.2	5:09	5:01	1	M	12:57	4.6	1:37	3.6	7:40	7:22
2	S	11:56	3.5	...	...	5:57	5:41	2	T	2:01	4.6	2:42	3.7	8:58	8:57
3	S	12:26	4.3	12:53	3.4	7:06	6:45	3	W	3:08	4.7	3:50	4.0	10:07	10:17
4	M	1:25	4.3	1:57	3.4	8:26	8:16	4	T	4:20	4.8	5:00	4.3	11:07	11:23
5	T	2:31	4.4	3:10	3.5	9:35	9:34	5	F	5:27	5.1	6:02	4.9	...	12:01
6	W	3:44	4.6	4:23	3.8	10:35	10:39	6	S	6:27	5.3	6:56	5.4	12:21	12:49
7	T	4:52	5.0	5:25	4.3	11:28	11:37	7	S	7:19	5.5	7:45	5.8	1:16	1:38
8	F	5:50	5.4	6:18	4.8	...	12:19	8	M	8:09	5.6	8:32	6.1	2:10	2:26
9	S	6:41	5.6	7:07	5.3	12:33	1:08	9	T	8:57	5.5	9:19	6.1	3:03	3:13
10	S	*8:30	5.7	*8:55	5.6	1:27	*2:55	10	W	9:47	5.3	10:07	5.9	3:53	3:59
11	M	9:18	5.7	9:43	5.7	3:19	3:41	11	T	10:38	5.0	10:57	5.6	4:41	4:43
12	T	10:08	5.4	10:33	5.6	4:10	4:25	12	F	11:33	4.6	11:50	5.2	5:29	5:28
13	W	10:59	5.1	11:24	5.4	4:58	5:09	13	S	...	...	12:31	4.3	6:20	6:17
14	T	11:53	4.7	...	...	5:48	5:54	14	S	12:46	4.9	1:29	4.1	7:18	7:15
15	F	12:18	5.1	12:50	4.3	6:43	6:44	15	M	1:42	4.6	2:25	4.0	8:24	8:23
16	S	1:13	4.8	1:48	4.0	7:46	7:44	16	T	2:37	4.3	3:21	3.9	9:29	9:33
17	S	2:09	4.5	2:46	3.7	8:56	8:54	17	W	3:34	4.2	4:18	4.0	10:25	10:33
18	M	3:07	4.2	3:47	3.6	10:03	10:02	18	T	4:33	4.2	5:14	4.2	11:13	11:25
19	T	4:10	4.1	4:51	3.7	11:02	11:02	19	F	5:30	4.2	6:04	4.5	11:55	...
20	W	5:14	4.2	5:50	3.9	11:51	11:53	20	S	6:18	4.4	6:46	4.8	12:11	12:33
21	T	6:09	4.3	6:39	4.2	...	12:34	21	S	7:00	4.5	7:24	5.0	12:55	1:11
22	F	6:55	4.5	7:20	4.4	12:39	1:14	22	M	7:38	4.5	7:59	5.2	1:37	1:48
23	S	7:34	4.6	7:57	4.7	1:23	1:52	23	T	8:14	4.5	8:31	5.3	2:19	2:24
24	S	8:10	4.7	8:32	4.8	2:05	2:28	24	W	8:49	4.5	9:03	5.3	3:00	3:00
25	M	8:44	4.6	9:05	4.9	2:46	3:03	25	T	9:24	4.3	9:34	5.3	3:40	3:35
26	T	9:17	4.5	9:36	4.9	3:24	3:35	26	F	10:00	4.2	10:09	5.2	4:18	4:08
27	W	9:49	4.3	10:06	4.9	4:01	4:05	27	S	10:41	4.1	10:50	5.1	4:56	4:43
28	T	10:21	4.2	10:37	4.8	4:36	4:34	28	S	11:30	4.0	11:42	5.0	5:37	5:21
29	F	10:57	4.0	11:13	4.7	5:11	5:01	29	M	...	...	12:29	3.9	6:26	6:10
30	S	11:41	3.8	11:59	4.7	5:48	5:33	30	T	12:44	4.9	1:31	4.0	7:26	7:21
31	S	...	...	12:35	3.7	6:35	6:16								

Dates when Ht. of **Low** Water is below Mean Lower Low with Ht. of lowest given for each period and Date of lowest in ( ):

7th–14th: -1.3' (11th)   5th–12th: -0.9' (8th, 9th)

Average Rise and Fall 4.7 ft.

When a high tide exceeds avg. ht., the *following* low tide will be lower than avg.

2024 HIGH & LOW WATER
SANDY HOOK, NJ
40°28.1'N, 74°00.6'W

Daylight Saving Time   **Daylight Saving Time**

DAY OF MONTH	DAY OF WEEK	MAY HIGH a.m.	Ht.	HIGH p.m.	Ht.	LOW a.m.	LOW p.m.	DAY OF MONTH	DAY OF WEEK	JUNE HIGH a.m.	Ht.	HIGH p.m.	Ht.	LOW a.m.	LOW p.m.
1	W	1:48	4.9	2:32	4.2	8:34	8:46	1	S	3:32	4.9	4:13	5.3	10:07	10:50
2	T	2:50	4.9	3:33	4.5	9:39	10:02	2	S	4:34	4.8	5:13	5.6	11:00	11:48
3	F	3:55	4.9	4:37	4.9	10:37	11:07	3	M	5:37	4.8	6:09	5.9	11:51	...
4	S	5:01	5.0	5:37	5.4	11:29	...	4	T	6:36	4.9	7:00	6.1	12:43	12:41
5	S	6:01	5.2	6:32	5.8	12:04	12:19	5	W	7:29	4.9	7:49	6.1	1:36	1:32
6	M	6:56	5.3	7:22	6.1	12:59	1:08	6	T	8:19	4.9	8:35	6.0	2:29	2:22
7	T	7:47	5.3	8:09	6.2	1:53	1:57	7	F	9:09	4.8	9:22	5.8	3:19	3:12
8	W	8:37	5.2	8:56	6.2	2:45	2:46	8	S	10:00	4.7	10:09	5.5	4:06	3:59
9	T	9:27	5.0	9:43	6.0	3:36	3:34	9	S	10:52	4.5	10:57	5.2	4:50	4:44
10	F	10:19	4.8	10:31	5.6	4:24	4:20	10	M	11:44	4.4	11:47	4.9	5:33	5:28
11	S	11:13	4.6	11:23	5.3	5:10	5:05	11	T	...	...	12:37	4.3	6:17	6:14
12	S	...	...	12:10	4.4	5:58	5:52	12	W	12:37	4.7	1:26	4.3	7:02	7:07
13	M	12:18	4.9	1:06	4.2	6:49	6:45	13	T	1:25	4.5	2:12	4.4	7:51	8:08
14	T	1:12	4.6	1:59	4.2	7:46	7:47	14	F	2:11	4.3	2:57	4.5	8:41	9:10
15	W	2:04	4.4	2:49	4.2	8:44	8:54	15	S	2:57	4.1	3:43	4.6	9:30	10:08
16	T	2:54	4.3	3:39	4.3	9:38	9:56	16	S	3:46	4.0	4:31	4.8	10:16	11:01
17	F	3:45	4.2	4:31	4.5	10:25	10:49	17	M	4:41	4.0	5:19	4.9	11:01	11:49
18	S	4:40	4.1	5:20	4.7	11:08	11:38	18	T	5:37	4.0	6:06	5.2	11:45	...
19	S	5:33	4.2	6:06	5.0	11:48	...	19	W	6:29	4.1	6:49	5.4	12:37	12:28
20	M	6:21	4.2	6:47	5.2	12:23	12:27	20	T	7:15	4.2	7:31	5.6	1:24	1:13
21	T	7:04	4.3	7:24	5.4	1:07	1:07	21	F	8:00	4.3	8:12	5.8	2:12	2:01
22	W	7:44	4.4	7:59	5.5	1:51	1:47	22	S	8:44	4.4	8:55	5.8	2:59	2:49
23	T	8:23	4.4	8:34	5.6	2:36	2:28	23	S	9:30	4.5	9:41	5.8	3:45	3:37
24	F	9:03	4.3	9:12	5.6	3:19	3:09	24	M	10:19	4.6	10:32	5.8	4:29	4:25
25	S	9:45	4.3	9:53	5.6	4:02	3:51	25	T	11:13	4.7	11:26	5.6	5:13	5:14
26	S	10:31	4.2	10:40	5.5	4:44	4:33	26	W	...	...	12:10	4.8	5:58	6:08
27	M	11:25	4.2	11:36	5.3	5:28	5:19	27	T	12:23	5.4	1:06	5.0	6:48	7:10
28	T	...	...	12:24	4.3	6:15	6:12	28	F	1:19	5.2	2:00	5.2	7:42	8:20
29	W	12:36	5.2	1:22	4.5	7:10	7:19	29	S	2:15	5.0	2:54	5.4	8:40	9:29
30	T	1:35	5.1	2:18	4.8	8:09	8:35	30	S	3:11	4.8	3:50	5.5	9:38	10:34
31	F	2:33	5.0	3:15	5.0	9:10	9:46								

Dates when Ht. of **Low** Water is below Mean Lower Low with Ht. of lowest given for each period and Date of lowest in ( ):

4th–10th: -0.5' (6th–9th)   6th–7th: -0.2'
                                         25th: -0.2'

Average Rise and Fall 4.7 ft.

When a high tide exceeds avg. ht., the *following* low tide will be lower than avg.

2024 HIGH & LOW WATER
SANDY HOOK, NJ
40°28.1'N, 74°00.6'W

Daylight Saving Time   **Daylight Saving Time**

DAY OF MONTH	DAY OF WEEK	JULY HIGH a.m.	Ht.	p.m.	Ht.	LOW a.m.	p.m.	DAY OF MONTH	DAY OF WEEK	AUGUST HIGH a.m.	Ht.	p.m.	Ht.	LOW a.m.	p.m.
1	M	4:12	4.6	4:49	5.6	10:34	11:33	1	T	6:04	4.3	6:27	5.4	12:13	12:05
2	T	5:16	4.5	5:48	5.7	11:28	...	2	F	6:59	4.5	7:17	5.5	1:04	12:56
3	W	6:18	4.5	6:42	5.8	12:28	12:20	3	S	7:47	4.6	8:01	5.5	1:52	1:45
4	T	7:14	4.6	7:32	5.8	1:21	1:12	4	S	8:32	4.7	8:42	5.5	2:37	2:32
5	F	8:03	4.6	8:18	5.7	2:12	2:03	5	M	9:14	4.8	9:21	5.3	3:19	3:16
6	S	8:52	4.7	9:02	5.6	3:00	2:52	6	T	9:55	4.8	10:00	5.2	3:56	3:57
7	S	9:39	4.6	9:46	5.4	3:45	3:39	7	W	10:36	4.8	10:38	4.9	4:31	4:36
8	M	10:26	4.6	10:30	5.2	4:26	4:21	8	T	11:17	4.8	11:16	4.7	5:03	5:13
9	T	11:13	4.5	11:13	4.9	5:04	5:02	9	F	11:58	4.7	11:56	4.4	5:33	5:52
10	W	11:59	4.5	11:58	4.7	5:41	5:43	10	S	...	...	12:39	4.7	6:04	6:34
11	T	...	...	12:46	4.5	6:17	6:28	11	S	12:39	4.2	1:20	4.7	6:37	7:27
12	F	12:42	4.5	1:29	4.5	6:56	7:19	12	M	1:24	4.0	2:02	4.7	7:18	8:33
13	S	1:26	4.2	2:11	4.6	7:38	8:19	13	T	2:13	3.9	2:48	4.8	8:17	9:41
14	S	2:10	4.1	2:53	4.7	8:27	9:22	14	W	3:08	3.8	3:43	4.9	9:26	10:43
15	M	2:56	3.9	3:38	4.7	9:19	10:21	15	T	4:14	3.8	4:46	5.1	10:32	11:39
16	T	3:50	3.8	4:29	4.9	10:13	11:16	16	F	5:23	4.0	5:49	5.4	11:31	...
17	W	4:53	3.8	5:24	5.1	11:05	...	17	S	6:22	4.4	6:44	5.8	12:30	12:26
18	T	5:54	4.0	6:17	5.4	12:07	12:01	18	S	7:14	4.8	7:33	6.1	1:20	1:21
19	F	6:48	4.2	7:06	5.7	12:57	12:47	19	M	8:02	5.2	8:21	6.2	2:08	2:15
20	S	7:37	4.4	7:53	5.9	1:47	1:39	20	T	8:50	5.5	9:09	6.2	2:56	3:08
21	S	8:24	4.7	8:40	6.1	2:36	2:32	21	W	9:39	5.7	9:58	6.1	3:41	3:59
22	M	9:12	4.9	9:27	6.1	3:23	3:24	22	T	10:29	5.8	10:50	5.8	4:25	4:50
23	T	10:01	5.1	10:17	6.0	4:08	4:14	23	F	11:23	5.8	11:45	5.4	5:09	5:41
24	W	10:54	5.2	11:10	5.8	4:51	5:04	24	S	...	...	12:18	5.8	5:55	6:38
25	T	11:48	5.4	...	...	5:35	5:57	25	S	12:42	5.1	1:14	5.6	6:45	7:42
26	F	12:05	5.5	12:44	5.4	6:22	6:56	26	M	1:40	4.7	2:10	5.4	7:44	8:53
27	S	1:01	5.2	1:38	5.5	7:13	8:02	27	T	2:39	4.5	3:08	5.2	8:50	10:01
28	S	1:57	4.8	2:32	5.5	8:11	9:12	28	W	3:40	4.3	4:09	5.1	9:56	11:03
29	M	2:54	4.6	3:28	5.4	9:12	10:18	29	T	4:46	4.2	5:13	5.1	10:57	11:56
30	T	3:55	4.4	4:28	5.4	10:13	11:18	30	F	5:49	4.4	6:11	5.2	11:51	...
31	W	5:00	4.3	5:31	5.4	11:11	...	31	S	6:42	4.6	6:58	5.3	12:43	12:40

Dates when Ht. of **Low** Water is below Mean Lower Low with Ht. of lowest given for each period and Date of lowest in ( ):

22nd–26th: -0.5' (24th)   19th–24th: -0.6' (21st, 22nd)

Average Rise and Fall 4.7 ft.

When a high tide exceeds avg. ht., the *following* low tide will be lower than avg.

2024 HIGH & LOW WATER
SANDY HOOK, NJ
40°28.1'N, 74°00.6'W

		Daylight Saving Time							Daylight Saving Time				
DAY OF MONTH	DAY OF WEEK	**SEPTEMBER**				DAY OF MONTH	DAY OF WEEK	**OCTOBER**					
		HIGH		LOW				HIGH			LOW		
		a.m.	Ht.	p.m.	Ht.	a.m.	p.m.		a.m.	Ht.	p.m.	Ht.	a.m.	p.m.
1	S	7:27	4.8	**7:40**	5.3	1:27	**1:26**	1	T	7:39	5.2	**7:50**	5.1	1:32	**1:45**
2	M	8:07	5.0	**8:18**	5.3	2:07	**2:10**	2	W	8:14	5.4	**8:25**	5.1	2:08	**2:27**
3	T	8:45	5.1	**8:54**	5.3	2:45	**2:52**	3	T	8:48	5.4	**8:59**	4.9	2:43	**3:07**
4	W	9:23	5.1	**9:29**	5.1	3:21	**3:32**	4	F	9:21	5.4	**9:32**	4.7	3:16	**3:45**
5	T	9:57	5.1	**10:03**	4.9	3:54	**4:10**	5	S	9:51	5.3	**10:05**	4.5	3:48	**4:21**
6	F	10:32	5.1	**10:37**	4.6	4:24	**4:46**	6	S	10:22	5.2	**10:39**	4.3	4:18	**4:57**
7	S	11:07	4.9	**11:13**	4.4	4:53	**5:21**	7	M	10:56	5.0	**11:21**	4.1	4:46	**5:34**
8	S	11:43	4.9	**11:54**	4.2	5:20	**5:59**	8	T	11:39	4.9	...	...	5:16	**6:18**
9	M	...	...	**12:25**	4.8	5:48	**6:45**	9	W	12:15	3.9	**12:36**	4.9	5:54	**7:18**
10	T	12:44	4.0	**1:13**	4.8	6:25	**7:49**	10	T	1:18	3.9	**1:38**	4.9	6:52	**8:33**
11	W	1:40	3.9	**2:07**	4.8	7:21	**9:05**	11	F	2:20	4.0	**2:42**	5.0	8:22	**9:42**
12	T	2:40	3.8	**3:08**	4.9	8:47	**10:13**	12	S	3:24	4.2	**3:48**	5.1	9:46	**10:40**
13	F	3:45	4.0	**4:15**	5.1	10:07	**11:10**	13	S	4:29	4.6	**4:54**	5.3	10:53	**11:32**
14	S	4:55	4.3	**5:21**	5.4	11:11	...	14	M	5:31	5.1	**5:54**	5.6	11:51	...
15	S	5:57	4.7	**6:20**	5.8	12:02	**12:09**	15	T	6:26	5.6	**6:48**	5.8	12:20	**12:46**
16	M	6:50	5.2	**7:11**	6.1	12:51	**1:03**	16	W	7:16	6.1	**7:38**	5.9	1:07	**1:40**
17	T	7:39	5.7	**8:00**	6.2	1:38	**1:57**	17	T	8:03	6.4	**8:27**	5.8	1:55	**2:33**
18	W	8:26	6.1	**8:48**	6.2	2:25	**2:51**	18	F	8:50	6.5	**9:17**	5.6	2:43	**3:26**
19	T	9:14	6.3	**9:37**	6.0	3:12	**3:43**	19	S	9:39	6.4	**10:09**	5.3	3:31	**4:16**
20	F	10:03	6.3	**10:29**	5.6	3:57	**4:33**	20	S	10:30	6.1	**11:05**	5.0	4:18	**5:06**
21	S	10:55	6.1	**11:24**	5.3	4:42	**5:24**	21	M	11:25	5.8	...	...	5:05	**5:59**
22	S	11:51	5.9	...	...	5:29	**6:18**	22	T	12:05	4.7	**12:24**	5.4	5:56	**6:57**
23	M	12:24	4.9	**12:49**	5.6	6:19	**7:21**	23	W	1:06	4.4	**1:24**	5.1	6:53	**8:03**
24	T	1:24	4.6	**1:48**	5.3	7:19	**8:31**	24	T	2:06	4.3	**2:21**	4.8	8:02	**9:10**
25	W	2:24	4.4	**2:47**	5.0	8:28	**9:40**	25	F	3:03	4.3	**3:17**	4.6	9:12	**10:08**
26	T	3:25	4.3	**3:47**	4.9	9:38	**10:41**	26	S	3:59	4.3	**4:14**	4.6	10:15	**10:56**
27	F	4:27	4.3	**4:49**	4.9	10:40	**11:31**	27	S	4:55	4.5	**5:09**	4.6	11:08	**11:38**
28	S	5:27	4.5	**5:45**	4.9	11:33	...	28	M	5:45	4.7	**5:58**	4.6	11:54	...
29	S	6:18	4.7	**6:33**	5.0	12:15	**12:20**	29	T	6:28	5.0	**6:41**	4.7	12:16	**12:37**
30	M	7:00	5.0	**7:13**	5.1	12:54	**1:03**	30	W	7:07	5.2	**7:20**	4.7	12:53	**1:19**
								31	T	7:42	5.4	**7:57**	4.7	1:29	**2:01**

Dates when Ht. of **Low** Water is below Mean Lower Low with Ht. of lowest given for each period and Date of lowest in ( ):

17th–21st: -0.7' (19th)   15th–20th: -0.6' (17th, 18th)

Average Rise and Fall 4.7 ft.

When a high tide exceeds avg. ht., the *following* low tide will be lower than avg.

2024 HIGH & LOW WATER
SANDY HOOK, NJ
40°28.1'N, 74°00.6'W

*Standard Time starts Nov. 3 at 2 a.m.   Standard Time

DAY OF MONTH	DAY OF WEEK	NOVEMBER HIGH a.m.	Ht.	HIGH p.m.	Ht.	LOW a.m.	LOW p.m.	DAY OF MONTH	DAY OF WEEK	DECEMBER HIGH a.m.	Ht.	HIGH p.m.	Ht.	LOW a.m.	LOW p.m.
1	F	8:16	5.5	8:32	4.6	2:05	2:42	1	S	7:22	5.3	7:46	4.1	1:12	2:02
2	S	8:48	5.4	9:06	4.5	2:41	3:22	2	M	7:57	5.3	8:25	4.1	1:52	2:44
3	S	*8:19	5.4	*8:41	4.3	*2:17	*3:01	3	T	8:34	5.2	9:06	4.0	2:32	3:24
4	M	8:52	5.2	9:19	4.1	2:51	3:39	4	W	9:17	5.2	9:54	3.9	3:12	4:05
5	T	9:28	5.1	10:04	4.0	3:24	4:19	5	T	10:05	5.0	10:49	3.9	3:53	4:49
6	W	10:16	5.0	11:01	3.9	4:00	5:03	6	F	11:02	4.9	11:48	4.1	4:40	5:37
7	T	11:15	4.9	...	...	4:43	5:58	7	S	...	...	12:01	4.8	5:38	6:33
8	F	12:03	3.9	12:19	4.9	5:43	7:03	8	S	12:45	4.3	1:00	4.7	6:52	7:34
9	S	1:04	4.1	1:20	4.9	7:07	8:09	9	M	1:41	4.6	1:58	4.6	8:08	8:33
10	S	2:03	4.4	2:22	4.9	8:28	9:07	10	T	2:39	4.9	2:59	4.5	9:17	9:30
11	M	3:04	4.8	3:26	5.0	9:35	10:00	11	W	3:39	5.2	4:04	4.5	10:18	10:23
12	T	4:05	5.2	4:28	5.1	10:35	10:50	12	T	4:39	5.5	5:05	4.6	11:15	11:15
13	W	5:02	5.7	5:25	5.2	11:30	11:39	13	F	5:34	5.7	6:01	4.7	...	12:09
14	T	5:53	6.1	6:18	5.3	...	12:24	14	S	6:25	5.9	6:53	4.7	12:06	1:03
15	F	6:42	6.3	7:08	5.3	12:28	1:17	15	S	7:13	5.8	7:44	4.7	12:58	1:55
16	S	7:30	6.3	7:59	5.2	1:18	2:09	16	M	8:01	5.7	8:35	4.5	1:50	2:44
17	S	8:18	6.2	8:51	4.9	2:08	3:00	17	T	8:49	5.4	9:26	4.4	2:39	3:30
18	M	9:08	5.8	9:46	4.7	2:57	3:49	18	W	9:38	5.1	10:19	4.2	3:26	4:14
19	T	10:01	5.5	10:44	4.4	3:45	4:38	19	T	10:28	4.8	11:12	4.1	4:11	4:58
20	W	10:57	5.1	11:43	4.2	4:33	5:30	20	F	11:19	4.5	...	...	4:56	5:43
21	T	11:54	4.8	...	...	5:26	6:26	21	S	12:04	4.0	12:08	4.2	5:47	6:31
22	F	12:39	4.2	12:48	4.5	6:27	7:26	22	S	12:52	4.0	12:56	4.0	6:46	7:22
23	S	1:32	4.2	1:39	4.3	7:34	8:22	23	M	1:38	4.0	1:43	3.8	7:49	8:13
24	S	2:22	4.2	2:30	4.2	8:38	9:11	24	T	2:25	4.1	2:32	3.6	8:50	9:02
25	M	3:13	4.3	3:23	4.1	9:34	9:54	25	W	3:14	4.2	3:27	3.5	9:45	9:49
26	T	4:03	4.5	4:16	4.1	10:23	10:34	26	T	4:06	4.3	4:25	3.5	10:36	10:34
27	W	4:50	4.8	5:05	4.1	11:08	11:13	27	F	4:55	4.5	5:18	3.6	11:23	11:18
28	T	5:32	5.0	5:50	4.2	11:51	11:52	28	S	5:40	4.8	6:05	3.7	...	12:09
29	F	6:11	5.2	6:30	4.2	...	12:35	29	S	6:21	4.9	6:47	3.8	12:02	12:55
30	S	6:47	5.3	7:09	4.2	12:31	1:18	30	M	7:01	5.1	7:28	3.9	12:47	1:41
								31	T	7:40	5.2	8:07	4.0	1:33	2:25

Dates when Ht. of **Low** Water is below Mean Lower Low with Ht. of lowest given for each period and Date of lowest in ( ):

12th–18th: -0.6' (15th, 16th)   10th–18th: -0.6' (14th–16th)
                                        30th–31st: -0.4'

Average Rise and Fall 4.7 ft.

When a high tide exceeds avg. ht., the *following* low tide will be lower than avg.

2024 CURRENT TABLE
DELAWARE BAY ENTRANCE
38°51.22'N, 75°04.62'W

Standard Time | **Standard Time**

JANUARY

DAY OF MONTH	DAY OF WEEK	NORTHWEST Flood Starts a.m.	p.m.	Kts.	SOUTHEAST Ebb Starts a.m.	p.m.	Kts.
1	M	7:30	8:30	a1.3	1:54	1:54	1.1
2	T	8:18	9:06	1.1	2:42	2:42	1.0
3	W	9:12	10:00	1.1	3:36	3:36	1.0
4	T	10:13	10:48	p1.2	4:24	4:36	p1.1
5	F	11:12	11:36	p1.3	5:12	5:24	p1.2
6	S	...	12:01	1.2	5:54	6:12	p1.3
7	S	12:12	12:42	a1.5	6:42	7:00	p1.5
8	M	12:54	1:30	a1.7	7:24	7:42	p1.6
9	T	1:36	2:24	a1.9	8:12	8:36	a1.7
10	W	2:18	3:12	a2.0	8:54	9:24	a1.9
11	T	3:00	4:00	a2.2	9:42	10:12	a2.1
12	F	3:48	4:48	a2.2	10:24	11:00	a2.2
13	S	4:36	5:42	a2.3	11:12	11:54	a2.2
14	S	5:36	6:30	a2.3	...	12:06	2.2
15	M	6:36	7:18	a2.2	12:42	1:00	p2.0
16	T	7:42	8:06	a2.0	1:36	1:54	p1.9
17	W	8:48	9:00	1.9	2:36	2:54	1.8
18	T	10:00	10:00	p2.0	3:42	4:00	a1.8
19	F	11:18	11:06	p2.1	4:48	5:00	1.7
20	S	...	12:24	1.6	5:54	6:00	p1.8
21	S	12:01	1:30	a2.2	6:54	6:54	p1.8
22	M	12:54	2:30	a2.3	8:00	7:48	1.8
23	T	1:48	3:24	a2.3	8:54	8:48	p1.8
24	W	2:42	4:12	a2.2	9:42	9:42	1.7
25	T	3:30	5:00	a2.0	10:18	10:36	1.6
26	F	4:18	5:42	a1.9	11:00	11:24	a1.6
27	S	5:06	6:18	a1.8	11:36	...	1.6
28	S	5:48	6:48	a1.7	12:06	12:12	1.5
29	M	6:30	7:12	1.5	12:48	12:42	1.4
30	T	7:12	7:36	1.4	1:24	1:24	p1.4
31	W	7:48	8:06	p1.4	2:00	2:00	1.3

FEBRUARY

DAY OF MONTH	DAY OF WEEK	NORTHWEST Flood Starts a.m.	p.m.	Kts.	SOUTHEAST Ebb Starts a.m.	p.m.	Kts.
1	T	8:24	8:48	1.3	2:36	2:48	p1.3
2	F	9:06	9:36	p1.4	3:18	3:36	p1.3
3	S	10:00	10:30	p1.4	4:12	4:30	p1.3
4	S	11:07	11:18	p1.5	5:00	5:18	p1.3
5	M	...	12:06	1.1	5:54	6:12	1.3
6	T	12:06	1:06	a1.7	6:42	7:12	a1.5
7	W	12:54	2:12	a1.9	7:36	8:18	a1.7
8	T	1:48	3:06	a2.0	8:30	9:12	a1.9
9	F	2:42	3:54	a2.1	9:24	10:06	a2.0
10	S	3:42	4:42	a2.2	10:18	10:54	a2.2
11	S	4:42	5:24	a2.3	11:06	11:42	a2.3
12	M	5:42	6:06	a2.3	...	12:01	2.3
13	T	6:36	6:54	a2.3	12:30	12:48	p2.2
14	W	7:36	7:36	p2.2	1:18	1:36	2.1
15	T	8:36	8:30	p2.2	2:12	2:30	2.0
16	F	9:42	9:24	p2.1	3:12	3:24	1.8
17	S	10:54	10:24	p2.1	4:24	4:24	p1.7
18	S	-A-	12:06	1.2	5:30	5:24	p1.5
19	M	...	1:18	1.2	6:36	6:30	p1.5
20	T	12:30	2:24	a2.0	7:36	7:36	a1.5
21	W	1:30	3:12	a1.9	8:36	8:42	a1.5
22	T	2:30	4:00	a1.8	9:18	9:42	a1.5
23	F	3:24	4:36	a1.7	10:00	10:24	1.5
24	S	4:12	5:12	1.7	10:36	11:06	a1.6
25	S	4:54	5:36	1.7	11:06	11:42	1.6
26	M	5:30	6:00	p1.8	11:42	...	1.7
27	T	6:06	6:24	1.7	12:12	12:18	p1.7
28	W	6:36	6:54	p1.7	12:42	12:48	p1.7
29	T	7:06	7:24	p1.6	1:12	1:24	1.6

A also at 11:30 p.m. (2.0)

The Kts. (knots) columns show the **maximum** predicted velocities of the stronger one of the Flood Currents and the stronger one of the Ebb Currents for each day.

The letter "a" means the velocity shown should occur **after** the **a.m.** Current Change. The letter "p" means the velocity shown should occur **after** the **p.m.** Current Change (even if next morning). No "a" or "p" means a.m. and p.m. velocities are the same for that day.

Avg. Max. Velocity: Flood 1.8 Kts., Ebb 1.9 Kts.

Max. Flood 3 hrs. 5 min. after Flood Starts, ±15 min.

Max. Ebb 3 hrs. 5 min. after Ebb Starts, ±15 min.

See pp. 22-29 for Current Change at other points.

2024 CURRENT TABLE
DELAWARE BAY ENTRANCE
38°51.22'N, 75°4.62'W

*Daylight Time starts March 10 at 2 a.m.   Daylight Saving Time

		MARCH								APRIL					
		CURRENT TURNS TO								CURRENT TURNS TO					
		NORTHWEST Flood Starts			SOUTHEAST Ebb Starts					NORTHWEST Flood Starts			SOUTHEAST Ebb Starts		
DAY OF MONTH	DAY OF WEEK	a.m.	p.m.	Kts.	a.m.	p.m.	Kts.	DAY OF MONTH	DAY OF WEEK	a.m.	p.m.	Kts.	a.m.	p.m.	Kts.
1	F	7:42	8:00	p1.6	1:48	2:00	1.5	1	M	9:42	9:42	p1.6	3:36	3:48	a1.5
2	S	8:18	8:42	p1.6	2:30	2:42	1.4	2	T	10:54	10:42	p1.5	4:30	5:06	a1.4
3	S	9:12	9:30	p1.5	3:18	3:30	a1.4	3	W	...	12:24	0.9	5:42	6:36	a1.4
4	M	10:25	10:24	p1.6	4:12	4:36	a1.3	4	T	12:02	1:42	a1.5	6:48	7:54	a1.4
5	T	11:42	11:24	p1.6	5:12	5:48	a1.3	5	F	1:24	2:42	a1.7	8:00	9:00	a1.7
6	W	...	12:54	1.0	6:12	7:00	a1.4	6	S	2:36	3:30	a1.9	9:06	9:48	a1.9
7	T	12:30	2:00	a1.8	7:12	8:12	a1.7	7	S	3:48	4:12	2.1	10:00	10:36	p2.2
8	F	1:36	2:54	a1.9	8:18	9:06	a1.9	8	M	4:42	4:54	p2.4	10:54	11:24	p2.4
9	S	2:42	3:36	a2.0	9:12	9:54	a2.1	9	T	5:36	5:36	p2.7	11:36	...	2.5
10	S	*4:42	*5:18	a2.2	*11:06	*11:42	2.2	10	W	6:24	6:18	p2.8	12:06	12:18	2.5
11	M	5:42	6:00	2.4	11:54	...	2.4	11	T	7:18	7:00	p2.8	12:54	1:00	2.5
12	T	6:36	6:42	p2.6	12:30	12:42	2.4	12	F	8:06	7:42	p2.6	1:42	1:42	p2.3
13	W	7:30	7:30	p2.6	1:12	1:30	2.4	13	S	8:54	8:30	p2.3	2:30	2:24	p2.0
14	T	8:24	8:12	p2.5	2:00	2:12	a2.3	14	S	10:00	9:18	p1.9	3:24	3:18	p1.6
15	F	9:12	9:00	p2.4	2:54	2:54	2.0	15	M	11:18	10:12	p1.6	4:24	4:24	1.2
16	S	10:18	9:48	p2.1	3:48	3:42	p1.8	16	T	-B-	12:42	0.8	5:36	5:54	a1.0
17	S	11:36	10:48	p1.9	4:54	4:48	p1.5	17	W	...	1:48	0.9	6:42	7:18	a1.0
18	M	-A-	1:00	0.9	6:06	6:00	1.2	18	T	1:00	2:42	1.2	7:42	8:30	a1.1
19	T	...	2:12	1.0	7:12	7:18	1.1	19	F	2:12	3:18	p1.4	8:36	9:18	1.2
20	W	1:06	3:12	a1.6	8:12	8:36	a1.2	20	S	3:12	3:54	p1.5	9:24	10:00	p1.4
21	T	2:18	3:54	a1.5	9:12	9:42	a1.3	21	S	3:54	4:18	p1.7	10:00	10:30	1.5
22	F	3:24	4:30	1.5	9:54	10:30	a1.4	22	M	4:24	4:42	p1.8	10:30	11:00	p1.7
23	S	4:12	5:00	p1.6	10:30	11:06	1.5	23	T	4:54	5:06	p1.9	11:06	11:24	1.8
24	S	4:54	5:30	p1.8	11:06	11:36	1.6	24	W	5:18	5:36	p2.0	11:36	11:54	1.9
25	M	5:30	5:54	p1.9	11:36	...	1.7	25	T	5:48	6:00	p2.1	...	12:06	2.0
26	T	6:00	6:18	p1.9	12:06	12:12	p1.8	26	F	6:18	6:30	p2.2	12:24	12:36	2.0
27	W	6:30	6:42	p2.0	12:36	12:42	p1.9	27	S	6:54	7:06	p2.1	1:00	1:12	a2.0
28	T	6:54	7:12	p2.0	1:06	1:12	p1.9	28	S	7:36	7:42	p2.0	1:36	1:48	a1.9
29	F	7:30	7:42	p1.9	1:36	1:42	1.8	29	M	8:24	8:24	p1.8	2:18	2:30	a1.8
30	S	8:06	8:18	p1.8	2:12	2:18	1.7	30	T	9:24	9:12	p1.6	3:06	3:30	a1.6
31	S	8:48	8:54	p1.7	2:48	3:00	a1.6								

A also at 11:54 p.m. (1.7)   **B** also at 11:36 p.m. (1.3)

The Kts. (knots) columns show the **maximum** predicted velocities of the stronger one of the Flood Currents and the stronger one of the Ebb Currents for each day.

The letter "a" means the velocity shown should occur **after** the **a.m.** Current Change. The letter "p" means the velocity shown should occur **after** the **p.m.** Current Change (even if next morning). No "a" or "p" means a.m. and p.m. velocities are the same for that day.

Avg. Max. Velocity: Flood 1.8 Kts., Ebb 1.9 Kts.

Max. Flood 3 hrs. 5 min. after Flood Starts, ±15 min.

Max. Ebb 3 hrs. 5 min. after Ebb Starts, ±15 min.

See pp. 22-29 for Current Change at other points.

2024 CURRENT TABLE
DELAWARE BAY ENTRANCE
38°51.22'N, 75°04.62'W

		Daylight Saving Time						Daylight Saving Time			
		MAY						**JUNE**			
DAY OF MONTH	DAY OF WEEK	CURRENT TURNS TO				DAY OF MONTH	DAY OF WEEK	CURRENT TURNS TO			
		NORTHWEST Flood Starts			SOUTHEAST Ebb Starts			NORTHWEST Flood Starts			SOUTHEAST Ebb Starts
		a.m. **p.m.** Kts.			a.m. **p.m.** Kts.			a.m. **p.m.** Kts.			a.m. **p.m.** Kts.
1	W	10:36 **10:24** p1.5			4:06 **4:54** a1.5	1	S	12:06 **12:36** 1.6			6:24 **7:06** p1.6
2	T	... **12:06** 1.0			5:18 **6:24** a1.4	2	S	1:18 **1:36** p2.0			7:24 **8:06** p1.9
3	F	12:01 **1:12** a1.5			6:36 **7:36** a1.5	3	M	2:24 **2:24** p2.3			8:24 **9:00** p2.2
4	S	1:25 **2:12** 1.7			7:48 **8:36** p1.8	4	T	3:25 **3:12** p2.5			9:18 **9:54** p2.3
5	S	2:36 **3:00** p2.1			8:48 **9:24** p2.1	5	W	4:18 **4:00** p2.7			10:06 **10:48** 2.3
6	M	3:36 **3:42** p2.4			9:42 **10:18** p2.4	6	T	5:06 **4:42** p2.7			10:48 **11:36** a2.3
7	T	4:30 **4:24** p2.6			10:30 **11:06** p2.5	7	F	6:00 **5:30** p2.7			11:30 ... 2.3
8	W	5:18 **5:12** p2.8			11:12 **11:48** 2.5	8	S	6:48 **6:12** p2.5			12:18 **12:18** 2.1
9	T	6:12 **5:54** p2.9			11:54 ... 2.5	9	S	7:42 **7:00** p2.2			1:06 **1:06** 1.8
10	F	7:00 **6:36** p2.8			12:36 **12:36** p2.4	10	M	8:30 **7:48** p1.8			1:48 **2:00** a1.6
11	S	7:54 **7:18** p2.5			1:24 **1:18** p2.1	11	T	9:18 **8:36** p1.5			2:30 **3:00** a1.3
12	S	8:42 **8:06** p2.1			2:12 **2:06** 1.7	12	W	10:12 **9:36** p1.2			3:18 **4:00** a1.1
13	M	9:42 **8:54** p1.7			3:00 **3:00** a1.4	13	T	11:12 **10:54** a1.1			4:06 **5:12** a1.0
14	T	10:54 **9:54** p1.3			3:48 **4:12** a1.1	14	F	... **12:06** 1.1			5:12 **6:12** 0.9
15	W	-A- **12:12** 0.9			4:54 **5:42** a0.9	15	S	12:06 **12:54** p1.2			6:12 **7:00** p1.0
16	T	... **1:06** 1.0			6:00 **7:00** a0.9	16	S	1:00 **1:30** p1.3			7:00 **7:42** 1.1
17	F	12:48 **1:54** p1.2			7:06 **7:54** 1.0	17	M	1:42 **2:00** p1.5			7:48 **8:18** 1.3
18	S	1:48 **2:30** p1.4			7:54 **8:36** p1.2	18	T	2:18 **2:36** p1.6			8:24 **8:54** a1.5
19	S	2:36 **3:06** p1.5			8:36 **9:12** p1.4	19	W	2:54 **3:06** p1.8			9:06 **9:36** 1.6
20	M	3:12 **3:30** p1.7			9:18 **9:48** 1.5	20	T	3:30 **3:42** p1.9			9:48 **10:12** 1.7
21	T	3:42 **3:54** p1.8			9:54 **10:18** 1.7	21	F	4:12 **4:12** p2.0			10:24 **10:48** p1.9
22	W	4:12 **4:24** p1.9			10:24 **10:48** 1.8	22	S	4:54 **4:48** p2.1			11:06 **11:24** p2.0
23	T	4:42 **4:54** p2.1			11:00 **11:18** 1.9	23	S	5:36 **5:30** p2.2			11:48 ... 1.7
24	F	5:18 **5:24** p2.2			11:30 **11:54** 2.0	24	M	6:24 **6:12** p2.2			12:06 **12:36** a2.1
25	S	5:54 **5:54** p2.2			... **12:06** 1.9	25	T	7:12 **7:06** p2.1			12:54 **1:24** a2.1
26	S	6:36 **6:36** p2.2			12:30 **12:48** a2.1	26	W	8:00 **8:06** p1.9			1:42 **2:18** a2.0
27	M	7:24 **7:18** p2.0			1:12 **1:30** a2.0	27	T	8:54 **9:12** p1.8			2:36 **3:18** a1.8
28	T	8:12 **8:06** p1.8			1:54 **2:24** a1.9	28	F	9:48 **10:30** p1.7			3:42 **4:24** a1.7
29	W	9:12 **9:06** p1.6			2:48 **3:24** a1.7	29	S	10:54 **11:54** 1.7			4:48 **5:36** 1.6
30	T	10:18 **10:30** p1.6			3:48 **4:48** a1.6	30	S	... **12:01** 1.9			6:00 **6:36** p1.8
31	F	11:30 ... 1.3			5:06 **6:00** a1.5						

A also at 11:18 p.m. (1.1)

The Kts. (knots) columns show the **maximum** predicted velocities of the stronger one of the Flood Currents and the stronger one of the Ebb Currents for each day.
The letter "a" means the velocity shown should occur **after** the a.m. Current Change. The letter "p" means the velocity shown should occur **after** the p.m. Current Change (even if next morning). No "a" or "p" means a.m. and p.m. velocities are the same for that day.
Avg. Max. Velocity: Flood 1.8 Kts., Ebb 1.9 Kts.
Max. Flood 3 hrs. 5 min. after Flood Starts, ±15 min.
Max. Ebb 3 hrs. 5 min. after Ebb Starts, ±15 min.

See pp. 22-29 for Current Change at other points.

2024 CURRENT TABLE
DELAWARE BAY ENTRANCE
38°51.22'N, 75°4.62'W

Daylight Saving Time							Daylight Saving Time					
JULY							**AUGUST**					
DAY OF MONTH	DAY OF WEEK	CURRENT TURNS TO					DAY OF MONTH	DAY OF WEEK	CURRENT TURNS TO			
		NORTHWEST Flood Starts			SOUTHEAST Ebb Starts				NORTHWEST Flood Starts			SOUTHEAST Ebb Starts
		a.m.	p.m.	Kts.	a.m.	p.m.	Kts.		a.m.	p.m.	Kts.	a.m.	p.m.	Kts.

Day	Wk	a.m.	p.m.	Kts.	a.m.	p.m.	Kts.	Day	Wk	a.m.	p.m.	Kts.	a.m.	p.m.	Kts.
1	M	1:06	1:00	p2.1	7:00	7:42	p1.9	1	T	3:00	2:18	p2.3	8:18	9:24	1.8
2	T	2:12	1:54	p2.4	7:54	8:42	p2.0	2	F	4:00	3:12	p2.2	9:24	10:18	1.8
3	W	3:12	2:42	p2.5	8:48	9:36	2.1	3	S	4:54	4:12	p2.1	10:24	11:00	p1.8
4	T	4:07	3:36	p2.6	9:36	10:30	a2.1	4	S	5:43	5:06	p2.0	11:18	11:42	p1.8
5	F	5:00	4:24	p2.5	10:30	11:18	a2.1	5	M	6:24	5:54	p1.9	...	12:12	1.6
6	S	5:54	5:12	p2.4	11:18	...	1.9	6	T	7:00	6:48	p1.8	12:24	12:54	a1.7
7	S	6:42	6:00	p2.2	12:01	12:12	a1.9	7	W	7:36	7:30	1.7	1:00	1:36	a1.6
8	M	7:30	6:48	p1.9	12:48	1:06	a1.7	8	T	8:06	8:06	a1.7	1:36	2:12	a1.5
9	T	8:12	7:42	p1.7	1:24	1:54	a1.6	9	F	8:30	8:36	a1.5	2:12	2:48	a1.5
10	W	8:48	8:30	1.4	2:06	2:42	a1.4	10	S	9:00	9:12	a1.4	2:48	3:24	a1.4
11	T	9:18	9:18	a1.3	2:42	3:30	a1.2	11	S	9:36	9:48	a1.4	3:24	4:06	a1.3
12	F	10:00	10:06	a1.2	3:30	4:18	a1.1	12	M	10:12	10:36	a1.3	4:12	4:48	a1.3
13	S	10:42	11:00	a1.2	4:18	5:06	a1.1	13	T	11:00	11:36	a1.4	5:00	5:42	a1.2
14	S	11:30	11:54	a1.2	5:12	5:54	a1.1	14	W	11:54	...	1.4	5:54	6:30	a1.2
15	M	...	12:18	1.3	6:06	6:42	1.1	15	T	12:36	12:42	p1.5	6:48	7:18	p1.3
16	T	12:36	12:54	p1.4	6:48	7:24	1.2	16	F	1:42	1:30	p1.7	7:48	8:12	p1.5
17	W	1:24	1:36	p1.6	7:36	8:06	a1.4	17	S	2:48	2:24	p1.8	8:54	9:06	p1.7
18	T	2:12	2:18	p1.7	8:24	8:48	1.5	18	S	3:42	3:24	p1.9	9:54	10:00	p1.9
19	F	3:06	3:00	p1.9	9:12	9:36	p1.7	19	M	4:30	4:18	p2.0	10:48	10:54	p2.1
20	S	3:54	3:42	p2.0	10:06	10:18	p1.9	20	T	5:12	5:18	p2.2	11:36	11:42	p2.2
21	S	4:42	4:30	p2.0	10:54	11:06	p2.0	21	W	5:54	6:12	p2.3	...	12:18	2.0
22	M	5:30	5:18	p2.1	11:42	11:54	p2.1	22	T	6:42	7:12	p2.3	12:30	1:06	a2.3
23	T	6:12	6:12	p2.2	...	12:30	1.7	23	F	7:24	8:06	a2.3	1:24	1:48	a2.3
24	W	7:00	7:12	p2.2	12:42	1:18	a2.2	24	S	8:06	9:00	a2.3	2:06	2:42	a2.2
25	T	7:48	8:12	p2.0	1:36	2:06	a2.1	25	S	8:54	10:00	a2.3	2:54	3:36	a2.1
26	F	8:30	9:12	1.9	2:24	3:00	a2.0	26	M	9:42	11:12	a2.3	3:48	4:36	a1.9
27	S	9:24	10:18	a2.0	3:24	4:00	a1.9	27	T	10:42	...	2.2	4:42	5:48	a1.8
28	S	10:18	11:36	a2.0	4:24	5:06	1.8	28	W	12:30	-A-	1.2	5:48	7:00	a1.6
29	M	11:18	...	2.1	5:24	6:12	a1.8	29	T	1:48	12:54	p2.0	6:54	8:06	1.5
30	T	12:48	12:24	p2.2	6:24	7:18	1.7	30	F	2:54	2:00	p2.0	8:12	9:06	p1.6
31	W	1:54	1:18	p2.3	7:18	8:24	1.8	31	S	3:54	3:06	p1.9	9:24	10:00	p1.6

A also at 11:48 a.m. (2.1)

The Kts. (knots) columns show the **maximum** predicted velocities of the stronger one of the Flood Currents and the stronger one of the Ebb Currents for each day.

The letter "a" means the velocity shown should occur **after** the **a.m.** Current Change. The letter "p" means the velocity shown should occur **after** the **p.m.** Current Change (even if next morning). No "a" or "p" means a.m. and p.m. velocities are the same for that day.

Avg. Max. Velocity: Flood 1.8 Kts., Ebb 1.9 Kts.
Max. Flood 3 hrs. 5 min. after Flood Starts, ±15 min.
Max. Ebb 3 hrs. 5 min. after Ebb Starts, ±15 min.

See pp. 22-29 for Current Change at other points.

2024 CURRENT TABLE
DELAWARE BAY ENTRANCE
38°51.22'N, 75°04.62'W

Daylight Saving Time	Daylight Saving Time
SEPTEMBER	**OCTOBER**

DAY OF MONTH	DAY OF WEEK	CURRENT TURNS TO						DAY OF MONTH	DAY OF WEEK	CURRENT TURNS TO					
		NORTHWEST Flood Starts			SOUTHEAST Ebb Starts					NORTHWEST Flood Starts			SOUTHEAST Ebb Starts		
		a.m.	**p.m.**	Kts.	a.m.	**p.m.**	Kts.			a.m.	**p.m.**	Kts.	a.m.	**p.m.**	Kts.
1	S	4:42	**4:06**	p1.8	10:24	**10:42**	p1.7	1	T	4:48	**4:48**	a1.8	10:54	**10:54**	p1.7
2	M	5:18	**5:00**	p1.8	11:12	**11:24**	p1.7	2	W	5:18	**5:24**	a1.9	11:30	**11:30**	p1.8
3	T	5:54	**5:48**	1.8	11:54	**...**	1.6	3	T	5:42	**5:54**	a1.9	11:54	**...**	1.7
4	W	6:31	**6:24**	a1.9	12:01	**12:30**	1.7	4	F	6:13	**6:18**	a2.0	12:01	**12:24**	a1.9
5	T	6:54	**7:00**	a1.9	12:30	**1:06**	1.7	5	S	6:36	**6:42**	a2.0	12:30	**12:54**	a1.9
6	F	7:18	**7:30**	a1.9	1:06	**1:36**	a1.7	6	S	7:00	**7:12**	a2.0	1:00	**1:24**	a1.9
7	S	7:42	**7:54**	a1.8	1:36	**2:06**	a1.7	7	M	7:30	**7:48**	a1.9	1:30	**1:54**	a1.8
8	S	8:12	**8:24**	a1.7	2:06	**2:36**	a1.7	8	T	8:00	**8:24**	a1.8	2:00	**2:30**	a1.7
9	M	8:42	**9:00**	a1.6	2:42	**3:12**	a1.6	9	W	8:36	**9:12**	a1.7	2:36	**3:12**	1.4
10	T	9:18	**9:42**	a1.5	3:18	**3:54**	a1.4	10	T	9:18	**10:18**	a1.5	3:24	**4:06**	p1.3
11	W	10:00	**10:48**	a1.5	4:00	**4:48**	a1.3	11	F	10:12	**11:42**	a1.4	4:36	**5:06**	p1.3
12	T	10:54	**...**	1.4	5:06	**5:42**	p1.2	12	S	11:30	**...**	1.4	6:06	**6:18**	p1.3
13	F	12:06	**-A-**	0.8	6:18	**6:42**	p1.3	13	S	1:06	**12:54**	p1.5	7:24	**7:30**	p1.5
14	S	1:24	**1:06**	p1.5	7:36	**7:48**	p1.5	14	M	2:06	**2:12**	p1.7	8:30	**8:36**	p1.8
15	S	2:30	**2:12**	p1.7	8:48	**8:48**	p1.7	15	T	3:00	**3:18**	p2.0	9:24	**9:36**	p2.0
16	M	3:24	**3:18**	p1.9	9:48	**9:48**	p1.9	16	W	3:42	**4:12**	p2.2	10:12	**10:24**	p2.2
17	T	4:12	**4:18**	p2.1	10:36	**10:42**	p2.1	17	T	4:24	**5:06**	2.3	10:54	**11:12**	2.4
18	W	4:54	**5:18**	p2.3	11:18	**11:30**	p2.3	18	F	5:06	**5:54**	a2.6	11:36	**11:54**	2.5
19	T	5:36	**6:06**	p2.4	...	**12:01**	2.4	19	S	5:48	**6:42**	a2.8	...	**12:24**	2.5
20	F	6:12	**7:00**	a2.5	12:18	**12:42**	p2.5	20	S	6:30	**7:36**	a2.9	12:36	**1:12**	a2.5
21	S	7:00	**7:48**	a2.7	1:00	**1:30**	2.4	21	M	7:12	**8:30**	a2.8	1:18	**2:00**	a2.4
22	S	7:42	**8:42**	a2.7	1:42	**2:18**	a2.4	22	T	8:00	**9:24**	a2.5	2:00	**2:54**	a2.1
23	M	8:24	**9:42**	a2.5	2:24	**3:12**	a2.2	23	W	8:48	**10:42**	a2.2	2:48	**3:48**	a1.7
24	T	9:12	**10:54**	a2.3	3:12	**4:12**	a1.9	24	T	9:42	**...**	1.8	3:54	**5:00**	a1.4
25	W	10:12	**...**	2.0	4:12	**5:24**	a1.6	25	F	12:06	**-C-**	0.9	5:24	**6:12**	1.1
26	T	12:24	**-B-**	1.0	5:24	**6:36**	a1.3	26	S	1:18	**12:36**	p1.3	6:54	**7:18**	p1.3
27	F	1:42	**12:36**	p1.6	6:48	**7:42**	p1.3	27	S	2:12	**1:54**	1.3	8:06	**8:18**	p1.3
28	S	2:42	**2:00**	p1.6	8:12	**8:48**	p1.4	28	M	3:00	**2:54**	a1.5	9:00	**9:06**	p1.4
29	S	3:30	**3:06**	p1.6	9:18	**9:36**	p1.5	29	T	3:36	**3:42**	a1.6	9:42	**9:48**	p1.5
30	M	4:12	**4:00**	1.6	10:12	**10:18**	p1.6	30	W	4:06	**4:18**	a1.7	10:18	**10:18**	p1.7
								31	T	4:36	**4:48**	a1.8	10:48	**10:48**	p1.8

A also at 11:54 a.m. (1.4)   B also at 11:18 a.m. (1.8)   C also at 11:00 a.m. (1.5)

The Kts. (knots) columns show the **maximum** predicted velocities of the stronger one of the Flood Currents and the stronger one of the Ebb Currents for each day.

The letter "a" means the velocity shown should occur **after** the **a.m.** Current Change. The letter "p" means the velocity shown should occur **after** the **p.m.** Current Change (even if next morning). No "a" or "p" means a.m. and p.m. velocities are the same for that day.

Avg. Max. Velocity: Flood 1.8 Kts., Ebb 1.9 Kts.

Max. Flood 3 hrs. 5 min. after Flood Starts, ±15 min.

Max. Ebb 3 hrs. 5 min. after Ebb Starts, ±15 min.

See pp. 22-29 for Current Change at other points.

2024 CURRENT TABLE
DELAWARE BAY ENTRANCE
38°51.22'N, 75°4.62'W

*Standard Time starts Nov. 3 at 2 a.m.   Standard Time

DAY OF MONTH	DAY OF WEEK	NORTHWEST Flood Starts			SOUTHEAST Ebb Starts			DAY OF MONTH	DAY OF WEEK	NORTHWEST Flood Starts			SOUTHEAST Ebb Starts		
		a.m.	p.m.	Kts.	a.m.	p.m.	Kts.			a.m.	p.m.	Kts.	a.m.	p.m.	Kts.
1	F	5:00	5:12	a1.9	11:18	11:18	p1.9	1	S	3:42	4:00	a2.0	10:06	10:18	p1.9
2	S	5:24	5:36	a2.0	11:48	11:48	p2.0	2	M	4:06	4:36	a2.1	10:42	10:48	1.8
3	S	*4:48	*5:06	a2.1	*11:12	*11:18	p2.0	3	T	4:42	5:18	a2.1	11:12	11:30	a1.9
4	M	5:19	5:42	a2.1	11:48	11:54	1.9	4	W	5:19	6:00	a2.1	11:54	...	1.9
5	T	5:48	6:18	a2.1	...	12:18	1.8	5	T	6:00	6:48	a2.0	12:12	12:36	p1.9
6	W	6:24	7:00	a1.9	12:30	1:00	p1.7	6	F	6:48	7:42	a1.8	1:00	1:24	p1.7
7	T	7:00	7:54	a1.7	1:12	1:42	p1.6	7	S	7:42	8:36	a1.6	2:00	2:18	p1.6
8	F	7:48	9:00	a1.5	2:06	2:36	p1.4	8	S	8:54	9:48	a1.5	3:06	3:30	p1.5
9	S	8:54	10:18	a1.4	3:24	3:42	p1.4	9	M	10:24	10:54	1.5	4:24	4:48	p1.5
10	S	10:24	11:36	a1.4	4:48	5:00	p1.4	10	T	11:42	11:54	p1.8	5:30	5:54	p1.6
11	M	11:54	...	1.6	6:00	6:12	p1.5	11	W	...	12:48	1.9	6:30	6:48	p1.9
12	T	12:36	1:06	p1.8	7:00	7:18	p1.8	12	T	12:48	1:48	a2.1	7:24	7:42	2.1
13	W	1:24	2:06	p2.1	7:54	8:12	p2.1	13	F	1:36	2:48	a2.4	8:18	8:36	2.2
14	T	2:12	3:00	2.2	8:42	9:00	2.3	14	S	2:24	3:42	a2.6	9:12	9:18	2.3
15	F	2:54	3:54	a2.5	9:30	9:48	2.4	15	S	3:12	4:30	a2.7	10:06	10:06	2.3
16	S	3:36	4:42	a2.7	10:18	10:30	2.5	16	M	4:00	5:24	a2.7	10:54	10:54	2.2
17	S	4:24	5:30	a2.9	11:06	11:12	2.4	17	T	4:48	6:18	a2.6	11:42	11:48	2.0
18	M	5:06	6:24	a2.9	11:54	11:54	2.2	18	W	5:36	7:12	a2.4	...	12:24	1.8
19	T	5:54	7:18	a2.7	...	12:42	1.9	19	T	6:30	8:00	a2.0	12:42	1:12	a1.7
20	W	6:42	8:18	a2.3	12:48	1:30	a1.9	20	F	7:24	8:48	a1.7	1:42	2:00	a1.4
21	T	7:30	9:24	a1.9	1:42	2:24	a1.5	21	S	8:30	9:42	1.3	2:42	2:54	1.2
22	F	8:30	10:36	a1.5	2:54	3:24	a1.2	22	S	9:42	10:42	1.2	3:48	3:54	p1.1
23	S	10:00	11:36	a1.2	4:18	4:36	1.0	23	M	10:54	11:30	p1.3	4:54	4:54	1.0
24	S	11:30	...	1.1	5:36	5:42	p1.0	24	T	11:48	...	1.1	5:42	5:42	p1.1
25	M	12:30	12:36	a1.3	6:36	6:36	p1.2	25	W	12:12	12:30	a1.4	6:24	6:30	p1.2
26	T	1:12	1:24	a1.5	7:24	7:24	p1.3	26	T	12:48	1:12	a1.5	7:06	7:06	p1.4
27	W	1:48	2:00	a1.6	8:00	8:00	p1.5	27	F	1:18	1:48	a1.6	7:42	7:48	p1.5
28	T	2:18	2:36	a1.7	8:36	8:36	p1.6	28	S	1:54	2:24	a1.7	8:18	8:30	p1.6
29	F	2:48	3:00	a1.8	9:06	9:12	p1.8	29	S	2:24	3:00	a1.8	8:54	9:12	1.6
30	S	3:12	3:30	a1.9	9:36	9:42	p1.8	30	M	3:00	3:36	a1.9	9:36	9:54	a1.7
								31	T	3:36	4:18	a2.0	10:12	10:36	a1.9

The Kts. (knots) columns show the **maximum** predicted velocities of the stronger one of the Flood Currents and the stronger one of the Ebb Currents for each day.

The letter "a" means the velocity shown should occur **after** the a.m. Current Change. The letter "p" means the velocity shown should occur **after** the p.m. Current Change (even if next morning). No "a" or "p" means a.m. and p.m. velocities are the same for that day.

Avg. Max. Velocity: Flood 1.8 Kts., Ebb 1.9 Kts.

Max. Flood 3 hrs. 5 min. after Flood Starts, ±15 min.

Max. Ebb 3 hrs. 5 min. after Ebb Starts, ±15 min.

See pp. 22-29 for Current Change at other points.

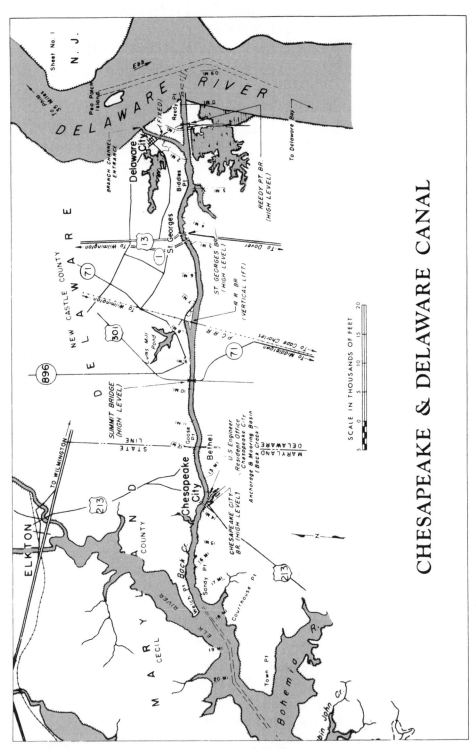

CHESAPEAKE & DELAWARE CANAL

See Chesapeake & Delaware Canal Current Tables, pp. 154-159

Chesapeake & Delaware Canal Regulations

(Traffic Dispatcher is located at Chesapeake City and monitors Channel 13.)

Philadelphia District Engineer issues notices periodically showing available channel depths and navigation conditions.

Projected Channel dimensions are 35 ft. deep and 450 ft. wide. (The branch to Delaware City is 8 ft. deep and 50 ft. wide.) The distance from the Delaware River Ship Channel to the Elk River is 19.1 miles.

1. Traffic controls, located at Reedy Point and Old Town Point Wharf, flash green when Canal is open, flash red when it is closed.
2. Vessel identification and monitoring are performed by TV cameras at Reedy Point and Old Town Point Wharf.
3. The following vessels, tugs and tows are required to have radiotelephones:
   a. Power vessels of 300 gross tons and upward.
   b. All commercial vessels of 100 gross tons and upward carrying 1 or more passengers for hire.
   c. Every towing vessel of 26 feet or over.
4. Vessels listed in 3. will not enter the Canal until radio communication is made with the dispatcher and clearance is received. Ships' captains will tell the dispatcher the estimated time of passing Reedy Point or Town Point. Communication is to be established on Channel 13 (156.65 MHz) two hours prior to entering the canal. Dispatcher also monitors Channel 16 (156.8 MHz) to respond to emergencies.
5. A westbound vessel must be able to pass Reedy Is. or Pea Patch Is. within 2 hours of receiving clearance; an eastbound vessel must be able to pass Arnold Point within 2 hours. If passage is not made within 2 hours, a new clearance must be solicited. Vessels must also report to the dispatcher the time of passing the outer end of the jetties at Reedy Point and Old Town Point Wharf.
6. Maximum combined extreme breadth of vessels meeting and overtaking each other is 190 feet.
7. Vessels of all types are required to travel at a safe speed to avoid damage by suction or wash to wharves, landings, other boats, etc. Operators of yachts, motorboats, etc. are cautioned that there are many large, deep-draft ocean-going and commercial vessels using the Canal. There is "no anchoring" in the canal at any time. Moor or anchor outside of Reedy Point, near Arnold Point, or in Chesapeake City Basin.
8. Vessels proceeding *with* the current shall have the right-of-way but all small pleasure craft shall relinquish the right-of-way to deeper draft vessels which have a limited maneuvering ability.
9. Vessels under sail will not be permitted in the Canal.
10. Vessels difficult to handle must use the Canal during daylight hours and must have tug assistance. They should clear Reedy Point Bridge (going east) or Chesapeake City Bridge (going west) before dark.
11. Any tows over 760' contact dispatcher 72 hours prior to passage.

Anchorage and wharfage facilities for small vessels only are at Chesapeake City and permission to use them for more than 24 hours must be obtained from Chesapeake City.

The **railroad bridge** has a clearance when closed of 45 ft. at MHW. The bridge monitors Channel 13 and gives 30 minutes notice prior to lowering.

The **five highway bridges** are high level and fixed.

Normal tide range is 5.4 ft. at Delaware R. end of the Canal and 2.6 ft. at Chesapeake City. Local mean low water at Courthouse Pt. is 2.5 ft. and decreases gradually eastward to 0.6 ft. at Delaware R. (See pp. 18 and 19 for times of High Water in this area.)
Note: A violent northeast storm may raise tide 4 to 5 ft. above normal in the Canal; a westerly storm may cause low tide to fall slightly below normal at Chesapeake City and as much as 4.0 ft. below normal at Reedy Point.

2024 CURRENT TABLE
CHESAPEAKE & DELAWARE CANAL
39°31.83'N, 75°49.66'W at Chesapeake City

Standard Time							Standard Time					
JANUARY							**FEBRUARY**					
DAY OF MONTH	DAY OF WEEK	CURRENT TURNS TO					DAY OF MONTH	DAY OF WEEK	CURRENT TURNS TO			
		EAST Flood Starts			WEST Ebb Starts				EAST Flood Starts			WEST Ebb Starts
		a.m.	**p.m.**	Kts.	a.m. **p.m.**	Kts.			a.m.	**p.m.**	Kts.	a.m. **p.m.** Kts.
1	M	7:42	**7:54**	p1.8	1:54 **1:06**	p1.9	1	T	8:36	**8:24**	p1.8	1:54 **2:30** a1.9
2	T	8:24	**8:36**	p1.7	2:24 **1:54**	p1.7	2	F	9:36	**9:06**	p1.7	2:30 **3:36** a1.9
3	W	9:12	**9:12**	p1.7	2:54 **2:54**	a1.6	3	S	10:36	**9:54**	p1.6	3:12 **4:48** a2.0
4	T	10:07	**10:00**	p1.6	3:30 **4:00**	a1.7	4	S	11:37	**10:48**	p1.6	4:00 **6:12** a2.1
5	F	11:12	**10:42**	p1.6	4:06 **5:18**	a1.8	5	M	...	**12:42**	1.5	4:54 **7:18** a2.2
6	S	-A-	**12:12**	1.4	4:54 **6:30**	a1.9	6	T	12:01	**1:42**	1.6	5:54 **8:24** a2.2
7	S	...	**1:18**	1.5	5:42 **7:42**	a2.1	7	W	1:06	**2:42**	p1.8	6:54 **9:18** a2.3
8	M	12:36	**2:18**	p1.6	6:30 **8:48**	a2.2	8	T	2:18	**3:36**	p2.0	7:54 **10:00** a2.4
9	T	1:36	**3:12**	p1.8	7:24 **9:48**	a2.3	9	F	3:12	**4:24**	p2.1	9:00 **10:36** a2.5
10	W	2:42	**4:00**	p2.0	8:18 **10:36**	a2.5	10	S	4:06	**5:12**	a2.2	10:00 **11:12** a2.6
11	T	3:36	**4:48**	p2.1	9:12 **11:18**	a2.6	11	S	4:54	**5:54**	a2.4	11:00 **11:48** a2.5
12	F	4:24	**5:36**	p2.2	10:06 **11:59**	a2.6	12	M	5:48	**6:42**	a2.5	... **12:01** 2.3
13	S	5:18	**6:18**	2.1	11:00 ...	2.6	13	T	6:42	**7:24**	a2.5	12:24 **1:00** 2.1
14	S	6:06	**7:06**	a2.2	12:36 **12:01**	p2.5	14	W	7:36	**8:06**	a2.4	1:00 **2:00** a2.2
15	M	7:00	**7:54**	a2.3	1:06 **1:00**	p2.3	15	T	8:42	**8:54**	a2.2	1:36 **3:12** a2.3
16	T	7:54	**8:36**	a2.3	1:42 **2:06**	p2.0	16	F	9:48	**9:42**	a2.0	2:24 **4:24** a2.3
17	W	8:54	**9:24**	a2.2	2:18 **3:12**	a2.0	17	S	10:54	**10:36**	a1.8	3:12 **5:36** a2.2
18	T	10:00	**10:12**	a2.0	3:00 **4:24**	a2.1	18	S	11:59	**11:36**	a1.7	4:12 **6:48** a2.1
19	F	11:06	**11:06**	a1.9	3:48 **5:42**	a2.1	19	M	...	**1:00**	1.8	5:12 **7:42** a2.1
20	S	...	**12:18**	1.8	4:42 **7:00**	a2.2	20	T	12:42	**1:54**	p1.9	6:12 **8:36** a2.0
21	S	12:01	**1:24**	p1.8	5:36 **8:06**	a2.2	21	W	1:48	**2:48**	p1.9	7:12 **9:18** a1.9
22	M	1:00	**2:24**	p1.9	6:36 **9:06**	a2.2	22	T	2:42	**3:30**	p1.9	8:12 **9:54** a1.9
23	T	2:00	**3:12**	p2.0	7:30 **9:54**	a2.2	23	F	3:30	**4:06**	p1.8	9:00 **10:30** a1.9
24	W	3:00	**4:00**	p2.0	8:24 **10:30**	a2.2	24	S	4:12	**4:42**	p1.8	9:48 **10:54** a1.9
25	T	3:48	**4:36**	p2.0	9:12 **11:06**	a2.1	25	S	4:48	**5:12**	p1.8	10:36 **11:24** a1.8
26	F	4:36	**5:12**	p2.0	10:00 **11:42**	a2.1	26	M	5:24	**5:42**	1.8	11:18 **11:42** 1.8
27	S	5:12	**5:48**	p1.9	10:42 ...	2.1	27	T	6:00	**6:12**	a1.9	... **12:01** 1.7
28	S	5:54	**6:18**	p1.9	12:12 **-B-**	1.5	28	W	6:42	**6:36**	1.8	12:06 **12:42** a1.9
29	M	6:30	**6:48**	p1.9	12:36 **12:06**	p1.9	29	T	7:24	**7:06**	1.8	12:30 **1:24** a2.0
30	T	7:06	**7:18**	1.8	1:00 **12:48**	p1.8						
31	W	7:48	**7:48**	p1.8	1:24 **1:36**	a1.8						

A also at 11:36 p.m. (1.5)   **B** also at 11:24 a.m. (2.0)

The Kts. (knots) columns show the **maximum** predicted velocities of the stronger one of the Flood Currents and the stronger one of the Ebb Currents for each day.

The letter "a" means the velocity shown should occur **after** the **a.m.** Current Change. The letter "p" means the velocity shown should occur **after** the **p.m.** Current Change (even if next morning). No "a" or "p" means a.m. and p.m. velocities are the same for that day.

Avg. Max. Velocity: Flood 2.0 Kts., Ebb 1.9 Kts.

Max. Flood 3 hrs. 10 min. after Flood Starts ±45 min.

Max. Ebb 2 hrs. 45 min. after Ebb Starts ±45 min.

See pp. 22-29 for Current Change at other points.

Note *from NOS: These predictions should be considered questionable. Caution is advised.*

2024 CURRENT TABLE
CHESAPEAKE & DELAWARE CANAL

39°31.83'N, 75°49.66'W at Chesapeake City

*Daylight Time starts March 10 at 2 a.m.   Daylight Saving Time

MARCH | APRIL

D A Y O F M O N T H	D A Y O F W E E K	EAST Flood Starts a.m.	EAST Flood Starts p.m.	EAST Flood Starts Kts.	WEST Ebb Starts a.m.	WEST Ebb Starts p.m.	WEST Ebb Starts Kts.	D A Y O F M O N T H	D A Y O F W E E K	EAST Flood Starts a.m.	EAST Flood Starts p.m.	EAST Flood Starts Kts.	WEST Ebb Starts a.m.	WEST Ebb Starts p.m.	WEST Ebb Starts Kts.
1	F	8:12	7:42	p1.8	1:06	2:18	a2.1	1	M	10:36	10:12	a1.7	2:54	5:24	a2.2
2	S	9:06	8:30	p1.7	1:42	3:24	a2.1	2	T	11:36	11:24	a1.7	3:48	6:18	a2.2
3	S	10:00	9:24	p1.6	2:24	4:36	a2.2	3	W	...	12:36	1.7	5:00	7:12	a2.1
4	M	11:07	10:30	p1.6	3:18	5:48	a2.2	4	T	12:31	1:36	1.7	6:12	8:00	a2.1
5	T	-A-	12:06	1.6	4:18	6:48	a2.2	5	F	1:36	2:36	1.8	7:30	8:42	a2.1
6	W	...	1:06	1.7	5:24	7:42	a2.2	6	S	2:36	3:30	a2.1	8:42	9:18	a2.1
7	T	12:48	2:06	p1.8	6:36	8:30	a2.3	7	S	3:30	4:24	a2.4	9:48	10:00	p2.2
8	F	1:54	3:06	1.9	7:48	9:12	a2.3	8	M	4:30	5:06	a2.5	10:54	10:36	p2.4
9	S	2:54	3:54	a2.2	8:54	9:48	a2.4	9	T	5:24	5:48	a2.6	11:54	11:12	p2.6
10	S	*4:48	*5:42	a2.4	*10:54	*11:24	a2.3	10	W	6:18	6:30	a2.6	-C-	12:54	1.6
11	M	5:36	6:24	a2.6	11:54	...	2.2	11	T	7:12	7:18	a2.5	...	1:54	1.3
12	T	6:30	7:06	a2.6	12:01	12:54	a2.3	12	F	8:06	8:00	a2.3	12:36	2:54	a2.6
13	W	7:24	7:48	a2.6	12:36	1:54	a2.4	13	S	9:06	9:00	a2.1	1:24	3:54	a2.5
14	T	8:24	8:36	a2.4	1:18	3:00	a2.5	14	S	10:00	10:00	a1.9	2:12	4:54	a2.3
15	F	9:24	9:24	a2.1	2:00	4:06	a2.4	15	M	10:54	11:06	a1.8	3:06	5:48	a2.0
16	S	10:30	10:18	a1.9	2:48	5:12	a2.3	16	T	11:48	...	1.7	4:06	6:36	a1.8
17	S	11:30	11:18	a1.8	3:36	6:18	a2.2	17	W	12:06	12:42	p1.7	5:18	7:18	a1.7
18	M	...	12:30	1.7	4:36	7:18	a2.0	18	T	1:06	1:30	p1.6	6:30	8:00	1.5
19	T	12:24	1:24	p1.7	5:48	8:06	a1.9	19	F	2:00	2:18	p1.6	7:36	8:36	p1.6
20	W	1:30	2:18	p1.8	6:54	8:54	a1.7	20	S	2:48	3:06	p1.6	8:42	9:12	p1.8
21	T	2:30	3:06	p1.7	8:00	9:30	a1.7	21	S	3:36	3:48	1.6	9:36	9:42	p1.9
22	F	3:18	3:54	p1.7	9:00	10:06	1.6	22	M	4:18	4:24	a1.7	10:30	10:12	p2.1
23	S	4:06	4:30	p1.7	9:54	10:36	p1.7	23	T	5:00	4:54	a1.8	11:18	10:36	p2.2
24	S	4:48	5:06	1.7	10:42	11:06	p1.8	24	W	5:42	5:24	a1.9	-D-	12:06	1.2
25	M	5:24	5:36	a1.8	11:24	11:30	p1.9	25	T	6:24	5:54	a1.9	-E-	12:54	1.1
26	T	6:06	6:06	a1.9	-B-	12:12	1.5	26	F	7:06	6:30	a1.9	...	1:42	1.0
27	W	6:42	6:30	a1.9	...	12:54	1.4	27	S	7:48	7:12	a1.9	12:12	2:30	a2.4
28	T	7:24	7:00	a1.9	12:18	1:36	a2.2	28	S	8:30	8:06	a1.8	12:48	3:18	a2.4
29	F	8:06	7:36	a1.8	12:48	2:24	a2.3	29	M	9:18	9:06	a1.8	1:36	4:12	a2.3
30	S	8:48	8:18	1.7	1:24	3:18	a2.3	30	T	10:12	10:12	a1.8	2:30	5:00	a2.2
31	S	9:42	9:12	a1.7	2:06	4:18	a2.3								

A also at 11:42 p.m. (1.6)   B also at 11:54 p.m. (2.1)   C also at 11:54 p.m. (2.7)
D also at 11:06 p.m. (2.3)   E also st 11:36 p.m. (2.4)

The Kts. (knots) columns show the **maximum** predicted velocities of the stronger one of the Flood Currents and the stronger one of the Ebb Currents for each day.
The letter "a" means the velocity shown should occur **after** the a.m. Current Change. The letter "p" means the velocity shown should occur **after** the p.m. Current Change (even if next morning). No "a" or "p" means a.m. and p.m. velocities are the same for that day.
Avg. Max. Velocity: Flood 2.0 Kts., Ebb 1.9 Kts.
Max. Flood 3 hrs. 10 min. after Flood Starts ±45 min.
Max. Ebb 2 hrs. 45 min. after Ebb Starts ±45 min.
See pp. 22-29 for Current Change at other points.
Note *from NOS: These predictions should be considered questionable. Caution is advised.*

2024 CURRENT TABLE
CHESAPEAKE & DELAWARE CANAL

39°31.83'N, 75°49.66'W at Chesapeake City

Daylight Saving Time   Daylight Saving Time

MAY								JUNE					
DAY OF MONTH	DAY OF WEEK	CURRENT TURNS TO											
		EAST Flood Starts			WEST Ebb Starts			EAST Flood Starts			WEST Ebb Starts		
		a.m.	p.m.	Kts.	a.m.	p.m.	Kts.	a.m.	p.m.	Kts.	a.m.	p.m.	Kts.
DAY OF MONTH	DAY OF WEEK						DAY OF MONTH	DAY OF WEEK					
1	W	11:06	11:18	a1.8	3:36	5:48	a2.1	1	S	12:06	12:30	a1.9	6:12	6:30	p2.0
2	T	...	12:06	1.8	4:48	6:30	a2.0	2	S	1:12	1:24	a2.0	7:30	7:12	p2.3
3	F	12:18	1:06	a1.8	6:12	7:12	a1.9	3	M	2:12	2:12	a2.1	8:36	7:54	p2.5
4	S	1:19	2:00	a2.0	7:30	7:54	p2.0	4	T	3:13	3:00	a2.2	9:48	8:36	p2.7
5	S	2:18	2:54	a2.2	8:36	8:30	p2.3	5	W	4:12	3:54	a2.3	10:48	9:24	p2.8
6	M	3:18	3:42	a2.4	9:48	9:12	p2.5	6	T	5:06	4:42	a2.3	11:48	10:06	p2.8
7	T	4:18	4:30	a2.5	10:48	9:54	p2.7	7	F	5:54	5:30	a2.3	-D-	12:42	1.0
8	W	5:12	5:12	a2.5	11:48	10:36	p2.8	8	S	6:42	6:24	a2.2	-E-	1:30	1.0
9	T	6:06	6:00	a2.5	-A-	12:48	1.2	9	S	7:24	7:18	a2.2	...	2:12	1.1
10	F	7:00	6:48	a2.4	...	1:48	1.1	10	M	8:06	8:18	a2.1	12:24	2:54	a2.3
11	S	7:48	7:36	a2.2	12:06	2:36	a2.6	11	T	8:42	9:12	a2.0	1:12	3:36	a2.1
12	S	8:36	8:36	a2.1	12:48	3:30	a2.4	12	W	9:24	10:12	a1.9	2:06	4:12	a1.8
13	M	9:24	9:42	a2.0	1:42	4:18	a2.2	13	T	10:06	11:00	a1.8	3:06	4:48	a1.6
14	T	10:12	10:42	a1.8	2:36	5:06	a1.9	14	F	10:48	11:54	a1.7	4:18	5:24	p1.6
15	W	11:00	11:42	a1.8	3:36	5:48	a1.7	15	S	11:36	...	1.7	5:30	6:00	p1.8
16	T	11:48	...	1.7	4:48	6:24	1.5	16	S	12:48	12:18	p1.6	6:42	6:36	p2.0
17	F	12:36	12:36	p1.6	6:06	7:06	p1.7	17	M	1:42	1:06	p1.6	7:48	7:18	p2.2
18	S	1:24	1:24	p1.6	7:12	7:42	p1.8	18	T	2:36	1:48	p1.6	8:54	7:54	p2.3
19	S	2:18	2:06	p1.6	8:18	8:12	p2.0	19	W	3:30	2:36	a1.7	10:00	8:30	p2.5
20	M	3:06	2:48	1.6	9:18	8:48	p2.1	20	T	4:18	3:24	a1.8	10:54	9:12	p2.6
21	T	3:54	3:30	a1.7	10:12	9:18	p2.3	21	F	5:06	4:18	a1.9	11:48	9:54	p2.6
22	W	4:42	4:12	a1.8	11:12	9:48	p2.4	22	S	5:48	5:06	a2.0	-F-	12:36	0.8
23	T	5:24	4:48	a1.9	11:59	10:24	p2.5	23	S	6:30	6:00	a2.0	-G-	1:18	0.9
24	F	6:06	5:30	a1.9	-B-	12:48	0.8	24	M	7:12	6:54	a2.1	...	2:00	1.0
25	S	6:48	6:12	a1.9	-C-	1:36	0.8	25	T	8:00	7:48	a2.0	12:24	2:36	a2.5
26	S	7:30	7:06	a2.0	...	2:24	0.9	26	W	8:42	8:48	a2.0	1:18	3:12	a2.3
27	M	8:18	8:00	a2.0	12:30	3:06	a2.5	27	T	9:30	9:48	a1.9	2:24	3:48	a2.1
28	T	9:00	9:00	a1.9	1:24	3:48	a2.3	28	F	10:24	10:54	p1.9	3:36	4:24	a1.9
29	W	9:54	10:06	a1.9	2:24	4:30	a2.2	29	S	11:12	...	1.8	4:54	5:06	p2.0
30	T	10:48	11:06	1.8	3:36	5:06	a2.0	30	S	12:01	12:01	a1.9	6:12	5:48	p2.3
31	F	11:36	...	1.8	4:54	5:48	a1.9								

A also at 11:18 p.m. (2.8)   B also at 11:00 p.m. (2.5)   C also at 11:42 p.m. (2.5)
D also at 10:54 p.m. (2.7)   E also at 11:36 p.m. (2.5)   F also at 10:42 p.m. (2.6)
G also at 11:30 p.m. (2.6)

The Kts. (knots) columns show the **maximum** predicted velocities of the stronger one of the Flood Currents and the stronger one of the Ebb Currents for each day.
The letter "a" means the velocity shown should occur **after** the **a.m.** Current Change. The letter "p" means the velocity shown should occur **after** the **p.m.** Current Change (even if next morning). No "a" or "p" means a.m. and p.m. velocities are the same for that day.
Avg. Max. Velocity: Flood 2.0 Kts., Ebb 1.9 Kts.
Max. Flood 3 hrs. 10 min. after Flood Starts ±45 min.
Max. Ebb 2 hrs. 45 min. after Ebb Starts ±45 min.

See pp. 22-29 for Current Change at other points.

Note *from NOS: These predictions should be considered questionable. Caution is advised.*

2024 CURRENT TABLE
CHESAPEAKE & DELAWARE CANAL
39°31.83'N, 75°49.66'W at Chesapeake City

Daylight Saving Time							Daylight Saving Time					
JULY							**AUGUST**					
DAY OF MONTH	DAY OF WEEK	CURRENT TURNS TO					DAY OF MONTH	DAY OF WEEK	CURRENT TURNS TO			
		EAST Flood Starts			WEST Ebb Starts				EAST Flood Starts			WEST Ebb Starts	
		a.m.	**p.m.**	Kts.	a.m.	**p.m.**	Kts.			a.m.	**p.m.**	Kts.	a.m.	**p.m.**	Kts.
1	M	1:00	**12:48**	a1.9	7:30	**6:36**	p2.5	1	T	2:54	**2:18**	a2.0	9:36	**8:00**	p2.5
2	T	2:06	**1:36**	a2.0	8:42	**7:24**	p2.6	2	F	3:48	**3:18**	a2.1	10:24	**8:54**	p2.4
3	W	3:06	**2:30**	a2.1	9:48	**8:12**	p2.7	3	S	4:36	**4:12**	a2.1	11:06	**9:42**	p2.3
4	T	4:01	**3:30**	a2.2	10:42	**9:00**	p2.7	4	S	5:19	**5:06**	a2.1	11:48	**10:30**	p2.2
5	F	4:54	**4:24**	a2.2	11:36	**9:48**	p2.6	5	M	5:54	**5:54**	a2.0	-E-	**12:24**	1.3
6	S	5:36	**5:18**	a2.2	-A-	**12:18**	1.0	6	T	6:24	**6:36**	a1.9	...	**12:54**	1.4
7	S	6:18	**6:12**	a2.1	-B-	**1:00**	1.1	7	W	6:54	**7:18**	a1.9	12:01	**1:24**	a1.9
8	M	6:54	**7:00**	a2.1	...	**1:36**	1.2	8	T	7:24	**8:00**	a1.9	12:42	**1:48**	a1.8
9	T	7:30	**7:48**	a2.0	12:06	**2:12**	a2.1	9	F	7:54	**8:48**	a1.8	1:30	**2:18**	1.7
10	W	8:06	**8:36**	a1.9	12:54	**2:42**	a2.0	10	S	8:30	**9:42**	a1.8	2:24	**2:48**	p1.8
11	T	8:36	**9:30**	a1.9	1:48	**3:18**	a1.8	11	S	9:00	**10:36**	a1.8	3:18	**3:18**	p1.9
12	F	9:18	**10:18**	a1.8	2:42	**3:48**	1.6	12	M	9:42	**11:36**	a1.8	4:30	**4:00**	p2.1
13	S	9:54	**11:12**	a1.8	3:42	**4:24**	p1.8	13	T	10:24	...	1.8	5:42	**4:42**	p2.2
14	S	10:36	...	1.7	4:54	**5:00**	p1.9	14	W	12:36	**-F-**	1.4	7:00	**5:36**	p2.3
15	M	12:12	**-C-**	1.4	6:12	**5:36**	p2.1	15	T	1:30	**12:18**	p1.7	8:06	**6:30**	p2.4
16	T	1:12	**12:06**	p1.7	7:24	**6:24**	p2.3	16	F	2:24	**1:24**	p1.7	9:06	**7:24**	p2.5
17	W	2:06	**12:54**	p1.7	8:36	**7:06**	p2.4	17	S	3:18	**2:36**	1.8	9:54	**8:24**	p2.5
18	T	3:00	**1:54**	p1.7	9:36	**7:54**	p2.5	18	S	4:12	**3:36**	1.9	10:36	**9:24**	p2.6
19	F	3:54	**2:54**	a1.8	10:30	**8:42**	p2.6	19	M	4:54	**4:30**	p2.1	11:18	**10:24**	p2.6
20	S	4:36	**3:54**	a1.9	11:18	**9:36**	p2.6	20	T	5:42	**5:24**	p2.2	11:54	**11:24**	p2.5
21	S	5:24	**4:54**	a2.0	11:59	**10:30**	p2.6	21	W	6:30	**6:18**	p2.3	...	**12:30**	1.7
22	M	6:06	**5:42**	a2.1	-D-	**12:42**	1.1	22	T	7:12	**7:12**	p2.3	12:24	**1:00**	a2.3
23	T	6:54	**6:36**	a2.1	...	**1:18**	1.3	23	F	7:54	**8:12**	p2.2	1:24	**1:36**	2.1
24	W	7:36	**7:30**	2.0	12:24	**1:48**	a2.4	24	S	8:36	**9:18**	p2.1	2:30	**2:18**	p2.2
25	T	8:24	**8:30**	2.0	1:24	**2:24**	a2.2	25	S	9:24	**10:24**	p1.9	3:42	**3:00**	p2.3
26	F	9:06	**9:36**	p2.0	2:30	**3:00**	a2.0	26	M	10:12	**11:36**	p1.8	4:54	**3:54**	p2.3
27	S	9:54	**10:42**	p1.9	3:42	**3:42**	p2.0	27	T	11:00	...	1.6	6:06	**4:48**	p2.3
28	S	10:42	**11:48**	p1.9	4:54	**4:24**	p2.2	28	W	12:36	**12:01**	a1.8	7:18	**5:48**	p2.3
29	M	11:30	...	1.7	6:12	**5:18**	p2.4	29	T	1:36	**1:06**	a1.8	8:18	**6:48**	p2.2
30	T	12:54	**12:18**	a1.8	7:30	**6:12**	p2.5	30	F	2:36	**2:12**	a1.9	9:06	**7:48**	p2.1
31	W	1:54	**1:18**	a1.9	8:36	**7:06**	p2.5	31	S	3:24	**3:12**	a1.9	9:54	**8:48**	p2.0

A also at 10:36 p.m. (2.4)   B also at 11:24 p.m. (2.3)   C also at 11:18 a.m. (1.7)
D also at 11:24 p.m. (2.6)   E also at 11:18 p.m. (2.1)   F also at 11:18 a.m. (1.7)

The Kts. (knots) columns show the **maximum** predicted velocities of the stronger one of the Flood Currents and the stronger one of the Ebb Currents for each day.
The letter "a" means the velocity shown should occur **after** the a.m. Current Change. The letter "p" means the velocity shown should occur **after** the p.m. Current Change (even if next morning). No "a" or "p" means a.m. and p.m. velocities are the same for that day.
Avg. Max. Velocity: Flood 2.0 Kts., Ebb 1.9 Kts.
Max. Flood 3 hrs. 10 min. after Flood Starts ±45 min.
Max. Ebb 2 hrs. 45 min. after Ebb Starts ±45 min.
See pp. 22-29 for Current Change at other points.
Note *from NOS: These predictions should be considered questionable. Caution is advised.*

2024 CURRENT TABLE
CHESAPEAKE & DELAWARE CANAL
39°31.83'N, 75°49.66'W at Chesapeake City

Daylight Saving Time   Daylight Saving Time

SEPTEMBER

Day of Month	Day of Week	EAST Flood Starts a.m.	**p.m.**	Kts.	WEST Ebb Starts a.m.	**p.m.**	Kts.
1	S	4:06	**4:00**	a1.9	10:30	**9:36**	p2.0
2	M	4:48	**4:48**	a1.9	11:06	**10:24**	p1.9
3	T	5:24	**5:30**	a1.8	11:36	**11:12**	p1.8
4	W	5:55	**6:12**	a1.8	-A-	**12:06**	1.6
5	T	6:24	**6:48**	a1.8	...	**12:30**	1.7
6	F	6:48	**7:30**	a1.8	12:36	**12:54**	p1.9
7	S	7:18	**8:18**	a1.8	1:24	**1:24**	p2.0
8	S	7:42	**9:06**	a1.8	2:12	**1:54**	p2.1
9	M	8:18	**10:00**	a1.8	3:06	**2:30**	p2.1
10	T	9:00	**11:00**	a1.8	4:06	**3:12**	p2.2
11	W	9:54	**11:54**	a1.7	5:18	**4:00**	p2.2
12	T	10:54	**...**	1.7	6:30	**5:00**	p2.3
13	F	12:54	**12:01**	p1.7	7:30	**6:00**	p2.3
14	S	1:48	**1:12**	p1.8	8:18	**7:06**	p2.4
15	S	2:42	**2:12**	p1.9	9:06	**8:12**	p2.4
16	M	3:36	**3:18**	p2.1	9:48	**9:18**	p2.4
17	T	4:30	**4:12**	p2.3	10:24	**10:18**	p2.4
18	W	5:12	**5:06**	p2.4	11:06	**11:24**	p2.2
19	T	6:00	**6:00**	p2.5	11:36	**...**	2.1
20	F	6:42	**7:00**	p2.4	12:24	**12:18**	p2.3
21	S	7:24	**8:00**	p2.3	1:24	**12:54**	p2.4
22	S	8:06	**9:06**	p2.1	2:30	**1:42**	p2.5
23	M	8:54	**10:06**	p1.9	3:36	**2:30**	p2.4
24	T	9:42	**11:12**	p1.8	4:42	**3:24**	p2.3
25	W	10:42	**...**	1.5	5:48	**4:24**	p2.2
26	T	12:12	**-B-**	1.7	6:48	**5:30**	p2.0
27	F	1:06	**12:54**	a1.7	7:42	**6:36**	p1.9
28	S	2:00	**1:54**	a1.7	8:24	**7:36**	p1.8
29	S	2:48	**2:54**	a1.7	9:06	**8:36**	p1.7
30	M	3:36	**3:42**	a1.7	9:48	**9:30**	p1.7

OCTOBER

Day of Month	Day of Week	EAST Flood Starts a.m.	**p.m.**	Kts.	WEST Ebb Starts a.m.	**p.m.**	Kts.
1	T	4:12	**4:30**	a1.7	10:18	**10:18**	1.6
2	W	4:48	**5:12**	1.7	10:48	**11:06**	a1.7
3	T	5:24	**5:48**	1.7	11:18	**11:54**	a1.9
4	F	5:49	**6:30**	1.7	11:42	**...**	2.0
5	S	6:12	**7:12**	1.7	12:36	**12:06**	p2.1
6	S	6:42	**7:54**	a1.8	1:24	**12:36**	p2.2
7	M	7:12	**8:42**	a1.8	2:06	**1:12**	p2.3
8	T	7:48	**9:30**	a1.8	3:00	**1:54**	p2.3
9	W	8:36	**10:24**	a1.7	3:54	**2:36**	p2.3
10	T	9:36	**11:18**	a1.7	4:54	**3:30**	p2.2
11	F	10:42	**...**	1.7	5:48	**4:30**	p2.2
12	S	12:12	**-C-**	1.6	6:42	**5:42**	p2.2
13	S	1:12	**12:54**	p1.8	7:30	**6:54**	p2.2
14	M	2:06	**1:54**	p2.0	8:12	**8:06**	p2.1
15	T	3:06	**2:54**	p2.2	8:54	**9:12**	p2.1
16	W	3:54	**3:54**	p2.4	9:36	**10:18**	2.0
17	T	4:42	**4:54**	p2.5	10:18	**11:18**	a2.2
18	F	5:30	**5:48**	p2.5	10:54	**...**	2.5
19	S	6:12	**6:48**	p2.5	12:24	**-D-**	1.7
20	S	6:54	**7:48**	p2.3	1:24	**12:18**	p2.7
21	M	7:36	**8:42**	p2.1	2:24	**1:06**	p2.6
22	T	8:30	**9:42**	p2.0	3:24	**2:00**	p2.4
23	W	9:24	**10:36**	p1.8	4:18	**2:54**	p2.2
24	T	10:30	**11:30**	p1.7	5:12	**3:54**	p2.0
25	F	11:36	**...**	1.4	6:06	**5:06**	p1.8
26	S	12:24	**12:36**	a1.6	6:54	**6:12**	p1.6
27	S	1:12	**1:30**	a1.5	7:36	**7:18**	p1.5
28	M	2:06	**2:24**	a1.5	8:18	**8:24**	a1.6
29	T	2:48	**3:18**	1.5	8:54	**9:18**	a1.7
30	W	3:30	**4:06**	p1.6	9:30	**10:12**	a1.8
31	T	4:12	**4:48**	p1.7	10:00	**11:00**	a1.9

A also at 11:54 p.m. (1.7)   **B** also at 11:48 a.m. (1.4)   **C** also at 11:48 a.m. (1.7)
D also at 11:36 a.m. (2.6)

The Kts. (knots) columns show the **maximum** predicted velocities of the stronger one of the Flood Currents and the stronger one of the Ebb Currents for each day.

The letter "a" means the velocity shown should occur **after** the **a.m.** Current Change. The letter "p" means the velocity shown should occur **after** the **p.m.** Current Change (even if next morning). No "a" or "p" means a.m. and p.m. velocities are the same for that day.

Avg. Max. Velocity: Flood 2.0 Kts., Ebb 1.9 Kts.

Max. Flood 3 hrs. 10 min. after Flood Starts ±45 min.

Max. Ebb 2 hrs. 45 min. after Ebb Starts ±45 min.

See pp. 22-29 for Current Change at other points.

Note *from NOS: These predictions should be considered questionable. Caution is advised.*

2024 CURRENT TABLE
CHESAPEAKE & DELAWARE CANAL
39°31.83'N, 75°49.66'W at Chesapeake City

*Standard Time starts Nov. 3 at 2 a.m.   Standard Time

NOVEMBER | DECEMBER

Day of Month	Day of Week	EAST Flood Starts a.m.	p.m.	Kts.	WEST Ebb Starts a.m.	p.m.	Kts.	Day of Month	Day of Week	EAST Flood Starts a.m.	p.m.	Kts.	WEST Ebb Starts a.m.	p.m.	Kts.
1	F	4:48	5:36	p1.8	10:30	11:48	a2.1	1	S	3:42	5:00	p1.8	9:18	11:36	a2.3
2	S	5:18	6:18	p1.8	11:00	...	2.2	2	M	4:24	5:42	p1.9	10:00	...	2.4
3	S	*4:42	*5:54	p1.8	12:36	-A-	1.1	3	T	5:00	6:18	p1.9	12:18	-F-	0.9
4	M	5:19	6:36	p1.8	12:24	-B-	1.0	4	W	5:49	7:00	p1.9	12:54	-G-	1.0
5	T	5:54	7:18	1.7	1:06	-C-	1.0	5	T	6:30	7:42	p1.9	1:30	12:12	p2.4
6	W	6:36	8:06	1.7	1:54	12:24	p2.4	6	F	7:24	8:24	1.8	2:06	1:06	p2.3
7	T	7:30	8:48	1.7	2:36	1:18	p2.3	7	S	8:18	9:12	a1.9	2:42	2:06	p2.1
8	F	8:30	9:42	1.7	3:24	2:12	p2.2	8	S	9:12	10:06	a1.9	3:24	3:12	p2.0
9	S	9:30	10:36	a1.8	4:06	3:18	p2.1	9	M	10:18	11:00	a1.9	4:06	4:24	p1.8
10	S	10:30	11:36	a1.8	4:54	4:30	p2.0	10	T	11:24	11:54	a2.0	4:48	5:42	a1.8
11	M	11:36	...	1.9	5:36	5:48	p1.9	11	W	...	12:30	2.0	5:36	7:00	a2.0
12	T	12:30	12:42	p2.1	6:24	7:00	1.8	12	T	12:48	1:36	p2.1	6:24	8:12	a2.2
13	W	1:24	1:42	p2.2	7:06	8:12	a2.0	13	F	1:42	2:42	p2.2	7:12	9:18	a2.4
14	T	2:18	2:48	p2.3	7:48	9:18	a2.3	14	S	2:36	3:42	p2.3	8:06	10:18	a2.6
15	F	3:06	3:48	p2.4	8:36	10:24	a2.5	15	S	3:30	4:36	p2.3	8:54	11:12	a2.7
16	S	3:54	4:42	p2.4	9:18	11:18	a2.7	16	M	4:18	5:24	p2.3	9:48	11:59	a2.7
17	S	4:42	5:36	p2.4	10:06	...	2.7	17	T	5:12	6:12	p2.2	10:36	...	2.6
18	M	5:24	6:30	p2.3	12:18	-D-	1.3	18	W	6:00	6:54	p2.1	12:42	-H-	1.3
19	T	6:18	7:18	p2.1	1:06	-E-	1.2	19	T	6:54	7:30	p2.0	1:24	12:18	p2.2
20	W	7:12	8:12	p2.0	1:54	12:36	p2.3	20	F	7:42	8:12	p1.9	2:00	1:12	p1.9
21	T	8:06	8:54	p1.8	2:42	1:30	p2.0	21	S	8:36	8:48	p1.7	2:36	2:06	p1.7
22	F	9:06	9:42	p1.7	3:30	2:30	p1.8	22	S	9:30	9:30	p1.6	3:12	3:06	a1.6
23	S	10:06	10:30	p1.6	4:12	3:36	p1.6	23	M	10:18	10:18	p1.5	3:54	4:06	a1.6
24	S	11:00	11:18	p1.5	4:54	4:42	a1.5	24	T	11:18	11:00	1.4	4:30	5:18	a1.7
25	M	...	12:01	1.3	5:36	5:54	a1.6	25	W	-I-	12:18	1.3	5:12	6:30	a1.8
26	T	12:06	12:54	1.4	6:18	7:00	a1.7	26	T	...	1:18	1.4	5:54	7:42	a1.9
27	W	12:54	1:48	p1.5	6:54	8:00	a1.8	27	F	12:42	2:12	p1.5	6:36	8:48	a2.0
28	T	1:42	2:42	p1.6	7:30	9:00	a1.9	28	S	1:36	3:06	p1.6	7:18	9:42	a2.2
29	F	2:24	3:30	p1.7	8:06	9:54	a2.1	29	S	2:24	3:54	p1.8	8:06	10:36	a2.3
30	S	3:06	4:18	p1.8	8:42	10:48	a2.2	30	M	3:18	4:36	p1.9	8:54	11:18	a2.4
								31	T	4:06	5:18	p1.9	9:36	11:54	a2.5

A also at *10:30 a.m. (2.3)   B also at 11:00 a.m. (2.4)   C also at 11:42 a.m. (2.4)
D also at 10:54 a.m. (2.7)   E also at 11:42 a.m. (2.6)   F also at 10:42 a.m. (2.5)
G also at 11:24 a.m. (2.5)   H also at 11:30 a.m. (2.4)   I also at 11:48 p.m. (1.4)

The Kts. (knots) columns show the **maximum** predicted velocities of the stronger one of the Flood Currents and the stronger one of the Ebb Currents for each day.
The letter "a" means the velocity shown should occur **after** the **a.m.** Current Change. The letter "p" means the velocity shown should occur **after** the **p.m.** Current Change (even if next morning). No "a" or "p" means a.m. and p.m. velocities are the same for that day.
Avg. Max. Velocity: Flood 2.0 Kts., Ebb 1.9 Kts.
Max. Flood 3 hrs. 10 min. after Flood Starts ±45 min.
Max. Ebb 2 hrs. 45 min. after Ebb Starts ±45 min.

See pp. 22-29 for Current Change at other points.

Note *from NOS: These predictions should be considered questionable. Caution is advised.*

Upper Chesapeake Bay Currents

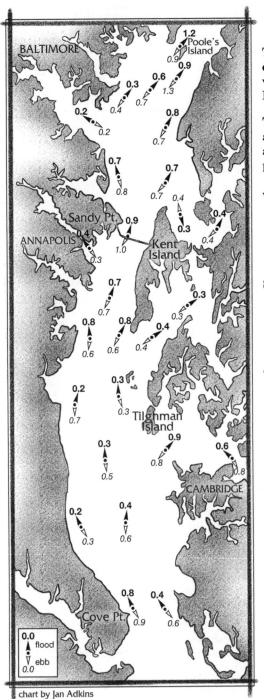

The arrows in this diagram denote **direction** and **average maximum velocities** for Flood (dark arrow) and Ebb (light arrow) currents.

Times of current change for the four areas listed below are in hours, before or after **High Water at Baltimore**, pp. 162-165.

West of Pooles Island:
Flood begins 3 1/2 before
Flood max. 1 1/2 before (1.2 kts.)
Ebb begins 2 1/2 after
Ebb max. 4 1/2 after (0.9 kts.)

Sandy Point:
Flood begins 3 1/2 before
Flood max. 1 1/2 before (0.9 kts.)
Ebb begins 1 1/2 after
Ebb max. 4 1/2 after (1.0 kts.)

off Tilghman Island:
Flood begins 5 1/2 before
Flood max. 3 1/2 before (0.3 kts.)
Ebb begins 1/2 after
Ebb max. 3 1/2 after (0.7 kts.)

off Cove Point:
Flood begins 6 1/2 before
Flood max. 4 1/2 before (0.9 kts.)
Ebb begins 1/2 before
Ebb max. 1 1/2 after (0.8 kts.)

Note:
From the beginning of the Flood Current at Cove Point until the Ebb Current begins off Baltimore, a north-bound vessel will have over 8 hours of fair current. A vessel bound southward from Sandy Point can expect only 4 hours of fair current.

chart by Jan Adkins

Relationship of High Water and Ebb Current

Many people wonder why the times of High Water and the start of Ebb Current at the mouths of bays and inlets are not simultaneous. (See p. 10, Why Tides and Currents Often Behave Differently.) The twelve diagrams below show the hourly stages of the Tide in the Ocean and a Bay connected by a narrow Inlet.

Picture the rising Tide, borne by the Flood Current, as a long wave. The wave enters the inlet and the crest reaches its maximum height in or at the inlet. But, the body of water inside the inlet - in the bay - has yet to be filled and the Flood Current continues to pour water through the inlet for a good period after the crest has already passed the inlet. The Ebb Current will not start until the level of the water in the ocean is lower than the water in the bay.

This does not necessarily apply to the mouths of small bays with wide entrances. The narrowness of the inlet and the size of the bay are the controlling factors.

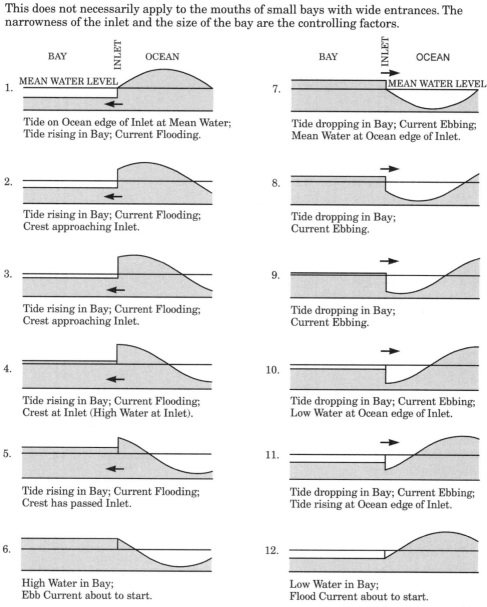

BAY   INLET   OCEAN

1. MEAN WATER LEVEL
Tide on Ocean edge of Inlet at Mean Water;
Tide rising in Bay; Current Flooding.

2. Tide rising in Bay; Current Flooding;
Crest approaching Inlet.

3. Tide rising in Bay; Current Flooding;
Crest approaching Inlet.

4. Tide rising in Bay; Current Flooding;
Crest at Inlet (High Water at Inlet).

5. Tide rising in Bay; Current Flooding;
Crest has passed Inlet.

6. High Water in Bay;
Ebb Current about to start.

BAY   INLET   OCEAN

7. MEAN WATER LEVEL
Tide dropping in Bay; Current Ebbing;
Mean Water at Ocean edge of Inlet.

8. Tide dropping in Bay;
Current Ebbing.

9. Tide dropping in Bay;
Current Ebbing.

10. Tide dropping in Bay; Current Ebbing;
Low Water at Ocean edge of Inlet.

11. Tide dropping in Bay; Current Ebbing;
Tide rising at Ocean edge of Inlet.

12. Low Water in Bay;
Flood Current about to start.

161

2024 HIGH WATER
BALTIMORE, MD

At Ft. McHenry 39°16'N, 76°34.7'W

Standard Time   Standard Time   *Daylight Time starts Mar. 10 at 2 a.m.

Day of Month	Day of Week	JANUARY a.m.	Ht.	p.m.	Ht.	Day of Week	FEBRUARY a.m.	Ht.	p.m.	Ht.	Day of Week	MARCH a.m.	Ht.	p.m.	Ht.	Day of Month
1	M	10:14	0.6	10:32	0.9	T	11:11	0.7	11:04	0.5	F	10:19	1.0	10:22	0.6	1
2	T	11:12	0.6	11:15	0.8	F	11:58	0.8	11:47	0.4	S	11:11	1.1	11:11	0.6	2
3	W	11:59	0.6	11:56	0.7	S	...	...	12:50	0.9	S	...	...	12:08	1.1	3
4	T	...	...	12:53	0.7	S	12:34	0.4	1:46	0.9	M	12:06	0.6	1:07	1.1	4
5	F	12:36	0.6	1:43	0.8	M	1:27	0.4	2:49	1.0	T	1:04	0.6	2:14	1.1	5
6	S	1:20	0.5	2:35	0.9	T	2:31	0.4	3:48	1.1	W	2:11	0.6	3:21	1.2	6
7	S	2:11	0.4	3:27	1.0	W	3:34	0.4	4:43	1.1	T	3:18	0.7	4:18	1.3	7
8	M	3:07	0.4	4:16	1.1	T	4:31	0.5	5:35	1.2	F	4:16	0.8	5:10	1.3	8
9	T	3:59	0.4	5:05	1.2	F	5:26	0.6	6:26	1.2	S	5:12	1.0	6:01	1.3	9
10	W	4:50	0.4	5:55	1.2	S	6:22	0.7	7:15	1.2	S	*7:07	1.1	*7:50	1.2	10
11	T	5:42	0.4	6:46	1.3	S	7:17	0.8	8:00	1.1	M	8:01	1.3	8:36	1.1	11
12	F	6:37	0.5	7:34	1.3	M	8:10	0.9	8:45	1.0	T	8:52	1.4	9:20	1.0	12
13	S	7:31	0.6	8:21	1.2	T	9:03	1.0	9:30	0.9	W	9:42	1.5	10:05	0.9	13
14	S	8:25	0.6	9:07	1.1	W	10:01	1.1	10:21	0.7	T	10:36	1.4	10:54	0.8	14
15	M	9:21	0.7	9:57	1.0	T	11:05	1.1	11:15	0.6	F	11:36	1.4	11:50	0.8	15
16	T	10:25	0.8	10:50	0.9	F	...	...	12:09	1.1	S	...	...	12:42	1.3	16
17	W	11:31	0.9	11:43	0.7	S	12:10	0.6	1:14	1.1	S	12:49	0.7	1:48	1.2	17
18	T	...	...	12:34	1.0	S	1:05	0.5	2:25	1.0	M	1:47	0.8	2:58	1.1	18
19	F	12:35	0.6	1:37	1.0	M	2:05	0.5	3:34	1.0	T	2:48	0.8	4:09	1.1	19
20	S	1:28	0.5	2:44	1.0	T	3:07	0.6	4:30	1.0	W	3:52	0.9	5:04	1.1	20
21	S	2:25	0.4	3:46	1.1	W	4:03	0.6	5:17	1.0	T	4:48	0.9	5:46	1.1	21
22	M	3:23	0.4	4:41	1.0	T	4:53	0.7	5:58	1.0	F	5:37	1.0	6:23	1.1	22
23	T	4:16	0.5	5:31	1.0	F	5:41	0.7	6:35	1.0	S	6:22	1.1	6:59	1.1	23
24	W	5:06	0.5	6:18	1.0	S	6:27	0.8	7:09	1.0	S	7:04	1.2	7:34	1.1	24
25	T	5:56	0.5	7:00	1.0	S	7:10	0.8	7:41	1.0	M	7:44	1.2	8:08	1.0	25
26	F	6:45	0.5	7:36	1.0	M	7:48	0.9	8:11	0.9	T	8:20	1.3	8:40	1.0	26
27	S	7:31	0.6	8:09	1.0	T	8:24	0.9	8:41	0.8	W	8:53	1.4	9:11	0.9	27
28	S	8:13	0.6	8:41	0.9	W	8:58	1.0	9:11	0.8	T	9:26	1.4	9:42	0.9	28
29	M	8:53	0.6	9:13	0.8	T	9:35	1.0	9:43	0.7	F	10:01	1.4	10:15	0.8	29
30	T	9:35	0.6	9:47	0.7						S	10:42	1.4	10:56	0.8	30
31	W	10:21	0.7	10:23	0.6						S	11:35	1.4	11:51	0.8	31

Dates when Ht. of **Low** Water is below Mean Low with Ht. of lowest given for each period and Date of lowest in ( ):

3rd–31st: -0.6' (11th–13th)   1st–26th: -0.6' (9th–11th)   3rd–14th: -0.3' (7th–12th) April Low Tide(s)

Average Rise and Fall 1.1 ft.

When a high tide exceeds avg. ht., the *following* low tide will be lower than avg.

2024 HIGH WATER
BALTIMORE, MD
At Ft. McHenry 39°16'N, 76°34.7'W

		Daylight Saving Time APRIL					Daylight Saving Time MAY					Daylight Saving Time JUNE				
DAY OF MONTH	DAY OF WEEK	a.m.	Ht.	p.m.	Ht.	DAY OF WEEK	a.m.	Ht.	p.m.	Ht.	DAY OF WEEK	a.m.	Ht.	p.m.	Ht.	DAY OF MONTH
1	M	...	...	12:37	1.4	W	12:47	1.1	1:16	1.6	S	2:38	1.6	2:43	1.4	1
2	T	12:53	0.8	1:39	1.4	T	1:49	1.2	2:16	1.5	S	3:38	1.8	3:42	1.3	2
3	W	1:55	0.9	2:44	1.4	F	2:51	1.3	3:17	1.5	M	4:35	2.0	4:39	1.2	3
4	T	3:01	1.0	3:50	1.4	S	3:54	1.5	4:16	1.4	T	5:28	2.1	5:32	1.2	4
5	F	4:05	1.1	4:49	1.4	S	4:50	1.7	5:10	1.3	W	6:18	2.1	6:25	1.1	5
6	S	5:04	1.3	5:41	1.4	M	5:42	1.9	6:00	1.2	T	7:10	2.1	7:18	1.2	6
7	S	5:57	1.5	6:31	1.3	T	6:33	2.0	6:51	1.2	F	8:01	2.1	8:11	1.2	7
8	M	6:50	1.6	7:21	1.2	W	7:24	2.1	7:42	1.1	S	8:48	2.0	9:01	1.2	8
9	T	7:42	1.8	8:09	1.2	T	8:15	2.0	8:32	1.1	S	9:33	1.9	9:51	1.2	9
10	W	8:33	1.8	8:55	1.1	F	9:04	2.0	9:20	1.1	M	10:17	1.8	10:44	1.3	10
11	T	9:22	1.8	9:41	1.0	S	9:52	1.9	10:09	1.1	T	11:04	1.6	11:45	1.3	11
12	F	10:12	1.7	10:30	1.0	S	10:43	1.7	11:06	1.2	W	11:52	1.5	...	...	12
13	S	11:08	1.6	11:27	1.0	M	11:40	1.6	...	...	T	12:44	1.4	12:39	1.5	13
14	S	...	...	12:13	1.5	T	12:10	1.2	12:38	1.5	F	1:37	1.4	1:23	1.4	14
15	M	12:30	1.0	1:17	1.4	W	1:11	1.2	1:31	1.4	S	2:26	1.5	2:07	1.3	15
16	T	1:30	1.0	2:19	1.3	T	2:08	1.3	2:20	1.3	S	3:15	1.6	2:54	1.2	16
17	W	2:31	1.1	3:20	1.2	F	3:04	1.4	3:10	1.3	M	4:02	1.7	3:47	1.1	17
18	T	3:32	1.1	4:15	1.2	S	3:58	1.5	4:00	1.2	T	4:45	1.8	4:38	1.0	18
19	F	4:28	1.2	4:59	1.2	S	4:44	1.6	4:46	1.1	W	5:27	1.9	5:25	1.0	19
20	S	5:15	1.3	5:38	1.2	M	5:24	1.7	5:28	1.1	T	6:08	2.0	6:11	1.0	20
21	S	5:56	1.4	6:15	1.1	T	6:01	1.8	6:09	1.0	F	6:52	2.0	7:00	1.0	21
22	M	6:35	1.5	6:53	1.1	W	6:39	1.9	6:51	1.0	S	7:38	2.0	7:51	1.1	22
23	T	7:12	1.6	7:31	1.1	T	7:18	1.9	7:34	1.0	S	8:23	2.0	8:40	1.2	23
24	W	7:48	1.7	8:08	1.0	F	7:59	2.0	8:16	1.0	M	9:08	2.0	9:29	1.2	24
25	T	8:24	1.7	8:43	1.0	S	8:40	2.0	8:58	1.1	T	9:52	2.0	10:22	1.3	25
26	F	8:59	1.8	9:18	1.0	S	9:21	1.9	9:42	1.1	W	10:40	1.9	11:22	1.4	26
27	S	9:37	1.8	9:56	1.0	M	10:06	1.9	10:33	1.1	T	11:32	1.7	...	...	27
28	S	10:20	1.7	10:42	1.0	T	10:57	1.8	11:35	1.2	F	12:26	1.6	12:27	1.6	28
29	M	11:13	1.7	11:43	1.0	W	11:55	1.7	...	...	S	1:25	1.7	1:20	1.5	29
30	T	...	...	12:15	1.6	T	12:40	1.3	12:53	1.6	S	2:22	1.9	2:14	1.3	30
31						F	1:40	1.5	1:47	1.5						31

Dates when Ht. of **Low** Water is below Mean Low with Ht. of lowest given for each period and Date of lowest in ( ):

Average Rise and Fall 1.1 ft.

When a high tide exceeds avg. ht., the *following* low tide will be lower than avg.

163

2024 HIGH WATER
BALTIMORE, MD
At Ft. McHenry 39°16'N, 76°34.7'W

		Daylight Saving Time					Daylight Saving Time					Daylight Saving Time				
DAY OF MONTH	DAY OF WEEK	JULY				DAY OF WEEK	AUGUST				DAY OF WEEK	SEPTEMBER				DAY OF MONTH
		a.m.	Ht.	p.m.	Ht.		a.m.	Ht.	p.m.	Ht.		a.m.	Ht.	p.m.	Ht.	
1	M	3:21	2.0	3:12	1.2	T	5:08	2.0	4:53	1.2	S	6:27	1.9	6:29	1.5	1
2	T	4:20	2.1	4:13	1.1	F	6:00	2.0	5:49	1.3	M	7:05	1.9	7:19	1.6	2
3	W	5:15	2.1	5:10	1.1	S	6:48	2.0	6:43	1.4	T	7:40	1.8	8:04	1.7	3
4	T	6:09	2.1	6:04	1.2	S	7:33	1.9	7:36	1.4	W	8:15	1.8	8:44	1.7	4
5	F	6:59	2.0	6:58	1.2	M	8:11	1.9	8:26	1.5	T	8:46	1.7	9:20	1.8	5
6	S	7:49	2.0	7:53	1.3	T	8:46	1.9	9:10	1.5	F	9:16	1.6	9:55	1.8	6
7	S	8:33	1.9	8:44	1.3	W	9:18	1.8	9:52	1.6	S	9:46	1.5	10:32	1.9	7
8	M	9:12	1.9	9:32	1.4	T	9:50	1.7	10:34	1.6	S	10:15	1.4	11:14	1.9	8
9	T	9:49	1.8	10:20	1.4	F	10:22	1.6	11:19	1.7	M	10:47	1.3	11:59	1.9	9
10	W	10:26	1.7	11:12	1.4	S	10:56	1.5	...	...	T	11:32	1.2	...	...	10
11	T	11:05	1.6	...	...	S	12:05	1.7	-B-	...	W	12:55	1.9	12:32	1.2	11
12	F	12:06	1.5	-A-	...	M	12:51	1.8	12:18	1.2	T	1:50	1.9	1:36	1.2	12
13	S	12:55	1.6	12:29	1.4	T	1:37	1.9	1:05	1.2	F	2:49	1.9	2:44	1.2	13
14	S	1:40	1.6	1:11	1.2	W	2:27	1.9	1:59	1.1	S	3:51	2.0	3:56	1.3	14
15	M	2:25	1.7	1:54	1.1	T	3:24	1.9	3:05	1.1	S	4:47	2.0	4:58	1.4	15
16	T	3:14	1.8	2:45	1.1	F	4:23	2.0	4:15	1.2	M	5:36	2.0	5:53	1.6	16
17	W	4:04	1.9	3:46	1.0	S	5:15	2.0	5:15	1.2	T	6:23	2.0	6:47	1.8	17
18	T	4:54	2.0	4:45	1.0	S	6:04	2.1	6:11	1.4	W	7:11	1.9	7:41	1.9	18
19	F	5:41	2.0	5:38	1.1	M	6:52	2.1	7:07	1.5	T	7:58	1.8	8:33	2.1	19
20	S	6:29	2.1	6:32	1.2	T	7:40	2.1	8:02	1.6	F	8:44	1.7	9:23	2.2	20
21	S	7:17	2.1	7:27	1.2	W	8:26	2.0	8:54	1.8	S	9:29	1.6	10:15	2.2	21
22	M	8:05	2.1	8:22	1.4	T	9:10	1.9	9:45	1.9	S	10:16	1.4	11:14	2.1	22
23	T	8:50	2.1	9:13	1.5	F	9:54	1.8	10:39	2.0	M	11:10	1.3	...	...	23
24	W	9:33	2.0	10:05	1.6	S	10:41	1.6	11:39	2.1	T	12:20	2.1	12:13	1.3	24
25	T	10:18	1.8	11:03	1.7	S	11:34	1.4	...	...	W	1:27	2.0	1:17	1.3	25
26	F	11:07	1.7	...	...	M	12:43	2.1	12:33	1.3	T	2:33	1.9	2:21	1.3	26
27	S	12:05	1.9	12:01	1.5	T	1:45	2.1	1:32	1.3	F	3:39	1.8	3:28	1.4	27
28	S	1:05	2.0	12:55	1.4	W	2:51	2.0	2:33	1.3	S	4:34	1.8	4:32	1.4	28
29	M	2:03	2.0	1:50	1.3	T	3:59	2.0	3:39	1.3	S	5:17	1.8	5:25	1.5	29
30	T	3:05	2.0	2:49	1.2	F	4:58	2.0	4:42	1.4	M	5:53	1.7	6:12	1.6	30
31	W	4:09	2.1	3:53	1.2	S	5:46	1.9	5:38	1.4						31

A also at 11:46 a.m. (1.5)   B also at 11:34 a.m. (1.4)

Dates when Ht. of **Low** Water is below Mean Low with Ht. of lowest given for each period and Date of lowest in ( ):

Average Rise and Fall 1.1 ft.

When a high tide exceeds avg. ht., the *following* low tide will be lower than avg.

2024 HIGH WATER
BALTIMORE, MD
At Ft. McHenry 39°16'N, 76°34.7'W

Daylight Saving Time | ***Standard Time starts Nov. 3 at 2 a.m.** | **Standard Time**

DAY OF MONTH	DAY OF WEEK	OCTOBER a.m.	Ht.	p.m.	Ht.	DAY OF WEEK	NOVEMBER a.m.	Ht.	p.m.	Ht.	DAY OF WEEK	DECEMBER a.m.	Ht.	p.m.	Ht.	DAY OF MONTH
1	T	6:28	1.7	6:56	1.7	F	7:01	1.2	7:42	1.7	S	6:04	0.7	6:53	1.5	1
2	W	7:03	1.6	7:36	1.8	S	7:38	1.1	8:18	1.8	M	6:44	0.7	7:33	1.5	2
3	T	7:38	1.6	8:14	1.8	S	*7:14	1.0	*7:53	1.8	T	7:25	0.6	8:12	1.5	3
4	F	8:13	1.5	8:48	1.9	M	7:49	1.0	8:30	1.7	W	8:07	0.6	8:53	1.4	4
5	S	8:45	1.4	9:21	1.9	T	8:22	0.9	9:10	1.7	T	8:52	0.6	9:39	1.4	5
6	S	9:15	1.3	9:55	1.9	W	9:01	0.9	9:59	1.7	F	9:49	0.7	10:32	1.3	6
7	M	9:44	1.2	10:35	1.9	T	9:56	0.9	10:56	1.6	S	10:59	0.7	11:27	1.2	7
8	T	10:17	1.2	11:24	1.9	F	11:09	0.9	11:54	1.6	S	...	...	12:06	0.8	8
9	W	11:05	1.1	...	...	S	...	...	12:19	1.0	M	12:20	1.1	1:07	1.0	9
10	T	12:22	1.8	12:17	1.1	S	12:48	1.5	1:23	1.1	T	1:12	1.0	2:08	1.1	10
11	F	1:21	1.8	1:26	1.1	M	1:43	1.5	2:26	1.3	W	2:08	0.9	3:08	1.3	11
12	S	2:18	1.8	2:34	1.2	T	2:40	1.4	3:26	1.5	T	3:04	0.8	4:03	1.4	12
13	S	3:17	1.8	3:42	1.3	W	3:34	1.3	4:19	1.6	F	3:58	0.7	4:56	1.5	13
14	M	4:14	1.8	4:42	1.5	T	4:24	1.2	5:10	1.8	S	4:49	0.7	5:49	1.5	14
15	T	5:05	1.8	5:36	1.7	F	5:13	1.1	6:02	1.9	S	5:40	0.7	6:44	1.5	15
16	W	5:53	1.7	6:28	1.9	S	6:03	1.0	6:55	1.9	M	6:33	0.7	7:35	1.4	16
17	T	6:41	1.6	7:20	2.0	S	6:53	1.0	7:47	1.8	T	7:24	0.7	8:23	1.3	17
18	F	7:29	1.5	8:12	2.1	M	7:43	1.0	8:37	1.7	W	8:15	0.7	9:09	1.2	18
19	S	8:18	1.4	9:03	2.1	T	8:32	0.9	9:31	1.6	T	9:07	0.7	9:56	1.1	19
20	S	9:05	1.3	9:54	2.1	W	9:26	0.9	10:30	1.5	F	10:06	0.7	10:44	1.0	20
21	M	9:53	1.2	10:51	2.0	T	10:31	0.9	11:29	1.3	S	11:12	0.7	11:32	0.9	21
22	T	10:47	1.2	11:57	1.8	F	11:41	0.9	...	...	S	...	...	12:12	0.7	22
23	W	11:53	1.1	...	...	S	12:21	1.2	12:45	0.9	M	12:16	0.8	1:07	0.8	23
24	T	1:04	1.7	1:01	1.1	S	1:08	1.2	1:47	1.0	T	12:59	0.7	2:00	0.8	24
25	F	2:03	1.6	2:07	1.2	M	1:54	1.1	2:45	1.1	W	1:45	0.6	2:53	0.9	25
26	S	2:59	1.5	3:13	1.2	T	2:41	1.0	3:35	1.2	T	2:35	0.5	3:40	1.0	26
27	S	3:50	1.5	4:15	1.3	W	3:25	0.9	4:17	1.3	F	3:23	0.5	4:23	1.1	27
28	M	4:34	1.4	5:05	1.4	T	4:06	0.9	4:56	1.4	S	4:08	0.4	5:05	1.1	28
29	T	5:12	1.4	5:48	1.5	F	4:45	0.8	5:34	1.4	S	4:49	0.4	5:48	1.2	29
30	W	5:48	1.3	6:27	1.6	S	5:24	0.7	6:13	1.5	M	5:32	0.4	6:32	1.2	30
31	T	6:24	1.2	7:05	1.7						T	6:18	0.4	6:59	1.2	31

Dates when Ht. of **Low** Water is below Mean Low with Ht. of lowest given for each period and Date of lowest in ( ):

10th–19th: -0.4' (13th–17th)
25th–31st: -0.4'

Average Rise and Fall 1.1 ft.

When a high tide exceeds avg. ht., the *following* low tide will be lower than avg.

2024 HIGH WATER
MIAMI HARBOR ENTRANCE, FL
25°45.8'N, 80°07.8'W

		Standard Time — JANUARY					Standard Time — FEBRUARY					*Daylight Time starts Mar. 10 at 2 a.m. — MARCH				
DAY OF MONTH	DAY OF WEEK	a.m.	Ht.	p.m.	Ht.	DAY OF WEEK	a.m.	Ht.	p.m.	Ht.	DAY OF WEEK	a.m.	Ht.	p.m.	Ht.	DAY OF MONTH
1	M	...	...	12:01	2.1	T	12:29	1.9	12:33	1.8	F	11:54	1.9	...	...	1
2	T	12:22	2.0	12:40	2.0	F	1:17	1.8	1:16	1.8	S	12:40	2.0	12:36	1.8	2
3	W	1:11	1.9	1:22	2.0	S	2:12	1.8	2:08	1.7	S	1:35	1.9	1:29	1.8	3
4	T	2:05	1.9	2:09	1.9	S	3:17	1.8	3:10	1.7	M	2:42	1.9	2:37	1.8	4
5	F	3:01	1.9	3:01	1.9	M	4:23	1.9	4:19	1.8	T	3:52	1.9	3:54	1.9	5
6	S	4:00	2.0	3:58	1.9	T	5:27	2.0	5:26	1.9	W	5:00	2.1	5:07	2.0	6
7	S	4:59	2.1	4:56	1.9	W	6:25	2.2	6:27	2.1	T	5:59	2.3	6:11	2.3	7
8	M	5:55	2.2	5:52	2.0	T	7:17	2.4	7:24	2.3	F	6:51	2.5	7:08	2.5	8
9	T	6:48	2.3	6:47	2.2	F	8:05	2.5	8:17	2.5	S	7:40	2.6	8:01	2.7	9
10	W	7:38	2.5	7:39	2.3	S	8:51	2.6	9:08	2.6	S	*9:26	2.7	*9:52	2.8	10
11	T	8:26	2.6	8:31	2.4	S	9:37	2.7	9:59	2.7	M	10:11	2.8	10:41	2.9	11
12	F	9:13	2.6	9:22	2.5	M	10:22	2.6	10:51	2.6	T	10:56	2.7	11:31	2.8	12
13	S	10:00	2.7	10:14	2.5	T	11:08	2.5	11:43	2.5	W	11:42	2.6	...	...	13
14	S	10:47	2.6	11:08	2.5	W	11:56	2.4	...	...	T	12:21	2.7	12:30	2.4	14
15	M	11:34	2.5	...	...	T	12:38	2.4	12:47	2.2	F	1:13	2.5	1:21	2.2	15
16	T	12:03	2.4	12:24	2.4	F	1:36	2.2	1:43	2.0	S	2:10	2.3	2:17	2.1	16
17	W	1:01	2.3	1:16	2.3	S	2:41	2.0	2:46	1.9	S	3:12	2.1	3:20	1.9	17
18	T	2:03	2.2	2:13	2.1	S	3:50	2.0	3:55	1.8	M	4:21	2.0	4:30	1.9	18
19	F	3:08	2.2	3:14	2.0	M	4:58	2.0	5:02	1.8	T	5:29	2.0	5:39	1.9	19
20	S	4:14	2.1	4:17	2.0	T	5:57	2.0	6:00	1.9	W	6:28	2.0	6:38	2.0	20
21	S	5:17	2.1	5:19	2.0	W	6:46	2.1	6:50	2.0	T	7:15	2.1	7:27	2.1	21
22	M	6:14	2.2	6:16	2.0	T	7:27	2.1	7:33	2.1	F	7:55	2.2	8:09	2.2	22
23	T	7:05	2.2	7:06	2.0	F	8:04	2.2	8:13	2.1	S	8:30	2.2	8:48	2.3	23
24	W	7:49	2.2	7:51	2.1	S	8:38	2.2	8:50	2.2	S	9:04	2.3	9:24	2.3	24
25	T	8:29	2.2	8:32	2.1	S	9:10	2.2	9:26	2.2	M	9:37	2.3	10:00	2.4	25
26	F	9:06	2.2	9:12	2.1	M	9:42	2.2	10:02	2.2	T	10:09	2.3	10:36	2.4	26
27	S	9:40	2.2	9:50	2.1	T	10:14	2.2	10:38	2.2	W	10:42	2.2	11:12	2.4	27
28	S	10:14	2.2	10:28	2.0	W	10:46	2.1	11:15	2.1	T	11:15	2.2	11:50	2.3	28
29	M	10:47	2.1	11:06	2.0	T	11:18	2.0	11:55	2.0	F	11:50	2.1	...	...	29
30	T	11:21	2.0	11:46	1.9						S	12:31	2.2	12:28	2.0	30
31	W	11:55	1.9	...	...						S	1:17	2.2	1:13	2.0	31

Dates when Ht. of **Low** Water is below Mean Low with Ht. of lowest given for each period and Date of lowest in ( ):

8th: -0.3'	5th–6th: -0.4'	6th: -0.3'
10th–21st: -0.6' (11th–14th)	8th–17th: -0.7' (9th–13th)	8th–15th: -0.8' (11th, 12th)
23rd–28th: -0.3' (23rd–26th)	22nd–27th: -0.2'	

Average Rise and Fall 2.3 ft.

When a high tide exceeds avg. ht., the *following* low tide will be lower than avg.

2024 HIGH WATER
MIAMI HARBOR ENTRANCE, FL
25°45.8'N, 80°07.8'W

		Daylight Saving Time					Daylight Saving Time					Daylight Saving Time				
DAY OF MONTH	DAY OF WEEK	APRIL				DAY OF WEEK	MAY				DAY OF WEEK	JUNE				DAY OF MONTH
		a.m.	Ht.	p.m.	Ht.		a.m.	Ht.	p.m.	Ht.		a.m.	Ht.	p.m.	Ht.	
1	M	2:12	2.1	2:10	1.9	W	2:57	2.2	3:13	2.1	S	4:29	2.3	5:15	2.4	1
2	T	3:17	2.0	3:21	2.0	T	3:59	2.2	4:25	2.2	S	5:27	2.3	6:17	2.5	2
3	W	4:25	2.1	4:38	2.0	F	5:00	2.3	5:33	2.4	M	6:24	2.4	7:14	2.6	3
4	T	5:32	2.2	5:50	2.2	S	5:59	2.4	6:36	2.6	T	7:20	2.4	8:07	2.7	4
5	F	6:29	2.4	6:54	2.5	S	6:52	2.5	7:32	2.8	W	8:11	2.5	8:58	2.7	5
6	S	7:22	2.5	7:50	2.7	M	7:43	2.6	8:25	2.9	T	9:02	2.5	9:46	2.7	6
7	S	8:11	2.7	8:43	2.9	T	8:33	2.7	9:15	2.9	F	9:50	2.4	10:33	2.6	7
8	M	8:59	2.8	9:33	3.0	W	9:21	2.7	10:03	2.9	S	10:37	2.4	11:18	2.5	8
9	T	9:45	2.8	10:22	3.0	T	10:09	2.6	10:51	2.8	S	11:24	2.3	...	...	9
10	W	10:31	2.7	11:10	2.9	F	10:56	2.5	11:39	2.7	M	12:03	2.4	12:10	2.2	10
11	T	11:18	2.6	11:59	2.7	S	11:44	2.4	...	...	T	12:46	2.3	12:58	2.1	11
12	F	...	...	12:06	2.5	S	12:27	2.5	12:34	2.2	W	1:29	2.2	1:47	2.0	12
13	S	12:50	2.5	12:56	2.3	M	1:16	2.3	1:26	2.1	T	2:13	2.1	2:39	1.9	13
14	S	1:43	2.3	1:51	2.1	T	2:07	2.2	2:21	2.0	F	2:57	2.0	3:33	1.9	14
15	M	2:42	2.1	2:52	2.0	W	3:00	2.1	3:21	1.9	S	3:44	1.9	4:28	1.9	15
16	T	3:44	2.0	3:59	1.9	T	3:52	2.0	4:22	1.9	S	4:33	1.9	5:23	2.0	16
17	W	4:46	2.0	5:05	1.9	F	4:44	2.0	5:19	2.0	M	5:24	1.9	6:16	2.1	17
18	T	5:42	2.0	6:04	2.0	S	5:33	2.0	6:11	2.1	T	6:15	2.0	7:06	2.2	18
19	F	6:29	2.1	6:54	2.1	S	6:19	2.1	6:58	2.2	W	7:05	2.0	7:55	2.3	19
20	S	7:11	2.2	7:37	2.2	M	7:03	2.1	7:42	2.3	T	7:53	2.1	8:42	2.4	20
21	S	7:49	2.2	8:17	2.4	T	7:45	2.2	8:25	2.4	F	8:41	2.2	9:28	2.5	21
22	M	8:25	2.3	8:55	2.5	W	8:27	2.2	9:06	2.5	S	9:28	2.2	10:14	2.5	22
23	T	9:02	2.3	9:33	2.5	T	9:08	2.2	9:49	2.5	S	10:16	2.3	10:59	2.5	23
24	W	9:38	2.3	10:11	2.5	F	9:49	2.2	10:32	2.5	M	11:05	2.3	11:45	2.5	24
25	T	10:14	2.3	10:50	2.5	S	10:32	2.2	11:16	2.5	T	11:57	2.3	...	...	25
26	F	10:51	2.2	11:31	2.5	S	11:17	2.2	...	...	W	12:32	2.5	12:51	2.3	26
27	S	11:30	2.2	...	...	M	12:02	2.5	12:06	2.2	T	1:20	2.5	1:49	2.3	27
28	S	12:15	2.4	12:13	2.1	T	12:51	2.4	1:00	2.2	F	2:11	2.4	2:49	2.3	28
29	M	1:04	2.3	1:04	2.1	W	1:42	2.4	2:00	2.2	S	3:05	2.3	3:52	2.3	29
30	T	1:58	2.2	2:05	2.1	T	2:35	2.3	3:04	2.2	S	4:02	2.3	4:56	2.4	30
31						F	3:31	2.3	4:10	2.3						31

Dates when Ht. of **Low** Water is below Mean Low with Ht. of lowest given for each period and Date of lowest in ( ):

6th–12th: -0.7' (8th, 9th)   4th–11th: -0.6' (7th, 8th)   1st–9th: -0.5' (4th–6th)
23rd–26th: -0.2'   20th–25th: -0.4' (23rd)
29th–30th: -0.3'

Average Rise and Fall 2.3 ft.

When a high tide exceeds avg. ht., the *following* low tide will be lower than avg.

2024 HIGH WATER
MIAMI HARBOR ENTRANCE, FL
25°45.8'N, 80°07.8'W

		Daylight Saving Time JULY					Daylight Saving Time AUGUST					Daylight Saving Time SEPTEMBER				
DAY OF MONTH	DAY OF WEEK	a.m.	Ht.	p.m.	Ht.	DAY OF WEEK	a.m.	Ht.	p.m.	Ht.	DAY OF WEEK	a.m.	Ht.	p.m.	Ht.	DAY OF MONTH
1	M	5:01	2.2	5:59	2.4	T	6:47	2.3	7:39	2.5	S	8:14	2.6	8:44	2.7	1
2	T	6:02	2.2	6:58	2.5	F	7:42	2.3	8:28	2.5	M	8:55	2.7	9:19	2.7	2
3	W	7:00	2.3	7:53	2.5	S	8:31	2.4	9:11	2.5	T	9:34	2.7	9:52	2.7	3
4	T	7:56	2.3	8:43	2.5	S	9:17	2.4	9:50	2.5	W	10:11	2.7	10:25	2.7	4
5	F	8:46	2.3	9:30	2.5	M	9:58	2.4	10:26	2.5	T	10:46	2.7	10:57	2.7	5
6	S	9:33	2.3	10:14	2.5	T	10:38	2.4	11:01	2.5	F	11:23	2.7	11:30	2.6	6
7	S	10:19	2.3	10:55	2.4	W	11:16	2.4	11:34	2.4	S	...	...	12:01	2.6	7
8	M	11:02	2.2	11:34	2.4	T	11:55	2.4	...	...	S	12:04	2.5	12:40	2.5	8
9	T	11:45	2.2	...	...	F	12:08	2.4	12:34	2.3	M	12:41	2.4	1:25	2.5	9
10	W	12:12	2.3	12:27	2.1	S	12:43	2.3	1:16	2.2	T	1:23	2.3	2:17	2.4	10
11	T	12:49	2.2	1:11	2.1	S	1:20	2.2	2:01	2.2	W	2:14	2.3	3:19	2.4	11
12	F	1:26	2.1	1:56	2.0	M	2:02	2.1	2:53	2.2	T	3:17	2.3	4:27	2.4	12
13	S	2:06	2.0	2:45	2.0	T	2:51	2.1	3:53	2.1	F	4:29	2.4	5:32	2.6	13
14	S	2:49	2.0	3:38	2.0	W	3:49	2.1	4:58	2.2	S	5:39	2.5	6:30	2.7	14
15	M	3:38	1.9	4:35	2.0	T	4:54	2.1	6:01	2.3	S	6:42	2.7	7:22	2.9	15
16	T	4:32	1.9	5:34	2.1	F	6:00	2.2	6:59	2.5	M	7:39	3.0	8:10	3.1	16
17	W	5:31	2.0	6:32	2.2	S	7:01	2.4	7:51	2.7	T	8:32	3.2	8:56	3.2	17
18	T	6:29	2.0	7:26	2.3	S	7:58	2.6	8:39	2.8	W	9:23	3.4	9:42	3.3	18
19	F	7:25	2.2	8:17	2.4	M	8:51	2.8	9:25	2.9	T	10:13	3.4	10:28	3.2	19
20	S	8:18	2.3	9:05	2.6	T	9:42	2.9	10:10	3.0	F	11:03	3.4	11:15	3.2	20
21	S	9:09	2.4	9:52	2.7	W	10:33	3.0	10:55	3.0	S	11:55	3.3	...	...	21
22	M	10:00	2.5	10:37	2.7	T	11:24	3.1	11:41	3.0	S	12:04	3.0	12:48	3.1	22
23	T	10:51	2.6	11:22	2.7	F	...	...	12:16	3.0	M	12:57	2.9	1:46	2.9	23
24	W	11:43	2.7	...	...	S	12:29	2.9	1:10	2.9	T	1:54	2.7	2:49	2.8	24
25	T	12:08	2.7	12:36	2.6	S	1:20	2.7	2:08	2.8	W	2:59	2.6	3:56	2.7	25
26	F	12:55	2.6	1:31	2.6	M	2:16	2.6	3:11	2.6	T	4:08	2.5	5:03	2.6	26
27	S	1:45	2.5	2:30	2.5	T	3:18	2.5	4:18	2.5	F	5:17	2.5	6:03	2.7	27
28	S	2:39	2.4	3:32	2.5	W	4:26	2.4	5:26	2.5	S	6:17	2.6	6:52	2.7	28
29	M	3:38	2.3	4:37	2.4	T	5:33	2.4	6:28	2.5	S	7:07	2.7	7:33	2.8	29
30	T	4:41	2.3	5:43	2.4	F	6:35	2.5	7:21	2.6	M	7:51	2.8	8:10	2.8	30
31	W	5:46	2.2	6:44	2.4	S	7:28	2.5	8:05	2.7						31

Dates when Ht. of **Low** Water is below Mean Low with Ht. of lowest given for each period and Date of lowest in ( ):

1st–7th: -0.4' (3rd, 4th)   19th–24th: -0.2'   19th–20th: -0.2'
19th–28th: -0.4' (21st, 22nd)

Average Rise and Fall 2.3 ft.

When a high tide exceeds avg. ht., the *following* low tide will be lower than avg.

2024 HIGH WATER
MIAMI HARBOR ENTRANCE, FL
25°45.8'N, 80°07.8'W

		Daylight Saving Time					*Standard Time starts Nov. 3 at 2 a.m.					Standard Time		
DAY OF MONTH	**DAY OF WEEK**	**OCTOBER**				**DAY OF WEEK**	**NOVEMBER**				**DAY OF WEEK**	**DECEMBER**			**DAY OF MONTH**
		a.m.	Ht.	p.m.	Ht.		a.m.	Ht.	p.m.	Ht.		a.m.	Ht.	p.m.	Ht.	
1	T	8:30	2.9	8:44	2.8	F	9:14	3.0	9:17	2.7	S	8:30	2.7	8:30	2.5	1
2	W	9:06	2.9	9:17	2.9	S	9:52	3.0	9:54	2.7	M	9:12	2.7	9:11	2.4	2
3	T	9:42	3.0	9:50	2.8	S	*9:30	2.9	*9:30	2.6	T	9:54	2.7	9:54	2.4	3
4	F	10:19	3.0	10:23	2.8	M	10:12	2.8	10:09	2.6	W	10:39	2.6	10:41	2.4	4
5	S	10:54	2.9	10:57	2.7	T	10:54	2.8	10:51	2.5	T	11:24	2.6	11:32	2.3	5
6	S	11:32	2.8	11:32	2.6	W	11:41	2.7	11:41	2.5	F	...	...	12:12	2.5	6
7	M	...	...	12:13	2.8	T	...	...	12:33	2.6	S	12:29	2.3	1:03	2.5	7
8	T	12:10	2.5	12:59	2.7	F	12:39	2.4	1:30	2.6	S	1:31	2.4	1:58	2.5	8
9	W	12:55	2.5	1:52	2.6	S	1:45	2.5	2:29	2.6	M	2:36	2.4	2:55	2.4	9
10	T	1:51	2.4	2:54	2.6	S	2:55	2.6	3:28	2.7	T	3:42	2.5	3:53	2.5	10
11	F	2:58	2.5	3:59	2.6	M	4:02	2.7	4:25	2.8	W	4:45	2.7	4:51	2.5	11
12	S	4:12	2.5	5:01	2.7	T	5:04	2.9	5:19	2.9	T	5:44	2.8	5:48	2.6	12
13	S	5:21	2.7	5:58	2.9	W	6:01	3.1	6:11	3.0	F	6:39	2.9	6:43	2.6	13
14	M	6:23	3.0	6:50	3.0	T	6:55	3.3	7:02	3.0	S	7:32	2.9	7:35	2.7	14
15	T	7:20	3.2	7:39	3.2	F	7:46	3.3	7:52	3.1	S	8:22	2.9	8:26	2.7	15
16	W	8:13	3.4	8:27	3.3	S	8:36	3.3	8:41	3.0	M	9:10	2.8	9:15	2.6	16
17	T	9:04	3.5	9:14	3.3	S	9:25	3.2	9:31	3.0	T	9:57	2.7	10:03	2.5	17
18	F	9:53	3.5	10:02	3.3	M	10:15	3.1	10:21	2.8	W	10:42	2.6	10:52	2.4	18
19	S	10:43	3.5	10:51	3.2	T	11:05	2.9	11:13	2.7	T	11:27	2.5	11:40	2.2	19
20	S	11:34	3.3	11:41	3.0	W	11:57	2.8	...	...	F	...	...	12:11	2.3	20
21	M	...	...	12:27	3.1	T	12:08	2.5	12:50	2.6	S	12:31	2.1	12:55	2.2	21
22	T	12:35	2.9	1:23	2.9	F	1:06	2.4	1:44	2.5	S	1:23	2.0	1:40	2.1	22
23	W	1:33	2.7	2:23	2.8	S	2:07	2.3	2:37	2.4	M	2:18	2.0	2:28	2.0	23
24	T	2:36	2.6	3:25	2.7	S	3:09	2.3	3:29	2.3	T	3:14	2.0	3:18	2.0	24
25	F	3:44	2.5	4:27	2.6	M	4:07	2.3	4:18	2.3	W	4:10	2.0	4:10	1.9	25
26	S	4:50	2.5	5:23	2.6	T	4:59	2.4	5:04	2.3	T	5:03	2.1	5:01	2.0	26
27	S	5:48	2.6	6:11	2.6	W	5:45	2.5	5:47	2.4	F	5:53	2.2	5:52	2.0	27
28	M	6:38	2.7	6:52	2.7	T	6:28	2.6	6:28	2.4	S	6:41	2.3	6:39	2.1	28
29	T	7:21	2.8	7:30	2.7	F	7:09	2.7	7:09	2.4	S	7:26	2.3	7:25	2.2	29
30	W	8:00	2.9	8:06	2.8	S	7:49	2.7	7:50	2.5	M	8:11	2.4	8:11	2.2	30
31	T	8:37	2.9	8:42	2.8						T	8:54	2.5	8:54	2.3	31

Dates when Ht. of **Low** Water is below Mean Low with Ht. of lowest given for each period and Date of lowest in ( ):

18th–19th: -0.2'   14th–17th: -0.3'   11th–12th: -0.4'
                                                     14th–18th: -0.5' (15th)
                                                     30th–31st: -0.3'

Average Rise and Fall 2.3 ft.

When a high tide exceeds avg. ht., the *following* low tide will be lower than avg.

My dear Captain and M. Mate,

As I cannot talk with you, I will do the next best thing. I will write you a letter.

Do you know, Captain and M. Mate of a place on the Atlantic Coast that is called "The Graveyard"? I propose to tell you something about it, and do what I can to keep vessels out of it. "The Graveyard" so called, is that part of the coast which lies between Sow and Pigs Rocks and Naushon Island. This place has been called "The Graveyard" for many years, — because many a good craft has laid her bones there, and many a captain has lost his reputation there also. If a vessel gets into this graveyard, there must be a cause for it. Did it ever occur to you that seldom does a vessel go ashore on Gay Head, or on the south side of the Sound? but that hundreds of them have been piled up in "The Graveyard", or on the north side of the Sound? I will explain why this is so, if you are bound into Vineyard Sound in thick weather, you will probably refer to the "Gay Head and Cross Rip" table in this book, to see when the tide turns in or out. You will notice at the — head of each table that it says, "This table shows the time that the current turns Easterly and — Westerly, off Gay Head in ship channel." That — means off Gay Head when it bears about South; Now, as a rule, captains figure on the currents after they leave the Lightship, as running Easterly into the Sound, when as a matter of fact the first of the flood between the Lightship and Gay Head runs nearly North; and the current does not begin to run to the eastward until you are well into the Sound, as shewn by the chart on the opposite page. Vessels bound into — Vineyard Sound from the Westward, will have the current of ebb on the starboard bow. (see arrows on the hulls in the chart on the opposite page)

I have explained this matter, and I leave the rest to your judgment and careful consideration; and thus you will undoubtedly keep your vessel out of "The Graveyard".

Yours for a fair tide,

Geo. W. Eldridge.

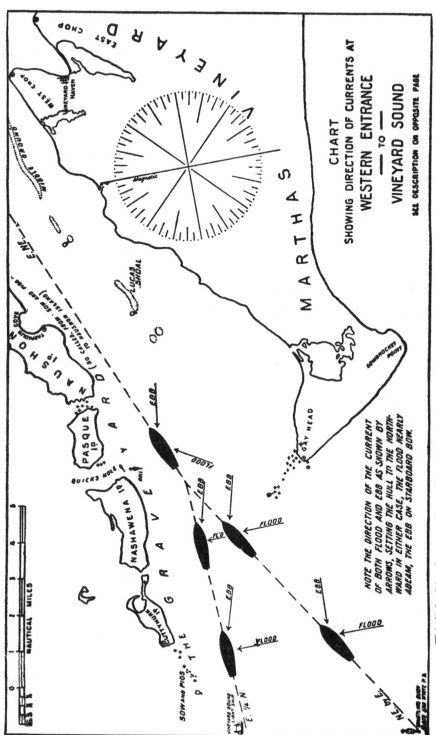

This lightship, shown on Capt. Eldridge's chart, on the Western edge, was replaced many years ago by a buoy.

CHARACTERISTICS OF LIGHT SIGNALS
(see footnote on next page for abbreviations used.)

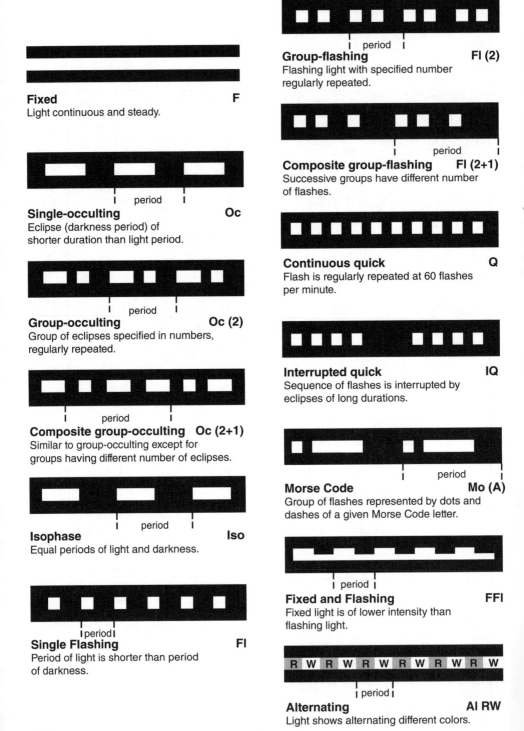

Fixed   **F**
Light continuous and steady.

Single-occulting   **Oc**
Eclipse (darkness period) of
shorter duration than light period.

Group-occulting   **Oc (2)**
Group of eclipses specified in numbers,
regularly repeated.

Composite group-occulting   **Oc (2+1)**
Similar to group-occulting except for
groups having different number of eclipses.

Isophase   **Iso**
Equal periods of light and darkness.

Single Flashing   **Fl**
Period of light is shorter than period
of darkness.

Group-flashing   **Fl (2)**
Flashing light with specified number
regularly repeated.

Composite group-flashing   **Fl (2+1)**
Successive groups have different number
of flashes.

Continuous quick   **Q**
Flash is regularly repeated at 60 flashes
per minute.

Interrupted quick   **IQ**
Sequence of flashes is interrupted by
eclipses of long durations.

Morse Code   **Mo (A)**
Group of flashes represented by dots and
dashes of a given Morse Code letter.

Fixed and Flashing   **FFl**
Fixed light is of lower intensity than
flashing light.

Alternating   **Al RW**
Light shows alternating different colors.

LIGHTS, FOG SIGNALS and OFFSHORE BUOYS

NOVA SCOTIA, EAST COAST

Cranberry Is. Lt., off Cape Canso, S. part of Is. – Fl. W. ev. 15 s., 2 Horns 2 bl. ev. 60 s., Horns point 066° and 141°, Ht. 16.9 m. (56'), Rge. 21 mi., Racon (B), (45-19-29.6N/60-55-38.2W)

White Head Is. Lt., SW side of Is. – LFl. W. ev. 6 s., Ht. 18.2 m. (60'), Rge. 10 mi., (45-11-49.1N/61-08-10.8W)

Country Is. Lt., S. side of Is. – Fl. W. ev. 20 s., Ht. 16.5 m. (54'), Rge. 10 mi., (45-05-59.8N/61-32-31.9W)

Liscomb Is. Lt., near Cranberry Pt. – Fl. W. ev. 10 s., Horn 1 bl. ev. 30 s., Ht. 21.9 m. (72'), Rge. 14 mi., (44-59-15.8N/61-57-58.4W)

Beaver Is. Lt., E. end of Is. – Fl. W. ev. 7 s., Ht. 19.9 m. (66'), Rge. 14 mi., (44-49-29.2N/62-20-16W)

Ship Harbour Lt., on Wolfes Pt. – LFl. G. ev. 6 s., Ht. 18.2 m. (60'), Rge. 4 mi., (44-44-55.4N/62-45-23.6W)

Owls Head Lt., at end of head – Fl. W. ev. 4 s., Ht. 25.8 m. (84'), Rge. 6 mi., (44-43-14.6N/62-47-59.5W)

Egg Is. Lt., center of Is. – LFl. W. ev. 6 s., Ht. 7.6 m. (25'), Rge. 12 mi., (44-39-52.7N/62-51-48.4W)

Jeddore Rock Lt., summit of rock – LFl. W. ev. 12 s., Ht. 29.5 m. (97'), Rge. 8 mi., (44-39-47.1N/63-00-37.3)

Bear Cove Lt. & Bell By. "H6," NE of cove, Q. R., Racon (N), Red, (44-32-36.3N/63-31-19.6W)

Sambro Harbor Lt. & Wh. By. "HS," S. of SW breaker, Halifax Hbr. app. – Mo(A)W ev. 6 s., RWS, (44-24-30N/63-33-36.5W)

Chebucto Head Lt., on summit, Halifax Hbr. app. – Fl. W. ev. 20 s., Ht. 47.8 m. (157'), Rge. 10 mi., Racon (Z), (44-30-26.6N/63-31-21.8W)

Halifax Alpha Lt. & Wh. By. "HA," Halifax app. – Mo(A)W ev. 6 s., RWS, (44-21-45N/63-24-15W)

Sambro Is. Lt., center of Is. – Fl. W. ev. 6 s., Ht. 42.7 m. (145'), Rge. 23 mi., (44-26-12N/63-33-48W)

Ketch Harbour Lt. By. "HE 19," Ketch Harbour entr. – Fl. G. ev 4 s., Green (44-28-19.6N/63-32-16W)

Betty Is. Lt., on Brig Pt. – LFl. W. ev. 6 s., Ht. 19.2 m. (63'), Rge. 13 mi., (44-26-19.7N/63-46-00.4W)

Pearl Is. Lt., off St. Margaret's & Mahone Bays – Fl. W. ev. 10 s., Ht. 19.0 m. (63'), Rge. 8 mi., (44-22-57.2N/64-02-54W)

East Ironbound Is. Lt., center of Is. – Iso. W. ev. 6 s., Ht. 44.5 m. (147'), Rge. 13 mi., (44-26-22.4N/64-04-59.7W)

East Point Island Lt., Mahone Bay – LFl G ev. 6 s., Ht. 9.6 m. (31'), Rge. 6 mi., (44-20-59.2N/64-12-15W)

Abbreviations: Alt., Alternating; **App.**, Approach; **By.**, Buoy; **Ch.**, Channel; **Entr.**, Entrance; **ev.**, every; **F.**, Fixed; **fl.**, flash; **Fl.**, Flashing; **Fl(2)**, Group Flashing; **LFl**, 2 s. flash.; **G.**, Green; **Hbr.**, Harbor or Harbour, **Ht.**, height; **Is.**, Island; **Iso.**, Isophase (Equal interval); **Iso. W.**, Isophase White (Red sector(s) of Lights warn of dangerous angle of approach. Bearings and ranges are from the observer to the aid.); **Jct.**, Junction; **Keyed**, Fog signal is radio activated. During times of reduced visibility, within ½ mile of the fog signal, turn VHF marine radio to channel 83A and 81A as alternate. Key microphone 5–10 times consecutively to activate fog signal for 45 minutes (Boston Lt. 60 minutes). **Lt.**, Light; **Ltd.**, Lighted.; **mi.**, miles; **Mo(A)**, Morse Code "A," **Mo(U)**, Morse Code "U"; **Oc.**, Occulting; **Pt.**, Point; **Q.**, Quick (Flashing); **RaRef.**, Radar Reflector; **R.**, Red; **rge.**, range; **RWS**, R.&W. Stripes; **RWSRST**, RWS with R. Spherical Topmarks; **s.**, seconds; **Wh.**, Whistle; **W.**, White; **Y.**, Yellow

Notices To Mariners: Keep informed of important changes. Visit www.navcen.uscg.gov to receive Local Notices to Mariners via email. When reporting discrepancies in navigational aids, contact nearest C.G. unit and give official name of the aid.

Table for Converting Seconds to Decimals of a Minute, p. 262, for standard GPS input of Lat/Lon.

Dangerous Current

by Jan Adkins

THE RIP TIDE, like the Jabberwocky, doesn't exist. The *rip current*, however, is a real and frightening phenomena that can be deadly unless you understand how it works.

The first lesson in beach physics is that waves don't move water. Waves are pulses of energy (often built up by offshore winds) moving *through* the water. In a traveling wave, a single molecule of water moves up and a bit in the direction of the wave, then down, then rotates against the wave direction, circling back to the surface. Bigger waves, bigger circles. The wave goes on and the water molecule stays put.

When these energy pulses approach the shore, their energy begins to reflect from the bottom, steepening the wave's form until it can't stand. The momentum of breaking waves carries them up the beach, stirring up sand and silt from the shallow bottom. The beach-thrown water carries sediment out to sea under the incoming waves and rushes offshore on the bottom. You've felt this return flow tugging at your ankles in the shallows, the *undertow* that tries to knock you off your feet. The return flow slows quickly and drops its sediment, building up a *bar* parallel to the beach. There may be small bars near the beach, but the big bar farther out is where the large waves (heightened by the reflected energy from that bar) break. Every beach with waves has a bar. Bars change with weather and waves—growing, subsiding, and occasionally *failing*.

In a falling tide, a bar partially dams up the water between bar and beach. A random flaw in the bar is blown out by escaping water. Dammed up water begins to flow through the break with real force creating a *rip current*, narrow or wide. A swimmer caught in a rip current is carried *away* from the beach. *Do not try to outswim the rip current!* You're not as strong as the sea. Swim *parallel* to the beach, right or left, usually only a hundred yards or less. When you're outside the rip current, swim back to shore and take a break. Beach physics has given you a scare.

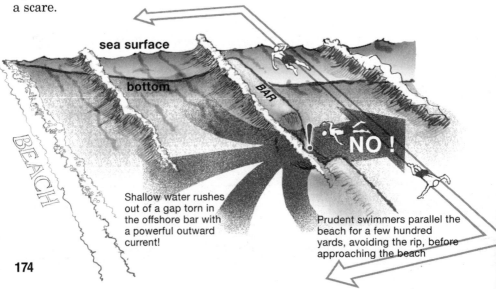

sea surface

bottom

BAR

BEACH

! NO !

Shallow water rushes out of a gap torn in the offshore bar with a powerful outward current!

Prudent swimmers parallel the beach for a few hundred yards, avoiding the rip, before approaching the beach

Cross Is. Lt., E. Pt. of Is. – Fl. W. ev. 10 s., Ht. 24.9 m. (82'), Rge. 10 mi., (44-18-43.7N/64-10-06.4W)

West Ironbound Is. Lt., Entr. to La Have R. – LFl. W. ev. 12 s., Ht. 23.6 m. (77'), Rge. 8 mi., (44-13-43.7N/64-16-28W)

Moshers Is. Lt., W. side Entr. to La Have R. – F.W., Ht. 23.3 m. (77'), Rge. 13 mi., (44-14-14.6N/64-18-59.1W)

Cherry Cove Lt., betw. Little Hbr. & Back Cove – Iso. G. ev. 4 s., Ht. 6.7 m. (22'), Rge. 8 mi., (44-09-29.8N/64-28-53.2W)

Medway Head Lt., W. side entr. to Pt. Medway – Fl. W. ev. 12 s., Ht. 24.2 m. (80'), Rge. 11 mi., (44-06-10.6N/64-32-23.3W)

Western Head Lt., W. side entr. to Liverpool Bay – Fl. W. ev. 15 s., Horn 1 bl. ev. 60 s., Horn points 104°, Ht. 16.8 m. (55'), Rge. 15 mi., (43-59-20.8N/64-39-44.5W)

Lockeport Lt., on Gull Rock, entr. to hbr. – LFl. W. ev. 15 s., Horn 1 bl. ev. 30 s., Ht. 16.7 m. (56'), Rge. 12 mi., (43-39-18.3N/65-05-55.9W)

Cape Roseway Lt., near SE Pt. of McNutt Is. – Fl. W. ev. 10 s., Ht. 33.1 m. (109'), Rge. 10 mi., (43-37-21.4N/65-15-50W)

Long Rock Lt., on SE end of Is. – LFl W. ev. 6 s., Horn 1 bl. ev. 60 s., Ht. 28.3 m. (92'), Rge. 11 mi., (43-30-26.2N/65-20-44.2W)

The Salvages Lt., SE end of Is. – LFl. W. ev. 12 s., Horn 3 bl. ev. 60 s., Ht. 15.6 m. (51'), Rge. 10 mi., (43-28-08.1N/65-22-44W)

Baccaro Point Lt., E. side entr. to Barrington Bay – Mo(D)W ev. 10 s., Horn 1 bl. ev. 20 s., Horn points 200°, Ht. 15.0 m. (49'), Rge. 15 mi., (43-26-59N/65-28-15W)

Cape Sable Lt., on cape – Fl. W. ev. 5 s., Horn 1 bl. ev. 60 s., Horn points 150°, Ht. 29.7 m. (97'), Rge. 18 mi., Racon (C), (43-23-24N/65-37-16.9W)

West Head Lt., Cape Sable Is. – F.R., Horn 2 bl. ev. 60 s., Horn points 254°, Ht. 15.6 m. (51'), Rge. 7 mi., (43-27-23.8N/65-39-16.9W)

Outer Island Lt., on S. Pt. of Outer Is. – Fl. W. ev. 10 s., Ht. 13.7 m. (46'), Rge. 10 mi., (43-27-23.2N/65-44-36.2W)

Seal Is. Lt., S. Pt. of Is. – Fl. W. ev. 10 s., Horn 3 bl. ev. 60 s., Horn points 183°, Ht. 33.4 m. (110'), Rge. 19 mi., (43-23-40N/66-00-51W)

NOVA SCOTIA, WEST COAST

Peases Is. Lt., S. Pt. of one of the Tusket Is. – LFl. W. ev. 6 s., Horn 2 bl. ev. 60 s., Ht. 16 m. (53'), Rge. 9 mi., (43-37-42.6N/66-01-34.9W)

Cape Forchu Lt., E. Cape S. Pt. Yarmouth Sd. – LFl. W. ev. 12 s., Ht. 34.5 m. (113'), Rge. 12 mi., Racon (B), (43-47-38.8N/66-09-19.3W)

Lurcher Shoal Bifurcation Light By. "NM," W. of SW shoal – Fl.(2+1) R. ev. 6 s., Racon (K), R.G.R. marked "NM," (43-48-57.2N/66-29-58W)

Cape St. Marys Lt., E. side of Bay – Fl. W. ev. 5 s., Horn 1 bl. ev. 60 s., Horn points 251° 30', Ht. 31.8 m (105'), Rge. 13 mi., (44-05-09.2N/66-12-39.6W)

Brier Is. Lt., on W. side of Is. R. & W. Tower – Fl(3) W. ev. 18 s., Ht. 22.2 m. (72'), Rge. 14 mi., (44-14-55N/66-23-32W)

Boars Head Lt., W. side of N. entr. to Petit Passage – Fl. W. ev. 4 s., Ht. 28.0 m. (91'), Rge. 7 mi., (44-24-14.5N/66-12-55W)

Prim Pt. Lt., Digby Gut, W. Pt. of entr. to Annapolis Basin – Iso. W. ev. 6 s., Ht. 24.8 m. (82'), Rge. 12 mi., (44-41-28N/65-47-10.8W)

Ile Haute Lt., on highest Pt. – Fl. W. ev. 4 s., Ht. 112 m. (367'), Rge. 7 mi., (45-15-03.3N/65-00-19.8W)

NEW BRUNSWICK COAST

Cape Enrage Lt., at pitch of cape – Fl. G. ev. 6 s., Horn 3 bl. ev. 60 s., Horn points 220°, Ht. 40.7 m. (134'), Rge. 10 mi., (45-35-38.1N/64-46-47.7W)

Quaco Lt., tower on head – Fl. W. ev. 10 s., Horn 1 bl. ev. 30 s., Horn points 130°, Ht. 26.0 m. (86'), Rge. 21 mi., (45-19-25.3N/65-32-08.8W)

For abbreviations see footnote p. 173

Weather Notes
From Maine to the Chesapeake

Sea Fog

There is always invisible moisture in the air, and the warmer the air, the more moisture it can contain invisibly. But when such a mass of moist air is cooled off, as it does when passing over a body of cooler water, the moisture often condenses into visible vapor, or fog. The fog clears when the air temperature rises, from the sun or a warm land mass, or by a warm, dry wind.

To predict fog accurately, you can use a "sling psychrometer." This instrument uses two thermometers side by side, one of which has a wick fastened to the bulb end. After wetting the wick on the "wet bulb" thermometer, the user swings the instrument in a circle for 60-90 seconds. This causes water to evaporate from the wet bulb thermometer, lowering its reading. The dry bulb thermometer simply tells air temperature. The difference in readings between the dry bulb and wet bulb thermometers determines the relative humidity of the air, and - especially valuable for determining the likelihood of fog - the dew point. The dew point is the (lower) temperature to which air must be cooled for condensation, or fog, to occur.

Eastport, Maine to Cape Cod

Cold water (48°-55°) off the northern New England coast often causes heavy fog conditions in the spring and summer, when a warm moist southwesterly flow of air passes over it. East of Portland to the Bay of Fundy, fog is not apt to occur when the dew point is under 55°, unless there is a very warm moist wind. The effect of the cold water on the warm air is reduced if the winds become brisk, as they are apt to do in the afternoon. Visibility should then improve.

Long Island Sound and the New Jersey Coast

Summertime warm water (in the 70s) in this area rarely cools down any warm air mass enough to produce fog. This is not the case farther offshore, where cooler water temperatures (in the 50s) can produce fog.

On the south coast of Long Island, when the southwest wind blows toward the shore at the same time as the ebb tide, inlets can become dangerous with short, steep seas. Also, offshore swells can become very high near the mouths of inlets.

On the New Jersey shore, prevailing winds in summer are southerly, increasing in mid-morning to rarely more than 20 knots and usually dying down at dusk. Occasional summer thunderstorms can be expected. Any brisk winds from the east, northeast, or southeast can produce dangerous conditions along this lee shore and at the mouths of inlets. When the wind is from offshore like this, inlets should be entered on a flood tide.

At the mouth of Delaware Bay, seas can build up to a hazardous degree when there is a southeast wind at the same time as an ebb current at the mouth of the Bay.

Chesapeake Bay

There is little chance of fog in this region because of the warmth of the water. The Bay has quirks of its own in weather and sea conditions. It is a narrow and fairly shallow body of water, and winds tend to blow up or down it. Sharp seas can result, depending on the direction of the current and the wind. Opposing forces make for rough water.

Prevailing winds in spring and summer are southerly, freshening in the afternoon after a morning of calm. Summer thunderstorms occur frequently in afternoon and early evening, usually from the west. In the fall, after a cold front passes through, the winds will shift into the north or northeast, usually for three days, and increase in velocity, causing seas to build up. Calm follows for a day or so until the wind shifts to the southwest.

Cape Spencer Lt., pitch of cape – Fl. W. ev. 11 s., Ht. 61.6 m. (203′), Rge. 14 mi., (45-11-42.5N/65-54-35.5W)

Partridge Is. Lt., highest pt. of Is., Saint John Harbour – Fl. W. ev. 7.5 s., Ht. 35.3 m. (116′), Rge. 19 mi., (45-14-21N/66-03-13.8W)

Musquash Head Lt., E. side entr. to Musquash Hbr. – Fl. W. ev. 3 s., Horn 1 bl. ev. 60 s., Horn points 180°, Ht. 35.1 m. (116′), Rge. 20 mi., (45-08-37.1N/66-14-14.2W)

Pt. Lepreau Lt., on point – Fl. W. ev. 5 s., Horn 3 bl. ev. 60 s., Horn points 190°, Ht. 25.5 m. (84′), Rge. 14 mi., (45-03-31.7N/66-27-31.3W)

Pea Pt. Lt., E. side entr. to Letang Hbr. – F.W. visible 251° thru N & E to 161°, Horn 2 bl. ev. 60 s., Horn points 180°, Ht. 17.2 m. (56′), Rge. 12 mi., (45-02-20.4N/66-48-28.2W)

Head Harbour Lt., outer rock of E. Quoddy Head – F.R., Horn 1 bl. ev. 60 s., Horn points 116°, Ht. 17.6 m. (58′), Rge. 13 mi., (44-57-28.6N/66-54-00.2W)

Swallowtail Lt., NE Pt. of Grand Manan – Oc. W. ev. 6 s., Horn 1 bl. ev. 20 s., Horn points 100°, Ht. 37.1 m. (122′), Rge. 12 mi., (44-45-51.1N/66-43-57.5W)

Great Duck Is. Lt., S. end of Is. – Fl. W. ev. 10 s., Horn 1 bl. ev. 60 s., Horn points 120°, Ht. 16.5 m. (54′), Rge. 18 mi., (44-41-03.5N/66-41-36.4W)

Southwest Head Lt., S. end of Grand Manan – Fl. W. ev. 10 s., Ht. 47.5 m. (156′), Rge. 16 mi., (44-36-02.9N/66-54-19.8W)

Gannet Rock North Lt. – Oc. W. ev. 3 s. visible 58° through E, S & W to 348°, Ht. 12.9 m. (42′), Rge. 11 mi., (44-30-38N/66-46-53.6W)

Gannet Rock South Lt. – Oc. W. ev. 3 s. visible 193° through W, N & E to 164°, Ht. 13.6 m. (44′), Rge. 11 mi., (44-30-37.2N/66-46-53.7W)

Machias Seal Is. Lt., On Is. summit – Fl. W. ev. 3 s., Ht. 25 m. (83′), Rge. 17 mi., (44-30-06.6N/67-06-04.1W)

MAINE

West Quoddy Head Lt., Entr. Quoddy Roads – Fl(2) W. ev. 15 s., Keyed (VHF 83A) Horn 2 bl. ev. 30 s., Ht. 83′, Rge. 14 mi., (44-48-54N/66-57-02W)

Libby Island Lt., Entr. Machias Bay – Fl(2) W. ev. 20 s., Keyed (VHF 83A) Horn 1 bl. ev. 15 s., Ht. 91′, Rge. 18 mi., (44-34-06N/67-22-03W)

Moose Peak Lt., E. end Mistake Is. – Fl. W. ev. 30 s., Keyed (VHF 83A) Horn 2 bl. ev. 30 s., Ht. 72′, Rge. 20 mi., (44-28-28N/67-31-55W)

Petit Manan Lt., E. Pt. of Is. – Fl. W. ev. 10 s., Keyed (VHF 83A) Horn 1 bl. ev. 30 s., Ht. 123′, Rge. 19 mi., (44-22-03N/67-51-52W)

Prospect Harbor Point Lt. – Fl. R. ev. 6 s., (2 W. sect.), Ht. 42′, Rge. R. 7 mi., W. 9 mi., ltd. 24 hrs., (44-24-12N/68-00-47W)

Mount Desert Lt., 20 mi. S. of island – Fl. W. ev. 15 s., Keyed (VHF 83A) Horn 2 bl. ev. 30 s., Ht. 75′, Rge. 14 mi., (43-58-07N/68-07-42W)

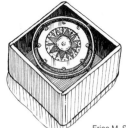

Erica M. Szuplat

Great Duck Island Lt., S. end of island – Fl. R. ev. 5 s., Keyed (VHF 83A) Horn 1 bl. ev. 15 s., Ht. 67′, Rge. 14 mi., (44-08-31N/68-14-45W)

Frenchman Bay Ltd. By. "FB," Fl. (2+1) R. ev. 6 s., Rge. 4 mi., R&G Bands, Racon (B), (44-19-21N/68-07-24W)

Egg Rock Lt., Frenchman Bay – Fl. R. ev. 5 s., Keyed (VHF 83A) Horn 2 bl. ev. 30 s., Ht. 64′, Rge. 18 mi., (44-21-14N/68-08-18W)

Baker Island Lt., SW Entr. Somes Sound – Fl. W. ev. 10 s., Ht. 105′, Rge. 10 mi., (44-14-28N/68-11-56W)

Bass Harbor Head Lt., SW Pt. Mt. Desert Is. – Oc. R. ev. 4 s., Ht. 56′, Rge. 13 mi., (44-13-19N/68-20-14W)

Blue Hill Bay Lt. #3, on Green Is. – Fl. G. ev. 4 s., Ht. 21′, Rge. 5 mi., SG on tower, (44-14-55N/68-29-52W)

For abbreviations see footnote p. 173

was a woman. Molly's organizational and proofreading skills, in addition to her nearly 40 years of involvement with the book, perfectly suited her to her new title. Listed after her were the next generation, Robert Eldridge (Ridge) White, Jr., and his wife Linda Foster White. Linda became a nearly constant assistant to Molly and made countless enhancements to the production of the book. Pollution regulations, fishing articles, and a story contest became regular components.

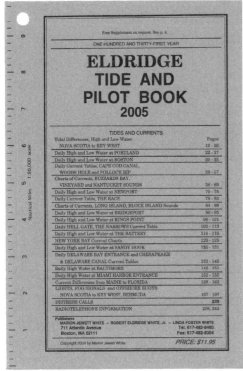

2005, prior to the present cover design

With the passing of Molly in 2004, Ridge and Linda became co-Publishers. Both avid sailors, Ridge and Linda each taught several classes using ELDRIDGE as a guide. Thanks to Linda's tech savvy, production of ELDRIDGE was ushered into the digital age. The face of the book underwent a significant makeover in 2006. In 2015, with Linda and Ridge taking the first steps towards retirement, daughter Jenny and husband Peter Kuliesis stepped forward and joined the crew. The timing would prove to be fortuitous, as Linda was to lose her bout with cancer at the end of that year. She was relieved to know that the book would continue in their hands.

Captain George W Eldridge

Since joining Ridge at the helm for the 2016 edition, Jenny (now the sixth generation of the Eldridge family to work on the book) and Peter have continued to refine the production of the book, placing an emphasis on new content for novices and old salts alike.

We are proud to continue the tradition as ELDRIDGE begins its 16th decade. In the words of our predecessors, we hope the book continues to be a means of ensuring you a fair tide and the safety of your ship.

Jenny White Kuliesis
Peter Kuliesis
Robert Eldridge White, Jr.

178

Burnt Coat Harbor Lt. – Oc. W. ev. 4 s., Ht. 75′, Rge. 9 mi., (44-08-03N/68-26-50W)

Halibut Rocks Lt., Jericho Bay – Fl. W. ev. 6 s., Horn 1 bl. ev. 10 s., Ht. 25′, Rge. 6 mi., NR on tower, (44-08-02N/68-31-31W)

Eggemoggin Ltd. Bell By. "EG" – Mo(A)W, Rge. 4 mi., RWSRST, (44-19-13N/68-44-34W)

Eggemoggin Reach Bell By. "ER" – RWSRST, (44-18-00N/68-46-29W)

Crotch Island Lt. #21, Deer Is. Thorofare – Fl. G. ev. 4 s., Ht. 20′, Rge. 5 mi., SG on tower, (44-08-46N/68-40-39W)

Saddleback Ledge Lt., Isle au Haut Bay – Fl. W. ev. 6 s., Horn 1 bl. ev. 10 s., Ht. 52′, Rge. 9 mi., (44-00-52N/68-43-35W)

Isle Au Haut Lt., Isle au Haut Bay – Fl. R. ev. 4 s., W. Sect. 034°-060°, Ht. 48′, Rge. R. 6 mi., W. 8 mi., (44-03-53N/68-39-05W)

Deer Island Thorofare Lt., W. end of thorofare – Fl. W. ev. 6 s., Horn 1 bl. ev. 15 s., Ht. 52′, Rge. 8 mi., Obscured from 240°-335°, (44-08-04N/68-42-12W)

Goose Rocks Lt., E. Entr. Fox Is. Thorofare – Fl. R. ev. 6 s., W. Sect. 301°-304°, Keyed (VHF 83A) Horn 1 bl. ev. 10 s., Ht. 51′, Rge. R. 7 mi., W. 12 mi., (44-08-08N/68-49-50W)

Eagle Island Lt., E. Penobscot Bay – Fl. W. ev. 4 s., Ht. 106′, Rge. 9 mi., (44-13-04N/68-46-04W)

Green Ledge Lt. #4, E. Penobscot Bay – Fl. R. ev. 6 s., Ht. 31′, Rge. 5 mi., TR on tower, (44-17-25N/68-49-42W)

Erica M. Szuplat

Heron Neck Lt., E. Entr. Hurricane Sound – F.R., W. Sect. 030°-063°, Keyed (VHF 83A) Horn 1 bl. ev. 30 s., Ht. 92′, Rge. R. 7 mi., W. 9 mi., (44-01-30N/68-51-44W)

Matinicus Rock Lt., Penobscot Bay App. – Fl. W. ev. 10 s., Keyed (VHF 83A) Horn 1 bl. ev. 15 s., Ht. 90′, Rge. 20 mi., (43-47-01N/68-51-18W)

Grindel Pt. Lt., West Penobscot Bay – Fl. W. ev. 4 s., Ht. 39′, Rge. 7 mi., (44-16-53N/68-56-35W)

Two Bush Island Lt., Two-Bush Ch. – Fl. W. ev. 5 s., R. Sect. 061°-247°, Keyed (VHF 83A) Horn 1 bl. ev. 15 s., Ht. 65′, Rge. W. 21 mi., R. 15 mi., (43-57-51N/69-04-26W)

Two Bush Island Ltd. Wh. By. "TBI" – Mo(A)W, Rge. 6 mi., RWS, (43-58-17N/69-00-16W)

Whitehead Lt., W. side of S. entr. Muscle Ridge Ch. – Oc.G. ev. 4 s., Keyed (VHF 83A) Horn 2 bl. ev. 30 s., Ht. 75′, Rge. 6 mi., (43-58-43N/69-07-27W)

Owls Head Lt., S. side Rockland Entr. – F.W., Keyed (VHF 83A) Horn 2 bl. ev. 20 s., Ht. 100′, Rge. 16 mi., Obscured from 324°-354° by Monroe Island, ltd. 24 hrs., (44-05-32N/69-02-38W)

Rockland Harbor Breakwater Lt., S. end of breakwater – Fl. W. ev. 5 s., Keyed (VHF 83A) Horn 1 bl. ev. 15 s., Ht. 39′, Rge. 14 mi., (44-06-15N/69-04-39W)

Lowell Rock Lt. #2, Rockport Entr. – Fl. R. ev. 6 s., Ht. 25′, Rge. 5 mi., TR on spindle, (44-09-46N/69-03-37W)

Browns Head Lt., W. Entr. Fox Is. Thorofare – F.W., 2 R. Sect. 001°-050° and 061°-091°, Keyed (VHF 83A) Horn 1 bl. ev. 10 s., Ht. 39′, Rge. R. 11 mi., F.W. 14 mi., ltd. 24 hrs., (44-06-42N/68-54-34W)

Curtis Island Lt., S. side Camden Entr. – Oc.G. ev. 4 s., Ht. 52′, Rge. 6 mi., (44-12-05N/69-02-56W)

Northeast Point Lt. #2, Camden Entr. – Fl. R. ev. 4 s., Ht. 20′, Rge. 5 mi., TR on white tower, (44-12-31N/69-02-47W)

Dice Head Lt., N. side Entr. to Castine – Fl. W. ev. 6 s., Ht. 134′, Rge. 11 mi., White tower, (44-22-58N/68-49-08W)

Fort Point Lt., W. side Entr. to Penobscot R. – F.W., Keyed (VHF 83A) Horn 1 bl. ev. 10 s., Ht. 88′, Rge. 15 mi., ltd. 24 hrs., (44-28-02N/68-48-42W)

For abbreviations see footnote p. 173

Marshall Point Lt., E. side of Pt. Clyde Hbr. S. Entr. – F.W., Keyed (VHF 83A) Horn 1 bl. ev. 10 s., Ht. 30', Rge. 13 mi., ltd. 24 hrs., (43-55-03N/69-15-41W)

Marshall Point Ltd. By. "MP" – Mo(A)W, Rge. 4 mi., RWSRST, (43-55-18N/69-10-52W)

Monhegan Island Lt., Penobscot Bay – Fl. W. ev. 15 s., Ht. 178', Rge. 20 mi., Obscured between west and southwest within 3 mi of island (43-45-53N/69-18-57W)

Franklin Is. Lt., Muscongus Bay – Fl. W. ev. 6 s., Ht. 57', Rge. 8 mi., Obscured from 253°-352° by trees (43-53-31N/69-22-29W)

Pemaquid Pt. Lt., W. side Muscongus Bay Entr. – Fl. W. ev. 6 s., Ht. 79', Rge. 14 mi., (43-50-12N/69-30-21W)

Ram Is. Lt., Fisherman Is. Passage S. side – Iso. R. ev. 6 s., 2 W. Sect. 258°-261° and 030°-046°, Covers fairways, Keyed (VHF 83A) Horn 1 bl. ev. 30 s., Ht. 36', Rge. W. 11 mi., R. 9 mi., W. 9 mi. (43-48-14N/69-35-57W)

Burnt Is. Lt., Boothbay Hbr. W. side Entr. – Fl. R. ev. 6 s., 2 W. Sect. 307°-316° and 355°-008°, Covers fairways. Keyed (VHF 83A) Horn 1 bl. ev. 10 s., Ht. 61', Rge. W. 8 mi., R. 6 mi., (43-49-31N/69-38-25W)

The Cuckolds Lt., Boothbay – Fl(2) W. ev. 6 s., Keyed (VHF 83A) Horn 1 bl. ev. 15 s., Ht. 59', Rge. 12 mi., (43-46-46N/69-39-00W)

Seguin Lt., 2 mi. S. of Kennebec R. mouth – F.W., Keyed (VHF 83A) Horn 2 bl. ev. 20 s., Ht. 180', Rge. 14 mi., (43-42-27N/69-45-29W)

Hendricks Head Lt., Sheepscot R. mouth E. side – F.W., R. Sect. 180°-000°, Ht. 43', Rge. R. 7 mi., F.W. 9 mi., (43-49-21N/69-41-23W)

Pond Is. Lt., Kennebec R. mouth W. side – Iso. W. ev. 6 s., Keyed (VHF 83A) Horn 2 bl. ev. 30 s., Ht. 52', Rge. 9 mi., (43-44-24N/69-46-13W)

Perkins Is. Lt., Kennebec R. – Fl. R. ev. 2.5 s., 2 W. Sect. 018° – 038°, 172° – 188°, Covers fairways, Ht. 41', Rge. R. 5 mi., W. 6 mi., (43-47-12N/69-47-07W)

Squirrel Pt. Lt., Kennebec R. – Iso. R. ev. 6 s., W. Sect. 321° - 324°, Covers fairway, Ht. 25', Rge. R. 7 mi., W. 9 mi., (43-48-59N/69-48-09W)

Erica M. Szuplat

Fuller Rock Lt., off Cape Small – Fl. W. ev. 4 s., Ht. 17', Rge. 6 mi., NR on tower, (43-41-45N/69-50-01W)

White Bull Ltd. Gong By. "WB" – Mo(A)W, Rge. 6 mi., RWS, (43-42-49N/69-55-13W)

Whaleboat Island Lt., Broad Sd., Casco Bay – Fl. W. ev. 6 s., Ht. 47', Rge. 4 mi., NR on tower, (43-44-31N/70-03-40W)

Cow Island Ledge Lt., Portland to Merepoint – Fl. W. ev. 6 s., Ht. 23', Rge. 8 mi., RaRef., NR on spindle, (43-42-11N/70-11-19W)

Halfway Rock Lt., midway betw. Cape Small Pt. and Cape Eliz. – Fl. R. ev. 5 s., Keyed (VHF 83A) Horn 2 bl. ev. 30 s., Ht. 76', Rge. 14 mi., (43-39-21N/70-02-12W)

Portland Ltd. Wh. By. "P", Portland Hbr. App. – Mo(A)W, Rge. 6 mi., Racon (M), RWSRST, (43-31-36N/70-05-28W)

Ram Island Ledge Lt., N. side of Portland Hbr. Entr. – Fl. (2) W. ev. 6 s., Keyed (VHF 83A) Horn 1 bl. ev. 10 s., Ht. 77', Rge. 9 mi., (43-37-53N/70-11-15W)

Cape Elizabeth Lt., S. of Portland Hbr. Entr. – Fl(4) W. ev. 15 s., Keyed (VHF 83A) Horn 2 bl. ev. 60 s., Ht. 129', Rge. 15 mi., ltd. 24 hrs., (43-33-58N/70-12-00W)

Portland Head Lt., SW side Portland Hbr. Entr. – Fl. W. ev. 4 s., Keyed (VHF 83A) Horn 1 bl. ev. 15 s., Ht. 101', Rge. 19 mi., ltd. 24 hrs., (43-37-23N/70-12-28W)

Spring Pt. Ledge Lt., Portland main ch. W. side – Fl. W. ev. 6 s., 2 R. Sect., 2 W. Sectors 331°-337° Covers fairway entrance, and 074°-288°, Keyed (VHF 83A) Horn 1 bl. ev. 10 s., Ht. 54', Rge. R. 10 mi., W. 12 mi., ltd. 24 hrs., (43-39-08N/70-13-26W)

Wood Island Lt., S. Entr. Wood Is. Hbr. N. side – Alt. W. and G. ev. 10 s., Keyed (VHF 83A) Horn 2 bl. ev. 30 s., Ht. 71', Rge. W. 13 mi., G. 13 mi., (43-27-25N/70-19-45W)

Goat Is. Lt., Cape Porpoise Hbr. Entr. – Fl. W. ev. 6 s., Keyed (VHF 83A) Horn 1 bl. ev. 15 s., Ht. 38', Rge. 12 mi., (43-21-28N/70-25-30W)

Cape Neddick Lt., On N. side of Nubble – Iso. R. ev. 6 s., Keyed (VHF 83A) Horn 1 bl. ev. 10 s., Ht. 88', Rge. 13 mi., ltd. 24 hrs., (43-09-55N/70-35-28W)

Jaffrey Point Lt. #4 – Fl. R. ev. 4 s., Ht. 22', rge. 4 mi., TR on tower, (43-03-18N/70-42-49W)

Boon Is. Lt., 6.5 mi. off coast – Fl. W. ev. 5 s., Horn 1 bl. ev. 10 s., Ht. 137', Rge. 14 mi., (43-07-17N/70-28-35W)

York Harbor Ltd. Bell By. "YH" – Mo(A)W, Rge. 5 mi., RWSRST, (43-07-45N/70-37-01W)

NEW HAMPSHIRE

Whaleback Lt., Portsmouth Entr. NE side –Fl(2) W. ev. 10 s., Keyed (VHF 83A) Horn 2 bl. ev. 30 s., Ht. 59', Rge. 11 mi., (43-03-32N/70-41-47W)

Portsmouth Harbor Lt. (New Castle), on Fort Point – F. G., Keyed (VHF 83A) Horn 1 bl. ev. 10 s., Ht. 52', Rge. 12 mi., (43-04-16N/70-42-31W)

Rye Harbor Entr. Ltd. Wh. By. "RH" – Mo(A)W, Rge. 6 mi., RWSRST, (42-59-38N/70-43-45W)

Isles Of Shoals Lt., 5.5 mi. off coast – Fl. W. ev. 15 s., Keyed (VHF 83A) Horn 1 bl. ev. 30 s., Ht. 82', Rge. 14 mi., (42-58-02N/70-37-24W)

MASSACHUSETTS

Newburyport Harbor Lt., N. end of Plum Is. – Oc.(2) G. ev. 15 s., Obscured from 165°-192° and 313°-344°, Ht. 50', Rge. 10 mi., (42-48-55N/70-49-08W)

Merrimack River Entr. Ltd. Wh. By. "MR"– Mo(A)W, Rge. 4 mi., RWSRST, (42-48-34N/70-47-03W)

Ipswich Lt., Ipswich Entr. S. side – Oc.W. ev. 4 s., Ht. 30', Rge. 5 mi., NR on tower, (42-41-07N/70-45-58W)

Rockport Breakwater Lt. #6, W. side Entr. Rockport inner hbr. – Fl. R. ev. 4 s., Ht. 32', Rge. 4 mi., TR on spindle, (42-39-39N/70-36-43W)

Annisquam Harbor Lt., E. side Entr. – Fl. W. ev. 7.5 s., R. Sector 180°-217°, Horn 2 bl. ev. 60 s., Ht. 45', Rge. R. 11 mi., W. 14 mi., (42-39-43N/70-40-53W)

Straitsmouth Lt., Rockport Entr. S. side – Fl. G. ev. 6 s., Keyed (VHF 83A) Horn 1 bl. ev. 15 s., Ht. 46', Rge. 6 mi., (42-39-44N/70-35-17W)

Cape Ann Lt., E. side Thacher Is. – Fl. R. ev. 5 s., Keyed (VHF 83A) Horn 2 bl. ev. 60 s., Ht. 166', Rge. 17 mi., (42-38-12N/70-34-30W)

Eastern Point Ltd. Wh. By. #2 – Fl. R. ev. 4 s., Rge. 3 mi., (42-34-14N/70-39-50W)

Eastern Point Lt., Gloucester Entr. E. side – Fl. W. ev. 5 s., Ht. 57', Rge. 20 mi., (42-34-49N/70-39-52W)

Gloucester Breakwater Lt., W. end – Oc.R. ev. 4 s., Keyed (VHF 83A) Horn 1 bl. ev. 10 s., Ht. 45', Rge. 6 mi., (42-34-57N/70-40-20W)

Bakers Island Lt., Salem Ch. – Alt. Fl. W. and R. ev. 20 s., Keyed (VHF 83A) Horn 1 bl. ev. 30 s., Ht. 111', Rge. W. 16 mi., R. 14 mi., (42-32-11N/70-47-09W)

Hospital Point Range Front Lt., Beverly Cove W. side – F.W., Ht. 69', Higher intensity on range line (42-32-47N/70-51-21W)

Marblehead Lt., N. point Marblehead Neck – F.G., Ht. 130', Rge. 7 mi., (42-30-19N/70-50-01W)

The Graves Ltd. Wh. By. #5 – Fl. G. ev. 4 s., Rge. 4 mi., Green, (42-22-33N/70-51-28W)

The Graves Lt., Boston Hbr. S. Ch. Entr. – Fl(2) W. ev. 12 s., Keyed (VHF 83A) Horn 2 bl. ev. 20 s., Ht. 98', Rge. 15 mi., (42-21-54N/70-52-09W)

Boston App. Ltd. By. "BG"– Mo(A)W, Rge. 4 mi., RWSRST, (42-23-27N/70-51-29W)

Deer Island Lt., President Roads, Boston Hbr. – Alt. W. and R. ev. 10 s., Keyed (VHF 83A) Horn 1 bl. ev. 10 s., Ht. 53', Rge. 9 mi., (42-20-22N/70-57-16W)

For abbreviations see footnote p. 173

Long Island Head Lt., President Roads, Boston Hbr. – Fl. W. ev. 2.5 s., Ht. 120', Rge. 6 mi., (42-19-49N/70-57-28W)

Boston Ltd. Wh. By. "B", Boston Hbr. Entr. – Mo(A)W, Rge. 6 mi., Racon (B), RWSRST, (42-22-42N/70-46-58W)

Boston App. Ltd. By. "BF" (NOAA-44013) –Fl(4) Y. ev. 20 sec, Rge. 7 mi., Yellow, (42-20-44N/70-39-04W)

Boston North Ch.Entr. Ltd. Wh. By. "NC" – Mo(A)W, Rge. 6 mi., RWSRST, Racon (N), (42-22-32N/70-54-18W)

Minots Ledge Lt., Boston Hbr. Entr. S. side – Fl(1+4+3) W. ev. 45 s., Keyed (VHF 83A) Horn 1 bl. ev. 10 s., Ht. 85', Rge. 10 mi., (42-16-11N/70-45-33W)

Boston Lt., SE side Little Brewster Is. – Fl. W. ev. 10 s., Keyed (VHF 83A) Horn 1 bl. ev. 30 s., Ht. 102', Rge. 27 mi., (42-19-41N/70-53-24W)

Scituate App. Ltd. Gong By. "SA"– Mo(A)W, Rge. 4 mi., RWSRST, (42-12-08N/70-41-49W)

Plymouth Lt. (Gurnet), N. side Entr. to hbr. – Fl(3) W. ev. 30 s., R. Sect. 323°-352°, Keyed (VHF 83A) Horn 2 bl. ev. 15 s., Ht. 102', Rge. R. 15 mi., W. 17 mi., (42-00-13N/70-36-02W)

Race Point Lt., NW Point of Cape Cod – Fl. W. ev. 10 s., Ht. 41', Rge. 14 mi., Obscured 220°-292°, (42-03-44N/70-14-35W)

Wood End Lt., Entr. to Provincetown – Fl. R. ev. 10 s., Keyed (VHF 83A) Horn 1 bl. ev. 30 s., Ht. 45', Rge. 3 mi., (42-01-17N/70-11-37W)

Long Point Lt., Provincetown Entr. SW side – Oc.G. ev. 4 s., Keyed (VHF 83A) Horn 1 bl. ev. 15 s., Ht. 36', Rge. 8 mi., (42-01-59N/70-10-07W)

Mary Ann Rocks Ltd. Wh. By. #12 – Fl. R. ev. 2.5 s., Rge. 4 mi., Red, (41-55-07N/70-30-22W)

Cape Cod Canal App. Ltd. Bell By. "CC" – Mo(A) W, Rge. 4 mi., RWSRST, (41-48-53N/70-27-39W)

Cape Cod Canal Breakwater Lt. #6, E. Entr. – Fl. R. ev. 5 s., Keyed (VHF 83A) Horn 1 bl. ev. 15 s., Ht. 43', Rge. 9 mi., (41-46-47N/70-29-23W)

Highland Lt., NE side of Cape Cod – Fl. W. ev. 5 s., Ht. 170', Rge. 14 mi., ltd. 24 hrs., (42-02-22N/70-03-39W)

Nauset Beach Lt., E. side of Cape Cod – Alt. W. R. ev. 10 s., Ht. 120', (41-51-36N/69-57-12W)

Chatham Beach Ltd. Wh. By. "C" – Mo(A)W, Rge. 4 mi., RWSRST, (41-39-12N/69-55-30W)

Sam O. White

Chatham Lt., W. side of hbr. – Fl(2)W. ev. 10 s., Ht. 80', Rge. 24 mi., ltd. 24 hrs., (41-40-17N/69-57-01W)

Chatham Inlet Bar Guide Lt., Fl. Y. ev. 2.5 s., Ht. 62', Rge. 11 mi., (41-40-18N/69-57-00W)

Hyannis Harbor App. Ltd. Bell By. "HH" – Mo(A)W, Rge. 4 mi., RWSRST, (41-35-57N/70-17-22W)

Pollock Rip Ch. Ltd. By. #8 – Fl. R. ev. 6 s., Rge. 3 mi., Red, (41-32-43N/69-58-56W)

A Quarter Mile from Harbor
by Will Sofrin

I've always loved mythology, be it Roman or Greek. The many overnight sailing passages I've made throughout my life continue to fuel my lure for these myths that inspired the names of the constellations I trust to find on a star-filled night, surrounded by a horizon made only of water and sky.

One of my favorite Greek myths is the story of Icarus. The son of a craftsman, Daedalus, Icarus was imprisoned with his father by King Minos for providing the king's daughter, Ariadne, with the clew that Theseus used to escape the labyrinth after killing the Minotaur. In this tale, the word clew is a ball of thread and the origination of the modern word clue. To escape their imprisonment, Daedalus, using wax and feathers, made two pairs of wings so he and his son could take to the air to get free. Before departing, Daedalus warned his son to follow him and not fly too close to the sun or the water. Naive of the danger and intoxicated by the experience of flight, Icarus ignored the warning and flew higher and higher. The heat from the sun melted the wax, causing the feathers to fall from the wings. As a result, Icarus, no longer able to fly, fell to the sea and drowned.

Icarus, Célestin Nanteuil

This story weighs heavily on me regarding foresight, understanding, and ignorance. It reminds me to stay present and be aware of where I am relative to the obstacles around me.

Today, many of us have become indifferent to the daily headlines announcing some sort of new technological breakthrough. Don't get me wrong, technology is impressive, but I can't help but feel concerned that all of these incredible amenities, in some way or another, dull our senses and reduce the potential of our resourcefulness at times when we may need it most. An easy example of this could be when a chart plotter dies in the middle of a fog bank on a boat without a paper chart. Maybe you've got a navigational app on your cell phone, but what happens if you don't have an electronic backup? Do you actually know exactly where you are?

In 2019, to meet the growing demand for ENCs (Electronic Navigational Charts), NOAA (National Oceanic Atmospheric Administration) began the process of stopping the production and maintenance of traditional paper and raster charts. I understand and won't argue the benefits of a chart plotter that can be more regularly updated and has the capability to show more detail than any paper chart ever could.

186

Continued on p. 210

Nantucket Lt., (Great Point), Nantucket, N. end of Is., – Fl. W. ev. 5 s., R. sect. 084°-106° (Covers Cross Rip & Tuckernuck Shoals), Ht. 71', Rge. W. 14 mi., R. 12 mi., (41-23-25N/70-02-54W)

Sankaty Head Lt., E. end of Is. – Fl. W. ev. 7.5 s., Ht. 158', Rge. 20 mi., ltd. 24 hrs., (41-17-04N/69-57-58W)

Nantucket East Breakwater Lt. #3, Outer Entr. to hbr. – Fl. G. ev. 4 s., Ht. 30', Rge. 3 mi., (41-18-37N/70-06-00W)

Brant Point Lt., Hbr. Entr. W. side – Oc.R. ev. 4 s., Keyed (VHF 83A) Horn 1 bl. ev. 10 s., Ht. 26', Rge. 9 mi., (41-17-24N/70-05-25W)

Cape Poge Lt., NE point of Chappaquiddick Is. – Fl. W. ev. 6 s., Ht. 65', Rge. 9 mi., (41-25-10N/70-27-08W)

Muskeget Ch. Ltd. Wh. By. "MC" – Mo(A)W, Rge. 4 mi., RWSRST, (41-15-00N/70-26-10W)

Edgartown Harbor Lt., Inner end of hbr. W. side – Fl. R. ev. 6 s., Ht. 45', Rge. 5 mi., (41-23-27N/70-30-11W)

East Chop Lt., E. side Vineyard Haven Hbr. Entr. – Iso. G. ev. 6 s., Ht. 79', Rge. 9 mi., (41-28-13N/70-34-03W)

West Chop Lt., W. side Vineyard Haven Hbr. Entr. – Oc.W. ev. 4 s., R. Sect. 281°-331° (covers Squash Meadow and Norton Shoals), Keyed (VHF 83A) Horn 1 bl. ev. 30 s., Ht. 84', Rge. R. 10 mi., W. 14 mi., (41-28-51N/70-35-59W)

Nobska Point Lt., Woods Hole E. Entr. – Fl. W. ev. 6 s., Obscured 125°-195°, R. Sect. 263°-289° (covers Hedge Fence and L'Hommedieu Shoal), Keyed (VHF 83A) Horn 2 bl. ev. 30 s., Ht. 87', Rge. R. 11 mi., W. 13 mi., ltd 24 hrs., (41-30-57N/70-39-18W)

Tarpaulin Cove Lt., SE side Naushon Is. – Fl. W. ev. 6 s., Ht. 78', Rge. 9 mi., (41-28-08N/70-45-27W)

Menemsha Creek Entr. Jetty Lt. #3 – Fl. G. ev. 4 s., Ht. 25', Rge. 5 mi., (41-21-16N/70-46-07W)

Gay Head Lt., W. point of Martha's Vineyard – Alt. W. and R. ev. 15 s., Ht. 175', Rge. W. 24 mi., R. 20 mi., Obscured 342°-359° by Nomans Land, ltd. 24 hrs., (41-20-54N/70-50-04W)

Cuttyhunk East Entr. Ltd. Bell By. "CH" – Mo(A)W, Rge. 4 mi., RWSRST, (41-26-34N/70-53-22W)

BUZZARDS BAY

Buzzards Bay Entr. Lt., W. Entr. – Fl. W. ev. 2.5 s., Keyed (VHF 83A) Horn 2 bl. ev. 30 s., Ht. 67', Rge. 14 mi., Racon (B), (41-23-49N/71-02-05W)

Dumpling Rocks Lt. #7, off Round Hill Pt. – Fl. G. ev. 6 s., Ht. 52', Rge. 8 mi., (41-32-18N/70-55-17W)

Buzzards Bay Midch. Ltd. Bell By. "BB" (east of Wilkes Ledge) – Mo(A)W, Rge. 4 mi., RWSRST, (41-30-33N/70-49-54W)

New Bedford West Barrier Lt. – Q.G., Keyed (VHF 83A) Horn 1 bl. ev. 10 s., Ht. 48', Rge. 8 mi., (41-37-27N/70-54-22W)

New Bedford East Barrier Lt. – Q. R., Ht. 33', Rge. 8 mi., (41-37-29N/70-54-19W)

Padanaram Breakwater Lt. #8 – Fl. R. ev. 4 s., Ht. 25', Rge. 5 mi., (41-34-27N/70-56-21W)

Cleveland East Ledge Lt., Cape Cod Canal App. E. side of S. Entr. – Fl. W. ev. 10 s., Keyed (VHF 83A) Horn 1 bl. ev. 15 s., Ht. 74', Rge. 14 mi., Racon (C), (41-37-51N/70-41-39W)

Ned Point Lt. – Iso. W. ev. 6 s., Ht. 41', Rge. 12 mi., (41-39-03N/70-47-44W)

Westport Harbor Entr. Lt. #7, W. side – Fl. G. ev. 6 s., Ht. 35', Rge. 9 mi., (41-30-27N/71-05-17W)

Westport Harbor App. Ltd. Bell By. 1, Fl. G. ev. 2.5s, Rge. 4 mi., (41-29-15N/71-04-04W)

For abbreviations see footnote p. 173

Weather Signs In the Sky

"When the rain before the wind, topsail sheets and halyards mind,
But when the wind before the rain, then you may set sail again."

Signs of Good Weather

- A gray sky in the morning or a "low dawn" – when the day breaks near the horizon, with the first streaks of light low in the sky – brings fair weather.
- "Rain before 7, clear before 11"
- Light, delicate tints with soft, undefined clouds accompany fine weather.
- Seabirds flying out early and far to sea suggest moderate wind, fair weather.
- A rosy sky at sunset, clear or cloudy: "Red sky at night, sailor's delight."
- High, wispy cirrus clouds, or even high cumulus, indicate immediate fair weather, with a possible change from a front within 24 hours.
- High contrails disappearing quickly show dry air aloft.
- Steady mild-to-moderate winds from the same direction indicate continuing fair weather.
- A low dew point relative to temperature means dry air.

Signs of Bad Weather

- "Red sky at morning, sailor take warning." Poor weather, wind, maybe rain.
- A "high dawn" – when the first streaks of daylight appear above a bank of clouds – often precedes a turn for worse weather.
- Light scud clouds driving across higher, heavy clouds show wind and rain.
- Hard-edged, inky clouds foretell rain and strong wind.
- Seabirds hanging over the land or headed inland suggest wind and rain.
- Remarkable clearness of atmosphere near the horizon, when distant hills or vessels are raised by refraction, are signs of an Easterly wind and indicate coming wet weather.
- Long-lasting contrails indicate humid air aloft.
- Low-level clouds, and clouds at several heights
- Rising humidity, dewpoint close to temperature

Signs of Wind

- Soft-looking, delicate clouds indicate light to moderate wind.
- Stronger wind is suggested by hard-edged, oily-looking, ragged clouds, or a bright yellow sky at sunset.
- A change in wind is indicated by high clouds crossing the sky in a different direction from that of lower clouds.
- Increasing wind and possibly rain are preceded by greater than usual twinkling of stars, indistinctness of the moon's horns, "wind dogs" (fragments of rainbows) seen on detached clouds, and the rainbow.
- "First rise after very low, indicates a stronger blow."

Sakonnet Lt. – Fl. W. ev. 6 s., R. sect. 195°-350°, Ht. 70', Rge. W. 7 mi., R. 5 mi., (41-27-11N/71-12-09W)

Sakonnet Breakwater Lt. #2, Entr. to hbr. – Fl. R. ev. 4 s., Ht. 29', Rge. 6 mi., (41-28-00N/71-11-43W)

Narragansett Bay Entr. Ltd. Wh. By. "NB" – Mo(A)W, Rge. 6 mi., Racon (B), RWSRST, (41-23-00N/71-23-21W)

Beavertail Lt. – Narrag. Bay E. passage – Fl. W. ev. 10 s., Obscured 175°-215°, Keyed (VHF 83A) Horn 1 bl. ev. 30 s., Ht. 64', Rge. 15 mi., ltd. 24 hrs., (41-26-58N/71-23-58W)

Castle Hill Lt. – Iso R. 6 s., Keyed (VHF 83A) Horn 1 bl. ev. 10 s., Ht. 40', Rge. 9 mi., (41-27-44N/71-21-47W)

Fort Adams Lt. #2, Narrag. Bay E. passage – Fl. R. ev. 6 s., Keyed (VHF 83A) Horn 1 bl. ev. 15 s., Ht. 32', Rge. 7 mi., (41-28-54N/71-20-12W)

Newport Harbor Lt., N. end of breakwater – F.G., Ht. 33', Rge. 9 mi., (41-29-36N/71-19-37W)

Rose Is. Lt., Fl W. ev. 6 s., Ht. 48', (41-29-44N/71-20-34W)

Prudence Is. Lt. (Sandy Pt.), Narrag. Bay E. passage – Fl. G. ev. 6 s., Ht. 28', Rge. 6 mi., (41-36-21N/71-18-13W)

Hog Island Shoal Lt., N. side Entr. to Mt. Hope Bay – Iso. W. ev. 6 s., Keyed (VHF 83A) Horn 2 bl. ev 30s., Ht. 54', Rge. 12 mi., (41-37-57N/71-16-24W)

Musselbed Shoals Lt.#6A, Mt. Hope Bay Ch. – Fl. R. ev. 6 s., Ht. 26', Rge. 6 mi., (41-38-10N/71-15-36W)

Castle Is. Lt. #2, N. of Hog Is. – Fl. R. ev. 6 s., Ht. 26', Rge. 3 mi., (41-39-14N/71-17-10W)

Bristol Harbor Lt. #4 – F.R., Ht. 25', Rge. 11 mi., (41-39-58N/71-16-42W)

Conimicut Lt., Providence R. App. – Fl. W. ev. 2.5 s., R. Sect. 322°-349° covers Ohio Ledge, Keyed (VHF 83A) Horn 2 bl. ev. 30 s., Ht. 58', Rge. W. 8 mi., R. 5 mi., (41-43-01N/71-20-42W)

Bullock Point Lt. "BP", Prov. R. – Oc.W. ev. 4 s., Ht. 29', Rge. 6 mi., (41-44-16N/71-21-51W)

Pomham Rocks Lt., Prov. R. – F.R., Ht. 54', Rge. 6 mi., (41-46-39N/71-22-10W)

Providence River Ch. Lt. #42, off rock – Iso. R. ev. 6 s., Ht. 31', Rge. 4 mi., (41-47-39N/71-22-47W)

Mt. Hope Bay Jct. Ltd. Gong By. "MH" – Fl(2+1) R. 6 s., Rge., 3 mi., R. & G. Bands, (41-39-32N/71-14-03W)

Borden Flats Lt., Mt. Hope Bay – Fl. W. ev. 2.5 s., Ht. 47', Rge. 9 mi., (41-42-16N/71-10-28W)

Wickford Harbor Lt. #1, Narrag. Bay W. passage – Fl. G. ev. 6 s., Ht. 40', Rge. 6 mi., (41-34-21N/71-26-13W)

Warwick Lt., Greenwich Bay App. – Oc.G. ev. 4 s., Keyed (VHF 81A) Horn 1 bl. ev. 15 s., Ht. 66', Rge. 10 mi., ltd. 24 hrs., (41-40-02N/71-22-42W)

Point Judith Lt., Block Is. Sd. Entr. – Oc(3)W. ev. 15 s., Keyed (VHF 83A) Horn 1 bl. ev. 15 s., Ht. 65', Rge. 16 mi., (41-21-40N/71-28-53W)

Block Island North Lt., N. end of Is. – Fl. W. ev. 5 s., Ht. 58', (41-13-39N/71-34-33W)

Block Island Southeast Lt., SE end of Is. – Fl. G. ev. 5 s., Keyed (VHF 83A) Horn 1 bl. ev. 30 s., Ht. 261', Rge. 17 mi., ltd. 24 hrs., (41-09-12N/71-33-07W)

Pt. Judith Harbor of Refuge W. Entr. Lt. #3 – Fl. G. ev. 6 s., Keyed (VHF 83A) Horn 1 bl. ev. 30 s., Ht. 35', Rge. 5 mi., (41-21-56N/71-30-53W)

Block Is. Breakwater Lt. #3 – Q. G., Keyed (VHF 81A) Horn 2 bl. ev. 30 s., Ht. 27', Rge. 6 mi., (41-10-38N/71-33-15W)

Watch Hill Lt., Fishers Is. Sd. E. Entr. – Alt. W. and R. ev. 5 s., Keyed (VHF 83A) Horn 1 bl. ev. 30 s., Ht. 61', Rge. 14 mi., ltd. 24 hrs., (41-18-14N/71-51-30W)

For abbreviations see footnote p. 173

FISHERS ISLAND SOUND

Latimer Reef Lt., Fishers Is. Sd. main ch. – Fl. W. ev. 6 s., Bell 2 strokes ev. 15 s., Ht. 55', Rge. 9 mi., (41-18-16N/71-56-00W)

N. Dumpling Lt., Fishers Is. Sd. main ch. – F.W., R. sector, Keyed (VHF 83A) Horn 1 bl. ev. 30 s., R. Sect. 257°-023°, Ht. 94', Rge. R. 7 mi., F.W. 9 mi., (41-17-17N/72-01-10W)

Stonington Outer Breakwater Lt. #4 – Fl. R. ev. 4 s., Horn 1 bl. ev. 10 s., Ht. 46', Rge. 5 mi., (41-19-00N/71-54-28W)

LONG ISLAND SOUND, NORTH SIDE

Race Rock Lt., SW end of Fishers Is. – Fl. R. ev. 10 s., Keyed (VHF 83A) Horn 2 bl. ev. 30 s., Ht. 67', Rge. 14 mi., (41-14-37N/72-02-50W)

Bartlett Reef Lt., S. end of reef – Fl. W. ev. 6 s., Keyed (VHF 83A) Horn 2 bl. ev. 60 s., Ht. 35', Rge. 8 mi., (41-16-28N/72-08-14W)

New London Ledge Lt., W. side of Southwest ledge –Fl(3+1) W. R. ev. 30 s., Keyed (VHF 83A) Horn 2 bl. ev. 20 s., Ht. 58', Rge. W. 17 mi., R. 14 mi., (41-18-21N/72-04-39W)

New London Harbor Lt., W. side Entr. – Iso. W. ev. 6 s., R. Sect. 000°-041° covers Sarah Ledge and shoals westward, Ht. 90', Rge. W. 17 mi., R. 14 mi., (41-19-00N/72-05-23W)

Saybrook Breakwater Lt., W. jetty – Fl. G. ev. 6 s., Keyed (VHF 83A) Horn 1 bl. ev. 30 s., Ht. 58', Rge. 11 mi., (41-15-48N/72-20-34W)

Lynde Pt. Lt., Conn. R. mouth W. side – F.W., Ht. 71', Rge. 14 mi., (41-16-17N/72-20-35W)

Twenty-Eight Foot Shoal Ltd. Wh. By. "TE" – Fl(2+1) R. ev. 6 s., , Rge. 4 mi., R&G Bands, (41-09-16N/72-30-25W)

Falkner Is. Lt., off Guilford Hbr. – Fl. W. ev. 10 s., Ht. 94', Rge. 13 mi., (41-12-43N/72-39-13W)

Branford Reef Lt., SE Entr. New Haven – Fl. W. ev. 6 s., Ht. 22', Rge. 7 mi., (41-13-17N/72-48-19W)

New Haven Hbr. Ltd. Wh. By. "NH" – Mo(A)W, Rge. 4 mi., RWSRST, (41-12-07N/72-53-47W)

Southwest Ledge Lt., E. side Entr. New Haven – Fl. R. ev. 5 s., Keyed (VHF 83A) Horn 1 bl. ev. 15 s., Ht. 57', Rge. 14 mi., (41-14-04N/72-54-44W)

New Haven Lt. – Fl. W. ev. 4 s., Ht. 27', Rge. 7 mi., (41-13-16N/72-56-32W)

Stratford Pt. Lt., W. side Entr. Housatonic R. – Fl(2)W. ev. 20 s., Ht. 52', Rge. 14 mi., (41-09-07N/73-06-12W)

Stratford Shoal Lt., Middle Ground – Fl. W. ev. 5 s., Horn 1 bl. ev. 15 s., Ht. 60', Rge. 13 mi., (41-03-35N/73-06-05W)

Tongue Pt. Lt., at Bridgeport Breakwater – Fl. G. ev. 4 s., Ht. 31', Rge. 5 mi., (41-10-00N/73-10-39W)

Penfield Reef Lt., S. side Entr. to Black Rock – Fl. R. ev. 6 s., Keyed (VHF 83A) Horn 1 bl. ev. 15 s., Ht. 51', Rge. 14 mi., (41-07-02N/73-13-20W)

Peck Ledge Lt., E. App. to Norwalk – Fl. G. ev. 2.5 s., Ht. 61', Rge. 5 mi., (41-04-39N/73-22-11W)

Greens Ledge Lt., W. end of ledge – Alt. Fl. W. and R. ev. 20 s., Keyed (VHF 83A) Horn 2 bl. ev. 20 s., Ht. 62', Rge. W. 14 mi., R. 14 mi., (41-02-30N/73-26-38W)

Stamford Harbor Ledge Obstruction Lt., on SW end of Harbor Ledge – Fl. W. ev. 4 s., (41-00-49N/73-32-34W)

Great Captain Is. Lt., SE Pt. of Is. – Alt. W. R. ev. 12 s., Keyed (VHF 83A) Horn 1 bl. ev. 15 s., Ht. 62', Rge. W. 14 mi., R. 14 mi., (40-58-57N/73-37-23W)

Larchmont Harbor Lt. #2, East Entr. – Fl. R. ev. 4 s., Ht. 26', Rge. 4 mi., (40-55-05N/73-43-52W)

For abbreviations see footnote p. 173

Heaving the Lead

In tidal water where depths were doubtfully marked on the chart, or in thick weather off shore, soundings were made to determine the ship's position. The leadsman stood in the fore channels and swung the lead. [Aft] in the main and mizzen channels were other men who held the line as it led aft to the stern, where the mate stood by the line tub. The leadsman called, "All ready there?" to the next man, the mate shouted "Heave!" and the lead went spinning forward. Each man let go as the line tautened, and the mate grasped the line as it ran from the tub, and made the sounding. If the lead struck bottom before it reached him, one of the others took the sounding and called the marks. Markers on the line indicated the depth in fathoms, and an "arming" of tallow in the end of the lead showed the nature of the bottom.

Reprinted from Sail Ho! Windjammer Sketches Alow and Aloft, by Gordon Grant, 1931, William Farquhar Payson, Inc., NY

Traditional Markings for Leadlines

2 fathoms – a 2-ended scrap of leather
3 fathoms – a 3-ended scrap of leather
5 fathoms – a scrap of white calico
7 fathoms – a strip of red wool bunting
10 fathoms – leather with a round hole

13 fathoms – a piece of thick blue serge
15 fathoms – a piece of white calico
17 fathoms – a piece of red wool bunting
20 fathoms – a cord with 2 knots
30 fathoms – a cord with 3 knots

LIGHTS, FOG SIGNALS and OFFSHORE BUOYS

LONG ISLAND SOUND, SOUTH SIDE

Little Gull Is. Lt., E. Entr. L.I. Sd. – Fl(2) W. ev. 15 s., Horn 1 bl. ev. 15 sec., Ht. 91', Rge. 14 mi., (41-12-23N/72-06-25W)

Plum Gut Lt. – Fl. W. ev. 2.5 s., Ht. 21' Rge. 5 mi., (41-10-26N/72-12-42W)

Plum Island Ltd. Wh. By. "PI" – Mo(A)W, Rge. 4 mi., RWSRST, (41-13-17N/72-10-48W)

Plum Is. Hbr. West Dolphin Lt., W. end of Is. – Q.G., (Maintained by DHS), (41-10-16N/72-12-24W)

Orient Pt. Lt., outer end of Oyster Pond Reef – Fl. W. ev. 5 s., Keyed (VHF 83A) Horn 2 bl. ev. 30 s., Ht. 64', Rge. 14 mi., (41-09-48N/72-13-25W)

Horton Pt. Lt., NW point of Horton Neck – Fl. G. ev. 10 s., Ht. 103', Rge. 14 mi., (41-05-06N/72-26-44W)

Mattituck Breakwater Lt. "MI" – Fl. W. ev. 4 s., Ht. 25', Rge. 6 mi., (41-00-55N/72-33-40W)

Old Field Pt. Lt. – Alt. Fl. R. and Fl. G. ev. 20 s., Ht. 74', Rge. 14 mi., (40-58-37N/73-07-07W)

Eatons Neck Lt., E. side Entr. Huntington Bay – F. W., Ht. 144', Rge. 14 mi., (40-57-14N/73-23-43W)

Cold Springs Hbr. Lt., on Pt. of shoal – F.W., R. Sect. 039°-125°, Ht. 37', Rge. W. Sect. 8 mi., R. Sect. 6 mi., (40-54-51N/73-29-35W)

Glen Cove Breakwater Lt. #5, E. side Entr. to hbr. – Fl. G. ev. 4 s., Ht. 24', Rge. 5 mi., (40-51-43N/73-39-37W)

Port Jefferson App. Ltd. Wh. By. "PJ" – Mo(A)W, Rge. 4 mi., RWSRST, (40-59-16N/73-06-27W)

Huntington Harbor Lt. – Iso. W. ev. 6 s., Keyed (VHF 81A) Horn 1 bl. ev. 15 s., Ht. 42', Rge. 9 mi., (40-54-39N/73-25-52W)

LONG ISLAND, OUTSIDE

Montauk Pt. Lt., E. end of L.I. – Fl. W. ev. 5 s., Keyed (VHF 83A) Horn 1 bl. ev. 15 s., Ht. 168', Rge. 14 mi., (41-04-15N/71-51-26W)

Montauk Hbr. Entr. Ltd. Bell By. "M" – Mo(A)W, Rge. 4 mi., RWSRST, (41-05-07N/71-56-23W)

Shinnecock Inlet App. Ltd. Wh. By. "SH" – Mo(A)W, Rge. 4 mi., RWSRST, (40-49-00N/72-28-35W)

Moriches Inlet App. Ltd. Wh. By. "M" – Mo(A)W, Rge. 6 mi., RWS, (40-44-08N/72-45-12W)

Shinnecock Lt., W. side of Inlet – Fl(2) W. ev. 15 s., Ht. 75', Rge. 11 mi., (40-50-31N/72-28-42W)

Jones Inlet Lt., end of breakwater – Fl. W. ev. 2.5 s., Ht. 33', Rge. 4 mi., (40-34-24N/73-34-32W)

Jones Inlet Ltd. Wh. By. "JI" – Mo(A)W, Rge. 4 mi., RWSRST, (40-33-38N/73-35-13W)

E. Rockaway Inlet Ltd. Bell By. "ER" – Mo(A)W, Rge. 5 mi., RWSRST, (40-34-17N/73-45-49W)

Fire Is. Lt., 5.5 mi. E. of inlet – Fl. W. ev. 7.5 s., Ht. 167', ltd. 24 hrs., (40-37-57N/73-13-07W)

Rockaway Point Breakwater Lt. #4, end of breakwater – Fl. R. ev. 4 s., Ht. 34', Rge. 5 mi., (40-32-25N/73-56-27W)

NEW YORK HARBOR & APPROACHES

Execution Rocks Lt. – Fl. W. ev. 10 s., Ht. 62', Rge. 14 mi., Racon (X), (40-52-41N/73-44-16W)

Hart Is. Lt. #46, off S. end of Is. – Fl. R. ev. 4 s., Ht. 23', Rge. 6 mi., (40-50-42N/73-46-00W)

Stepping Stones Lt., outer end of reef – Oc.G. ev. 4 s., Ht. 46', Rge. 8 mi., (40-49-28N/73-46-29W)

For abbreviations see footnote p. 173

Throgs Neck Lt., Fort Schuyler – F. R., Ht. 60′, Rge. 9 mi., (40-48-16N/73-47-26W)

Whitestone Pt. Lt. #1, East R. main ch. – Q.G., Ht. 56′, Rge. 3 mi., (40-48-06N/73-49-10W)

Kings Pt. Lt. – Iso. W. ev. 2 s., (Private Aid), (40-48-42N/73-45-48W)

Hell Gate Lt. #15, East R. Hallets Pt. – Fl. G. ev. 2.5 s., Ht. 33′, Rge. 4 mi., (40-46-41N/73-56-05W)

Mill Rock South Lt. #16, East R., main ch. – Fl. R. ev. 4 s., Ht. 37′, Rge. 4 mi., (40-46-46N/73-56-22W)

Governors Is. Lt. – Iso R. ev. 6 s., Ht. 75′, Rge. 7 mi., (40-41-35N/74-01-11W)

Verrazano-Narrows Bridge Sound Signal – (Private Aid), 2 Horns on bridge 1 bl. ev. 15 s., (40-36-31N/74-02-19W)

Coney Is. Lt., N.Y. Hbr. main ch. – Fl. R. ev. 5 s., Ht. 75′, Rge. 16 mi., ltd. 24 hrs., (40-34-36N/74-00-42W)

Romer Shoal Lt., N.Y. Hbr. S. App. – Fl(2) W. ev. 15 s., Horn 2 bl. ev. 30 s., Ht. 54′, Rge. 15 mi., (40-30-47N/74-00-49W)

West Bank (Range Front) Lt., Ambrose Ch. outer sect. – Iso. W. ev. 6 s., R. Sect. 004°-181° and W from 181° - 004°, Horn 2 bl. ev. 20 s., Ht. 69′, ltd. 24 hrs., (40-32-17N/74-02-34W)

Staten Island (Range Rear) Lt., Ambrose Ch. outer sect. – F. W. , Visible on range line only, Ht. 234′, ltd. 24 hrs., (40-34-34N/74-08-28W)

Old Orchard Shoal Lt., N.Y. Hbr. – Fl. W. ev. 6 s., Ht. 20′, Rge. 4 mi., (40-30-44N/74-05-55W)

Sandy Hook Lt. – F. W., Ht. 88′, Rge. 19 mi., ltd. 24 hrs., (40-27-42N/74-00-07W)

Sandy Hook Ch. (Range Front) Lt. – Q. W., G., and R. sectors, Red from 063°-073° and Green from 300.5°-315.5°, Ht. 45′, Rge. W. 6 mi., G. 4 mi., R. 4 mi. Racon (C), (40-29-15N/73-59-35W)

Southwest Spit Jct. Ltd. Gong By. "SP" – Fl(2+1) R. ev. 6 s., Rge. 3 mi., R. & G. Bands, (40-28-46N/74-03-18W)

Sandy Hook Pt. Lt. – Iso W. ev. 6 s., Ht. 38′, Rge. 7 mi., "NB" on Skeleton Tower, (40-28-15N/74-01-07W)

Scotland Ltd. Wh. By. "S", Sandy Hook Ch. App. – Mo(A)W, Rge. 6 mi., Racon (M), RWSRST, (40-26-33N/73-55-01W)

Ambrose Ch. Ltd. Wh. By. "A" – Mo(A)W, Rge. 6 mi., Racon (N), RWSRST, (40-27-28N/73-50-12W)

NEW JERSEY

Highlands Lt. – Iso W. ev. 10 s., Obscured 334°-140°, (40-23-48N/73-59-09W)

Atlantic Highlands Breakwater Lt. – Fl. W. ev. 4 s., Ht. 33′, Rge. 7 mi., (40-25-07N/74-01-10W)

Kill Van Kull Ch. Jct. Ltd. Wh. By. "KV"– Fl (2+1) R. ev. 6 s., Rge. 3 mi., R. & G. Bands, Racon (K), (40-39-02N/74-03-51W)

Kill Van Kull Ch. Jct. Ltd. By. "A"– Fl (2+1) G. ev. 6 s., Rge. 3 mi., G. & R. Bands (40-38-45N/74-10-07W)

Kill Van Kull Ch. East Jct. Ltd. By. "E"– Fl (2+1) G. ev. 6 s., Rge. 3 mi. G. & R. Bands (40-38-31N/74-09-15W)

Manasquan Inlet Lt. #3 - Fl. G. ev. 6 s., Keyed (VHF 83A) Horn 1 bl. ev. 30 s., Ht. 35′ Rge. 8 mi., (40-06-01N/74-01-54W)

Shark River Inlet S. Breakwater Lt. #1 – Fl. G. ev. 4s, Ht. 33′, Rge. 7 mi. (40-11-11N/74-00-27W)

Barnegat Inlet S. Breakwater Lt. #7 – Q. G., Ht. 35′, Rge. 5 mi., (39-45-26N/74-05-36W)

Barnegat Inlet Outer Ltd. Wh. By. "BI" – Mo(A)W, Rge. 6 mi., RWSRST, (39-44-19N/74-04-08W)

Little Egg Ltd. By. 3 – Q. G., Rge. 4 mi., Green, (39-28-14N/74-17-14W)

For abbreviations see footnote p. 173

Brigantine Inlet Wreck Ltd. By. "WR2" (455 yards, 103° from wreck) – Q. R., Rge. 5 mi., Red, (39-24-41N/74-13-43W)

Hereford Inlet Lt., S. side – Fl. W. ev. 10 s., Ht. 57', Rge. 18 mi., (39-00-24N/74-47-28W)

Five Fathom Bank Ltd. By. "F" – Fl. Y. ev. 2.5 s., Rge. 6 mi., Yellow, (38-46-49N/74-34-32W)

Cape May Lt. – Fl. W. ev. 15 s., Ht. 165', Rge. 22 mi., (38-55-59N/74-57-37W)

NEW JERSEY, DELAWARE AND MARYLAND

Delaware Bay Appr. Ltd. W. By "CH" – Mo(A)W, Rge. 6 mi., Racon (K), RWSRST, (38-46-14N/75-01-19W)

Delaware Ltd. By. "D" – Fl. Y. ev. 6 s., Rge. 6 mi., Yellow, (38-27-18N/74-41-47W)

Delaware Traffic Lane Ltd. By. "DA" – Fl. Y. ev. 2.5 s., Rge. 6 mi., Yellow, (38-32-45N/74-46-56W)

Delaware Traffic Lane Ltd. By. "DB" – Fl. Y. ev. 4 s., Rge. 7 mi., Yellow, (38-38-12N/74-52-11W)

Delaware Traffic Lane Ltd. By. "DC" – Fl. Y. ev. 2.5 s., Rge. 6 mi., Yellow, (38-43-47N/74-57-33W)

Harbor of Refuge Lt., Del. Bay – Fl. W. ev. 10 s., 2 R. Sect. 325°-351° and 127°-175°, Horn 2 bl. ev. 30 s., (Mar. 15 - Dec. 15), Ht. 72', Rge. W. 19 mi., R. 16 mi., (38-48-52N/75-05-33W)

Brown Shoal Lt., Del. Bay main ch. – Fl. W. ev. 2.5 s., Ht. 23', Rge. 7 mi., Racon (B), (38-55-21N/75-06-01W)

Brandywine Shoal Lt., Del. Bay main ch. on shoal – Fl. W. ev. 10 s., R. Sect. 151°-338°, Horn 1 bl. ev. 15 s. (Mar. 15 - Dec. 15), Ht. 60', Rge. W. 19 mi., R. 13 mi., (38-59-10N/75-06-47W)

Fourteen Foot Bank Lt., Del. Bay main ch. – Fl. W. ev. 9 s., R. Sect. 332.5°-151°, Horn 1 bl. ev. 30 s., (Mar. 15-Dec. 1), Ht. 59', Rge. W. 13 mi., R. 10 mi., (39-02-54N/75-10-56W)

Miah Maull Shoal Lt., Del. Bay main ch. – Oc. W. ev. 4 s., R. Sect. 137.5°-333°, Horn 1 bl. ev. 10 s., (Mar. 15-Dec. 15), Ht. 59', Rge. W. 10 mi., R. 10 mi., Racon (M), (39-07-36N/75-12-31W)

Elbow of Cross Ledge Lt., Del. Bay main ch. – Iso. W. ev. 6 s., Horn 2 bl. ev. 20 s., (Mar. 15-Dec. 15), Ht. 61', Rge. 16 mi., (39-10-56N/75-16-06W)

Ship John Shoal Lt., Del. Bay main ch. – Fl. W. ev. 5 s., R. Sect. 138°-321.5°, Horn 1 bl. ev. 15 s. (Mar. 15 - Dec. 15), Ht. 50', Rge. W. 16 mi., R. 12 mi., Racon (O), (39-18-19N/75-22-36W)

Egg Island Point Lt., Del. Bay East side – Fl. W. ev. 4 s., Ht. 27', Rge. 7 mi., (39-10-21N/75-07-55W)

Old Reedy Is. Lt. – Iso. W. ev. 6 s., R. Sect. 353°-014°, Ht. 20', Rge. W. 8 mi., R. 6 mi., (39-30-03N/75-34-08W)

Fenwick Is. Lt. – Iso. W. ev. 8 s., Ht. 83', (38-27-06N/75-03-18W)

Ocean City Inlet Jetty Lt., on end of jetty – Iso. W. ev. 6 s., Keyed (VHF 81A) Horn 1 bl. ev. 10 s., Ht. 38', Rge. 6 mi., (38-19-27N/75-05-06)

VIRGINIA

Assateague Lt., S. side of Is. – Fl(2) W. ev. 5 s., Ht. 154', Rge. 22 mi., (37-54-40N/75-21-22W)

Wachapreague Inlet Ltd. Wh. By. "W" – Mo(A)W, Rge. 6 mi., RWSRST, (37-34-54N/75-33-37W)

Great Machipongo Inlet Lt. #5, S. side – Fl. G. ev. 4 s., Ht. 15', Rge. 4 mi., (37-21-40N/75-44-06W)

Chesapeake Lts. (2), off Entr. to Ches. Bay – Fl W. ev. 4 s., Ht. 84', (36-54-17N/75-42-46W)

For abbreviations see footnote p. 173

First Love
by Joe Berkeley

Everybody remembers their first love, the one that got away. Precious few get their first love back. The first time I saw her I stopped and stared. I was completely gobsmacked. The boat was an International 110, 24 ft long, #632 that was built by the Graves Yacht Yard in 1958. The previous owner was more of a cruiser than a racer. He sailed the boat in an unconventional manner, with two genoas which he set wing and wing downwind.

Ahead of the forestay, where the spinnaker launcher normally went, was a hole in the deck where his poodle would poke his head out to look around. That was then. As I stood on my friend Will Craig's lawn, I looked at what was the most beautiful International 110 I had ever seen.

A painter by trade, an artist by disposition, Will Craig was a tall and taciturn man who spent his days making old houses beautiful while he listened to NPR on his headphones. In his spare time, in a basement that was barely big enough to fit an International 110, Will rebuilt #632. He lovingly replaced each of the bottom frames, the plywood gussets, the deck, the sides, and the bottom. Like all wooden boat projects, the restoration took more time than Will thought it would.

When I saw her on Will's lawn she was gleaming in the sun, near perfect. As a college student with limited resources, I was in no position to buy the boat. I did anyway. I didn't want to. I had to. That first summer I rigged the boat and Will made sure I did it right. The plywood the boat was rebuilt from is known as Okoume, which is light, but perishable, so every time I drilled a hole, Will insisted I fill it with epoxy before inserting the screw or bolt.

With the boat rigged, it was time to name her. I didn't know it when I bought the boat but Will had already christened her. A visitor saw Will's work and said, "Is that a new boat?" He replied, "No, it's a retread."

The name stuck. When *Retread* was launched she was light and fair, fast and a pleasure to sail. She had, and still has, an extra gear downwind such that when she is in the groove she just goes.

I teamed up with Dave McGrath, a former hockey player, and we sailed every regatta we could, finishing third in the Nationals three years in a row. We swore that if we finished third again, we would throw the trophy into the bay. Finally, after years of trying, we won the Nationals in Boston Harbor in 1992.

There is a cliché that climbing the mountain is the easy part. Getting back down is tough. A decade later in 2002, after finishing second at the 110 Nationals in Newport, I had found a new interest. Late in life I started sailing a Laser. To become more fit, I rode my bicycle. Before I knew it, I was riding more than I was sailing.

I rode my bicycle for fun. I rode my bicycle to raise funds for cancer survivors. I

Continued on p. 200

Chesapeake Bay Entr. Ltd. Wh. By. "CH" – Mo(A)W, Rge. 6 mi., Racon (C), RWSRST, (36-56-08N/75-57-27W)
Cape Henry Lt., S. side of Entr. to Ches. Bay – Mo (U) W ev. 20 s., R. Sect. 154°-233°, Ht. 164', Rge. W. 17 mi., R. 15 mi., (36-55-35N/76-00-26W)

CHESAPEAKE BAY

Old Point Comfort Lt., N. side Entr. to Hampton Roads – Fl(2) R. ev. 12 s., W. Sect. 265°-038°, Ht. 54', Rge. W. 16 mi., R. 14 mi., (37-00-06N/76-18-23W)
York Spit Lt., N. side Entr. to York R. – On pile, Fl. W. ev. 6 s., Ht. 30', Rge. 7 mi., (37-12-35N/76-15-15W)
Stingray Pt. Lt., Ches. Ch. – Fl. W. ev. 4 s., Ht. 34', Rge. 7 mi., (37-33-41N/76-16-12W)
Windmill Pt. Lt., Ches. Ch. – On pile. Fl. W. ev. 6 s., 2 R. Sectors 293°-082° and 091.5°-113°, Ht. 34', Rge. W. 9 mi., R. 7 mi., (37-35-49N/76-14-10W)
Tangier Sound Lt., Ches. Ch. – Fl. W. ev. 6 s., R. Sect. 110°-192°, Ht. 45', Rge. W. 12 mi., R. 9 mi., (37-47-17N/75-58-24W)
Smith Pt. Lt., Ches. Ch. – Fl. W. ev. 10 s., Ht. 52', Rge. 15 mi., (37-52-48N/76-11-01W)
Point Lookout Lt., Ches. Ch. – Fl(2) W. ev. 5 s., Ht. 39', Rge. 7 mi., (38-01-30N/76-19-25W)
Holland Is. Bar Lt., Ches. Ch. – Fl. W. ev. 2.5 s., Ht. 37', Rge. 6 mi., (38-04-07N/76-05-45W)
Point No Point Lt., Ches. Ch. – Fl. W. ev. 6 s., Ht. 52', Rge. 9 mi., (38-07-41N/76-17-25W)
Hooper Is. Lt., Ches. Ch. – Fl. W. ev. 6 s., Ht. 63', Rge. 9 mi., (38-15-23N/76-14-59W)
Drum Pt. Lt.#4, Ches. Ch. – Fl. R. ev. 2.5 s., Ht. 17', Rge. 5 mi., (38-19-08N/76-25-15W)
Cove Pt. Lt., Ches. Ch. – Fl. W. ev. 10 s., Ht. 45', Rge. 12 mi., ltd. 24 hrs, (38-23-11N/76-22-54W)
Bloody Point Bar Warning Lt. – Fl. W. ev. 6 s., Ht. 22', Rge. 7 mi., (38-50-00N/76-23-35W)
Thomas Pt. Shoal Lt., Ches. Ch. – Fl. W. ev. 5 s., 2 R. Sectors 011°-051.5° and 096.5°-202°, Ht. 43', Rge. W. 16 mi., R. 11 mi., (38-53-56N/76-26-09W)
Wm. P. Lane, Jr. Bridge West Ch. Fog Signal, on main ch. span – Horn 1 bl. ev. 15 s., 5 s. bl., Horn Points 017° & 197°, (38-59-36N/76-22-56W)
Wm. P. Lane, Jr. Bridge East Ch. Fog Signal, on main ch. span – Horn 1 bl. ev. 20 s., 2 s. bl., (38-59-20N/76-21-29W)
Baltimore Lt. – Fl. W. ev. 2.5 s., R. Sector 082°- 160°, Ht. 52', Rge. W. 7 mi., R. 5 mi., (39-03-33N/76-23-56W)

NORTH CAROLINA

Currituck Beach Lt. – Fl. W. ev. 20 s., Ht. 158', Rge. 18 mi., (36-22-37N/75-49-47W)
Bodie Is. Lt. – Fl(2) W. ev. 30 s., Ht. 156', Rge. 18 mi., (35-49-07N/75-33-48W)
Oregon Inlet Jetty Lt. – Fl. W. ev. 2.5 s., Ht. 28', Rge. 7 mi., (35-46-26N/75-31-30W)
Cape Hatteras Lt., – Fl. W. ev. 7.5 s., Ht. 192', Rge. 24 mi., (35-15-02N/75-31-44W)
Hatteras Inlet Lt. – Iso. W. ev. 6 s., Ht. 48', Rge. 10 mi., (35-11-52N/75-43-56W)
Ocracoke Lt., on W. part of island – F.W., Ht. 75', Rge. 15 mi., (35-06-32N/75-59-10W)
Cape Lookout Lt., on N. pt. of cape – Fl. W. ev. 15 s., Ht. 156', Rge. 14 mi., (34-37-22N/76-31-28W)
Beaufort Inlet Ch. Ltd. Wh. By. "BM" – Mo(A)W, Rge. 6 mi., RWSRST, (34-36-39N/76-41-10W)
New River Inlet Ltd. Wh. By. "NR" – Mo(A)W, Rge. 6 mi., RWSRST, (34-31-00N/77-19-36W)

Continued from p. 198

rode my bicycle from my home in Hull to my job in Boston. I did all of the charity rides I could find, then signed up to ride the entire Tour de France route one day ahead of the professionals.

The Tour would take up a lot of time and a lot of money. Since I wasn't racing *Retread* as much as I should have been, I sold her to some guy whose name I don't recall. Seeing her go down the driveway behind a stranger's car was sad, but it was time.

After the Tour, I trained for and competed in the Mt. Washington Hill Climb. I gave it a full effort and finished in the middle of the pack. Cycling is cruel sport in that it is a math problem. It's all about how much oxygen your body can process, how much you weigh, and how much power you can throw. After the Mt. Washington Hill Climb I had a call with my coach who said, "You're never going to catch the guys who rode in college. You should go back to sailing."

Well, the truth is the truth and it is not nasty by intention. It just has a way of making things clear. I had to agree with my coach because I had almost been hit by cars, trucks, eighteen wheelers, pickup trucks, panel vans, cement mixers and Brinks trucks more times than I could count. I had experienced all manner of unmentionable injuries that occur when riding 10,000 miles per year. I felt immortal when I was on the bike. The rest of the time I was a mess. And it was time.

As fate would have it, the guy who bought *Retread* lost interest in her and sold her to Will Laidlaw, a terrific craftsman who goes for a sail now and then when he isn't in his barn fixing boats. He bought *Retread* and installed a fancy new genoa trim system that was a huge upgrade over the vintage setup.

Best of all, Will agreed to sell me *Retread*. Some of her original woodwork needed attention and I thought it might be good to have a craftsman make new coamings. But Tom Craig strongly disagreed. He believed that his brother's work could be and should be revived. Tragically, Will Craig, who rebuilt *Retread*, passed away after a tough battle with ALS. Of all of Will's work, *Retread* is the most beautiful piece of craftsmanship his hands ever touched.

I couldn't disagree with Tom. I don't so much own *Retread* as I am her steward. If I do a good job, I am an honorary member of the Craig family. With some help from a talented craftsman, Prescott Cronin, *Retread's* coamings were restored.

Paying Prescott was not a problem, because at the time I was an important person in the big company where I worked. I had received the Man of the Year Award. I was part of "the company family." I was a leader. Then one day after 17 years of meritorious service, I wasn't. I was laid off.

That winter I rebuilt *Retread* as I rebuilt my life. I started my own creative business on my own terms. I recall one day when I was varnishing *Retread* and the phone rang. On the other end was Halsey Herreshoff returning my call for a quote that would appear in a story I was writing. I put down my Epifanes brush and ran up the stairs to open my computer. What a thrill.

Continued on p. 202

Oak Is. Lt., on SE pt. of island – Fl(4) W. ev. 10 s., Ht. 169', Rge. 22 mi., (33-53-34N/78-02-06W)

Cape Fear River Entr. Ltd. Wh. By. "CF" – Mo(A)W, Rge. 6 mi., Racon (C), RWSRST, (33-46-17N/78-03-02W)

SOUTH CAROLINA

Little River Inlet Ltd. By. "LR" – Mo(A)W, Rge. 5 mi., RWSRST, (33-49-50N/78-32-27W)

Little River Inlet North Jetty Lt. #2 – Fl. R. ev. 4 s., Ht. 24', Rge. 5 mi., (33-50-31N/78-32-39W)

Winyah Bay Ltd. Wh. By. "WB" – Mo(A)W, Rge. 6 mi., RWSRST, (33-11-37N/79-05-11W)

Georgetown Lt., E. side Entr. to Winyah Bay – Fl(2) W. ev. 15 s., Ht. 85', Rge. 15 mi., (33-13-21N/79-11-06W)

Charleston Entr. Ltd. By. "C" – Mo(A)W, Rge. 6 mi., Racon (K), RWSRST, (32-37-05N/79-35-30W)

Charleston Lt., S. side of Sullivans Is. – Fl(2) W. ev. 30 s., Ht. 163', Rge. 20 mi., (32-45-29N/79-50-36W)

GEORGIA

Tybee Lt., NE end of Is. – F. W., Ht. 144', Rge. 19 mi., ltd. 24 hrs., (32-01-20N/80-50-44W)

St. Simons Ltd. By. "STS" – Mo(A)W, Rge. 7 mi., RWSRST, (31-02-49N/81-14-25W)

St. Simons Lt., N. side Entr. to St. Simons Sd. – F. Fl. W. ev. 60 s., Ht. 104', Rge. F. W. 18 mi., Fl. W. 23 mi., (31-08-03N/81-23-37W)

FLORIDA

Amelia Is. Lt., 2 mi. from N. end of Is. – Fl. W. ev. 10 s., R. Sect. 344°-360°, Ht. 107', Rge. W. 23 mi., R. 19 mi., (30-40-23N/81-26-33W)

St. Johns Lt., on shore – Fl(4) W. ev. 20 s., Obscured 179°-354°, Ht. 83', Rge. 19 mi., (30-23-10N/81-23-53W)

St. Augustine Lt., N. end of Anastasia Is. – F. Fl. W. ev. 30 s., Ht. 161', Rge. F. W. 19 mi., Fl. W. 24 mi., (29-53-08N/81-17-19W)

Ponce De Leon Inlet Lt., S. side on inlet – Fl(6) W. ev. 30 s., Ht. 159', (29-04-50N/80-55-41W)

Cape Canaveral Lt., on Cape – Fl(2) W. ev. 20 s., Ht. 137', Rge. 24 mi., (28-27-37N/80-32-36W)

Sebastian Inlet N. Jetty Lt. – Fl. R. ev. 4 s., Ht. 27', (27-51-41N/80-26-51W)

Jupiter Inlet Lt., N. side of inlet – Fl(2) W. ev. 30 s., Obscured 231°-234°, Ht. 146', Rge. 25 mi., (26-56-55N/80-04-55W)

Hillsboro Inlet Entr. Lt., N. side of inlet – Fl. (2) W. ev. 20 s., Obscured 114°-119°, Ht. 136', Rge. 28 mi., (26-15-33N/80-04-51W)

Port Everglades Ltd. By. "PE" - Mo(A)W, Rge. 6 mi., RWSRST, (26-05-30N/80-04-46W)

Miami Ltd. By. "M" – E. end of Miami Beach, Mo(A)W, Rge. 7 mi., Racon (M), RWSRST, (25-46-06N/80-05-00W)

Fowey Rocks Lt., Hawk Ch. – Fl. W. ev. 10 s., Ht. 110', Rge. 7 mi., (25-35-26N/80-05-48W)

Carysfort Reef Lt., outer line of reefs – Fl(3) W. ev. 60 s., Ht. 40', Rge. 13 mi., (25-13-37N/80-12-33W)

Alligator Reef Lt., – Fl(4) W. ev. 60 s., Ht. 16', Rge. 7 mi., (24-51-05N/80-37-04W)

Sombrero Key Lt., outer line of reefs – Fl(5) W. ev. 60 s., Ht. 19', Rge.7 mi. (24-37-40N/81-06-31W)

American Shoal Lt. – Fl(4) W. ev. 60 s., Ht. 19', Rge. 7 mi., (24-31-32N/81-31-03W)

Continued from p. 200

That summer, *Retread* was launched with new paint, new varnish, new sails, and most importantly, new hope. I had made the journey from sailor to cyclist and back, from corporate cog to small business owner.

Dr. Linda Epstein agreed to sail with me, and we headed up to Marblehead for the 75th 110 Nationals hosted by Eastern Yacht Club. It was a good field of sailors, and we were fortunate to win the event.

Since then, the three of us have had some terrific adventures. *Retread* has won the Nationals five times, more than any other 110 in history. She has taken on many fiberglass boats that were built with more modern technology, but not one of them was built with more heart.

Last summer *Retread* lined up at the Great Chase Race in Hull, Massachusetts. At this pursuit event, where the slowest boast start first and if the judges have handicapped properly, all boats would finish at the same time, she squared off with all manner of big boats in a fleet of 85 boats and took home Line Honors.

That win earned her another complete makeover last winter. This summer we launched 110 #632 and Dr. Ep joked that after all the rehabs, the boat is really the "Re-re-re-retread." *Retread* looks just as beautiful as the first time I saw her. I made the mistake of letting my first love go once. But I got her back for good.

Joe Berkeley writes, shoots and directs from his studio in Hull, Massachusetts. His work is at joeberkeley.com

Key West Ltd. Wh. By. "KW" – Mo (A) W, Rge. 6 mi., RWSRST, (24-27-26N/81-48-00W)

Sand Key Lt., Fl(2) W. ev. 15 s., Ht. 40′, Rge. 13, (24-27-21N/81-52-38W)

BERMUDA – APPROACH LIGHTS FROM SEAWARD

North Rock Beacon – Fl(4)W. ev. 20 s. yellow, Ht. 70′, Rge. 12 mi., RaRef, (32-28.5N/64-46.1W)

North East Breaker Beacon – Fl. W. ev. 2.5 s., Ht. 45′, Rge. 12 mi., RaRef, (Red tower on red tripod base reading "Northeast," (32-28.7N/64-41.0W)

Kitchen Shoal Beacon – Fl(3)W. ev. 15 s., Ht. 45′, Rge. 12 mi., RaRef, RWS, Red "Kitchen" on White background, (32-26.1N/64-37.6W)

Eastern Blue Cut Beacon – Fl. W. Mo(U) ev. 10 s., Ht. 60′, Rge. 12 mi., RaRef, B&W Tower "Eastern Blue Cut" on white band, (32-23.9N/64-52.6W)

Chub Heads – Q. Fl(9) W. ev. 15 s., Ht. 60′, Rge. 12 mi., RaRef, Yellow and Black Horizontal Stripe Tower with "Chub Heads" in White on Black Central band, (32-17.2N/64-58.9W)

Spit By. – Q. Fl(3) W. ev. 10 s., Black "Spit" on yellow, (32-22.7N/64-38.5W)

Sea By. –Mo(A)W ev. 6 s., RWS, Red "SB" in white on side, (32-22.9N/64-37.1W)

St. David's Is. Lighthouse – F. R. and G. Sectors below Fl(2) W. ev. 20 s., Ht. 212′, Rge. W. 15 mi., R. and G. 20 mi., (32-21.8N/64-39.1W) Your bearing from seaward of G. Sector is 221°-276° True; remaining Sector is R. and partially obscured by land 044°-135° True.

Kindley Field Aero Beacon – Alt. W and G.; 1 White, 1 Green (rotating Aero Beacon), Ht. 140′, Rge. 15 mi., (32-21.95N/64-40.55W)

Gibbs Hill Lighthouse – Fl. W. ev. 10 s., Ht. 354′, Rge. 26 mi., (32-15.2N/64-50.1W)

Erica M. Szuplat

☆ **Note:** The information in this volume has been compiled from U. S. Government sources and others, and carefully checked. The Publishers cannot assume any liability for errors, omissions, or changes.

Foregoing information checked to date, September 2023. See p. 268 for free supplement in June 2024.

The Tide Cycle Simplified: The Rule of Twelfths

Since the average interval between high and low is just over six hours, we can divide the cycle into six segments of one hour each. On average the tide rises or falls approximately according to the fractions at right:

1st hour - 1/12
2nd hour - 2/12
3rd hour - 3/12
4th hour - 3/12
5th hour - 2/12
6th hour - 1/12

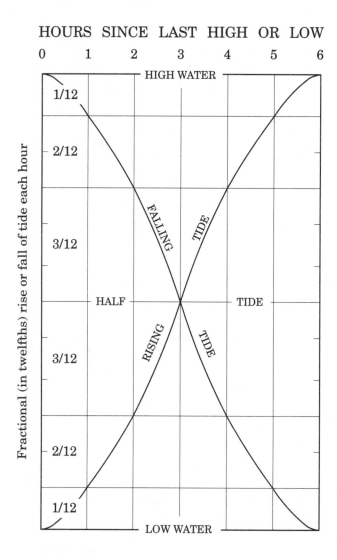

HOURS SINCE LAST HIGH OR LOW

Fractional (in twelfths) rise or fall of tide each hour

Mean tidal heights by the hour at five ports				
Boston	Newport	New York	Charleston	Savannah
9.6	3.5	4.6	5.2	6.9
8.8	3.2	4.2	4.8	6.3
7.2	2.6	3.4	3.9	5.2
4.8	1.8	2.3	2.6	3.5
2.4	0.9	1.2	1.3	1.7
0.8	0.3	0.4	0.4	0.6
0.0	0.0	0.0	0.0	0.0

Tidal Heights and Depths

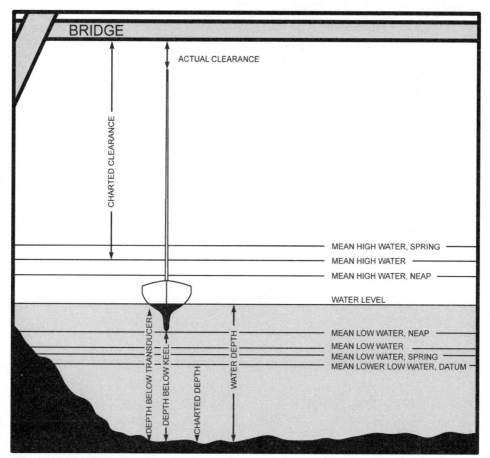

Mean High Water, Spring - the mean of high water heights of spring tides
Mean High Water - the mean of all high water heights; the charted clearance
  of bridges is measured from this height
Mean High Water, Neap - the mean of high water heights of neap tides
Mean Low Water, Neap - the mean of low water heights of neap tides
Mean Low Water - the mean of all low water heights
Mean Low Water, Spring - the mean of low water heights of spring tides
Mean Lower Low Water Datum - the mean of lower low water heights;
  charted depths originate from this reference height or datum

---

Spring Tides - tides of increased range, occurring twice a month, around the
  times of the new and full moons
Neap Tides - tides of decreased range, occurring twice a month, around the
  times of the half moons
Diurnal Inequality - the difference in height of the two daily low waters or
  the two daily high waters, a result of the moon's (and to a lesser extent the
  sun's) changing declination above and below the Equator

The Most Fun I've Had On A Boat

by Ann C. Logue

I didn't take up sailing until I was 55. At 57, as a rank beginner, I took up team racing, and it is so fun! I think that even if I had decades of sailing experience, it would still be the most fun I have ever had on a boat.

Although I've spent most of my life near the Great Lakes, I didn't grow up sailing and didn't have the time or money to get out on the water until my kid was out of college. I started out learning basic keelboat skills, cruising Lake Michigan on Friday evenings. As lovely as a sunset sail along the Chicago skyline is, I wanted to do more, so I signed up for team racing. Of course, I had no idea what I was in for.

Team racing is not a leisurely evening cruise. It's a fast, wild young person's sport, the province of high school and college sailors. My teammates are considerably younger and more experienced sailors than I am. Some have been sailing since they could walk. They know what they are doing. I must be told what to do on the jib when we get close to the mark, but that's okay, because I am learning so much. It helps that most of my teammates taught sailing as a summer job, so they are more patient with a middle-aged novice than you might expect.

Erica M. Szuplat

I am slowly understanding jib trim and boat handling. Even on nights when I'm serving up rail meat, I've observed how subtle shifts in weight or sail position make a huge difference in boat speed. Am I a sailor or a yogi, moving from side to side with each tack and gybe?

Team races are short but intense. A typical race has two teams of three boats each, Sonars or other small craft; each boat has three or four sailors. If one of your team's boats comes in last, your team will probably lose, so your goal is less about coming in first than it is about not coming in last. The skipper can choose to play offense and be the first around the mark or opt for the defense and push the other team's boats away from the team's leader. The choice happens in the moment, often when all six boats may be trying to round the mark without hitting each other. Trim the sails! Get on the high side! Steal their wind! Run the tape!

Did I mention that we use spinnakers?

When the wind and water are right, team racing delivers the joyful adrenaline

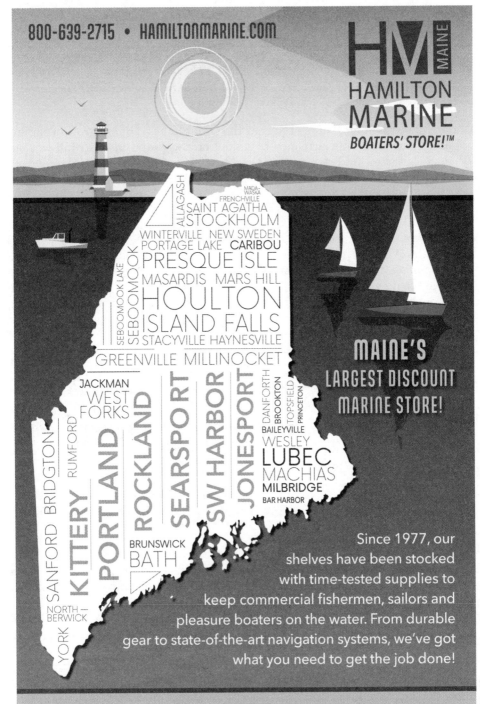

of the best roller coaster. You pop up on a swell, heel over into the waves, and get plenty wet. If you're beating the other team, it's even more fun.

But the best part of team racing, for me, is that it's impossible to think about anything except the boat, the wind, and the water. For a few hours each Tuesday evening, I cannot worry or mourn. To-do lists? Sick relatives? Existential dread? There's no time for any of that nonsense. I can't even feel the bruises that accumulate as surely as water is wet.

I don't even know much about my teammates, as we have no time for casual conversation. Instead, we have the camaraderie that comes from doing hard work together in pursuit of a goal, even if it's as fleeting as winning a race against friends on a summer weeknight. By the time we get back to the dock, we're exhilarated and exhausted. It's time to douse the sails and remember all the things we forgot on the water, at least until next week.

Story Contest 2025
Chronicles of the Coast

Do you have a captivating true story of your adventures along the East Coast? Your story should transport us to the waters, harbors, and shores of the East Coast, illustrating the maritime life that defines the region. Whether you've navigated rough seas, discovered hidden treasures, or forged unbreakable bonds with fellow sailors, we want to hear your tales of seafaring, coastal exploration, and nautical encounters that have left an indelible mark on you.

Deadline: 11:59 pm ET, August 3, 2024

Length: 600 words, give or take a few

How to submit: Email to pilot@eldridgetide.com (preferred), or mail to the address on the front cover. Submitted materials will not be returned.

The winning entry will be published in the 2025 edition, and the author will receive a copy of the book, an ELDRIDGE tote bag, and $200.

Erica M. Szuplat

Submissions must be original, previously unpublished works and grant the publisher nonexclusive rights to publish winning entries in the book and on our website.

But the idea of becoming entirely dependent on electronic charts terrifies me. Maybe that's because I am now in my early forties, and I have entered the stage of life when one likes to reminisce that things were better when younger and that the future generation is screwed.

All that said, I would be a hypocrite if I didn't embrace new technology. Thank god John Harrison invented the chronometer. Were it not for his diligent efforts, early explorers could have missed landfall by hundreds, if not thousands of miles. Before Mr. Harrison's breakthrough, navigating great distances at sea without any land references could be a real gamble due to the inability to calculate a vessel's longitudinal position accurately.

There is still a great benefit to navigating by using traditional methods. In my senior year of high school, I had a job delivering flowers for a florist. Three days a week, starting at 2:00, I would load up the van and assess the long list of deliveries I needed to accomplish in three hours. In those days, we didn't have Google Maps or Waze. I had to figure out how to get myself from A to B and then to C and D and E and then F. That meant being efficient in mapping my deliveries and learning how to strategize the order of stops. You see, I lived in a bustling suburb, which meant rush hour could cause many headaches, much like how the changing of the tides or the strength of the current can impact a long passage, especially when factoring in other variables such as unforeseen obstacles and the weather.

Earlier this summer, I was lucky enough to spend some time on the Cape and Islands offering talks while on tour promoting my book *All Hands on Deck*. My good friend Phil took his new boat from Stamford, CT, to Nantucket to visit me. The night before he departed from Nantucket for Shelter Island, he asked me when he should get underway. I was surprised by this question and said, "Don't you have an *Eldridge*?"

Phil said he did, but it was out on the boat, which was on a mooring. It was 1700, and we were getting ready to head out for some fun. I knew we could swing into Mitchell's Book Corner before it closed. Sure enough, we found a copy, checked the tide tables, found the applicable current chart, and figured out when best for him to get underway at 0430. There was no arguing. We knew it was the best call.

Hours later and a few rounds into it, I told Phil about one of my most memorable passages in Nantucket Sound on a foggy mid-August night. I was the mate on the twelve-meter yacht *Onawa*. She was a seventy-foot wooden sloop built in 1928. We didn't have a chart plotter or radar on board. Our navigational tools and electronics were limited to a rudimentary handheld GPS showing only the latitude and longitude coordinates, two VHF radios, our compass, depth sounder, speedo, paper charts, and an *Eldridge*.

The Captain, Casey, is one of the most competent sailors I've ever worked under. Casey knows his stuff, and he is a great teacher. On *Onawa*, each crew member had to participate in plotting our course whenever we were underway. Casey was diligent about maintaining and recording a dead reckoned position in our log book on or near the hour and whenever something worth noting should be recorded.

After three glorious weeks of cruising the coast of Maine, bound for Nantucket, we steamed out of Somes Sound on August 14 at 2335. The sea gods decided early on that this would be a difficult passage as a thick bank of fog rolled in, forcing us to strike sail, grab a mooring, and get a few hours of sleep before making another attempt at daybreak. The following morning, at 0640, the fog had thinned to one mile of visibility, so we got underway. We departed with a reefed mainsail and headed out the Western Way. By 1000, a nice breeze had filled in, allowing us to kill the engine and enjoy a bit of sailing. The water was choppy with 3-5 foot seas. We had taken on a fourth crew member to help us with the delivery, but the combination of the rough sea state and low visibility caused her to get seasick. Miserable and unable to help us, Casey decided we should lower our sails, pull into a harbor, and get her off the boat and into a launch without us even stopping to take a mooring.

With our crew down to three, two on deck and the third napping below, we continued pressing south through the night. The conditions were breathtaking. The fog lifted, the seas flattened, and the bright waxing gibbous moon made the lightly rippled surface of the water sparkle like a flattened disco ball. On the morning of August 16 at 0515, we passed Boon Island, one mile abeam to port. At 1600, we

Continued on p. 224

The Mystery *of the* Compass

H enry the Navigator's explorers (15th century Portugal) couldn't imagine boarding a vessel without saluting the holy shrine at its taffrail. It makes sense: heading offshore, always salute the mysteries, the unknowable currents of fate. When boarding a vessel today, you might salute one of our great mysteries – the compass.

CRUST
MOLTEN MOVING MANTLE
STABLE OUTER CORE
INNER CORE

RADIAL SPIN OF MOLTEN MANTLE $\neq$

MISSHAPEN OUTER CORE

The ideal model of orderly, geometric earth-layers has been disproved by deep-sounding exploration

History from Jan Adkins

H ow does a compass work? A mystery. We know the Earth's molten mantle revolves around the solid core at a separate rate of spin. This high temperature pirouette produces an electric charge and the magnetosphere, a mighty magnetic flux that surrounds the earth.

That magnetic cloak deflects fierce charged particles leaping from the Sun's nuclear surface, bends them around our precious orb, and allows them to slide into the magnetic wells of the north and south poles. Virtually nothing on earth could live without protection from those solar rays. As the charged particles fall toward the poles they collide with molecules in the atmosphere and fluoresce, creating the Aurora Borealis (North Pole) and the Aurora Australis (South Pole).

This global force commands our compasses – imperfectly. Does the compass point north? Not really. The needle of the compass aligns with the earth's magnetic lines, roughly north and south. We've learned that the molten mantle is lumpy, which skews the magnetic field. True North is the geographic North Pole, the axis of the pleasantly spinning earth. Magnetic North is the abstract pole of a misshapen magneto-sphere. That pole resided in Canada for many years but has been defecting toward Siberia by as much as 60 km a year. Your charts are orient-ed toward the geographical North Pole, but

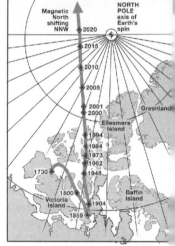

Chinese floating fish compass; south-pointing spoon, wrought from a lodestone.

within each chart's compass rose you'll find a disclaimer: magnetic *variation* defines the chart's difference between magnetic north and geographical north, east or west, and at what rate it's moving. This skewing *variation* differs – lumps and bumps – from place to place.

Further uncertainty: *deviation* is the magnetic effect of your boat on the compass – proximity to the engine and its generator, steel hardware here and there, and pistols kept in the binnacle against mutiny.

Lodestones were the first compasses – ferrous rock struck by lightning or shards of meteorites magnetized by their hot descent. Early compasses were probably Chinese; documents attest to South-pointing "spoons" fashioned from lodestone. Fish in a bowl came later, in the Han Dynasty around 200 BCE; a wooden fish backed by a thin, magnetized rod floated in a bowl of water and pointed south. Why not north? The Chinese knew little about earth's polar regions and the important direction was the grand progress of the sun in the south. These were land compasses, used only for magic shows and feng shui. Around the 11th century CE Chinese fish-in-bowl compasses were adapted for sailors. Yes, they were useful in fog or on overcast nights, but they were essentially backups – sun, moon, and star sights were more accurate.

Chinese mariner's dry-needle compass, 11th CE

Boxed Mediterranean mariner's dry-card compass, 12th C CE

Our Eurocentric sailor-heroes were gentlemen adventurers: Drake, Magellan, Hudson. But in the early 15th C – years before Vasco de Gama came close to the Cape of Good Hope – **Zheng He** was the Ming Dynasty's grand admiral. In vast fleets churning the seas around giant junk-rigged 9-sail ships, he voyaged south and west, through the Straits of Malacca, ranging the Indian Ocean, bringing back giraffes, lions, and elephants from Africa! In many voyages between 1405 and 1423, he expanded Chinese influence, exchanged treasure, sowed culture, and improved marine technology on the high seas, guided by sun, moon, and star sights, and assured by the night and storm backup of the Chinese compass. At left is Zheng He's enormous flagship with Columbus' *Niña* for comparison.

William Thomson was a polymath of voracious curiosity. He was a resourceful engineer, crack mathematician, and theoretical physicist. His fascination with electricity led him to establish the basic laws of thermodynamics and drew him into the political and financial furor of laying an Atlantic telegraph cable. Attempts had been made and bungled but Thomson paid out a successful Atlantic cable from Isambard Kingdom Brunel's giant steamship *Great Eastern*. Queen Victoria knighted him for this accomplishment in 1866. Sir William developed a lifelong love of seafaring. Predictably, he addressed the problems of magnetic compasses on iron ships, compensating the ship's deviation with adjustable iron balls to the right and left of a binnacle fitted with a new Thomson compass that became the Royal Navy standard for many years. Thomson's impact on science was so extraordinary that he was the first scientist to be raised to Britain's peerage, becoming **Lord Kelvin** in 1892.

The surety of the compass had traveled from China to the Mediterranean. The floating or silk-suspended needle evolved into a magnetized metal arrow pivoting on a needle in a glass bearing. In 1362 it is commonly believed that Flavio De Amalfi introduced a true mariner's compass: a magnetic needle or parallel needles were affixed to the underside of a flat card suspended on a pivot inside a dry bowl and marked with compass points. The compass encouraged more trade out of the Mediterranean and into the North Sea.

This flat disc arrangement persisted for five hundred years, giving navigators and quartermasters hissy fits. In a seaway, or with any kind of vibration, the card spun merrily. Naval gunfire knocked it off its pivots, and a rogue wave could jam the disc up against its glass cover.

In 1608, The Reverend William Barlow gimballed the entire compass to swing independently of the ship. Compass utility took a giant leap when American inventor Edward Samuel Ritchie patented a mariner's compass in 1863 filled with fluid that damped swing and vibration.

A Royal Navy binnacle fitted with Lord Kelvin's compensating iron balls

A flat-face, liquid-filled lifeboat compass with a small oil lamp for night illumination

Around 1918, Wilfrid O. White, a nautical instrument maker in Boston, forged a collaboration to sell Kelvin and White compasses. Wilfrid O. White also sold his own patented, liquid-filled compasses under the same name. In 1936 White solved a problem Lord Kelvin missed: any shift of direction set up liquid pressure currents between the flat reading disc and the glass face of a fluid-damped compass.

White encapsulated the entire card, magnetic elements, pivot, and damping fins into a spherical housing. A rubber diaphragm compensated for temperature and atmospheric pressure changes. This spherical compass had a splendid advantage: the clear hemispherical upper half of the compass acted as a lens, magnifying the compass card.

Scientific and engineering evolution has made the mariners compass more accurate and more convenient than ever. We consider a compass indispensable. It's a Boston fact that the White family of instrument makers was bound by marriage into the Eldridge family of hydrographers, which is why you are reading about the mysteries of the compass in the 150th Edition of the Eldridge Tide & Pilot Book. This is an apt venue from which to address the *GPS vs compass* brouhaha. Has electronic navigation eclipsed our need for the fish in a bowl?

Apples and oranges. Every navigator adores GPS, though traditionalists among us don't want our sextant skills to tarnish. GPS is about position. The compass is about steering. The boat compass is a moment by moment counselor keeping you on course and oriented to wind shifts. It is distinctly and heartily analog, a connection between helm, sea, pilot, and wind. It requires experience and sailor's cunning to steer small and make headway to your marks. The GPS is a marvel as a tool, but the compass is part of the visceral bond between you and the boat's progress. The deep magma may bump and grind, the magnetosphere may shift, but the compass remains a constant friend.

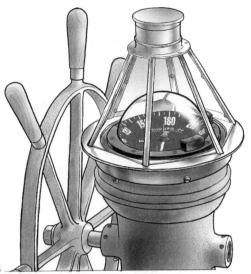

Spherical compasses are complex instruments aligning themselves with the inexplicable lines of magnetic force that embrace and protect our fragile planet. They align us with our boat's progress and guide us from mark to mark.

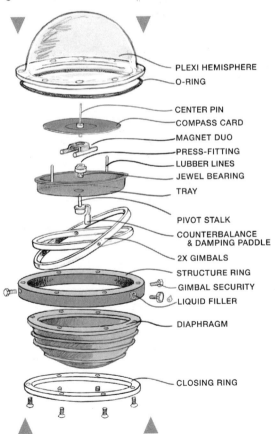

- PLEXI HEMISPHERE
- O-RING
- CENTER PIN
- COMPASS CARD
- MAGNET DUO
- PRESS-FITTING
- LUBBER LINES
- JEWEL BEARING
- TRAY
- PIVOT STALK
- COUNTERBALANCE & DAMPING PADDLE
- 2X GIMBALS
- STRUCTURE RING
- GIMBAL SECURITY
- LIQUID FILLER
- DIAPHRAGM
- CLOSING RING

IALA BUOYAGE SYSTEM

Lateral Aids marking the sides of channels seen when entering from Seaward

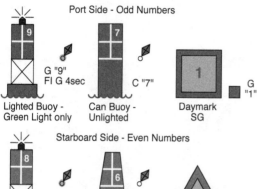

Port Side - Odd Numbers

Lighted Buoy -
Green Light only

G "9"
Fl G 4sec

Can Buoy -
Unlighted

C "7"

Daymark
SG

G "1"

Port- hand aids are Green, some with Flashing Green Lights.
Daymarks:
1st letter "S" = Square
2nd letter "G" = color Green

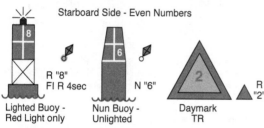

Starboard Side - Even Numbers

Lighted Buoy -
Red Light only

R "8"
Fl R 4sec

Nun Buoy -
Unlighted

N "6"

Daymark
TR

R "2"

Starboard-hand aids are Red, some with Flashing Red Lights.
Daymarks:
1st letter "T" = Triangle
2nd letter "R"= color Red

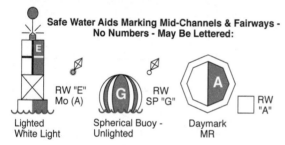

Safe Water Aids Marking Mid-Channels & Fairways - No Numbers - May Be Lettered:

Lighted
White Light

RW "E"
Mo (A)

Spherical Buoy -
Unlighted

RW
SP "G"

Daymark
MR

RW "A"

Red and White replaces vertical stripes. Buoys are spherical; or have a Red spherical topmark.
Flashing White Light only: Mo (A).
Daymarks:
1st letter "M" = Octagon
2nd letter "R" = color Red

Preferred Channel Aids - Mark Bifurcations - No Numbers - Preferred Ch. to Starboard (Aid to Port):

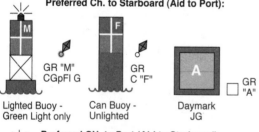

Lighted Buoy -
Green Light only

GR "M"
CGpFl G

Can Buoy -
Unlighted

GR
C "F"

Daymark
JG

GR "A"

Flashing Light (Red or Green) is Composite Gp. Fl. (2 + 1).
Daymarks: 1st letter "J" = Square or Triangle 2nd letter "R" or "G" is color of top band

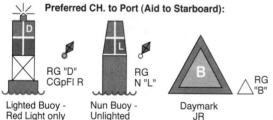

Preferred CH. to Port (Aid to Starboard):

Lighted Buoy -
Red Light only

RG "D"
CGpFl R

Nun Buoy -
Unlighted

RG
N "L"

Daymark
JR

RG "B"

Note: ISOLATED DANGER BUOYS, Black and Red with two Black spherical topmarks - no numbers, may be lettered (if lighted, white light only, Fl (2) 5s). Stay Clear. SPECIAL AIDS BUOYS will be all YELLOW (if lighted, with yellow light only, Fixed Flashing): Anchorage Areas, Fish Net Areas, Spoil Grounds, Military Exercise Zones, Dredging Buoys (where conventional markers would be confusing), Ocean Data Systems, some Traffic Separations Zone Mid-Channel Buoys.

FICTITIOUS NAUTICAL CHART

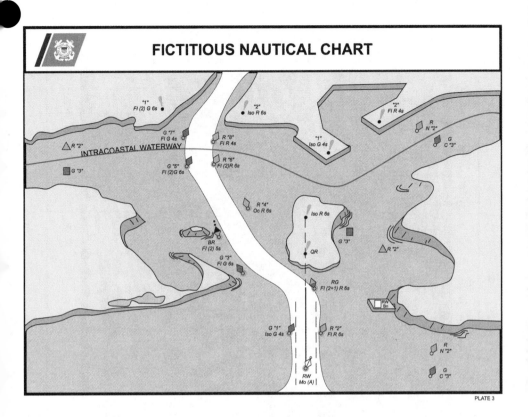

PLATE 3

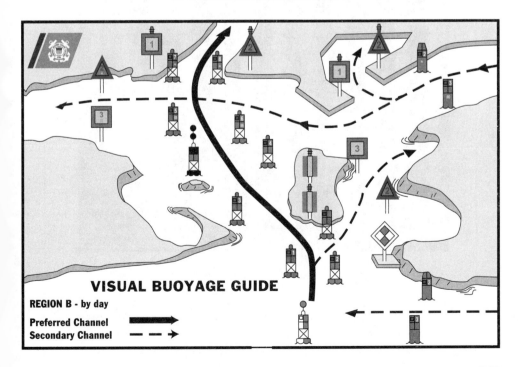

VISUAL BUOYAGE GUIDE

REGION B - by day

Preferred Channel

Secondary Channel

Daily Moon Phases 2024

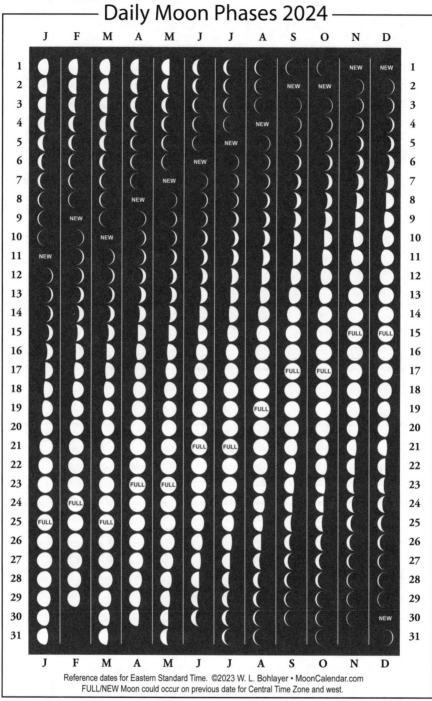

Reference dates for Eastern Standard Time. ©2023 W. L. Bohlayer • MoonCalendar.com
FULL/NEW Moon could occur on previous date for Central Time Zone and west.

Full collection of other moon calendars and astronomy
publications available at
Amazon.com/CelestialProducts

>> Use code word **Eldridge2024** for discount.   mooncalendar.com

CELESTIAL PRODUCTS™

If you have Easterly deviation, you must steer to the left of the desired Magnetic Course. If you have Westerly deviation, you must steer to the right of the desired Magnetic Course.

Table for Turning Compass Points into Degrees, and the Contrary
MERCHANT MARINE PRACTICE

NORTH----------	**0**	**EAST**------------	**90**	**SOUTH** ----------	**180**	**WEST**------------	**270**
N. 1/4E. -----------	2 3/4	E. 1/4S.------------	92 3/4	S. 1/4W. -----------	182 3/4	W. 1/4N. ----------	272 3/4
N. 1/2E. -----------	5 3/4	E. 1/2S.------------	95 3/4	S. 1/2W. -----------	185 3/4	W. 1/2N. ----------	275 3/4
N. 3/4E. -----------	8 1/2	E. 3/4S.------------	98 1/2	S. 3/4W. -----------	188 1/2	W. 3/4N. ----------	278 1/2
N. by E.-----------	11 1/4	E. by S. -----------	101 1/4	S. by W. -----------	191 1/4	W. by N. ----------	281 1/4
N. by E. 1/4E. ----	14	E. by S. 1/4S.-----	104	S. by W. 1/4W. ---	194	W. by N. 1/4N. ---	284
N. by E. 1/2E.----	17	E. by S. 1/2S.-----	107	S. by W. 1/2W. ---	197	W. by N. 1/2N. ---	287
N. by E. 3/4E. ----	19 3/4	E. by S. 3/4S.-----	109 3/4	S. by W. 3/4W. ---	199 3/4	W. by N. 3/4N. ---	289 3/4
N.N.E. ------------	**22 1/2**	**E.S.E.** ------------	**112 1/2**	**S.S.W.** ------------	**202 1/2**	**W.N.W.**-----------	**292 1/2**
N.E. by N. 3/4N.--	25 1/4	S.E. by E. 3/4E.--	115 1/4	S.W. by S. 3/4S.--	205 1/4	N.W. by W. 3/4W.	295 1/4
N.E. by N. 1/2N.--	28 1/4	S.E. by E. 1/2E. --	118 1/4	S.W. by S. 1/2S.--	208 1/4	N.W. by W. 1/2W.	298 1/4
N.E. by N. 1/4N.--	31	S.E. by E. 1/4E. --	121	S.W. by S. 1/4S.--	211	N.W. by W. 1/4W.	301
N.E. by N.---------	33 3/4	S.E. by E. --------	123 3/4	S.W. by S.--------	213 3/4	N.W. by W.-------	303 3/4
N.E. 3/4N. --------	36 1/2	S.E. 3/4E. --------	126 1/2	S.W. 3/4S.--------	216 1/2	N.W. 3/4W. -------	306 1/2
N.E. 1/2N.---------	39 1/2	S.E. 1/2E. ---------	129 1/2	S.W. 1/2S.---------	219 1/2	N.W. 1/2W. -------	309 1/2
N.E. 1/4N. ---------	42 1/4	S.E. 1/4E. ---------	132 1/4	S.W. 1/4S.---------	222 1/4	N.W. 1/4W. -------	312 1/4
N.E. --------------	**45**	**S.E.** --------------	**135**	**S.W.**----------------	**225**	**N.W.** --------------	**315**
N.E. 1/4E.---------	47 3/4	S.E. 1/4S. ---------	137 3/4	S.W. 1/4W.--------	227 3/4	N.W. 1/4N.--------	317 3/4
N.E. 1/2E.---------	50 3/4	S.E. 1/2S. ---------	140 3/4	S.W. 1/2W.--------	230 3/4	N.W. 1/2N.--------	320 3/4
N.E. 3/4E.---------	53 1/2	S.E. 3/4S. ---------	143 1/2	S.W. 3/4W.--------	233 1/2	N.W. 3/4N.--------	323 1/2
N.E. by E. --------	56 1/4	S.E. by S.---------	146 1/4	S.W. by W. -------	236 1/4	N.W. by N. -------	326 1/4
N.E. by E. 1/4E.--	59	S.E. by S. 1/4S. --	149	S.W. by W. 1/4W.	239	N.W. by N. 1/4N.	329
N.E. by E. 1/2E.--	62	S.E. by S. 1/2S. --	152	S.W. by W. 1/2W.	242	N.W. by N. 1/2N.	332
N.E. by E. 3/4E.--	64 3/4	S.E. by S. 3/4S. --	154 3/4	S.W. by W. 3/4W.	244 3/4	N.W. by N. 3/4N.	334 3/4
E.N.E. ------------	**67 1/2**	**S.S.E.** ------------	**157 1/2**	**W.S.W.** -----------	**247 1/2**	**N.N.W.** -----------	**337 1/2**
E. by N. 3/4N.----	70 1/4	S. by E. 3/4E.-----	160 1/4	W. by S. 3/4S. ----	250 1/4	N. by W. 3/4W.---	340 1/4
E. by N. 1/2N.----	73 1/4	S. by E. 1/2E.-----	163 1/4	W. by S. 1/2S. ----	253 1/4	N. by W. 1/2W.---	343 1/4
E. by N. 1/4N.----	76	S. by E. 1/4E.-----	166	W. by S. 1/4S. ----	256	N. by W. 1/4W.---	346
E. by N.-----------	78 3/4	S. by E. -----------	168 3/4	W. by S. ----------	258 3/4	N. by W. ---------	348 3/4
E. 3/4N. -----------	81 1/2	S. 3/4E.------------	171 1/2	W. 3/4S. -----------	261 1/2	N. 3/4W. ----------	351 1/2
E. 1/2N. -----------	84 1/2	S. 1/2E.------------	174 1/2	W. 1/2S. -----------	264 1/2	N. 1/2W. ----------	354 1/2
E. 1/4N. -----------	87 1/4	S. 1/4E.------------	177 1/4	W. 1/4S. -----------	267 1/4	N. 1/4W. ----------	357 1/4
EAST------------	**90**	**SOUTH** ----------	**180**	**WEST**------------	**270**	**NORTH**----------	**0**

The International Code of Signals

The Code comprises 40 flags: 1 Code Flag; 26 letters; 10 numerals; 3 repeaters. With this Code it is possible to converse freely at sea with ships of different countries.

Single Flag Signals

A :: I have a diver down; keep well clear at slow speed.

B :: I am taking in, or discharging, or carrying dangerous goods.

C :: Yes

D :: Keep clear of me; I am maneuvering with difficulty.

E :: I am altering my course to starboard.

F :: I am disabled; communicate with me.

G :: I require a pilot. (When made by fishing vessels when operating in close proximity on the fishing grounds it means; "I am hauling nets.")

H :: I have a pilot on board.

I :: I am altering my course to port.

J :: I am on fire and have dangerous cargo on board; keep well clear of me.

K :: I wish to communicate with you.

L :: You should stop your vessel instantly.

M:: My vessel is stopped and making no way through water.

N :: No

O :: Man overboard.

P :: *In harbor;* All persons should report on board as the vessel is about to proceed to sea.
   At sea; It may be used by fishing vessels to mean "My nets have come fast upon an obstruction."

Q :: My vessel is healthy and I request free pratique.

R :: *nothing currently assigned*

S :: My engines are going astern.

T :: Keep clear of me; I am engaged in pair trawling.

U :: You are running into danger.

V :: I require assistance.

W:: I require medical assistance.

X :: Stop carrying out your intentions and watch for my signals.

Y :: I am dragging my anchor.

Z :: I require a tug. (When made by fishing vessels operating in close proximity on the fishing grounds it means : "I am shooting nets.")

Flags Showing "Diver Down"

There are two flags that may be flown to indicate diving operations, and each has a distinct meaning.

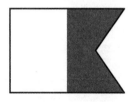

The **Alpha or "A" flag**, according to the U.S. Coast Guard, is to be flown on small vessels engaged in diving operations (1) whenever these vessels are restricted in their ability to maneuver (2) if divers are attached to the vessel. Generally, only vessels to which the divers are physically connected by communication lines, air hoses, or the like are affected by this requirement. The Alpha flag is a signal intended to *protect the vessel from collision.*

In sports diving, where divers are usually free-swimming, the Alpha flag does not have to be shown. The Coast Guard encourages the use of the traditional sports diver flag. The **sports diver flag** is an unofficial signal that, through custom, has come to be used to *protect the diver in the water.* To be most effective, the sports diver flag should be exhibited on a float in the water to mark the approximate location of the diver. Restrictions for nearby vessels vary from state to state, but typically they include a zone of 100' radius around the flag where no other boats are allowed, and a second larger zone in which speed is limited.

INTERNATIONAL SIGNAL FLAGS AND MORSE CODE

CODE FLAG	AND ANSWERING PENNANT

Alpha	Bravo	Charlie	Delta	Echo	Foxtrot
A • —	B — • • •	C — • — •	D — • •	E •	F • • — •

Golf	Hotel	India	Juliet	Kilo
G — — •	H • • • •	I • •	J • — — —	K — • —

Lima	Mike	November	Oscar	Papa
L • — • •	M — —	N — •	O — — —	P • — — •

Quebec	Romeo	Sierra	Tango	Uniform
Q — — • —	R • — •	S • • •	T —	U • • —

Victor	Whiskey	XRay	Yankee	Zulu
V • • • —	W • — —	X — • • —	Y — • — —	Z — — • •

NUMERAL PENNANTS

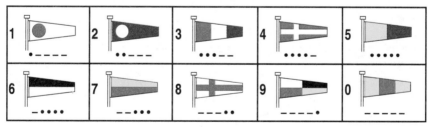

1 • — — — —	2 • • — — —	3 • • • — —	4 • • • • —	5 • • • • •
6 — • • • •	7 — — • • •	8 — — — • •	9 — — — — •	0 — — — — —

REPEATERS

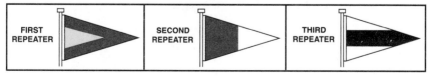

FIRST REPEATER	SECOND REPEATER	THIRD REPEATER

Yacht Flags and How To Fly Them

U.S. Ensign: 8 a.m. to sundown only. Not flown while racing.

At the stern staff of all vessels at anchor, or under way by power or sail.

At the leech of the aftermost sail, approximately 2/3 of the leech above the clew.

When the aftermost sail is gaff-rigged, the Ensign is flown immediately below the peak of the gaff.

U.S. Power Squadron Ensign: 8 a.m. to sundown when flown at the stern staff in place of the U.S. Ensign; otherwise, day and night from the starboard spreader. In either case it is flown only when a Squadron member is in command.

Club Burgee: Day and night. Not flown while racing.

At the bow staff of power vessels with one mast.

At the main peak of yawls, ketches, sloops, cutters, and catboats.

At the fore peak of schooners and power vessels with two masts.

Private Signal: Day and night.

At the bow staff of power vessels without a mast.

At the masthead of power and sailing vessels with one mast.

At the mizzen peak of yawls and ketches.

At the main peak of schooners and power vessels with two masts.

Flag Officers' Flags: Day and night. Flown in place of the private signal on all rigs except single-masted sailboats, when it is flown in place of the club burgee at the masthead.

Union Jack: 8 a.m. to sundown, only at anchor, and only on Sundays, holidays, or occasions for dressing ship, at the bow staff. Sailboats without a bow staff may fly it from the forestay a few feet above the stem head.

The Ship's Bell Code

Telling time by ship's bell has a romantic background that goes back hundreds of years. It is based in the workday routine of the ship's crew. A ship at sea requires a constant watch throughout the whole twenty-four hours of the day. To divide the duty, the day is broken up into six watches of four hours each and the crew into three divisions, or watches.

Each division of the crew stands two four-hour watches a day. In order to rotate the duty, so that a division does not have to stand the same watch day in and day out, the 4 to 8 watch in the afternoon is divided into two watches known as the dog watches.

The Mid-Watch - Midnight to 4 A.M.   *The 1st Dog Watch* - 4 P.M. to 6 P.M.
The Morning Watch - 4 A.M. to 8 A.M.   *The 2nd Dog Watch* - 6 P.M. to 8 P.M.
The Forenoon Watch - 8 A.M. to 12 Noon   *The First Watch* - 8 P.M. to Midnight
The Afternoon Watch - 12 Noon to 4 P.M.

To apprise the crew of the time, the ship's bell was struck by the watch officer at half hour intervals, the first half hour being one bell, the first hour two bells, hour and a half three bells, and so on up to eight bells, denoting time to relieve the watch. By this method of timekeeping eight bells marks 4, 8, or 12 o'clock.

8 Bells	4:00	8:00	12:00
1 Bell	4:30	8:30	12:30
2 Bells	5:00	9:00	1:00
3 Bells	5:30	9:30	1:30
4 Bells	6:00	10:00	2:00
5 Bells	6:30	10:30	2:30
6 Bells	7:00	11:00	3:00
7 Bells	7:30	11:30	3:30

Courtesy of Chelsea Clock Co., Chelsea, MA

U.S. Storm Signals

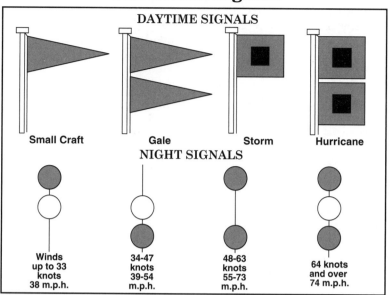

The above signals are displayed regularly on Light Vessels, at Coast Guard shore stations, and at many principal lighthouses. Each Coast and Geodetic Survey Chart lists those locations which appear within the area covered by that chart

Distance of Visibility

Given the curvature of the earth, can you see a 200' high headland from 20 miles away? (Answer below.) How far you can see depends on visibility, which we will assume is ideal, and the heights above water of your eye and the object.

To find the theoretical maximum distance of visibility, use the Table below. First, using your height of eye above water (say, 8'), the Table shows that at that height, your horizon is 3.2 n.m. away. Then, from our Lights, Fog Signals and Offshore Buoys (pp. 173-203), your chart, or the Light List, find the height of the object (say, 200'). The Table shows that object can be seen 16.2 n.m. from sea level. Add the two distances: 3.2 + 16.2 = 19.4 n.m. *Answer: not quite!*

(Heights below in feet, distance in nautical miles)

Ht.	Dist.	Ht.	Dist.	Ht.	Dist.	Ht.	Dist.	Ht.	Dist.
4	2.3	30	6.3	80	10.3	340	21.1	860	33.6
6	2.8	32	6.5	90	10.9	380	22.3	900	34.4
8	3.2	34	6.7	100	11.5	420	23.5	1000	36.2
10	3.6	36	6.9	120	12.6	460	24.6	1400	42.9
12	4.0	38	7.1	140	13.6	500	25.7	1800	48.6
14	4.3	40	7.3	160	14.5	540	26.7	2200	53.8
16	4.6	42	7.4	180	15.4	580	27.6	2600	58.5
18	4.9	44	7.6	200	16.2	620	28.6	3000	62.8
20	5.1	46	7.8	220	17.0	660	29.4	3400	66.9
22	5.4	48	8.0	240	17.8	700	30.4	3800	70.7
24	5.6	50	8.1	260	18.5	740	31.1	4200	74.3
26	5.9	60	8.9	280	19.2	780	32.0	4600	77.7
28	6.1	70	9.6	300	19.9	820	32.8	5000	81.0

sighted Provincetown off our starboard beam. We were flying, hitting 9.5 knots on a beam reach as we blew past Highland Light at 1710. Then, at 2000, the breeze died off when a thick bank of fog rolled in off Chatham Light, reducing our visibility to thirty yards. At 2045, we doused our jib and fired up the engine.

There are two channels for entering Nantucket Sound. The more direct Pollock Rip Channel is closer to the southern coast of Cape Cod, making it a preferred route for recreational vessels. Then, there is the Great Round Shoal Channel, which tends to be busier as it is the channel of choice for many commercial fishing vessels based out of Southern New England. Having been a commercial fisherman based out of Montauk earlier in his career, Casey was no stranger to either option and chose Great Round Shoal Channel.

The tidal current in Nantucket Sound floods east and ebbs west. The *Eldridge* tidal chart for Pollock Rip Channel shows that the flood starts four hours after high tide at Boston, which was at 1848. Thanks to Casey's timing, the ebbing current added another 1-2 knots to our SOG (speed over ground). At 2100, the Pollock Rip Buoy was abeam as we steered a course of 190°. At 2200, with the wind light and visibility at 50 yards, we powertacked into Great Round Channel steering for Nantucket.

This is where things got tense. We cleared Great Round Shoal Channel at 0025, pushing towards Nantucket. I felt like I was in *Das Boot*, the feature film based

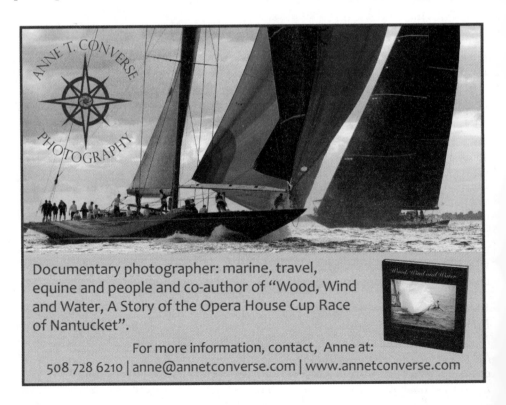

on Lothar-Günther Buchheim's book about an ill-fated German U-boat. There is a high-stakes scene in which the submarine attempts to motor on the surface through the Straits of Gibraltar in thick fog under the cover of darkness. Funny enough for me, a year prior, I was passing through the Straits of Gibraltar on a large cargo ship. It was the only foggy day of the entire passage. I think I saw the coast of Africa for ten minutes, tops.

Navigating westward through Nantucket Sound, the fog had become so thick that I couldn't see our mast, which was less than thirty feet from the helm. With our navigation lights and the red interior lights on only, Casey put me at the helm while he navigated our passage from the chart table down in our main saloon. He used our handheld GPS, a paper chart, and an *Eldridge*. Every couple of minutes, he would shout up course adjustment commands.

"HELMSMAN! Come right to 255°."

I'd shout back, "Come right to 255°." Repeating commands is the best way to acknowledge and ensure the order has been heard. Once on the new course, I would shout down to him that we were on course.

The three of us had been underway for close to forty-two hours. We were tired and cold. Water condensed on the standing and running rigging so much that it felt like I was standing under a hard showerhead. I couldn't wait for the misery to end. Still, due to the limited visibility, Casey made the call for us to furl the mainsail, and at 0150 on August 17, we dropped the hook just a quarter mile west of the main buoy, marking the channel entrance to Nantucket Harbor.

Our night did not stop there. We were on the edge of a busy channel, so we took turns standing watch at one-hour intervals. The person on watch sat on deck with a giant spotlight and foghorn in hand. We also verified our position with the handheld GPS on the hour to ensure our anchor was not dragging. At around 0600, the fog had lifted enough so we could weigh anchor and steam into the harbor. We were tied up by 0700, just in time to get a piping hot cup of coffee and some breakfast on shore.

Looking back on that passage, I still remember how frustrating it was to drop our anchor when we were so close! Hindsight is twenty-twenty. I so wanted to press on and get to the dock, but I know Casey made the right call. After all, we reached our final destination without suffering a collision or running aground or having our proverbial wings melt. Today, I follow Casey's lead. I am conservative, and when I'm the one in charge of a boat, I navigate with my compass and a chart. My chart plotter running in the background is just for verification.

Will Sofrin is a master shipwright who has taught at MIT and has built boats for Billy Joel and Estée Lauder. As a former professional sailor and licensed captain, he has tracked more than 30,000 blue-water miles. Today he is a freelance writer for numerous maritime periodicals, continues to race sailboats, and explores the coast of California with his wife and seven-year-old daughter. All Hands on Deck is his first book.

DIAL-A-BUOY Service

Dial-A-Buoy offers reports of conditions at numerous coastal and offshore locations. In all, there are approximately 65 buoy and 54 Coastal-Marine Automated Network (C-MAN) stations. The system is operated by the National Data Buoy Center (NDBC), part of the National Weather Service (NWS).

The reports from offshore buoys include wind speed, gusts, and direction, wave heights and periods, water temperature, and barometric pressure as recorded within the last hour or so. Reports from land stations cover wind speed and direction, temperature, and pressure; some land stations also add water temperature, visibility, and dew point.

On the next page, we give the station or buoy identifier, location name, and lat/long in degrees and hundredths, as provided by the NWS. To find station or buoy locations and identifiers using the Internet, visit www.ndbc.noaa.gov. To find locations by telephone, you can enter a latitude and longitude to receive the locations and identifiers of the closest stations.

Using GPS to Create a Deviation Table

Most compasses are subject to onboard magnetic influences, called deviation. You can make your compass more trustworthy by using your GPS to create a deviation table.

Choose a day when the wind is light and sea as calm as possible. Find a large open area with little or no current and a minimum of boat traffic. Bring aboard an assistant. In a notebook create two columns: in pencil, label the left column GPS and the right column COMPASS. Down the right column, number each successive line using intervals of 15° [24 lines] up to 360°. You can concentrate on noting the four Cardinal and four Inter Cardinal headings (N, NE, E, SE, S, SW, W, NW) and safely interpolate and fill in the missing numbers for every 15°. Note that the Default setting on a GPS display is TRUE. For this exercise, make sure that your GPS is displaying MAGNETIC- Course Over Ground (COG) heading. This may require going into the GPS setup to insure that the COG is displaying a MAGNETIC heading.

Choose a speed which provides responsive steering and which will make any current or leeway a negligible factor. Proceed on any of the numbered courses for at least 30 seconds, giving the GPS time to report a consistent direction. Once you have held a steady course long enough to get a repeated reading, record it in the left column. Proceed to the next heading. Completing the circle results in a deviation table for your steering compass. Now, erase the penciled column headings and relabel the GPS column TO GO, and the COMPASS column STEER. Example: TO GO 094°, STEER 090°.

A deviation table admittedly falls far short of the ideal of a compensated compass; however, such a table will allow you to use your compass with a measure of confidence before an adjuster comes aboard. And that is much better than trying to steer by your GPS.

DIAL-A-BUOY and C-MAN Stations

To access Dial-A-Buoy:

1. Call 888-701-8992.
2. If you know the identifier of the station or buoy, press 1. Press 2 to get station locations by entering an approximate lat/long.
3. Enter the five-digit (or character) station identifier.
4. If, after hearing the latest report, you wish to hear a forecast for that same location, press 1.
5. If you want to hear the report for another station, press 2.

Station ID	Location Name	Lat	Long
44027	JONESPORT, ME	44.28N	67.30W
MDRM1	MT DESERT ROCK, ME	43.97N	68.13W
MISM1	MATINICUS ROCK, ME	43.78N	68.86W
44007	PORTLAND, ME	43.53N	70.14W
44005	GULF OF MAINE	43.20N	69.13W
IOSN3	ISLE OF SHOALS, NH	42.97N	70.62W
44013	BOSTON, MA	42.35N	70.65W
44018	CAPE COD, MA	42.20N	70.15W
BUZM3	BUZZARDS BAY, MA	41.40N	71.03W
44011	GEORGES BANK, MA	41.09N	66.56W
44017	MONTAUK POINT, NY	40.69N	72.05W
44008	NANTUCKET, MA	40.50N	69.25W
44065	NEW YORK HARBOR ENT., NY	40.37N	73.70W
44025	LONG ISLAND, NY	40.25N	73.16W
44066	TEXAS TOWER #4, NJ	39.62N	72.64W
TPLM2	THOMAS POINT, MD	38.90N	76.44W
44009	DELAWARE BAY, NJ	38.46N	74.70W
44099	CAPE HENRY, VA	36.91N	75.72W
41025	DIAMOND SHOALS	35.01N	75.45W
44014	VIRGINIA BEACH, VA	36.60N	74.84W
DUKN7	DUCK PIER, NC	36.18N	75.75W
CLKN7	CAPE LOOKOUT, NC	34.62N	76.53W
41001	E. HATTERAS, NC	34.70N	72.24W
41013	FRYING PAN SHOAL, NC	33.44N	77.76W
41004	EDISTO, SC	32.50N	79.10W
41002	S. HATTERAS, SC	31.76N	74.94W
41008	GRAYS REEF, GA	31.40N	80.87W
SAUF1	ST AUGUSTINE, FL	29.86N	81.27W
41010	CANAVERAL EAST, FL	28.88N	78.49W
41009	CANAVERAL, FL	28.51N	80.19W
LKWF1	LAKE WORTH, FL	26.61N	80.03W
FWYF1	FOWEY ROCK, FL	25.59N	80.10W
LONF1	LONG KEY, FL	24.84N	80.86W
SMKF1	SOMBRERO KEY, FL	24.63N	81.11W
SANF1	SAND KEY, FL	24.46N	81.88W

Most stations can provide information via RSS feed using your web browser. For information on how to use this feature, visit www.ndbc.noaa.gov/rss_access.shtml

2024 SUN'S RISING AND SETTING AT BOSTON – 42° 20'N 71°W

Daylight Saving Time is March 10 – November 3, transitions are noted with an *

Times shown in table are first tip of Sun at Sunrise and last tip at Sunset.

Day	JAN. Rise h m	Set h m	FEB. Rise h m	Set h m	MAR. Rise h m	Set h m	APR. Rise h m	Set h m	MAY Rise h m	Set h m	JUN. Rise h m	Set h m	Day
01	7:13	16:22	6:58	16:58	6:18	17:35	6:26	19:10	5:39	19:44	5:10	20:15	01
02	7:13	16:23	6:57	16:59	6:17	17:36	6:24	19:12	5:37	19:45	5:09	20:15	02
03	7:13	16:24	6:56	17:00	6:15	17:37	6:22	19:13	5:36	19:46	5:09	20:16	03
04	7:13	16:25	6:55	17:01	6:14	17:38	6:20	19:14	5:35	19:47	5:08	20:17	04
05	7:13	16:26	6:54	17:03	6:12	17:39	6:19	19:15	5:33	19:49	5:08	20:17	05
06	7:13	16:26	6:52	17:04	6:10	17:41	6:17	19:16	5:32	19:50	5:08	20:18	06
07	7:13	16:27	6:51	17:05	6:09	17:42	6:15	19:17	5:31	19:51	5:08	20:19	07
08	7:13	16:29	6:50	17:07	6:07	17:43	6:14	19:18	5:30	19:52	5:07	20:19	08
09	7:13	16:30	6:49	17:08	6:05	17:44	6:12	19:19	5:29	19:53	5:07	20:20	09
10	7:12	16:31	6:48	17:09	*7:04	18:45	6:10	19:21	5:27	19:54	5:07	20:20	10
11	7:12	16:32	6:46	17:11	7:02	18:46	6:09	19:22	5:26	19:55	5:07	20:21	11
12	7:12	16:33	6:45	17:12	7:00	18:48	6:07	19:23	5:25	19:56	5:07	20:21	12
13	7:11	16:34	6:44	17:13	6:58	18:49	6:05	19:24	5:24	19:57	5:07	20:22	13
14	7:11	16:35	6:42	17:14	6:57	18:50	6:04	19:25	5:23	19:58	5:07	20:22	14
15	7:11	16:36	6:41	17:16	6:55	18:51	6:02	19:26	5:22	19:59	5:07	20:23	15
16	7:10	16:37	6:40	17:17	6:53	18:52	6:01	19:27	5:21	20:00	5:07	20:23	16
17	7:10	16:39	6:38	17:18	6:52	18:53	5:59	19:28	5:20	20:01	5:07	20:23	17
18	7:09	16:40	6:37	17:20	6:50	18:55	5:58	19:30	5:19	20:02	5:07	20:24	18
19	7:09	16:41	6:35	17:21	6:48	18:56	5:56	19:31	5:18	20:03	5:07	20:24	19
20	7:08	16:42	6:34	17:22	6:46	18:57	5:54	19:32	5:18	20:04	5:07	20:24	20
21	7:07	16:44	6:32	17:23	6:45	18:58	5:53	19:33	5:17	20:05	5:08	20:24	21
22	7:07	16:45	6:31	17:25	6:43	18:59	5:51	19:34	5:16	20:06	5:08	20:25	22
23	7:06	16:46	6:29	17:26	6:41	19:00	5:50	19:35	5:15	20:07	5:08	20:25	23
24	7:05	16:47	6:28	17:27	6:39	19:01	5:48	19:36	5:14	20:08	5:08	20:25	24
25	7:04	16:49	6:26	17:28	6:38	19:03	5:47	19:37	5:14	20:09	5:09	20:25	25
26	7:04	16:50	6:25	17:30	6:36	19:04	5:46	19:39	5:13	20:10	5:09	20:25	26
27	7:03	16:51	6:23	17:31	6:34	19:05	5:44	19:40	5:12	20:11	5:09	20:25	27
28	7:02	16:52	6:22	17:32	6:32	19:06	5:43	19:41	5:12	20:11	5:10	20:25	28
29	7:01	16:54	6:20	17:33	6:31	19:07	5:41	19:42	5:11	20:12	5:10	20:25	29
30	7:00	16:55			6:29	19:08	5:40	19:43	5:11	20:13	5:11	20:25	30
31	6:59	16:56			6:27	19:09			5:10	20:14			31

Day	JUL. Rise h m	Set h m	AUG. Rise h m	Set h m	SEP. Rise h m	Set h m	OCT. Rise h m	Set h m	NOV. Rise h m	Set h m	DEC. Rise h m	Set h m	Day
01	5:11	20:24	5:37	20:03	6:10	19:17	6:42	18:25	7:18	17:37	6:54	16:12	01
02	5:12	20:24	5:38	20:02	6:11	19:15	6:43	18:23	7:19	17:35	6:55	16:12	02
03	5:13	20:24	5:39	20:00	6:12	19:14	6:44	18:21	*6:20	16:34	6:56	16:12	03
04	5:13	20:24	5:40	19:59	6:13	19:12	6:45	18:19	6:22	16:33	6:57	16:12	04
05	5:14	20:23	5:41	19:58	6:14	19:10	6:46	18:18	6:23	16:32	6:58	16:11	05
06	5:14	20:23	5:42	19:57	6:15	19:08	6:47	18:16	6:24	16:31	6:59	16:11	06
07	5:15	20:23	5:43	19:55	6:16	19:07	6:48	18:14	6:25	16:30	7:00	16:11	07
08	5:16	20:22	5:44	19:54	6:17	19:05	6:49	18:13	6:27	16:28	7:01	16:11	08
09	5:16	20:22	5:46	19:53	6:18	19:03	6:51	18:11	6:28	16:27	7:02	16:11	09
10	5:17	20:21	5:47	19:51	6:19	19:01	6:52	18:09	6:29	16:26	7:03	16:11	10
11	5:18	20:21	5:48	19:50	6:20	19:00	6:53	18:08	6:30	16:25	7:03	16:12	11
12	5:19	20:20	5:49	19:48	6:21	18:58	6:54	18:06	6:32	16:24	7:04	16:12	12
13	5:20	20:20	5:50	19:47	6:22	18:56	6:55	18:04	6:33	16:23	7:05	16:12	13
14	5:20	20:19	5:51	19:46	6:23	18:54	6:56	18:03	6:34	16:22	7:06	16:12	14
15	5:21	20:19	5:52	19:44	6:25	18:53	6:57	18:01	6:35	16:22	7:06	16:12	15
16	5:22	20:18	5:53	19:43	6:26	18:51	6:59	18:00	6:37	16:21	7:07	16:13	16
17	5:23	20:17	5:54	19:41	6:27	18:49	7:00	17:58	6:38	16:20	7:08	16:13	17
18	5:24	20:16	5:55	19:40	6:28	18:47	7:01	17:56	6:39	16:19	7:08	16:13	18
19	5:25	20:16	5:56	19:38	6:29	18:46	7:02	17:55	6:40	16:18	7:09	16:14	19
20	5:26	20:15	5:57	19:37	6:30	18:44	7:03	17:53	6:41	16:18	7:09	16:14	20
21	5:26	20:14	5:58	19:35	6:31	18:42	7:04	17:52	6:43	16:17	7:10	16:15	21
22	5:27	20:13	5:59	19:33	6:32	18:40	7:06	17:50	6:44	16:16	7:10	16:15	22
23	5:28	20:12	6:00	19:32	6:33	18:39	7:07	17:49	6:45	16:16	7:11	16:16	23
24	5:29	20:11	6:01	19:30	6:34	18:37	7:08	17:47	6:46	16:15	7:11	16:16	24
25	5:30	20:10	6:02	19:29	6:35	18:35	7:09	17:46	6:47	16:15	7:12	16:17	25
26	5:31	20:09	6:03	19:27	6:36	18:33	7:11	17:45	6:49	16:14	7:12	16:18	26
27	5:32	20:08	6:05	19:25	6:37	18:31	7:12	17:43	6:50	16:14	7:12	16:19	27
28	5:33	20:07	6:06	19:24	6:38	18:30	7:13	17:42	6:51	16:13	7:13	16:19	28
29	5:34	20:06	6:07	19:22	6:39	18:28	7:14	17:41	6:52	16:13	7:13	16:20	29
30	5:35	20:05	6:08	19:20	6:41	18:26	7:15	17:39	6:53	16:13	7:13	16:21	30
31	5:36	20:04	6:09	19:19			7:17	17:38			7:13	16:22	31

2024 SUN'S RISING AND SETTING AT NEW YORK – 40° 42'N   74°W

Daylight Saving Time is March 10 – November 3 transitions are noted with an *

Times shown in table are first tip of Sun at Sunrise and last tip at Sunset.

	JAN. Rise	JAN. Set	FEB. Rise	FEB. Set	MAR. Rise	MAR. Set	APR. Rise	APR. Set	MAY Rise	MAY Set	JUN. Rise	JUN. Set	
Day	h m	h m	h m	h m	h m	h m	h m	h m	h m	h m	h m	h m	Day
01	7:26	16:33	7:11	17:09	6:31	17:46	6:37	19:23	5:50	19:57	5:20	20:28	01
02	7:26	16:34	7:10	17:10	6:29	17:47	6:36	19:24	5:48	19:58	5:20	20:29	02
03	7:26	16:34	7:09	17:11	6:27	17:49	6:34	19:25	5:47	19:59	5:20	20:29	03
04	7:26	16:35	7:07	17:13	6:26	17:50	6:32	19:26	5:46	20:00	5:19	20:30	04
05	7:26	16:36	7:06	17:14	6:24	17:51	6:30	19:27	5:45	20:01	5:19	20:31	05
06	7:26	16:37	7:05	17:15	6:22	17:52	6:29	19:28	5:43	20:03	5:19	20:31	06
07	7:26	16:38	7:04	17:17	6:21	17:54	6:27	19:30	5:42	20:04	5:18	20:32	07
08	7:26	16:39	7:03	17:18	6:19	17:55	6:25	19:31	5:41	20:05	5:18	20:33	08
09	7:26	16:40	7:02	17:19	6:17	17:56	6:24	19:32	5:40	20:06	5:18	20:33	09
10	7:26	16:42	7:00	17:21	*7:16	18:57	6:22	19:33	5:38	20:07	5:18	20:34	10
11	7:25	16:43	6:59	17:22	7:14	18:58	6:20	19:34	5:37	20:08	5:18	20:34	11
12	7:25	16:44	6:58	17:23	7:12	19:00	6:19	19:35	5:36	20:09	5:17	20:35	12
13	7:25	16:45	6:56	17:25	7:11	19:01	6:17	19:36	5:35	20:10	5:17	20:35	13
14	7:24	16:46	6:55	17:26	7:09	19:02	6:15	19:38	5:34	20:11	5:17	20:36	14
15	7:24	16:47	6:54	17:27	7:07	19:03	6:14	19:39	5:33	20:12	5:17	20:36	15
16	7:23	16:48	6:52	17:29	7:05	19:04	6:12	19:40	5:32	20:13	5:17	20:36	16
17	7:23	16:50	6:51	17:30	7:04	19:05	6:11	19:41	5:31	20:14	5:18	20:37	17
18	7:22	16:51	6:49	17:31	7:02	19:07	6:09	19:42	5:30	20:15	5:18	20:37	18
19	7:22	16:52	6:48	17:32	7:00	19:08	6:07	19:43	5:29	20:16	5:18	20:37	19
20	7:21	16:53	6:46	17:34	6:58	19:09	6:06	19:44	5:28	20:17	5:18	20:38	20
21	7:20	16:55	6:45	17:35	6:57	19:10	6:04	19:46	5:28	20:18	5:18	20:38	21
22	7:20	16:56	6:43	17:36	6:55	19:11	6:03	19:47	5:27	20:19	5:18	20:38	22
23	7:19	16:57	6:42	17:37	6:53	19:12	6:01	19:48	5:26	20:20	5:19	20:38	23
24	7:18	16:58	6:40	17:39	6:51	19:14	6:00	19:49	5:25	20:21	5:19	20:38	24
25	7:17	17:00	6:39	17:40	6:50	19:15	5:58	19:50	5:24	20:22	5:19	20:38	25
26	7:16	17:01	6:37	17:41	6:48	19:16	5:57	19:51	5:24	20:23	5:20	20:38	26
27	7:16	17:02	6:36	17:43	6:46	19:17	5:55	19:52	5:23	20:24	5:20	20:38	27
28	7:15	17:03	6:34	17:44	6:44	19:18	5:54	19:54	5:23	20:25	5:21	20:38	28
29	7:14	17:05	6:32	17:45	6:43	19:19	5:53	19:55	5:22	20:25	5:21	20:38	29
30	7:13	17:06			6:41	19:20	5:51	19:56	5:21	20:26	5:22	20:38	30
31	7:12	17:07			6:39	19:22			5:21	20:27			31

	JUL. Rise	JUL. Set	AUG. Rise	AUG. Set	SEP. Rise	SEP. Set	OCT. Rise	OCT. Set	NOV. Rise	NOV. Set	DEC. Rise	DEC. Set	
Day	h m	h m	h m	h m	h m	h m	h m	h m	h m	h m	h m	h m	Day
01	5:22	20:38	5:48	20:16	6:21	19:29	6:54	18:36	7:31	17:48	7:07	16:23	01
02	5:23	20:38	5:49	20:14	6:22	19:28	6:55	18:35	7:32	17:47	7:08	16:23	02
03	5:23	20:37	5:50	20:13	6:24	19:26	6:56	18:33	*6:33	16:45	7:09	16:23	03
04	5:24	20:37	5:51	20:12	6:25	19:24	6:57	18:31	6:34	16:44	7:10	16:22	04
05	5:24	20:37	5:52	20:11	6:26	19:22	6:58	18:29	6:36	16:43	7:11	16:22	05
06	5:25	20:36	5:54	20:09	6:27	19:21	6:59	18:28	6:37	16:42	7:12	16:22	06
07	5:26	20:36	5:55	20:08	6:28	19:19	7:01	18:26	6:38	16:41	7:13	16:22	07
08	5:27	20:36	5:56	20:07	6:29	19:17	7:02	18:24	6:40	16:40	7:14	16:22	08
09	5:27	20:35	5:57	20:05	6:30	19:15	7:03	18:23	6:41	16:39	7:15	16:22	09
10	5:28	20:35	5:58	20:04	6:31	19:14	7:04	18:21	6:42	16:37	7:16	16:22	10
11	5:29	20:34	5:59	20:03	6:32	19:12	7:05	18:19	6:43	16:36	7:17	16:22	11
12	5:30	20:34	6:00	20:01	6:33	19:10	7:06	18:18	6:45	16:35	7:17	16:22	12
13	5:30	20:33	6:01	20:00	6:34	19:08	7:07	18:16	6:46	16:34	7:18	16:23	13
14	5:31	20:32	6:02	19:58	6:35	19:07	7:09	18:14	6:47	16:34	7:19	16:23	14
15	5:32	20:32	6:03	19:57	6:36	19:05	7:10	18:13	6:48	16:33	7:20	16:23	15
16	5:33	20:31	6:04	19:55	6:37	19:03	7:11	18:11	6:50	16:32	7:20	16:23	16
17	5:34	20:30	6:05	19:54	6:39	19:01	7:12	18:10	6:51	16:31	7:21	16:24	17
18	5:35	20:30	6:06	19:52	6:40	18:59	7:13	18:08	6:52	16:30	7:22	16:24	18
19	5:36	20:29	6:07	19:51	6:41	18:58	7:15	18:06	6:53	16:29	7:22	16:25	19
20	5:36	20:28	6:08	19:49	6:42	18:56	7:16	18:05	6:54	16:29	7:23	16:25	20
21	5:37	20:27	6:10	19:48	6:43	18:54	7:17	18:03	6:56	16:28	7:23	16:26	21
22	5:38	20:26	6:11	19:46	6:44	18:52	7:18	18:02	6:57	16:27	7:24	16:26	22
23	5:39	20:25	6:12	19:44	6:45	18:51	7:19	18:00	6:58	16:27	7:24	16:27	23
24	5:40	20:24	6:13	19:43	6:46	18:49	7:21	17:59	6:59	16:26	7:25	16:27	24
25	5:41	20:23	6:14	19:41	6:47	18:47	7:22	17:57	7:00	16:26	7:25	16:28	25
26	5:42	20:22	6:15	19:40	6:48	18:45	7:23	17:56	7:02	16:25	7:25	16:29	26
27	5:43	20:21	6:16	19:38	6:49	18:43	7:24	17:55	7:03	16:25	7:26	16:29	27
28	5:44	20:20	6:17	19:36	6:50	18:42	7:26	17:53	7:04	16:24	7:26	16:30	28
29	5:45	20:19	6:18	19:34	6:52	18:40	7:27	17:52	7:05	16:24	7:26	16:31	29
30	5:46	20:18	6:19	19:33	6:53	18:38	7:28	17:51	7:06	16:23	7:26	16:32	30
31	5:47	20:17	6:20	19:31			7:29	17:49			7:26	16:32	31

2024 SUN'S RISING AND SETTING AT JACKSONVILLE – 30° 20'N   81° 37'W

Daylight Saving Time is March 10 – November 3, transitions are noted with an *

Times shown in table are first tip of Sun at Sunrise and last tip at Sunset.

	JAN. Rise	Set	FEB. Rise	Set	MAR. Rise	Set	APR. Rise	Set	MAY Rise	Set	JUN. Rise	Set	
Day	h m	h m	h m	h m	h m	h m	h m	h m	h m	h m	h m	h m	Day
01	7:23	17:37	7:17	18:03	6:52	18:26	7:15	19:46	6:43	20:05	6:25	20:24	01
02	7:23	17:38	7:17	18:04	6:51	18:26	7:14	19:46	6:42	20:05	6:25	20:25	02
03	7:23	17:38	7:16	18:05	6:50	18:27	7:13	19:47	6:41	20:06	6:25	20:25	03
04	7:24	17:39	7:16	18:05	6:49	18:28	7:11	19:48	6:40	20:07	6:24	20:26	04
05	7:24	17:40	7:15	18:06	6:47	18:29	7:10	19:48	6:39	20:07	6:24	20:26	05
06	7:24	17:41	7:14	18:07	6:46	18:29	7:09	19:49	6:38	20:08	6:24	20:27	06
07	7:24	17:41	7:14	18:08	6:45	18:30	7:08	19:49	6:38	20:09	6:24	20:27	07
08	7:24	17:42	7:13	18:09	6:44	18:31	7:07	19:50	6:37	20:09	6:24	20:27	08
09	7:24	17:43	7:12	18:10	6:43	18:31	7:06	19:51	6:36	20:10	6:24	20:28	09
10	7:24	17:44	7:11	18:10	*7:42	19:32	7:04	19:51	6:35	20:11	6:24	20:28	10
11	7:24	17:45	7:10	18:11	7:40	19:33	7:03	19:52	6:35	20:11	6:24	20:29	11
12	7:24	17:45	7:10	18:12	7:39	19:33	7:02	19:53	6:34	20:12	6:24	20:29	12
13	7:24	17:46	7:09	18:13	7:38	19:34	7:01	19:53	6:33	20:13	6:24	20:29	13
14	7:24	17:47	7:08	18:14	7:37	19:34	7:00	19:54	6:33	20:13	6:24	20:30	14
15	7:24	17:48	7:07	18:15	7:36	19:35	6:59	19:54	6:32	20:14	6:24	20:30	15
16	7:24	17:49	7:06	18:15	7:34	19:36	6:58	19:55	6:32	20:15	6:24	20:30	16
17	7:23	17:50	7:05	18:16	7:33	19:36	6:57	19:56	6:31	20:15	6:25	20:31	17
18	7:23	17:51	7:04	18:17	7:32	19:37	6:55	19:56	6:30	20:16	6:25	20:31	18
19	7:23	17:51	7:03	18:18	7:31	19:38	6:54	19:57	6:30	20:16	6:25	20:31	19
20	7:23	17:52	7:02	18:18	7:30	19:38	6:53	19:58	6:29	20:17	6:25	20:31	20
21	7:22	17:53	7:01	18:19	7:28	19:39	6:52	19:58	6:29	20:18	6:25	20:32	21
22	7:22	17:54	7:00	18:20	7:27	19:40	6:51	19:59	6:28	20:18	6:26	20:32	22
23	7:22	17:55	6:59	18:21	7:26	19:40	6:50	20:00	6:28	20:19	6:26	20:32	23
24	7:21	17:56	6:58	18:21	7:25	19:41	6:49	20:00	6:28	20:20	6:26	20:32	24
25	7:21	17:57	6:57	18:22	7:23	19:41	6:48	20:01	6:27	20:20	6:26	20:32	25
26	7:21	17:58	6:56	18:23	7:22	19:42	6:47	20:01	6:27	20:21	6:27	20:32	26
27	7:20	17:58	6:55	18:24	7:21	19:43	6:46	20:02	6:26	20:21	6:27	20:32	27
28	7:20	17:59	6:54	18:24	7:20	19:43	6:45	20:03	6:26	20:22	6:27	20:32	28
29	7:19	18:00	6:53	18:25	7:19	19:44	6:44	20:03	6:26	20:22	6:28	20:32	29
30	7:19	18:01			7:17	19:44	6:44	20:04	6:25	20:23	6:28	20:32	30
31	7:18	18:02			7:16	19:45			6:25	20:24			31

	JUL. Rise	Set	AUG. Rise	Set	SEP. Rise	Set	OCT. Rise	Set	NOV. Rise	Set	DEC. Rise	Set	
Day	h m	h m	h m	h m	h m	h m	h m	h m	h m	h m	h m	h m	Day
01	6:28	20:32	6:45	20:20	7:04	19:48	7:20	19:11	7:41	18:38	7:06	17:25	01
02	6:29	20:32	6:46	20:19	7:04	19:47	7:21	19:10	7:42	18:38	7:07	17:25	02
03	6:29	20:32	6:47	20:18	7:05	19:46	7:21	19:09	*6:43	17:37	7:07	17:25	03
04	6:30	20:32	6:47	20:17	7:05	19:45	7:22	19:07	6:44	17:36	7:08	17:26	04
05	6:30	20:32	6:48	20:17	7:06	19:44	7:23	19:06	6:44	17:35	7:09	17:26	05
06	6:31	20:32	6:48	20:16	7:06	19:42	7:23	19:05	6:45	17:35	7:10	17:26	06
07	6:31	20:32	6:49	20:15	7:07	19:41	7:24	19:04	6:46	17:34	7:10	17:26	07
08	6:32	20:32	6:50	20:14	7:07	19:40	7:25	19:03	6:47	17:33	7:11	17:26	08
09	6:32	20:31	6:50	20:13	7:08	19:39	7:25	19:02	6:48	17:33	7:12	17:26	09
10	6:33	20:31	6:51	20:12	7:09	19:37	7:26	19:00	6:48	17:32	7:13	17:26	10
11	6:33	20:31	6:51	20:11	7:09	19:36	7:26	18:59	6:49	17:32	7:13	17:27	11
12	6:34	20:31	6:52	20:10	7:10	19:35	7:27	18:58	6:50	17:31	7:14	17:27	12
13	6:34	20:30	6:53	20:09	7:10	19:34	7:28	18:57	6:51	17:30	7:15	17:27	13
14	6:35	20:30	6:53	20:08	7:11	19:32	7:28	18:56	6:52	17:30	7:15	17:28	14
15	6:35	20:30	6:54	20:07	7:11	19:31	7:29	18:55	6:53	17:29	7:16	17:28	15
16	6:36	20:29	6:54	20:06	7:12	19:30	7:30	18:54	6:53	17:29	7:16	17:28	16
17	6:36	20:29	6:55	20:05	7:12	19:29	7:30	18:53	6:54	17:29	7:17	17:29	17
18	6:37	20:28	6:56	20:04	7:13	19:27	7:31	18:52	6:55	17:28	7:18	17:29	18
19	6:38	20:28	6:56	20:03	7:13	19:26	7:32	18:51	6:56	17:28	7:18	17:30	19
20	6:38	20:27	6:57	20:02	7:14	19:25	7:32	18:49	6:57	17:27	7:19	17:30	20
21	6:39	20:27	6:57	20:01	7:15	19:24	7:33	18:48	6:58	17:27	7:19	17:31	21
22	6:39	20:26	6:58	20:00	7:15	19:22	7:34	18:47	6:58	17:27	7:20	17:31	22
23	6:40	20:26	6:58	19:59	7:16	19:21	7:35	18:46	6:59	17:27	7:20	17:32	23
24	6:40	20:25	6:59	19:58	7:16	19:20	7:35	18:46	7:00	17:26	7:21	17:32	24
25	6:41	20:25	7:00	19:57	7:17	19:19	7:36	18:45	7:01	17:26	7:21	17:33	25
26	6:42	20:24	7:00	19:56	7:17	19:17	7:37	18:44	7:02	17:26	7:21	17:33	26
27	6:42	20:23	7:01	19:54	7:18	19:16	7:37	18:43	7:03	17:26	7:22	17:34	27
28	6:43	20:23	7:01	19:53	7:19	19:15	7:38	18:42	7:03	17:26	7:22	17:35	28
29	6:43	20:22	7:02	19:52	7:19	19:14	7:39	18:41	7:04	17:26	7:22	17:35	29
30	6:44	20:21	7:02	19:51	7:20	19:12	7:40	18:40	7:05	17:26	7:23	17:36	30
31	6:45	20:21	7:03	19:50			7:40	18:39			7:23	17:37	31

2024 SUN'S SETTING AT OTHER LOCATIONS FOR FLAG USE
Daylight Saving Time is March 10 – November 3

Times shown in tables p. 228-230 are first tip of Sun at Sunrise and last tip at Sunset.

Vernal Equinox: March 19th, 11:06 p.m. E.D.T.   Summer Solstice: June 20th, 4:50 p.m. E.D.T.
Autumnal Equinox: Sept. 22nd, 8:43 a.m. E.D.T.   Winter Solstice: Dec. 21st, 4:20 a.m. E.S.T.

Add to or subtract from the referenced table

	Jan	Feb	Mar	Apr	May	Jun	Jul	Aug	Sep	Oct	Nov	Dec
BOSTON p. 228												
New London, CT	+7	+6	+4	+2	0	-1	0	+1	+2	+5	+6	+7
Newport, RI	+4	+3	+1	-1	-2	-3	-2	-1	0	+2	+4	+5
New Bedford, MA	+3	+2	0	-1	-2	-3	-2	-1	0	+1	+2	+3
Vineyard Haven, MA	+1	-1	-2	-4	-5	-6	-5	-4	-3	-2	0	+1
Nantucket, MA	-1	-2	-4	-6	-7	-8	-7	-6	-5	-3	-2	-1
Portland, ME	-8	-6	-3	-1	+1	+2	+1	0	-2	-4	-6	-7
Rockland, ME	-14	-12	-8	-6	-4	-2	-4	-5	-7	-10	-12	-14
Bar Harbor, ME	-18	-15	-11	-8	-5	-3	-5	-7	-9	-13	-17	-18
NEW YORK p. 229												
Hampton Roads, VA	+18	+15	+9	+2	0	-1	-1	+2	+7	+13	+18	+20
Oxford, MD	+14	+12	+9	+5	+4	+3	+3	+5	+8	+11	+14	+15
Annapolis, MD	+14	+13	+10	+7	+6	+5	+5	+7	+9	+12	+14	+15
Cape May, NJ	+8	+7	+4	+1	0	-1	-1	+1	+3	+6	+8	+9
Atlantic City, NJ	+5	+4	+2	0	-1	-2	-2	0	+2	+4	+6	+6
Mannasquan, NJ	+2	+1	0	-1	-2	-2	-2	-1	0	+1	+2	+2
Port Jefferson, NY	-5	-4	-4	-3	-3	-3	-3	-3	-4	-4	-5	-5
Bridgeport, CT	-4	-4	-3	-2	-2	-1	-1	-2	-3	-4	-4	-5
New Haven, CT	-7	-6	-4	-3	-3	-3	-3	-3	-4	-5	-6	-7
JACKSONVILLE p. 230												
Morehead City, NC	-28	-24	-20	-14	-10	-7	-9	-13	-19	-24	-28	-29
Wilmington, NC	-22	-18	-14	-10	-5	-3	-5	-8	-14	-18	-22	-23
Myrtle Beach, SC	-16	-14	-10	-6	-3	-1	-3	-5	-7	-12	-17	-17
Charleston, SC	-11	-9	-6	-3	+1	0	-1	-3	-7	-9	-11	-12
Savannah. GA	-1	0	+2	+4	+6	+6	+5	+4	+3	0	-2	-2
Brunswick, GA	+1	-1	0	+1	+2	+2	+1	+1	-1	+1	+2	+2
Ponce Inlet, FL	+1	-1	-1	-2	-4	-5	-5	-4	-2	0	+1	+1
Melbourne, FL	+1	-2	-4	-5	-7	-9	-9	-8	-5	-1	0	+1
N. Palm Beach, FL	+2	-2	-6	-8	-11	-14	-14	-11	-7	-4	0	+2
Miami, FL	+6	0	-3	-8	-13	-15	-15	-11	-7	-2	+3	+5
Key West, FL	+13	+7	+2	-3	-8	-12	-12	-6	-1	+6	+11	+14

The Wreck at Graves Island Light
by Eric Troels Wiberg

Young Russell Forsyth Craig must have been relieved to return to Earth relatively unscathed after World War II. The naval aviator was engaged in combat against the Japanese at Midway in early June, 1942, and campaigns in the Solomons, Santa Cruz, Gilberts, and Marshall Islands years later. Shot down over Majuro, he was rescued uninjured. Born in Seattle in 1919, Russell graduated from the University of Washington and was back stateside in time to marry Georgia Lybeck in 1945. His 31-year naval career brought him to the Boston area where he obtained his master's degree in ordnance (weaponry) engineering from MIT.

In 1947 the couple were living in Belmont and raising daughters Denise and Lorilee. He was based at Naval Air Station Squantum, begun in 1920 as the Harvard Aviation Field, and occupied by Boston Scientific and Marina Bay in Quincy today. On the evening of July 17 Lieutenant Commander Craig was pilot and sole occupant of a Grumman F6F-5N Hellcat single-engine carrier-borne fighter plane. According to the *Boston Globe*, he was "working on a Navy experimental project at Massachusetts Institute of Technology," in nearby Cambridge.

Jim Ignahser of New England Aviation History says the mission was "to test an experimental fire control tracking device." The target? Graves Light Station, situated on a jagged outcrop of rocks simply known as The Graves. For Craig, reaching the light, 10 miles northeast of Squantum, would have taken just minutes at the aircraft's max speed of 388 mph. On arrival he "began making simulated attack runs" on the manned lighthouse, probably to the terror of its three keepers taking turns trimming the wicks and winding the light.

That was when things went wrong. "While passing the lighthouse, the engine of his aircraft suddenly began to sputter and lose power. The pilot attempted to gain altitude, but the engine froze and lost all power. The oil pressure gauge read zero. With great skill, the pilot was able to make an emergency water landing northeast of the lighthouse. When the plane hit the water it flipped onto its back, trapping the pilot inside."

After a terrifying ordeal extracting himself, Craig floated alone on an inflatable life vest for half an hour, flashing his emergency beacon by hand in the cold waters "until rescued by a passing yacht." Leon Estabrook, owner of the cabin cruiser of *Dorcus II*, saw his light and pulled him out of the water. By good fortune a doctor named Walter Channing provided Craig with First Aid "for immersion and shock" while *Dorcus II* then headed north to Marblehead. Eight miles later the boat with Craig arrived at the Eastern Yacht Club.

Since Craig had sent a Mayday (French *m'aidez* for "*aid me*") to Squantum prior to ditching, two patrol bombers, two rescue boats from Squantum as well as two aircraft from Salem came to his aid. An ambulance driven by navy Pharmacist J. F. De Cordova returned him to Squantum, where Craig was examined and released that night to his wife's company. Thanks to this concerted rescue, he went on to earn the Distinguished Flying Cross, led air operations aboard the carrier

232   *Continued on p. 256*

LOCAL APPARENT NOON 2024

FOR THE CENTRAL MERIDIAN OF ANY TIME ZONE

	JAN. h:m:s	FEB. h:m:s	MAR. h:m:s	APR. h:m:s	MAY h:m:s	JUN. h:m:s	JUL. h:m:s	AUG. h:m:s	SEP. h:m:s	OCT. h:m:s	NOV. h:m:s	DEC. h:m:s
1	12:03:25	12:13:30	12:12:09	12:03:38	11:57:00	11:57:57	12:04:02	12:06:18	11:59:46	11:49:25	11:43:33	11:49:16
2	12:03:53	12:13:38	12:11:57	12:03:21	11:56:54	11:58:07	12:04:13	12:06:14	11:59:27	11:49:06	11:43:33	11:49:40
3	12:04:21	12:13:45	12:11:44	12:03:03	11:56:48	11:58:17	12:04:24	12:06:09	11:59:07	11:48:48	11:43:33	11:50:03
4	12:04:48	12:13:51	12:11:31	12:02:46	11:56:43	11:58:28	12:04:34	12:06:03	11:58:48	11:48:29	11:43:34	11:50:28
5	12:05:15	12:13:56	12:11:18	12:02:29	11:56:38	11:58:38	12:04:45	12:05:57	11:58:27	11:48:12	11:43:36	11:50:53
6	12:05:42	12:14:01	12:11:04	12:02:12	11:56:34	11:58:50	12:04:55	12:05:50	11:58:07	11:47:54	11:43:39	11:51:19
7	12:06:08	12:14:05	12:10:49	12:01:55	11:56:30	11:59:01	12:05:04	12:05:42	11:57:47	11:47:37	11:43:43	11:51:45
8	12:06:34	12:14:08	12:10:34	12:01:39	11:56:27	11:59:13	12:05:14	12:05:34	11:57:26	11:47:20	11:43:47	11:52:11
9	12:06:59	12:14:10	12:10:19	12:01:23	11:56:25	11:59:25	12:05:22	12:05:26	11:57:05	11:47:04	11:43:52	11:52:38
10	12:07:24	12:14:11	12:10:04	12:01:07	11:56:23	11:59:37	12:05:31	12:05:16	11:56:44	11:46:48	11:43:59	11:53:05
11	12:07:48	12:14:12	12:09:48	12:00:51	11:56:22	11:59:49	12:05:39	12:05:07	11:56:23	11:46:33	11:44:06	11:53:33
12	12:08:11	12:14:12	12:09:32	12:00:36	11:56:21	12:00:02	12:05:46	12:04:56	11:56:01	11:46:18	11:44:13	11:54:01
13	12:08:34	12:14:11	12:09:16	12:00:21	11:56:21	12:00:15	12:05:53	12:04:45	11:55:40	11:46:04	11:44:22	11:54:29
14	12:08:57	12:14:09	12:08:59	12:00:06	11:56:21	12:00:27	12:05:59	12:04:34	11:55:19	11:45:50	11:44:31	11:54:58
15	12:09:18	12:14:06	12:08:42	11:59:52	11:56:22	12:00:40	12:06:05	12:04:22	11:54:57	11:45:37	11:44:42	11:55:27
16	12:09:39	12:14:03	12:08:25	11:59:38	11:56:24	12:00:53	12:06:10	12:04:09	11:54:36	11:45:24	11:44:53	11:55:56
17	12:09:59	12:13:59	12:08:08	11:59:24	11:56:26	12:01:06	12:06:15	12:03:56	11:54:14	11:45:12	11:45:05	11:56:25
18	12:10:19	12:13:55	12:07:50	11:59:11	11:56:28	12:01:19	12:06:19	12:03:42	11:53:52	11:45:00	11:45:18	11:56:55
19	12:10:38	12:13:49	12:07:33	11:58:58	11:56:31	12:01:32	12:06:23	12:03:28	11:53:31	11:44:49	11:45:31	11:57:24
20	12:10:56	12:13:43	12:07:15	11:58:46	11:56:35	12:01:45	12:06:26	12:03:13	11:53:10	11:44:39	11:45:46	11:57:54
21	12:11:13	12:13:37	12:06:57	11:58:34	11:56:39	12:01:58	12:06:29	12:02:58	11:52:48	11:44:30	11:46:01	11:58:24
22	12:11:29	12:13:29	12:06:39	11:58:22	11:56:44	12:02:11	12:06:31	12:02:43	11:52:27	11:44:21	11:46:17	11:58:53
23	12:11:45	12:13:21	12:06:21	11:58:11	11:56:49	12:02:24	12:06:32	12:02:27	11:52:06	11:44:13	11:46:34	11:59:23
24	12:12:00	12:13:13	12:06:03	11:58:00	11:56:55	12:02:37	12:06:33	12:02:10	11:51:45	11:44:05	11:46:52	11:59:53
25	12:12:14	12:13:04	12:05:44	11:57:50	11:57:01	12:02:49	12:06:33	12:01:54	11:51:24	11:43:59	11:47:10	12:00:23
26	12:12:27	12:12:54	12:05:26	11:57:41	11:57:07	12:03:02	12:06:33	12:01:36	11:51:04	11:43:53	11:47:29	12:00:53
27	12:12:40	12:12:44	12:05:08	11:57:31	11:57:15	12:03:14	12:06:32	12:01:19	11:50:44	11:43:47	11:47:49	12:01:22
28	12:12:51	12:12:33	12:04:50	11:57:23	11:57:22	12:03:26	12:06:30	12:01:01	11:50:24	11:43:43	11:48:10	12:01:52
29	12:13:02	12:12:21	12:04:32	11:57:15	11:57:30	12:03:38	12:06:28	12:00:43	11:50:04	11:43:39	11:48:31	12:02:21
30	12:13:12		12:04:14	11:57:07	11:57:39	12:03:50	12:06:25	12:00:24	11:49:44	11:43:36	11:48:53	12:02:50
31	12:13:22		12:03:56		11:57:48		12:06:22	12:00:06		11:43:34		12:03:18

Explanatory Notes: The noon sight and the Sun's Declination (p. 235) result in the vessel's parallel of latitude. It is taken at the time of the sun's meridian passage, when the sun is at maximum altitude.

The moment of meridian passage is called Local Apparent Noon (L.A.N.), and only rarely is it the same time as noon Standard Time or Local Mean Time. Instead, as this Table shows, the sun is either ahead of or behind its theoretical schedule.

Two corrections are involved. 1) To correct for your difference in longitude from the central meridian of your time zone (i.e. 75° for U.S. Atlantic Coast), either a) subtract 4 minutes of time for each degree West of b) add 4 minutes of time for each degree East. 2) If necessary, convert from Daylight Savings Time to Standard Time by subtracting 1 hour from your watch.

Thus for Boston, at 71° West longitude (or 4° East of 75°), L.A.N. occurs 16 minutes before the times listed in the Table.

For New York, at 74° West (1° East of 75°), L.A.N. occurs 4 minutes earlier than times shown.

Converting arc to time:

360°	=	24	hours
15°	=	1	hour
1°	=	4	minutes
15'	=	1	minute
1'	=	4	seconds

Sun's True Bearing at Rising and Setting

To find compass deviation using the Sun.

Figures are correct for all Longitudes.

Sun's decl.	38°N Rise	38°N Set	40°N Rise	40°N Set	42°N Rise	42°N Set	44°N Rise	44°N Set	Sun's decl.
N 23°	60.3	299.7	59.3	300.7	58.3	301.7	57.1	302.9	N 23°
22	61.6	298.4	60.7	299.3	59.7	300.3	58.6	301.4	22
21	63.0	297.0	62.1	297.9	61.2	298.8	60.1	299.9	21
20	64.3	295.7	63.5	296.5	62.6	297.4	61.6	298.4	20
19	65.6	294.4	64.9	295.1	64.0	296.0	63.1	296.9	19
18	66.9	293.1	66.2	293.8	65.4	294.6	64.6	295.4	18
17	68.2	291.8	67.6	292.4	66.8	293.2	66.0	294.0	17
16	69.5	290.5	68.9	291.1	68.2	291.8	67.5	292.5	16
15	70.8	289.2	70.3	289.7	69.6	290.4	68.9	291.1	15
14	72.1	287.9	71.6	288.4	71.0	289.0	70.4	289.6	14
13	73.4	286.6	72.9	287.1	72.4	287.6	71.8	288.2	13
12	74.7	285.3	74.3	285.7	73.8	286.2	73.2	286.8	12
11	76.0	284.0	75.6	284.4	75.1	284.9	74.6	285.4	11
10	77.3	282.7	76.9	283.1	76.5	283.5	76.0	284.0	10
9	78.6	281.4	78.2	281.8	77.9	282.1	77.4	282.6	9
8	79.8	280.2	79.5	280.5	79.2	280.8	78.9	281.1	8
7	81.1	278.9	80.9	279.1	80.6	279.4	80.3	279.7	7
6	82.4	277.6	82.2	277.7	81.9	278.1	81.7	278.3	6
5	83.7	276.3	83.5	276.5	83.3	276.7	83.0	277.0	5
4	84.9	275.1	84.8	275.2	84.6	275.4	84.4	275.6	4
3	86.2	273.8	86.1	273.9	86.0	274.0	85.8	274.2	3
2	87.5	272.5	87.4	272.6	87.3	272.7	87.2	272.8	2
N 1°	88.7	271.3	88.7	271.3	88.7	271.3	88.6	271.4	N 1°
0	90.0	270.0	90.0	270.0	90.0	270.0	90.0	270.0	0
S 1°	91.3	268.7	91.3	268.7	91.3	268.7	91.4	268.6	S 1°
2	92.5	267.5	92.6	267.4	92.7	267.3	92.8	267.2	2
3	93.8	266.2	93.9	266.1	94.0	266.0	94.2	265.8	3
4	95.1	264.9	95.2	264.8	95.4	264.6	95.6	264.4	4
5	96.3	263.7	96.5	263.5	96.7	263.3	97.0	263.0	5
6	97.6	262.4	97.8	262.2	98.1	261.9	98.3	261.7	6
7	98.9	261.1	99.1	260.9	99.4	260.6	99.7	260.3	7
8	100.2	259.8	100.5	259.5	100.8	259.2	101.1	258.9	8
9	101.4	258.6	101.8	258.2	102.1	257.9	102.6	257.4	9
10	102.7	257.3	103.1	256.9	103.5	256.5	104.0	256.0	10
11	104.0	256.0	104.4	255.6	104.9	255.1	105.4	254.6	11
12	105.3	254.7	105.7	254.3	106.2	253.8	106.8	253.2	12
13	106.6	253.4	107.1	252.9	107.6	252.4	108.2	251.8	13
14	107.9	252.1	108.4	251.6	109.0	251.0	109.6	250.4	14
15	109.2	250.8	109.7	250.3	110.4	249.6	111.1	248.9	15
16	110.5	249.5	111.1	248.9	111.8	248.2	112.5	247.5	16
17	111.8	248.2	112.4	247.6	113.2	246.8	114.0	246.0	17
18	113.1	246.9	113.8	246.2	114.6	245.4	115.4	244.6	18
19	114.4	245.6	115.1	244.9	116.0	244.0	116.9	243.1	19
20	115.7	244.3	116.5	243.5	117.4	242.6	118.4	241.6	20
21	117.0	243.0	117.9	242.1	118.8	241.2	119.9	240.1	21
22	118.4	241.6	119.3	240.7	120.3	239.7	121.4	238.6	22
S 23°	119.7	240.3	120.7	239.3	121.7	238.3	122.9	237.1	S 23°

Instructions: (1) Knowing the date, find the Sun's Declination from the facing page. Find that Declination down the left column on this page. (2) Find the column with your Latitude, and choose either Rise or Set to determine the True Bearing. (3) Add the local Westerly Variation to the figure. (4) If you are a couple of minutes after sunrise or before sunset, the Sun's bearing changes about 1° each 6 minutes during the first hour after sunrise and before sunset. (5) The deviation found will be correct only for the heading you are on at that time.

The Sun's Declination 2024

For celestial navigators, the "noon sight" reading of the Sun's height above the horizon, together with the Sun's Declination from this table, determines latitude.

MEAN NOON – 75° MERIDIAN (1700 G.M.T.)

The Sun's Declination 2024

	JAN. South	FEB. South	MAR. South	APR. North	MAY North	JUN. North	JUL. North	AUG. North	SEP. North	OCT. South	NOV. South	DEC. South	
1	-23 00	-17 06	-7 13	+4 55	+15 22	+22 11	+23 02	+17 46	+7 55	-3 34	-14 44	-21 57	1
2	-22 55	-16 49	-6 50	+5 18	+15 40	+22 19	+22 58	+17 30	+7 33	-3 57	-15 03	-22 06	2
3	-22 49	-16 32	-6 27	+5 41	+15 58	+22 26	+22 52	+17 14	+7 11	-4 21	-15 22	-22 14	3
4	-22 43	-16 14	-6 04	+6 04	+16 15	+22 33	+22 47	+16 58	+6 49	-4 44	-15 40	-22 22	4
5	-22 37	-15 56	-5 40	+6 27	+16 32	+22 39	+22 41	+16 42	+6 26	-5 07	-15 58	-22 29	5
6	-22 30	-15 37	-5 17	+6 49	+16 49	+22 45	+22 35	+16 25	+6 04	-5 30	-16 16	-22 36	6
7	-22 22	-15 19	-4 54	+7 12	+17 05	+22 51	+22 28	+16 08	+5 42	-5 53	-16 34	-22 43	7
8	-22 15	-14 60	-4 30	+7 34	+17 21	+22 56	+22 21	+15 51	+5 19	-6 15	-16 51	-22 49	8
9	-22 06	-14 41	-4 07	+7 57	+17 37	+23 01	+22 14	+15 34	+4 56	-6 38	-17 08	-22 54	9
10	-21 57	-14 21	-3 43	+8 19	+17 53	+23 05	+22 06	+15 16	+4 34	-7 01	-17 25	-22 60	10
11	-21 48	-14 02	-3 20	+8 41	+18 08	+23 09	+21 58	+14 58	+4 11	-7 24	-17 41	-23 04	11
12	-21 39	-13 42	-2 56	+9 03	+18 23	+23 13	+21 49	+14 40	+3 48	-7 46	-17 57	-23 09	12
13	-21 29	-13 22	-2 32	+9 24	+18 38	+23 16	+21 41	+14 22	+3 25	-8 08	-18 13	-23 12	13
14	-21 18	-13 01	-2 09	+9 46	+18 52	+23 18	+21 31	+14 03	+3 02	-8 31	-18 29	-23 16	14
15	-21 08	-12 41	-1 45	+10 07	+19 06	+23 21	+21 22	+13 44	+2 39	-8 53	-18 44	-23 19	15
16	-20 56	-12 20	-1 21	+10 28	+19 20	+23 23	+21 12	+13 25	+2 15	-9 15	-18 59	-23 21	16
17	-20 45	-11 59	-0 57	+10 49	+19 33	+23 24	+21 01	+13 06	+1 52	-9 37	-19 13	-23 23	17
18	-20 33	-11 38	-0 34	+11 10	+19 46	+23 25	+20 51	+12 46	+1 29	-9 58	-19 27	-23 25	18
19	-20 20	-11 17	-0 10	+11 31	+19 59	+23 26	+20 40	+12 27	+1 06	-10 20	-19 41	-23 26	19
20	-20 07	-10 55	+0 14	+11 51	+20 11	+23 26	+20 28	+12 07	+0 43	-10 41	-19 54	-23 26	20
21	-19 54	-10 34	+0 37	+12 12	+20 23	+23 26	+20 16	+11 47	+0 19	-11 03	-20 07	-23 26	21
22	-19 41	-10 12	+1 01	+12 32	+20 35	+23 26	+20 04	+11 27	-0 04	-11 24	-20 20	-23 26	22
23	-19 27	-9 50	+1 25	+12 52	+20 46	+23 25	+19 52	+11 06	-0 28	-11 45	-20 32	-23 25	23
24	-19 13	-9 28	+1 48	+13 11	+20 57	+23 23	+19 39	+10 46	-0 51	-12 05	-20 44	-23 24	24
25	-18 58	-9 06	+2 12	+13 31	+21 07	+23 21	+19 26	+10 25	-1 14	-12 26	-20 56	-23 22	25
26	-18 43	-8 43	+2 35	+13 50	+21 18	+23 19	+19 13	+10 04	-1 38	-12 46	-21 07	-23 20	26
27	-18 28	-8 21	+2 59	+14 09	+21 28	+23 17	+18 59	+9 43	-2 01	-13 07	-21 18	-23 17	27
28	-18 12	-7 58	+3 22	+14 28	+21 37	+23 14	+18 45	+9 21	-2 24	-13 27	-21 28	-23 14	28
29	-17 56	-7 36	+3 46	+14 46	+21 46	+23 10	+18 30	+9 00	-2 48	-13 46	-21 38	-23 10	29
30	-17 40		+4 09	+15 04	+21 55	+23 06	+18 16	+8 39	-3 11	-14 06	-21 48	-23 06	30
31	-17 23		+4 32		+22 03		+18 01	+8 17		-14 25		-23 01	31

Vernal Equinox: March 19th, 10:06 p.m. E.S.T.
Summer Solstice: June 20th, 3:50 p.m. E.S.T.

Autumnal Equinox: September 22nd, 7:43 a.m. E.S.T.
Winter Solstice: December 21st, 4:20 a.m. E.S.T.

To find Sun's Declination in the Atlantic Time Zone (1 hour earlier than E.S.T.), take 1/24 of the difference between Day 1 and Day 2. Add or subtract this figure from Day 2 to find the Declination for Day 2.

If Declination is increasing (N. or S.), *subtract*.   If Declination is decreasing (N. or S.), *add*.

2024 MOON'S RISING AND SETTING AT BOSTON – 42° 20'N 71°W
Daylight Saving Time is March 10 – November 3, transitions are noted with an *

	JAN. Rise	Set	FEB. Rise	Set	MAR. Rise	Set	APR. Rise	Set	MAY Rise	Set	JUN. Rise	Set	
Day	h m	h m	h m	h m	h m	h m	h m	h m	h m	h m	h m	h m	Day
01	22:00	10:39	23:56	9:56	23:59	8:45	2:08	10:29	2:26	11:53	2:13	14:46	01
02	23:01	10:57	...	10:18	...	9:14	3:03	11:35	2:57	13:11	2:35	16:02	02
03	...	11:15	1:03	10:44	1:08	9:51	3:49	12:50	3:23	14:28	2:59	17:19	03
04	0:02	11:33	2:13	11:16	2:15	10:40	4:26	14:09	3:47	15:45	3:27	18:38	04
05	1:05	11:54	3:23	11:59	3:17	11:41	4:56	15:30	4:09	17:02	4:00	19:55	05
06	2:11	12:17	4:31	12:55	4:10	12:54	5:22	16:50	4:33	18:21	4:42	21:06	06
07	3:21	12:47	5:32	14:04	4:54	14:14	5:46	18:09	4:59	19:42	5:34	22:06	07
08	4:33	13:25	6:22	15:24	5:29	15:37	6:09	19:30	5:29	21:01	6:35	22:55	08
09	5:45	14:15	7:01	16:47	5:58	17:00	6:34	20:50	6:07	22:17	7:42	23:33	09
10	6:51	15:19	7:33	18:11	*7:23	19:21	7:02	22:11	6:53	23:24	8:51	...	10
11	7:47	16:34	8:00	19:32	7:46	20:41	7:35	23:29	7:49	...	9:58	0:03	11
12	8:32	17:56	8:24	21:00	8:10	22:00	8:16	...	8:53	0:19	11:02	0:27	12
13	9:07	19:18	8:47	22:07	8:36	23:19	9:06	0:39	10:00	1:02	12:05	0:47	13
14	9:35	20:37	9:11	23:24	9:06	...	10:05	1:40	11:07	1:36	13:06	1:06	14
15	10:00	21:54	9:37	...	9:41	0:37	11:08	2:28	12:12	2:02	14:07	1:23	15
16	10:22	23:09	10:08	0:39	10:25	1:49	12:14	3:06	13:15	2:24	15:09	1:41	16
17	10:45	...	10:45	1:52	11:17	2:53	13:20	3:36	14:17	2:44	16:13	2:00	17
18	11:08	0:22	11:30	2:59	12:16	3:47	14:24	4:00	15:17	3:01	17:21	2:23	18
19	11:35	1:36	12:24	3:59	13:20	4:30	15:26	4:20	16:19	3:19	18:30	2:50	19
20	12:07	2:49	13:24	4:49	14:25	5:05	16:27	4:39	17:22	3:37	19:39	3:25	20
21	12:46	3:59	14:28	5:29	15:30	5:32	17:28	4:56	18:28	3:58	20:44	4:10	21
22	13:34	5:05	15:34	6:01	16:33	5:55	18:30	5:14	19:37	4:22	21:40	5:07	22
23	14:30	6:02	16:38	6:27	17:35	6:14	19:34	5:32	20:46	4:52	22:25	6:15	23
24	15:33	6:49	17:41	6:49	18:36	6:32	20:41	5:54	21:54	5:30	23:01	7:31	24
25	16:38	7:27	18:42	7:08	19:37	6:49	21:49	6:19	22:54	6:18	23:31	8:49	25
26	17:43	7:58	19:43	7:25	20:39	7:07	22:58	6:51	23:46	7:19	23:56	10:06	26
27	18:47	8:22	20:44	7:43	21:44	7:27	...	7:32	...	8:28	...	11:22	27
28	19:49	8:43	21:47	8:01	22:50	7:49	0:02	8:23	0:27	9:43	0:18	12:36	28
29	20:50	9:02	22:52	8:21	23:58	8:16	1:00	9:26	1:00	11:00	0:40	13:51	29
30	21:51	9:19			1:00	8:50	1:47	10:37	1:27	12:16	1:03	15:06	30
31	22:53	9:37			1:06	9:34			1:51	13:31			31

	JUL. Rise	Set	AUG. Rise	Set	SEP. Rise	Set	OCT. Rise	Set	NOV. Rise	Set	DEC. Rise	Set	
Day	h m	h m	h m	h m	h m	h m	h m	h m	h m	h m	h m	h m	Day
01	1:28	16:22	2:12	18:43	4:26	18:59	5:28	18:02	7:27	17:25	7:35	16:07	01
02	1:59	17:38	3:14	19:28	5:31	19:19	6:28	18:19	8:33	17:53	8:37	16:58	02
03	2:37	18:51	4:21	20:03	6:34	19:38	7:29	18:37	8:39	17:27	9:32	17:59	03
04	3:24	19:55	5:29	20:31	7:35	19:55	8:32	18:57	*9:44	18:09	10:18	19:08	04
05	4:21	20:48	6:36	20:54	8:36	20:12	9:36	19:21	10:43	19:03	10:55	20:21	05
06	5:26	21:30	7:41	21:14	9:37	20:31	10:41	19:49	11:35	20:06	11:25	21:35	06
07	6:34	22:02	8:43	21:32	10:40	20:52	11:47	20:26	12:18	21:16	11:50	22:49	07
08	7:42	22:29	9:44	21:49	11:44	21:17	12:51	21:12	12:53	22:30	12:13	...	08
09	8:49	22:50	10:45	22:07	12:51	21:48	13:49	22:08	13:22	23:45	12:35	0:02	09
10	9:52	23:09	11:47	22:26	13:57	22:28	14:38	23:15	13:47	...	12:57	1:17	10
11	10:54	23:27	12:50	22:49	15:00	23:19	15:19	...	14:10	1:01	13:22	2:33	11
12	11:55	23:44	13:56	23:16	15:57	...	15:53	0:29	14:32	2:17	13:51	3:52	12
13	12:56	...	15:04	23:51	16:44	0:21	16:21	1:46	14:56	3:35	14:27	5:13	13
14	13:59	0:03	16:11	...	17:23	1:34	16:46	3:05	15:23	4:56	15:14	6:32	14
15	15:04	0:24	17:13	0:37	17:55	2:53	17:09	4:24	15:56	6:19	16:12	7:44	15
16	16:12	0:49	18:08	1:34	18:22	4:14	17:33	5:44	16:38	7:42	17:19	8:44	16
17	17:21	1:20	18:53	2:44	18:47	5:35	17:58	7:06	17:30	8:59	18:31	9:31	17
18	18:28	2:00	19:29	4:02	19:10	6:56	18:28	8:29	18:32	10:06	19:43	10:07	18
19	19:28	2:51	19:58	5:23	19:34	8:16	19:05	9:52	19:42	10:59	20:52	10:35	19
20	20:19	3:56	20:23	6:45	20:01	9:38	19:51	11:12	20:52	11:39	21:57	10:58	20
21	20:59	5:10	20:47	8:05	20:33	10:59	20:47	12:23	22:01	12:10	23:00	11:17	21
22	21:32	6:30	21:10	9:24	21:13	12:19	21:51	13:21	23:07	12:35	...	11:35	22
23	21:58	7:50	21:34	10:42	22:01	13:32	22:59	14:07	...	12:56	0:01	11:53	23
24	22:22	9:08	22:02	12:00	22:59	14:36	...	14:42	0:10	13:14	1:02	12:11	24
25	22:44	10:25	22:35	13:18	...	15:28	0:08	15:09	1:12	13:31	2:04	12:31	25
26	23:07	11:41	23:17	14:33	0:03	16:08	1:14	15:32	2:12	13:49	3:08	12:55	26
27	23:32	12:57	...	15:42	1:10	16:39	2:18	15:51	3:14	14:08	4:14	13:24	27
28	...	14:13	0:07	16:41	2:17	17:05	3:20	16:09	4:17	14:29	5:21	14:02	28
29	0:00	15:29	1:06	17:28	3:23	17:26	4:21	16:26	5:22	14:55	6:25	14:49	29
30	0:36	16:41	2:11	18:06	4:26	17:44	5:22	16:43	6:28	15:27	7:24	15:48	30
31	1:19	17:47	3:19	18:35			6:23	17:03			8:14	16:56	31

2024 MOON'S RISING AND SETTING AT NEW YORK – 40° 42'N 74°W

Daylight Saving Time is March 10 – November 3, transitions are noted with an *

	JAN. Rise	Set	FEB. Rise	Set	MAR. Rise	Set	APR. Rise	Set	MAY Rise	Set	JUN. Rise	Set	
Day	h m	h m	h m	h m	h m	h m	h m	h m	h m	h m	h m	h m	Day
01	22:12	10:52	...	10:08	...	8:56	2:23	10:39	2:39	12:05	2:25	14:59	01
02	23:13	11:10	0:10	10:29	0:13	9:25	3:18	11:46	3:10	13:23	2:47	16:15	02
03	...	11:27	1:17	10:55	1:22	10:02	4:03	13:01	3:36	14:40	3:11	17:33	03
04	0:15	11:45	2:26	11:27	2:30	10:50	4:39	14:21	3:59	15:58	3:38	18:51	04
05	1:18	12:05	3:37	12:10	3:32	11:52	5:09	15:42	4:22	17:15	4:11	20:09	05
06	2:25	12:29	4:45	13:06	4:24	13:05	5:34	17:02	4:45	18:35	4:53	21:20	06
07	3:35	12:58	5:46	14:15	5:07	14:25	5:58	18:22	5:10	19:55	5:45	22:21	07
08	4:48	13:36	6:35	15:35	5:42	15:49	6:21	19:43	5:40	21:16	6:46	23:09	08
09	6:00	14:26	7:15	16:59	6:10	17:12	6:45	21:04	6:18	22:32	7:53	23:47	09
10	7:06	15:30	7:46	18:23	7:35	19:33	7:13	22:25	7:04	23:39	9:02	...	10
11	8:01	16:45	8:13	19:44	7:58	20:54	7:46	23:43	8:00	...	10:09	0:16	11
12	8:46	18:07	8:36	21:03	8:22	22:14	8:27	...	9:04	0:33	11:14	0:40	12
13	9:20	19:29	8:59	22:21	8:47	23:33	9:17	0:54	10:11	1:16	12:17	1:00	13
14	9:48	20:49	9:22	23:37	9:17	...	10:15	1:54	11:18	1:49	13:18	1:18	14
15	10:12	22:06	9:48	...	9:52	0:51	11:19	2:42	12:24	2:16	14:19	1:35	15
16	10:34	23:21	10:19	0:53	10:36	2:03	12:26	3:19	13:27	2:37	15:22	1:53	16
17	10:56	...	10:56	2:06	11:27	3:08	13:31	3:49	14:29	2:56	16:27	2:12	17
18	11:20	0:35	11:41	3:14	12:27	4:01	14:36	4:13	15:30	3:14	17:34	2:34	18
19	11:46	1:49	12:34	4:13	13:31	4:44	15:38	4:33	16:32	3:31	18:44	3:01	19
20	12:18	3:03	13:35	5:03	14:36	5:18	16:39	4:51	17:36	3:49	19:54	3:36	20
21	12:57	4:14	14:40	5:43	15:41	5:45	17:41	5:08	18:42	4:09	20:58	4:21	21
22	13:45	5:19	15:45	6:14	16:45	6:07	18:43	5:25	19:51	4:33	21:54	5:18	22
23	14:41	6:16	16:50	6:40	17:47	6:27	19:48	5:44	21:01	5:03	22:39	6:26	23
24	15:44	7:03	17:53	7:01	18:48	6:44	20:55	6:05	22:08	5:41	23:15	7:42	24
25	16:49	7:41	18:55	7:20	19:50	7:01	22:03	6:31	23:09	6:29	23:44	9:00	25
26	17:55	8:11	19:56	7:38	20:52	7:19	23:12	7:02	...	7:29	...	10:18	26
27	18:59	8:35	20:57	7:55	21:57	7:38	...	7:43	0:00	8:39	0:08	11:34	27
28	20:02	8:56	22:00	8:13	23:04	8:00	0:17	8:34	0:41	9:55	0:30	12:49	28
29	21:03	9:14	23:05	8:33	...	8:27	1:14	9:37	1:13	11:12	0:52	14:04	29
30	22:04	9:32			0:12	9:01	2:01	10:48	1:40	12:28	1:14	15:19	30
31	23:06	9:49			1:20	9:44			2:03	13:44			31

	JUL. Rise	Set	AUG. Rise	Set	SEP. Rise	Set	OCT. Rise	Set	NOV. Rise	Set	DEC. Rise	Set	
Day	h m	h m	h m	h m	h m	h m	h m	h m	h m	h m	h m	h m	Day
01	1:40	16:36	2:23	18:57	4:37	19:12	5:40	18:14	7:41	17:37	7:49	16:18	01
02	2:10	17:52	3:25	19:42	5:43	19:32	6:41	18:31	8:46	18:04	8:51	17:09	02
03	2:48	19:05	4:32	20:17	6:46	19:50	7:42	18:49	8:53	17:37	9:46	18:10	03
04	3:35	20:09	5:40	20:44	7:48	20:07	8:45	19:08	9:58	18:20	10:32	19:19	04
05	4:32	21:02	6:48	21:07	8:49	20:24	9:49	19:32	10:58	19:13	11:08	20:32	05
06	5:37	21:43	7:52	21:26	9:50	20:42	10:55	20:00	11:49	20:17	11:38	21:47	06
07	6:45	22:16	8:55	21:44	10:53	21:03	12:01	20:36	12:32	21:27	12:03	23:01	07
08	7:54	22:42	9:57	22:01	11:58	21:28	13:05	21:22	13:06	22:41	12:26	...	08
09	9:00	23:03	10:58	22:18	13:04	21:59	14:03	22:19	13:35	23:57	12:47	0:15	09
10	10:04	23:22	12:00	22:38	14:11	22:39	14:52	23:26	14:00	...	13:09	1:30	10
11	11:06	23:39	13:04	23:00	15:14	23:29	15:33	...	14:22	1:13	13:33	2:46	11
12	12:07	23:56	14:10	23:27	16:11	...	16:06	0:40	14:44	2:30	14:02	4:06	12
13	13:09	...	15:18	...	16:58	0:32	16:34	1:58	15:08	3:48	14:38	5:27	13
14	14:12	0:15	16:25	0:02	17:37	1:45	16:58	3:17	15:35	5:09	15:25	6:47	14
15	15:18	0:35	17:28	0:47	18:08	3:04	17:21	4:37	16:07	6:33	16:22	7:59	15
16	16:26	1:00	18:22	1:45	18:35	4:26	17:44	5:57	16:49	7:56	17:30	8:59	16
17	17:35	1:30	19:06	2:55	18:59	5:47	18:10	7:19	17:41	9:13	18:42	9:45	17
18	18:42	2:10	19:42	4:13	19:22	7:08	18:40	8:42	18:43	10:20	19:54	10:21	18
19	19:42	3:02	20:11	5:35	19:46	8:29	19:16	10:06	19:53	11:13	21:03	10:48	19
20	20:33	4:06	20:36	6:57	20:13	9:51	20:02	11:26	21:04	11:53	22:09	11:11	20
21	21:13	5:21	20:59	8:17	20:44	11:13	20:57	12:37	22:13	12:23	23:12	11:30	21
22	21:45	6:41	21:22	9:36	21:23	12:33	22:02	13:35	23:19	12:48	...	11:47	22
23	22:11	8:02	21:46	10:55	22:12	13:47	23:10	14:21	...	13:08	0:14	12:05	23
24	22:34	9:21	22:13	12:14	23:09	14:50	...	14:55	0:23	13:26	1:15	12:23	24
25	22:56	10:38	22:46	13:32	...	15:42	0:19	15:22	1:24	13:43	2:17	12:43	25
26	23:19	11:54	23:27	14:48	0:14	16:22	1:26	15:44	2:25	14:01	3:22	13:06	26
27	23:43	13:10	...	15:56	1:21	16:53	2:30	16:03	3:27	14:19	4:28	13:35	27
28	...	14:26	0:18	16:55	2:29	17:18	3:32	16:21	4:30	14:40	5:35	14:12	28
29	0:12	15:43	1:17	17:42	3:35	17:39	4:33	16:38	5:35	15:06	6:40	15:00	29
30	0:46	16:56	2:22	18:19	4:38	17:57	5:34	16:55	6:42	15:37	7:38	15:58	30
31	1:30	18:02	3:30	18:48			6:37	17:14			8:28	17:07	31

Phases of the Moon 2024 E.T.

Daylight Saving Time is March 10 – November 3

● New Moon, ◐ 1st Quarter, ○ Full Moon, ◑ Last Quarter, A in Apogee,
P in Perigee, N, S Moon farthest North or South of Equator, E on Equator

January			February			March			April			May			June		
A	1	10AM	◐	2	6PM	◐	3	10AM	S	1	5AM	◐	1	7AM	E	1	4AM
E	3	4AM	S	6	1PM	S	4	9PM	◐	1	11PM	E	4	10PM	P	2	3AM
◐	3	10PM	●	9	6PM	P	10	3AM	E	7	12PM	P	5	6PM	●	6	9AM
S	10	3AM	P	10	2PM	●	10	5AM	P	7	2PM	●	7	11PM	N	7	1PM
●	11	7AM	E	12	2PM	E	11	1AM	●	8	2PM	N	11	4AM	◐	14	1AM
P	13	6AM	◑	16	10AM	◐	17	12AM	N	13	7PM	◐	15	8AM	A	14	10AM
E	16	6AM	N	19	4AM	N	17	11AM	◐	15	3PM	A	17	3PM	E	14	7PM
◐	17	11PM	○	24	7AM	A	23	12PM	A	19	10PM	E	18	12PM	○	21	9PM
N	22	11PM	A	25	10AM	E	24	11PM	E	21	5AM	○	23	10AM	S	21	11PM
○	25	1PM	E	26	4PM	○	25	3AM	○	23	8PM	S	25	4PM	P	27	7AM
A	29	3AM							S	28	11AM	◑	30	1PM	E	28	9AM
E	30	10AM													◑	28	6PM

July			August			September			October			November			December		
N	4	9PM	N	1	2AM	●	2	10PM	E	1	9PM	●	1	9AM	●	1	1AM
●	5	7PM	●	4	7AM	E	4	3PM	●	2	3PM	S	5	1PM	S	2	6PM
E	12	2AM	E	8	9AM	A	5	11AM	A	2	4PM	◐	9	1AM	◐	8	10AM
A	12	4AM	A	8	10PM	◐	11	2AM	S	9	8AM	E	12	4AM	E	9	10AM
◐	13	7PM	◐	12	11AM	S	12	1AM	◐	10	3PM	P	14	6AM	P	12	8AM
S	19	7AM	S	15	5PM	○	17	11PM	E	15	7PM	○	15	4PM	○	15	4AM
○	21	6AM	○	19	2PM	E	18	8AM	P	16	9PM	N	18	6AM	N	15	4PM
P	24	2AM	P	21	1AM	P	18	9AM	○	17	7AM	◑	22	8PM	E	22	4PM
E	25	2PM	E	21	10PM	N	24	1PM	N	21	9PM	E	25	9AM	◑	22	5PM
◑	27	11PM	◑	26	5AM	◑	24	3PM	◑	24	4AM	A	26	7AM	A	24	2AM
			N	28	7AM				E	29	3AM				S	30	1AM
									A	29	7PM				●	30	5PM

Midnight is the *beginning* of the day.

The Tides, The Moon and The Sun

Tides are created on the earth by the pull of gravity between the earth and moon, and to a lesser extent the sun. Since the moon's pull weakens with distance, its pull is stronger on water located on the near side of the earth than it is on the earth's center. This creates a bulge of water on the side facing the moon. Similarly, the moon's pull on the earth's center is stronger than it is on the water on the earth's far side. This tends to pull the earth away from the water, creating another bulge of water of equal size on the far side of the earth. High tides are where the bulges are. The two bulges can also be explained as the moon's gravity being dominant on the earth's near side, and centrifugal force being dominant on the earth's far side.

The earth rotates in the same direction as the moon orbits, but much more rapidly, with a period of 24 hours vs. 27.3 days. The earth thus spins rapidly under the slowly rotating bulges, which follow the moon. A given point on the earth thus takes 24 hours and 50 minutes to rotate from one tidal bulge around to the same bulge, so the tides occur 50 minutes later than the previous day. As there are usually two highs and two lows per day, highs and lows average about 6 hours 12 1/2 minutes apart. A handy fact for planners: in the course of 7 days, the tides are about the reverse of the previous week: if there is a low on Sunday at about noon, the following Sunday it will be about high at noon.

The time of high tide does not usually coincide exactly with the time the moon is overhead or underneath. The largest astronomical reason for this is the effect of the sun, which has its own tidal effect on the earth. Although the sun has a mass 27 million times that of the moon, it is the moon which dominates by being on average 390 times closer to earth. Since the sun's effect on the tides is about one-half that of the moon, the sun can shift tidal times by up to one hour or more, depending on its position. Tidal times are also greatly affected by land masses that impede the current flows necessary to create the tides, the speeds of traveling ocean waves, and underwater topography.

How much the ocean tides rise and fall depends basically on three conditions. (See Phases of the Moon, p. 238.) First, when the sun and moon are in a line with the earth, their gravitational forces work together to produce a greater range of tide than usual. This occurs both at full moon, when the moon is opposite the earth from the sun, and at new moon, when the moon is between the earth and sun. These higher tides are called "spring tides." But when the moon and sun are at right angles to the earth (first and last quarter, or half moon), their forces are working against each other, and the result is a lower range of tide than usual. These are called "neap tides." As each year has about 13 "lunar" months, we have 26 spring tides and 26 neap tides in the year.

Second, the moon's orbit around the earth is elliptical, ranging from 252,000 miles at apogee (A) down to 221,000 miles at perigee (P), so the moon's effect on the earth is greater at "P" than at "A." Note again in the High and Low Water Tables how much higher the tide is when the Full Moon is at "P" than when the Full Moon is at "A." The position of the moon along its elliptical path is very important to the height of the tides.

Third, the moon's orbit about the earth is inclined to the plane of the earth's equator, varying from 18° to 28°. The moon therefore travels above and below the earth's equator, and sits directly above the equator only twice a month When it is over the equator, the day's two high tides will be about the same height. The rest of the time the moon is either above the northern hemisphere or the southern hemisphere, and the two high water marks on the same day will differ in height. This is known as "semidiurnal inequality." When the moon has northern declination, the highest part of the nearside bulge is located under the moon in the north, and the highest part of the farside bulge is opposite the moon in the south. When the U.S. at northern latitudes is on the moon side, it therefore experiences a very high tide, but when it rotates around to be on the far side, it will find itself north of the maximum bulge and will experience a lower tide.

The height of tides is influenced most by the moon's phase, with the highest tides at Full and New Moon; second by the moon's distance from earth in its elliptical orbit, tides being highest when the moon is closest, at perigee; and last by the moon's declination, north or south, which creates tides of different heights on the same day.

The Publishers thank Nelson Caldwell, of the Smithsonian Astrophysical Observatory, Cambridge, MA, and Hale Bradt, Department of Physics, M.I.T., for their valuable contributions to this article.

Visibility of the Planets 2024

VENUS is a brilliant object in the morning sky from the beginning of the year until late April when it be-comes too close to the Sun for observation. In the second week of July, it reappears in the evening sky where it stays until the end of the year. Venus is in conjunction with Mars on February 22, with Saturn on March 22, and with Mercury on April 18 and August 6.

MARS can be seen in the second week in January in the morning sky in Sagittarius then it passes through Capricornus, Aquarius, Pisces, briefly into Cetus and back into Pisces, on to Aries, Taurus, and Gemini. It passes into Cancer in late October by which time it can be seen for more than half the night and where it remains for the rest of the year. Mars is in conjunction with Mercury on January 27, with Venus on February 22, with Saturn on April 11 and with Jupiter on August 14.

JUPITER is in Aries at the beginning of the year. From late January it can only be seen in the evening sky until early May when it becomes too close to the Sun for observation. It reappears in the morning sky in Taurus in early June remaining in this constellation for the rest of the year. Its westward elongation gradually increases until opposition on December 7 when it is visible throughout the night. Jupiter is in conjunction with Mercury on June 4 and with Mars on August 4.

SATURN can be seen in the evening sky in Aquarius until mid-February then it becomes too close to the Sun for observations. It reappears in the morning sky in mid-March still in Aquarius, in which constellation it remains throughout the year. Its westward elongation gradually increases until it is at opposition on September 8 when it is visible throughout the night. Its eastward elongation then gradually decreases until early December when it can only be seen in the evening sky. Saturn is in conjunction with Venus on March 22 and with Mars on April 11.

MERCURY can only be seen low in the east before sunrise, or low in the west after sunset. It is visible in the mornings from January 1 to February 16, April 20 to June 7, August 27 to September 20, and December 12 to December 31. It is brighter at the end of each period. It is visible in the evenings from March 9 to April 4, June 22 to August 12, and October 15 to November 30. It is brighter at the beginning of each period.

Conjunction occurs when a body has the same horizontal bearing from Earth as another. When Venus is in conjunction with Mercury on July 26, they appear one over the other, in the same sector of the sky.

Opposition occurs when a body, farther than Earth from the Sun, appears opposite the Sun. On a line drawn from the Sun through the Earth and beyond, the body lies on that extension. It is brightest at that time.

Elongation is apparent motion eastward (clockwise) or westward (counterclockwise) relative to the Sun across the sky. When a planet has 0° elongation, it lies on a line from Earth to the Sun, is in conjunction with the Sun and is not visible; when it has 90° elongation, it is in eastern quadrature; when it has 180° elongation, it is in opposition and has the best visibility; when it has 270° elongation, it is in western quadrature.

Where Have All The Bluefish Gone?
by Nick King

I think it was a mistake not to have a management plan for blues. Who knows when their bounteous stock may spontaneously and disastrously decline...
— *Blues* by John Hersey, 1987

Writer John Hersey, who fished the waters around Martha's Vineyard for decades, may well have been the one and only angler to posit the unthinkable nearly forty years ago: that the population of bluefish might someday decline as a result of anglers catching and keeping too many of them.

Really? Bluefish, so bounteous that you could legally keep 15 at a time? Blues, the fish that you sometimes couldn't avoid catching when you wanted stripers? Bluefish, the ones you would encounter in huge schools blitzing under screaming terns up and down the East Coast?

Sam O. White

Sadly, yes. Hersey was not only precise but prescient. In 2019 state and federal fisheries officials found that the once ubiquitous bluefish were "overfished," fisheries parlance signalling the sad news that the overall population of blues had fallen below the prescribed threshold of sustainability.

But the reason for the decline was surprising. It wasn't the net-wielding commercial guys who are usually the culprit, it was the hordes of meat-seeking recreational anglers taking advantage of the plentitude of blues and the lax 15-fish

241

bag limit on them. Indeed, rod and reel, not nets, were responsible for catching nearly eight of every ten bluefish harvested on the East Coast.

The ravaging of bluefish stocks peaked in the 1980s. That was when a staggering 150 million pounds of blues were taken annually by everyday anglers. Today the harvest has been regulated downwards with annual quotas of roughly 9.5 million pounds for recreational fishing and 2.8 million pounds for the commercial industry.

That's still a lot of bluefish, though, particularly for a species that lacks wide palette appeal. While blues are easy and fun to catch, and fight like hell on the hook, they lack commercial value because the oily meat doesn't freeze well and thus most commercial blue is either smoked or reduced to pate.

Assessing the strength and viability of any fish stock is both art and science, and fisheries officials cover the waterfront in their attempts to define the population. They conduct interviews of fishermen at boat ramps and shore sites, conduct mail surveys, anayze catch estimates from commercial boats, conduct trawl surveys and more.

But counting the population of any fish, much less blues, is easier said than done. Blues are migratory, fast-moving, elusive and visciously predatorial thanks to a scary set of needle-sharp teeth. Fishing pressure is considered the leading cause of the decline of blues but it's not happening in a vacuum. Many of the factors impacting fish stocks are difficult if not impossible to measure, notes Samuel Truesdell of the Massashuestts Division of Marine Fisheries. Disease, natural mortality , breeding cycles, pollution, and environmental conditions such as storms, declining ocean oxygen levels and warming water temperatures all take their toll.

All these issues aside, once the bluefish regulators—NOAA Fisheries, the Mid-Atlantic Fishery Management Council and the Atlantic States Marine Fisheries Commission—found that blues are "overfished," it triggered a seven-year management plan designed to rebuild the overfished stocks—exactly what John Hersey had called for way back when Ronald Reagan was president. The new plan put an end to the 15-fish limit that had been in effect since 2000 and instituted, effective in 2020, a three bluefish daily bag limit per fisherperson and a five blue limit for anglers in guide boats.

The new regs, which are reviewed annually, struck like a lightening bolt on the disbelieving angling community up and down the East Coast. It was as if saltwater fishing as we know it was coming to an end. Fishermen raised a stink, guides bellyached that their ability to make a living was in jeopardy, and various angling groups accused the regulators of mismanagement and bias against anglers.

None of which was all that surprising. Indeed, it mirrors the outoutcries over earlier fishing limits. But given the long and depressing history of how fishing depletes fish stocks, it raises the question of whether we've learned anything from those very public crises over the years, notably over cod and striped bass. The fishing threats to those species were, and still are, very real, and fisher folks

242

have slowly adapted to the severe restrictions in hopes of bringing them back to sustainability.

So why moan and groan over bag limits for the lowly bluefish? Why not support the measures to conserve and rebuild the bluefish stocks? Let's be honest. The old 15-fish "limit" for blues was madness. Who in the world needs to keep 15 fish of any kind? And what's wrong with a three-fish limit anyway? It doesn't mean you have to stop fishing or stop catching, it just means you have to stop keeping.

Anglers argue, not unreasonably, that catch-and-releasing a blue is no easy thing. But if you forego treble hooks, don't overplay the fish, and have an appropriate release tool at hand, it can be done successfully.

Granted, there are challenges to embracing a new fishing ethic for this day and age. Yes, it is hard to pass up that photograph showing the "success" of the hunt. Amd yes, it is counterintuitive not to gloat about how many you caught. But you can also brag about how many of those you put back. Enjoy the chase, relish the fight, maybe keep one fish for yourself, and feel good about returning the rest to live another day.

Author Hersey warned of this bluefish-in-decline scenario lo those many years ago, so let's let him have the last word on the uneasy relationship between bluefish and humankind:

> *The blue is a tough fish and so far its life-style has spared it hardships like those of the striper. But man is indeed careless... And the carelessness has a big reach, which the bluefish won't necessarily outdistance forever.*

Nick King, a retired reporter and editor from the Boston Globe, *is an avid angler in waters both fresh and salt. He is co-chair of the Board of Advisors of the Charles River Watershed Association.*

Hypothermia
and Cold Water Immersion

It is not uncommon for a boater to fall off a boat or dock. Most are rescued immediately. However, when rescue is delayed and conditions which threaten survival are present, all who go boating should know what to do.

Hypothermia is a state of low core body temperature—specifically below 95° F. This loss of body heat may be caused by exposure to cold air or cold water. Since water conducts heat away twenty-five times more quickly than air, time is critical for rescue. There are many variables beyond water temperature that combine to determine survival time: whether a life jacket is worn, body size and composition, type of clothing, movement in the water, etc. Unconsciousness in water temps of 50-60°F can occur in as little as one hour. Each 10°F drop cuts this time in half. Unconsciousness in water between 30-40°F occurs in as little as fifteen minutes.

Wearing a Personal Flotation Device (PFD) greatly extends survival time by keeping your head above water and allowing you to float without expending energy. A PFD will only work if you wear it. Consider carrying a personal locating device to aid rescuers in finding you.

Familiarize yourself with your survival gear. An emergency is not the time to learn.

What a person in the water should do:
- If at all possible, get out of the water, or at least grab hold of anything floating. If the boat is swamped, stay with it and crawl as far out of the water as possible.
- Do not try to swim unless a boat or floating object is very nearby and you are certain you can get to it.
- Control heat loss by keeping clothing on as partial insulation. In particular, keep your head out of water. To protect the groin, sides, and chest from heat loss, use the H.E.L.P. (Heat Escape Lessening Position), a fetal position with hands clasped around the legs, which extends survival time.
- Conserve energy by remaining as still as possible. Physical effort promotes heat loss. Swimming, or even treading water, reduces survival time.
- Pulling a large trash bag over your feet up to your shoulders will keep a warm layer of water around you and can extend survival time. Keep your life jacket on, remain in H.E.L.P. position. Do not try to swim or move.

What a rescuer should do:
- Stop heat loss, remove the victim from the cold environment, gently dry them off.
- Move the victim to a warm place, position on their back, and check breathing and signs of circulation.
- If victim is unconscious or minimally responsive, minimize sudden movements. Be gentle, as rough handling can induce cardiac arrest. If cardiac arrest occurs, start CPR (p. 247).
- Carefully remove wet clothing, cutting it away if necessary.
- Take steps to raise the body temperature gradually: cover the victim with blankets or a sleeping bag; apply warm moist towels to the neck, chest, and groin.
- Provide room temperature oral fluids when uncontrolled shivering stops, and the patient becomes more alert and is able to swallow.

Hypothermia
and Cold Water Immersion

What NOT to do:
- Do not attempt in-water rescue without proper equipment and training. **Avoid becoming an additional victim.**
- Do not give alcohol, coffee, tea, or nicotine. If the victim is not fully conscious, do not attempt to provide food or water.
- Do not massage arms or legs or handle the victim roughly, as this could cause cold blood from the periphery to circulate to the body's core.

The states of hypothermia:
- Mild: awake, **shivering**, cold sensation, lethargic, fast heart rate and breathing.
- Medium: drowsy, **not shivering**, may have slurred speech, loss of some muscle control, incoherence or combativeness, stupor, exhaustion.
- Severe: unconscious, **not shivering**, shallow or absent breathing, possible cardiac arrest.

Emergency First Aid

These are guidelines to be used only when professional help is not readily available or may be delayed. The following guidance reflects American Heart Association 2020 Guidelines, but it does not replace proper training in First Aid or CPR.

Good Samaritan laws were enacted to encourage people to help others in emergency situations. Laws vary from state to state, but all require that the caregiver use common sense and a reasonable level of skill. Care or assistance must be provided in good faith and cannot be considered gross negligence or wanton misconduct.

Before giving care to a conscious victim, you must first get consent. If the victim does not give consent, call 911. Consent may be implied if a victim is unconscious, confused, or seriously ill.

Prevent disease transmission by avoiding contact with bodily fluids. Use protective equipment such as disposable gloves and a Pocket Mask or barrier device. Thoroughly wash your hands after giving care.

For all life-threatening events, immediately contact USCG by marine radio on VHF Ch. 16, or call 911 by phone. **Be ready to provide your position or location to aid rescuers**; see call scripts on pp. 270-271. Trained dispatchers can provide instructions on how to properly perform CPR, apply an AED, or provide other assistance.

Continued on p. 246   **245**

Emergency First Aid
continued

Primary Assessment — In all cases, assure and maintain your own safety first. Avoid becoming an additional victim. Move the victim to a safe place prior to rendering aid if necessary. Check for:

1. Unresponsiveness,
2. Breathing—look for chest rise, listen for breath, feel for air movement, and
3. Signs of circulation—normal breathing, coughing, or movement.

If signs of circulation and breathing are present, check for and control any severe bleeding.

If unresponsive and not breathing – For victims of trauma, drowning/submersion, or suspected drug overdose, call for help and then begin CPR. For children and infants, check for breathing first. If no breathing, do 1 minute of CPR, call for help, then resume CPR.

If circulation is present but no breathing – Begin Rescue Breathing.

If airway is obstructed – Do Heimlich to clear airway. Do not use Heimlich if drowning is suspected; go to Rescue Breathing.

Rescue Breathing, no obstruction — Call or get someone to call for help.

Signs of circulation or pulse definitely present, unresponsive, no breathing.

Roll victim onto back and open airway. Tilt head back and lift chin except where neck or back injury is suspected. Place your ear close to the mouth. LOOK for chest rise, LISTEN for breathing, FEEL for breath on your cheek for not more than 10 seconds.

If no breathing is detected, keep head tilted back, pinch nose shut, seal your lips tight around victim's mouth, GIVE 2 BREATHS only until the chest rises.

For **Adults**: Continue in cycles of counting to FIVE: give breath during count ONE and TWO, allow exhalation for counts three, four, and five.

For **Children and Infants**: Continue in cycles of counting to THREE: give breath during count ONE, allow exhalation for counts two and three.

CHECK PULSE EVERY 2 MINUTES If victim has a pulse but is not breathing, continue rescue breathing; Look, listen and feel for return of breathing between breaths.

For Adults: Feel for pulse at side of the neck for not more than 10 seconds

For Infants and Children: Feel for pulse at the inside of the upper arm for not more than 10 seconds

If victim has no sign of life or breath, begin CPR.

Obstructed Airway —

If victim is conscious but cannot cough, breathe, or speak, use Heimlich. They may be giving the universal sign for choking by holding their hands over their throat.

If drowning suspected, use Rescue Breathing. Do not try to clear water from lungs. Roll to side if vomiting occurs to keep the airway clear.

If victim is unconscious, look in the mouth for obstruction, remove it ONLY if it can be seen. Do not reach deeply into the mouth as you may further lodge the obstructing object. If no object is seen and victim remains unresponsive, begin CPR.

Emergency First Aid
continued

Heimlich — If victim is conscious, stand behind them. Wrap your arms around victim's waist. Place your closed fist (thumbside) against the victim's stomach in the midline, just above the navel and well below the rib margin. Grasp your fist with other hand. Press into stomach with a quick upward thrust.

If victim is or becomes unconscious, commence CPR.

CPR - Cardiopulmonary Resuscitation — Use only when there is no sign of breathing and no sign of movement or life. First, call or get someone to call for help.

CPR has two components: high-quality chest compressions and rescue breathing. High-quality, uninterrupted chest compressions are the most important part of CPR.

If you are untrained in Rescue Breathing or how to properly perform CPR, the American Heart Association recommends hands-only chest compressions until help arrives. Follow these two important steps: 1) contact help and 2) provide continuous chest compressions until professional help or an AED arrives.

After determining unresponsiveness, roll victim onto back as a unit, being careful to keep the spine in alignment. Expose the chest.

For **Adults** (Age over 18 or signs of puberty present): Put the heel of 1 hand on the lower half of the breastbone. Put the heel of your other hand on top of the first hand. Push straight down at least 2 inches at a rate of 100-120 compressions per minute.

For **Children** (Age 1 to Adult): Use the palm of one hand or two fingers placed on the lower half of the breastbone at the level of the nipples. Push straight down about 2 inches at a rate of 100-120 compressions per minute.

For **Infants** (Birth to 1 year): Use two fingers placed on the lower half of the breastbone at the level of the nipples. Push straight down about 1 1/2 inches at a rate of 100-120 compressions per minute.

After each compression, let the chest recoil to its normal position, but do not lift your hands (or fingers) from the chest. Giving compressions is tiring. If someone else is available, switch compressors every 2 minutes, being careful to minimize interruptions in giving compressions.

If you are trained in how to perform CPR and do not have another trained person to help you, you may combine chest compressions with Rescue Breathing at a rate of 30 compressions to 2 breaths.

If you are trained in how to perform CPR and are accompanied by another trained rescuer, give 15 compressions and 2 breaths; alternate giving breaths and compressions every two minutes to avoid fatigue.

Bleeding — Apply pressure directly over wound with a clean sterile dressing until bleeding stops or until EMS rescuers arrive. If possible, press edges of a large wound together before using dressing and bandage.

If bleeding continues, apply additional bandages and continue to maintain pressure; place new dressings over any that are soaked through. Do not remove saturated dressings as this may cause continued bleeding. If bleeding from a wound on an extremity cannot be stopped, use a tourniquet above the wound. Tourniquet should be placed on single-bone extremities (upper arm or thigh, not on forearm or shin).

Continued on p. 248

Emergency First Aid

Bleeding (cont.)—

Even if the injury is to the hand or wrist, place the tourniquet on the upper arm as close to the torso as possible. Place the tourniquet "high and tight" against the torso or trunk. Tighten until bleeding stops. Commercially available tourniquets like the CAT Tourniquet work best. Do not use a belt or rope as this can cause further damage to blood vessels and may not stop the bleeding. A properly applied tourniquet is extremely painful, be prepared to treat for pain if possible. If necessary, apply a second tourniquet adjacent to the first. Never remove a tourniquet once it is applied. Make a note of what time the tourniquet is applied.

If possible, elevate wounded area, pad the injured extremity to prevent further injury. Keep the victim warm and dry, lay them flat, and be prepared to treat for shock.

Burns, Scalds — No open blisters: Use cool water, then cover with a dry sterile dressing.

Open blisters - Heat, Flame, or Fire: Cover injury with dry sterile dressing. Do not put water on burn or remove clothing sticking to burn. Keep victim warm, prepare to treat for shock

Open blisters - Chemical Agent: PROTECT YOURSELF FROM EXPOSURE. Brush away any loose dry chemical. Remove all clothing on which chemical has spilled. Flush all chemical burns continuously with water for 1 hour. Cover with dry sterile dressing and treat for shock. Eyes: Flush with cool water only for 1 hour. You may have to gently help hold victim's eyes open to allow proper flushing.

Shock — Characteristics include: confused behavior; rapid pulse and breathing; cool, moist skin; blue tinge to lips and nailbeds; weakness; nausea; vomiting. If possible, identify and correct the cause.

If pulse and breathing are present, keep victim lying on their left side in "recovery position." Remove wet clothing. Maintain normal body temperature. Do not give victim food or drink.

If pulse present but no breathing, begin Rescue Breathing p. 246.

If no pulse and no breathing, begin CPR, p. 247.

Fractures — Do not move victim or try to correct any deformity unless there is imminent danger for further injury. Immobilize the injured extremity. If bone penetrates the skin, cover and pad the extruding part with dry sterile dressing and control bleeding before splinting.

Splint a broken arm to the trunk or a broken leg to the other leg. A padded board or pole can be used along the side, front or back of a broken limb. A pillow or a rolled blanket can be used around the arm or leg.

For an injured shoulder put a pillow between the arm and chest and bind arm to body.

For an injured hip, place pillow between thighs and bind legs together.

Head, Neck, and Spine Injuries — Do not move victim or try to correct any deformity unless there is no breathing or signs of circulation, then gently align the head and neck to the neutral position to provide Rescue Breathing and CPR. Stabilize head, neck and torso to minimize movement and potential for further injury.

Emergency First Aid
continued

Poisoning — Call for help immediately: Poison Control Center 800-222-1222. Protect yourself from exposure, avoid becoming an additional victim. Have poison container available. Antidotes listed on the label may be wrong. DO NOT induce vomiting.

Heat Exposure — Remove from hot environment, prevent further warming. Remove excess clothing, maintaining modesty. Move to a shaded or air-conditioned area. Provide evaporative cooling. Wrap in cool, wet sheet, towel, or blanket. Treat for shock. Gradually reduce body temperature to normal, avoid causing shivering. Provide room temperature oral fluids.

Cold Exposure — Remove from the cold environment, prevent further cooling or heat loss. Provide a warm dry bunk and warm drink, not coffee, tea or alcohol.

Frostbite: rewarm slowly, beginning with the body core rather than the extremities. Elevate and protect affected area. Do not rub frozen area, break blisters or use dry heat to thaw. Pad any frozen parts with dry sterile dressings to prevent further injury. Treat for shock. See *Hypothermia and Cold Water Immersion*, p. 244.

Sunburn — Treat heat exposure if present. Cool the skin by using a damp cloth laid over the area. Do not apply ice as this may damage the skin further.

Over-the-Counter pain relievers such as acetaminophen (Tylenol) or Ibuprofen (Motrin) may be used for pain. Be sure to follow administration and dosing recommendations. Use topical skin care lotions to keep the skin moist and reduce dehydration. Those containing aloe work well. If the skin is blistering, do not break blisters. Prevent secondary infection by keeping the area clean.

Victim should rest and keep hydrated. Seek medical help if area does not improve.

Seasickness — This form of motion sickness is characterized by headache, drowsiness, dizziness and vertigo, nausea, and vomiting. It is often brought on by sailing in rough or inconsistent seas and can be difficult to control. Prevention is the most preferred treatment. Severity can range from mild to debilitating; not all people are affected the same way; even seasoned mariners can suffer from seasickness. Prevention: There are many herbal or natural treatments as well as over the counter or prescription medications available. Anti-seasickness wristbands are also known to prevent or relieve symptoms. Talk with your doctor or pharmacist about which approach might be right for you.

Generally, avoid strong odors, greasy, spicy, and high-fat foods, alcohol, and excessive sugar as they can make you more prone and contribute to seasickness severity. Avoid reading books and computer screens. Avoid confined spaces.

Coping with seasickness: take ginger, chew gum, look at the horizon, stay on deck, get fresh air, try to sleep. Stay as close to the center of the boat as possible. Keep hydrated.

Debilitating nausea and vomiting can become a true emergency requiring medical treatment or at-sea evacuation.

The Publishers thank Andrew N Sikes, CCP, FP-C, Flight Paramedic, Vanderbilt Life-Flight for his valuable contributions to the Hypothermia & Emergency First Aid sections.

Point Cruz, and was executive officer of the aircraft carrier *Princeton* in Korea. Craig was a leader in naval nuclear weapons testing, and according to his obituary in the *Washington Post* on March 26, 2001, he served in the Armed Forces Staff College in Norfolk, and "as nuclear weapons readiness officer for the commander of the Atlantic Fleet." Thus, it is fair to say that by pulling Craig in from the cold, Messrs. Estabrook and Channing helped their country win the Cold War.

Researching this incident with a view to ascertaining the location of the crash and then finding remains of the aircraft seemed – at first blush – within my reach. There are photos of Craig as he emerged from the ambulance, many images of the type of aircraft, of Graves Light, Eastern Yacht Club, and more. There is even a painting of an aircraft at the base of Graves Light being battered by waves. Yachts and owners are usually quite easy to track, particularly those with pedigreed yacht club affiliations.

But there's the rub, because "ordinary" searches for people, places, and things can soon became extraordinarily difficult. The usual resources – even plane-searching legends like Doug Campbell, Jim Ignahser, Larry Webster, and Joe Baugher - didn't pull up many hits, and many aviation databases don't track fighters, due to their sheer number and maneuverability. Even the precise location of the crash remains unconfirmed, with the *Boston Globe* saying the plane sank "in the water two and one- half miles northeast of Graves Light," and Craig's hometown paper, the *Bellingham Herald*, stating the "plane crashed into Boston Harbor .... in the outer harbor, two and a half miles northwest of Graves Light." These quotes alone are 5 miles apart.

Per Jim Ignahser, "The navy did not recover the aircraft, so the cause of the engine failure could not be determined." The most likely resting spot of the wreck is 2.5 nautical miles northeast of The Graves and 3.5 nautical miles east-southeast of Nahant. As precise and cool as he was, even Craig could make at best an educated guess while hurtling out of control, without an engine, at night, and with no land to reference. Despite all of this information nobody had found the crash. So, I set out to do just that.

Dawn of Sunday, July 30 found me hurtling around Winthrop, the northern half of the terrestrial embrace forming Boston's harbor. The skipper, Dave Waller of Malden, calculated we could nudge into a natural inlet at the base of Graves Light (using *Eldridge*, of course) and offload equipment and a film crew. We did. Dave has been making this 9-mile voyage sometimes several times a day, in snow or shine for a decade. That's because this Lynn native and his wife Lynn were the surprise winners of Graves Light when the federal government put it up for auction in 2013. Since then, the Wallers have partnered with another investor and poured countless hours into restoring the light. The film crew was there in an effort to document their efforts to 'cap off' the lighthouse by hoisting up and installing the only known private first-order Fresnel lens light to be approved by the US Coast Guard.

I expected to find a bit of Lt. Cdr. Craig's Hellcat sticking out of the rocks of

Graves Ledge at low tide, along with wreckage of the *City of Salisbury* from 1938. As Dave approached the dock he asked me to run forward and secure the boat. In doing so I unwittingly imitated a *Cirque du Soleil* trapeze artist, by overextending in a swell before the skipper brought the boat back to me. Within minutes a heap of passengers and crew were landed. I was surprised at the lack of a human footprint: no garbage or construction junk in sight. The crew are known to row after helium balloons to keep them from the mouths of nearby seals, gulls, or turtles.

Soon we were clambering up a wizened bronze ladder stuck like so many staples into the first third of a tower 113 feet high. One enters the light into a cave-like engine room with whirring dials and swish of water being created by reverse osmosis, and the whir of turbine windmills charging batteries. Then floor one: a bunk house with four well-appointed comfortable beds, storage for the tenants, and windows double-sealed when necessary. Dave and some of his specialists were weather-bound in a blizzard earlier this year for nearly a week, when boat ripped from its mooring and dashed to pieces on the mainland.

The second floor boasts an elegant bath and hot-water shower. The third is a room filled with two cozy couches and a wooden box-like square on the far wall adorned with a chart—that is one of two Murphy beds which fold down. Then further up to the office, with a large wooden desk and splendid views of Bos-

ton's skyline. Finally, the galley, with a wide deck at places made narrower by engineering equipment in support of the gas stove, plumbing and a US Coast Guard-approved active light which is roughly the size of a triple fire hydrant.

Then, the magic: the site of what had been a 12-foot tall, very rare first-order Fresnel lens. In 1942 Graves Light was used as a navigational aide by the German *Kapitän-leutnant* Joachim Berger in the submarine U-98 to lay mines off Graves Light, and later on for the film *Portrait of Jennie*. By 1976 Graves was automated, and in 1987 the Fresnel lens disassembled and shipped to the Smithsonian Institution in Washington. Dave took me from the galley to the penultimate platform, from which one could push a heavy glass and brass door outwards and stand astride the wide Atlantic and the perilous rocks outlying Boston's Harbor. I clung dizzily to the rails and gasped deeply the thick ocean air.

Graves Light, Allan Wood/shutterstock.com

Graves Light had my full attention. Over the next two weeks I joined an eclectic and yet highly-efficient team of volunteers and professionals, all there to restore the Fresnel lens to its rightful place. We toiled together along with two helicopters and a pilot who told us, "If things go south, I won't hit the lighthouse, I'll be sure to ditch in the sea," just as Craig had. The cooperative imperative to preserve the light echoed across time and space.

I returned often. The splendid serenity was not the central theme, not a newborn pink seal clinging to a rock, not the seagulls, and not even folk on boats watching us work. They would cheer and whistle when we hand-pulled a large beam up the side of the granite tower. The joy was in working shoulder-to-shoulder with men and women, teens and greybeards, captains, a prairie farmer and poet, his son the lead rigger, film makers, fish-grillers, divers, lamp-lighters, and an Australian who found, ushered, boxed, and hand-assembled 40 panels of lenses into place under the studious eye of Dave, whose family had pre-assembled the whole thing at home.

Like all that take flight, Newton's laws require them to also alight back on Earth or the seas. And so it was that Craig crashed into the sea, avoiding the tower for his sake and also, for the sake of the men of the US Light House Service. After the energy of the dozens of volunteers had peaked, and they went back to the mainland, I found myself one cold day with Dave, nudging into the empty outcrop, enshrouded in fog and wending our way to the pinnacle.

Atop the light we wedged the final 15 glass and bronze panels – orphans from various lighthouses in the Antipodes - into place and secured them. The soothing croon of folk vocals and the pelting rain against the glass kept the tempo. I felt what *J. Alfred Prufrock* described; "The yellow fog that rubs its back upon the window-panes." Our only company was a lobster boat, its skipper and stern man ignoring us. As well-built forts prevent attack by their very existence, lighthouses should be a deterrent to wrecks; they envelop the visitor, cloaking them in a sense of stolid security—in a sense of safety—even on a ledge which is not an island.

As Dave and I swept up for the day, we sealed the doors against the blast of North Atlantic winds which I'd endured as a mariner. To our east was nothing but open sea to the Azores, from Hull to Horta. Like the metal doors, Dave and Lynn are protecting the lenses, similar to others I have seen languishing in the Bahamas and since stripped out.

Before descending, I looked over the parapet one last time, trying to imagine what it was like for Russell Craig that night – how terrifying for him, as well as the keepers. It occurred to me that the magic of this story is not over there, on the horizon, in the future, or under the water, in the past, but right beneath our feet—at Graves Light—in the now.

Before we left for the night, Dave made sure to switch the lights *on*.

Capt. Eric Wiberg was for many years a yacht delivery skipper, with 33 Bermuda voyages, over 150 vessels served on over 80,000 miles. The author of over 40 books and 1,000 articles, he lives in East Boston. He has worked for owners of tanker, bulker, tugboat and salvage assets.

Beaufort Scale

Force	Knots	Wind Condition	Conditions at Sea	Conditions Ashore
0	0-1	Calm	Smooth, mirror-like sea	Calm, smoke rises vertically
1	1-3	Light Air	Scaly ripples, no foam crests	Smoke drifts at an angle, leaves move
2	4-6	Light Breeze	Small wavelets, crests glassy, not breaking	Leaves rustle, flags begin to move
3	7-10	Gentle Breeze	Large wavelets, some crests break, scattered whitecaps	Small branches move, light flags extended
4	11-16	Moderate Breeze	Small waves 1-4 ft. getting longer, numerous whitecaps	Leaves, loose paper lifted, larger flags flapping
5	17-21	Fresh Breeze	Moderate waves 4-8 ft., many whitecaps	Small trees in leaf begin to sway, flags extended
6	22-27	Strong Breeze	Larger waves 8-13 ft., more whitecaps, spray	Larger tree branches and small trees in motion
7	28-33	Near Gale	Sea heaps up, waves 13-20 ft., white foam streaks	Whole trees moving, resistance in walking
8	34-40	Gale	Waves 13-20 ft. of greater length, crests break, spindrift	Large trees in motion, small branches break
9	41-47	Strong Gale	High waves, 20+ ft., dense streaks of foam, spray reduces visibility	Slight structural damage, roof shingles may blow off, signs in motion
10	48-55	Storm	Very high waves, 20-30 ft., overhanging crests, lowered visibility, sea white with densely blown foam	Trees broken or uprooted, considerable structural damage, very high tides
11	56-63	Violent Storm	Exceptionally high waves, 30-45 ft., foam patches cover sea, visibility limited	Widespread damage, light structures in peril, coastal flooding
12	64+	Hurricane	Air filled with foam, waves 45+ ft., wind shrieks, sea white with spray, visibility poor	Storm surge at coast, serious beach erosion, extensive flooding, trees and wires down

NOTE: When the wind speed doubles, the pressure of the wind on an object *quadruples*. Example: the wind pressure at 40 kts. is *four times* what it is at 20 kts.

In many tidal waters wave heights are apt to increase considerably in a very short time, and conditions can be more dangerous near land than in the open sea.

Distance Table in Nautical Miles

*Approximate

Bar Harbor to
Halifax, N.S. 259
Yarmouth, N.S. 101
Saint John, N.B. 122
Machiasport 52
Rockland................................... 62
Boothbay Harbor 86
Portland................................... 115
Marblehead 169

Rockland to
Boothbay Harbor 42
Belfast 22
Bucksport 33

Boothbay Harbor to
Kennebec River......................... 11
Monhegan.................................. 15
Portland..................................... 36

Portland Ltd. Buoy "P" to
Biddeford.................................. 17
Portsmouth................................ 54
Cape Cod Light 99
Cape Cod Canal (E. Entr.)..... 118
Pollock Rip Slue 141

Portsmouth (Whaleback) to
York River 7
Biddeford Pool.......................... 30
Newburyport Entr..................... 15
Gloucester – via Annisquam...... 28

Gloucester to
Boston....................................... 26
Scituate 26
Plymouth................................... 43
Cape Cod Canal (E. Entr.)....... 52
Provincetown 45

Marblehead to
Portsmouth................................ 43
Biddeford Pool.......................... 68
Portland..................................... 87
Boothbay Harbor 104
Rockland................................... 133
Plymouth................................... 38
Cape Cod Canal (E. Entr.)....... 47

Boston (Commonwealth Pier)
Marblehead 17
Isles of Shoals 52
Portsmouth................................ 58
Portland..................................... 95
Kennebec River....................... 107
Boothbay Harbor 116
Rockland................................... 149
North Haven 148
Bangor...................................... 194
St. John, N.B. 286
Halifax, N.S. 380
Cohasset 14
Cape Cod Canal, E. Entr.......... 50
Provincetown 50
Vineyard Haven....................... 77
New Bedford 81
Fall River................................ 107
Newport................................... 122
New London 140
New York 234

****Western Entr., Cape Cod Canal to**
East Entrance 8
Woods Hole............................... 15
Quicks Hole............................... 20
New Bedford 24
Newport..................................... 50
New London 83

Woods Hole to
Hyannis..................................... 19
Chatham 32
Cuttyhunk................................. 14
Marion....................................... 11

Vineyard Haven to
Edgartown................................... 9
Marblehead – around Cape..... 114
Canal – via Woods Hole 20
Newport..................................... 45
New London 77
New Haven................................ 114
South Norwalk........................ 140
City Island 153

*Each distance is by the shortest route that safe navigation permits between the two ports concerned.

****Western entr.**, The beginning of the "land cut" at Bourne Neck, 7.3 nautical miles up the channel from Cleveland Ledge Lt.

Distance Table in Nautical Miles
*Approximate

Nantucket Entr. Bell NB to
Boston – around Cape............. 105
Boston – via Canal 94
Chatham 23
Edgartown.............................. 23
Hyannis 21
Woods Hole............................. 30
Cape Cod Canal (W. Entr.) 45
Newport.................................. 71

New Bedford (State Pier) to
Woods Hole 14
Newport.................................. 38
New London 74
New York (Gov. Is.)................ 166

Newport to
Providence............................... 21
Stonington.............................. 34
New London 48
New Haven............................... 84
City Island 122

Block Island (FR Horn) to
Nantucket 79
Vineyard Haven 52
Cleveland Ledge Lt.................. 50
New Bedford 44
Newport.................................. 22
Race Point Lt........................... 21
New London 29

New London to
Greenport................................ 25
New Haven............................... 49
Bridgeport 60
City Island 86

Port Jefferson to
Larchmont............................... 30
So. Norwalk............................. 15
Milford.................................... 14
Old Saybrook........................... 43
New London 53

City Island to
Governors Island 17
Execution Rocks........................ 3

Execution Rocks to
Port Chester............................. 8
Stamford.................................. 12
Oyster Bay Harbor 14
So. Norwalk............................. 19
Bridgeport 29

Port Jefferson.......................... 30
Milford.................................... 37
New Haven............................... 49
Conn. River 69
Mystic 84
Montauk Point 87

New York (Battery) to
Jones Inlet............................... 34
Fire Island Inlet...................... 47
Moriches Inlet......................... 74
Shinnecock Inlet...................... 88
Montauk Point 117
Keyport................................... 22
Asbury Park 35
Manasquan 40
Little Egg Inlet 81
Atlantic City............................ 97
Philadelphia.......................... 235
Chesapeake Lt. Stn................. 247
Cape Henry Lt. 262
Norfolk 288
Baltimore 418

Brielle-Manasquan to
E. Rockaway Inlet 32
Jones Inlet............................... 35
Fire Island Inlet...................... 45
Montauk Point 117
Barnegat Inlet......................... 21
Atlantic City............................ 51

Delaware Breakwater to
Reedy Pt. Entr. (C&D Canal) .. 51
Annapolis – via Canal.............. 97
Norfolk 167
New York 150
New London 242
Providence............................. 275
New Bedford 278
Boston (outside) 399
Portland (outside) 443

Old Point Comfort to
Baltimore 163
Philadelphia.......................... 240
New York 276
New London 363
Providence............................. 392
New Bedford 397
Boston (outside) 512
Portland................................. 553

The Saffir-Simpson Hurricane Wind Scale

CATEGORY ONE: Winds 74-95 mph: Very dangerous winds will produce some damage. Falling or flying debris. Damage primarily to power lines, mobile homes, shopping center roofs, shrubbery, and trees. Also, some coastal road flooding and minor pier damage.

CATEGORY TWO: Winds 96-110 mph: Extremely dangerous winds will cause extensive damage. Some roofing material, door, and window damage to buildings. Considerable damage to vegetation, mobile homes, and piers. Small craft in unprotected areas break moorings. Near-total power outages. Some water systems fail.

CATEGORY THREE: Winds 111-130 mph: Devastating damage will occur. Some structural damage to small residences. Mobile homes destroyed. Many trees snapped or uprooted. Coastal flooding may extend inland, destroying smaller structures, damaging larger structures. Electricity and water may be unavailable for days or weeks.

CATEGORY FOUR: Winds 131-155 mph: Catastrophic damage will occur. More extensive failures including roofs on small residences. Major erosion of beach areas. Major damage to lower floors of structures near the shore. Power poles down. Terrain may be flooded well inland. Long-term water shortages.

CATEGORY FIVE: Winds greater than 155 mph: Catastrophic damage will occur. Complete roof failure on many residences and industrial buildings. Some complete building failures with small utility buildings destroyed. Major damage to most structures located near the shoreline. Massive evacuation of residential areas may be required. Most of the area will be uninhabitable for weeks or months.

Hurricanes

For their awesome power to wreak havoc by wind and water, hurricanes have always been fascinating. Early warnings have all but eliminated surprise, yet these storms often defy attempts to prepare. Always vulnerable, we must know what to expect.

Hurricanes affecting the East Coast are born as tropical depressions in the Atlantic west of Africa, move westward through the eastern Caribbean, and eventually veer northwest and then north and northeast up our coast. Counter-clockwise winds spiral inward and accelerate toward the eye, the center of lowest pressure. The sharper the drop in pressure, the more violent the winds. Hurricanes lose power as they move north out of the tropics because warm ocean water, the energy source which helped create them, turns cooler.

A hurricane's forward motion, which can vary from 5 to 50+ knots, means that the winds are stronger on the right side. Winds of 100 knots spiraling around the eye, when you add a forward speed of 25 knots, create a speed of 125 knots on the right side, but only 75 knots on the left side, a dramatic difference. Note: a doubling of wind speed means the force on an object is increased four times, so that a wind of 100 knots has four times the power it does at 50 knots.

If the eye is moving directly toward you, the wind direction will remain fairly constant and the velocity will increase until the eye arrives. When the eye passes, the velocity will suddenly increase, rather stronger than before, from the opposite direction. These factors make the vicinity of the eye most dangerous.

In our diagram the hurricane is approaching, and vessels A, B, and C are at positions A1, B1, and C1 relative to the storm. When the storm passes, these vessels will be at positions A2, B2, and C2. Each will have experienced very different wind speeds and directions:

Vessel A, in the least dangerous semi-circle, will experience winds from the NE (at A1), backing to N (least velocity), NW, and finally W (at A2) as the storm passes.

Vessel B (at B1) will have ENE winds, increasing until the eye arrives. After the deceptive calm of the eye passes, the wind will rise, stronger than before, from the WSW (at B2), gradually decreasing.

Vessel C, in the most dangerous semi-circle, has the strongest winds, beginning (at C1) from the E, veering to SE, S (greatest velocity), and finally to SW (at C2).

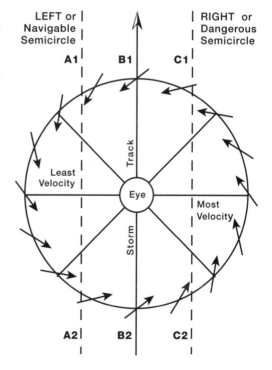

If space and time permit, try to reduce your vulnerability by proceeding at right angles to the storm track. Which way to go depends on a number of factors, including how far away the storm is, its speed, the speed of the vessel, and sea conditions or sea room on either side of the expected storm path.

Hurricane Precautions Alongshore

Extremely high tides accompany hurricanes. If the storm arrives anywhere near the usual time of high water, low-lying areas will be flooded. Especially high tides will occur in all bays or V-mouth harbors if they are facing the wind direction. High water in all storm areas will remain for much longer than usual.

At or near the coastline, pull small craft well above the high water mark, dismast sailboats, remove outboard motors, and remove or lash down loose objects.

Seek the most protected anchorage possible, considering possible wind direction reversals, extreme tides, and other vessels. If on a mooring or at anchor, use maximum scope, allowing for room to swing clear of other boats. In a real blow it is easy to slack off, but not to shorten scope. Use as much chain in your anchor rode as possible. Another piece of chain or a weight, attached halfway along your mooring or anchor line, will help absorb sudden strains. Use chafing gear liberally at bits and bow chocks to minimize fraying of lines. Rig fenders to minimize damage from/to other boats.

Shut off gas, stove tanks, etc. Douse any fires in heating stoves. Secure all portholes, skylights, ventilators, hatch covers, companionways, etc. Pump the boat dry. At a wharf or pier, use fenders liberally. If possible, rig one or more anchors abreast of the boat in the event the tide rises above pilings.

Boats are replaceable: don't wait for the last moment to get ashore!

Hurricane Precautions Offshore

Monitor storm reports on your radio. The U.S. Coast Guard warns all vessels offshore to seek shelter at least 72 hours ahead of a hurricane.

But, if caught offshore with no chance to reach shelter, watch the wind most carefully. First, note that if you face the wind, the eye is about 10 points or 112° to your right. If the wind "backs" (moves counter-clockwise), you are already on the less dangerous side of the storm track. If the wind "veers" (moves clockwise), you are on the right or more dangerous side. If the wind direction is constant, the hurricane's eye is headed directly at you, so make haste to get to the left side of the track.

Use your radiotelephone to advise the Coast Guard and other vessels of your position. Have a life raft and safety equipment (flares, flashlights, EPIRB, etc.) ready. Put on life jackets. If it is impossible to hold your intended course, head your powerboat directly into the wind and sea, using only enough power to maintain steerageway. If power fails, rig a sea anchor or drogue to keep the bow to the wind.

Sailing vessels heaving to should consider doing so on the starboard tack (boom to port) in the more dangerous semicircle, or on the port tack (boom to starboard) in the less dangerous semicircle, to keep the wind drawing aft.

NOTE: This information is necessarily very general, the diagram (p. 257) is over-simplified, and the suggestions assume a straight storm track. If the storm track curves to the right, vessels A and B will have an easier time of it, but C may wind up on the track. The best advice: monitor weather reports continuously and seek shelter well ahead of time.

National Weather Service – www.weather.gov
National Hurricane Center – www.nhc.noaa.gov
NOAA Hurricane Research – www.aoml.noaa.gov/hrd

Marine Weather Forecasts

VHF-FM, NOAA All-Hazards Weather Radio - Continuous broadcasts 24 hours a day are provided by the National Weather Service with messages repeated every 4-6 minutes. These are updated every 3-6 hours and include weather and radar summaries, wind observations, visibility, sea conditions and detailed local forecasts. Broadcasts can be received 20-40 miles from transmitting site.

	MHz		**MHz**
WX-1	162.550	WX-5	162.450
WX-2	162.400	WX-6	162.500
WX-3	162.475	WX-7	162.525
WX-4	162.425		

Jonesboro, ME (5)	Riverhead, NY (3)	Mamie, NC (4)	Jacksonville, FL (1)
Ellsworth, ME (2)	Philadelphia, PA (3)	Cape Hatteras, NC (3)	Daytona Bch., FL (2)
Dresden, ME (3)	Atlantic City, NJ (2)	New Bern, NC (2)	Melbourne, FL (1)
Gloucester, MA (4)	Lewes, DE (1)	Georgetown, SC (6)	Fort Pierce, FL (4)
Boston, MA (3)	Baltimore, MD (2)	Charleston, SC (1)	Miami, FL (1)
Hyannis, MA (1)	Hagerstown, MD (3)	Beaufort, SC (5)	Key West, FL (2)
Providence, RI (2)	Norfolk, VA (1)	Brunswick, GA (4)	

Time Signals

Bureau of Standards Time Signals: WWV, Ft. Collins, Col., every min. on 2500, 5000, 10000, 15000, 20000, and, on an experimental basis, 25000 kHz. **Canadian Time Signals:** CHU, (frequently easier to get than WWV) 45° 17' 47" N, 75° 45' 22" W. Continuous transmission on 3330, 7850, and 14670 kHz. For more information on time, visit www.nist.gov/pml/time-and-frequency-division.

The new minute is marked by the full tone immediately following the voice announcement. There is a pulse every second except on the 29th and 59th seconds of the minute.

Forecasting
with Wind Direction and Barometric Pressure

Wind Dir.	Pressure	Trend	Likely Forecast
SW to NW	30.1-30.2	Steady	Fair, little temp. change
	30.1-30.2	Rising rapidly	Fair, perhaps warmer with rain
	30.2+	Steady	Fair, no temp. change
	30.2+	Falling	Fair, gradual rise in temp.
S to SW	30.0	Rising slowly	Clearing, then fair
S to SE	30.2	Falling rapidly	Increasing wind, rain to follow
S to E	29.8	Falling rapidly	Severe NE gale, heavy rain/snow
SE to NE	30.1-30.2	Falling slowly	Rain
	30.1-30.2	Falling rapidly	Increasing wind and rain
	30.0	Falling slowly	Rain continuing
	30.0	Falling rapidly	Rain, high wind, then clearing and cooler
E to NE	30.0+	Falling slowly	Rain with light winds
	30.1	Falling rapidly	Rain or snow, increasing wind
Shifting W	29.8	Rising rapidly	Clearing and cooler

Pollution Regulations

Simplified Regulations for Waste Disposal Outside Special Areas

Prohibited in all waters: The discharge of garbage including synthetic ropes, fishing gear, plastics (including plastic waste bags), incinerator ashes, clinkers, paper, rags, packing materials, dunnage, metal, glass, bottles, cooking oil, crockery and similar refuse.

Food waste: The discharge of any garbage or ground food waste is prohibited within 3 n.m. of land. Beyond 3 n.m., food waste may be discharged if ground to particles less than 1 inch. Unground food waste may be discharged if 12 n.m. or more from land. In any case, the vessel must be *en route* and discharge should be as far from land as practicable.

The Damage Caused by Pollution

Sewage is not just a repulsive visual pollutant. The microorganisms in sewage, including pathogens and bacteria, degrade water quality by introducing diseases like hepatitis, cholera, typhoid fever and gastroenteritis, which can contaminate shellfish beds. Shellfish are filter feeders that eat tiny food particles filtered through their gills into their stomachs, along with bacteria from sewage. Nearly all waterborne pathogens can be conveyed by shellfish to humans.

Marine Sanitation Devices (MSDs)

USCG-certified MSDs are required on all vessels with installed toilets. Vessels under 65' may install type I, II or III MSD. Vessels over 65' must install a type II or III MSD.

Type I MSDs are allowed only on vessels under 65'. They treat sewage with disinfectant chemicals before discharge. The discharge must not show any visible floating solids, and must have a fecal coliform bacterial count not greater than 1000 per 100 milliliters of water.

Type II MSDs are allowed on vessels of any length. They provide a higher level of treatment than Type I, using greater levels of chemicals to create effluent having less than 200 per 100 milliliters and suspended solids not greater than 150 milligrams per liter.

Type III MSDs are allowed on vessels of any length. They do not allow discharge of sewage, except through a Y-valve to discharge at a pumpout facility, or overboard when outside the 3 nautical miles. They include holding tanks, recirculating and incinerating units.

Portable toilets or "porta-potties" are not considered installed toilets and are not subject to MSD regulations. They are, however, subject to the disposal regulations which prohibit the disposal of raw sewage within the 3 nautical miles of shore.

No Discharge Zones (NDZs)

NDZs are water bodies where the Environmental Protection Agency (EPA) and local communities prohibit the discharge of all vessel sewage. Many States are adding NDZs. **It is the boater's responsibility to be aware of where those NDZs are.** For NDZs by state see https://www.epa.gov/vessels-marinas-and-ports/no-discharge-zones-ndzs-state.

When operating vessel in NDZs, the operator must secure all Types of MSDs in a manner that prevents discharge of treated or untreated sewage. Acceptable methods of securing Type III MDSs include: closing appropriate valves, removing the handle, padlocking each valve, or using a non-reusable wire-tie to hold each valve in a closed position. Sewage held in Type III MSDs can be removed by making arrangements with pumpout stations or pumpout boats. Call Harbormaster for details.

Report sewage violations to the local USCG office or the USCG National Response Center (see contact details on p. 268).

Pumpout Information — State Sources

Please be sure to call or radio in advance for rates and availability. While we have taken all possible care in compiling this list, changes may have occurred and we cannot guarantee accuracy. For more current information check the state website or call the agency listed. See also *Pollution Regulations* on opposing page.

Look for the pumpout symbol

For more information on the Clean Vessel Act (CVA), see www.fws.gov/program/clean-vessel-act

Most major harbors now have a pumpout boat. Contact the local Harbormaster. Many monitor VHF channel 09.

MAINE: ME Dept. of Environ. Protection, 207-485-3038
www.maine.gov/dep/water/wd/vessel/pumpout/index.html

NEW HAMPSHIRE: Mobile pumpout boat, 603-670-5130
www.des.nh.gov/home-and-recreation/boating-and-fishing/boat-pumpouts

MASSACHUSETTS: MA Coastal Zone Mgmt., 978-282-0308, ext.119
www.mass.gov/service-details/boat-pumpout-facilities

RHODE ISLAND: RI Environ. Mgmt. Law Enforcement, 401-222-3070
RI Environmental Mgmt., Office of Water Resources, 401-222-4700 x277412
www.dem.ri.gov/maps/mapfile/pumpmap.pdf

CONNECTICUT: CT Energy and Environ. Protection, 860-447-4340
www.ct.gov/deep/pumpoutdirectory

NEW YORK: NY State Environmental Facilities Corp., 518-402-6924
www.efc.ny.gov/cvap (link to map at bottom of page)

NEW JERSEY: NJ Fish & Wildlife, 908-637-4125 ext. 0
NJBoating.org

DELAWARE: DE Division of Fish & Wildlife, 302-739-9915
dnrec.alpha.delaware.gov/fish-wildlife/boating/pumpout/

MARYLAND: MD Dept. of Natural Resources, 410-260-8772
dnr.maryland.gov/boating/pages/pumpout/locations.aspx

VIRGINIA: VA Dept. of Health, 804-864-7468
www.vdh.virginia.gov/environmental-health/marina-program/maps-marina/

NORTH CAROLINA: NC Div. of Coastal Management, 252-808-2808
deq.nc.gov/about/divisions/coastal-management/coastal-management-recognition-programs/nc-pumpout-program

SOUTH CAROLINA: SC Dept. of Natural Resources, 843-953-9062
www.dnr.sc.gov/marine/vessel/stationmaps.html

GEORGIA: Georgia Dept. of Natural Resources, 912-264-7218
coastalgadnr.org/pumpout — contact local marinas

FLORIDA: FL Dept. of Environmental Protection, Environmental Education Office, 850-245-2846
arcg.is/1quLP0

Got a Minute?
Angular and Linear Equivalents

Whether you are navigating purely by GPS or using a paper chart, it can be helpful to know how degrees, minutes, and seconds – or tenths or hundredths of a minute – translate into linear distance on the water. Knowing both is important because your GPS can display part of a coordinate as 41° 23' 25", or as 41° 23.42', where each is correct, but one is more accurate.

First, the basics. Latitude is the angular distance north or south of the Equator, and the parallels are equidistant. The latitude scale appears on the vertical edges of your chart. (Longitude, measured east and west of Greenwich and appearing along the top and bottom edges of your chart, is never used for distance measurement.) For practical purposes, the distance between parallels of latitude which are one degree (1°) apart is 60 nautical miles (n.m.).

- 1° (degree) = 60 nautical miles (Ex: from 42° North to 43° North is 60 n.m.)
- 1' (minute, or 1/60th of a degree) = 1 n.m., or 6076 feet
- 1" (second, or 1/60th of a minute) = 101.3 feet (acceptable for general purposes)

The U.S. Coast Guard gives positions of buoys, lights, and lighthouses in degrees, minutes, and seconds, or within roughly 100 feet. (See pp. 173-203).

Sometimes minutes are divided into tenths or hundredths instead of seconds.

- 1' (minute) = 1 n.m., or 6076 feet
- 0.1' (1/10th of a minute) = 608 feet (acceptable tolerance at sea; not so near shore)
- 0.01' (1/100th of a minute) = 61 feet (acceptable for almost any purpose)

Use the Table below to convert seconds to tenths or hundredths of a minute.

Table for Converting Seconds to Decimals of a Minute

From many sources, including charts, Light Lists, and Notices to Mariners, positions are in degrees, minutes, and seconds. These are written either 34° 54' 24" or 34-54-24

However, for navigating with GPS, Loran, chart plotters, and celestial calculators, it can be useful to convert the last increment – seconds – to either tenths or hundredths of a minute. The numbers above become 34° 54.40' or 34-54.4'

Secs.	Tenths	Hundredths	Secs.	Tenths	Hundredths	Secs.	Tenths	Hundredths
1	.0	.02	21	.4	.35	41	.7	.68
2	.0	.03	22	.4	.37	42	.7	.70
3	.1	.05	23	.4	.38	43	.7	.72
4	.1	.07	24	.4	.40	44	.7	.73
5	.1	.08	25	.4	.42	45	.8	.75
6	.1	.10	26	.4	.43	46	.8	.77
7	.1	.12	27	.5	.45	47	.8	.78
8	.1	.13	28	.5	.47	48	.8	.80
9	.2	.15	29	.5	.48	49	.8	.82
10	.2	.17	30	.5	.50	50	.8	.83
11	.2	.18	31	.5	.52	51	.9	.85
12	.2	.20	32	.5	.53	52	.9	.87
13	.2	.22	33	.6	.55	53	.9	.88
14	.2	.23	34	.6	.57	54	.9	.90
15	.3	.25	35	.6	.58	55	.9	.92
16	.3	.27	36	.6	.60	56	.9	.93
17	.3	.28	37	.6	.62	57	1.0	.95
18	.3	.30	38	.6	.63	58	1.0	.97
19	.3	.32	39	.7	.65	59	1.0	.98
20	.3	.33	40	.7	.67	60	1.0	1.00

Table of Equivalents
and other useful information

Length

English	Metric
1 inch	2.54 centimeters
1 foot	0.30 meters
1 fathom	1.61 meters
1 statute mile	1.61 kilometers
1 nautical mile	1.85 kilometers

Metric	English
1 meter	39.37 inches
"	3.28 feet
"	0.55 fathoms
1 kilometer	0.62 statute miles
"	0.54 nautical miles

Nautical	Terrestrial
1 fathom	6 feet
1 cable	608 feet
1 nautical mile	6076 feet
"	1.15 statute miles
1 knot	1.15 mph
7 knots	8 mph approx.

Capacity

English	Metric
1 quart	0.95 liters
1 gallon	3.78 liters

Metric	English
1 liter	1.06 quarts
"	0.26 US gallons

Weight

English	Metric
1 ounce	28.35 grams
1 pound	0.45 kilograms
1 US ton	0.907 metric tons
"	0.893 long tons

Metric	English
1 gram	0.035 ounces
1 kilogram	2.20 pounds
1 metric ton	2204.6 pounds

Weight of 1 US Gallon

Gasoline	6 pounds
Diesel fuel	7 pounds
Fresh water	8.3 pounds
Salt water	8.5 pounds

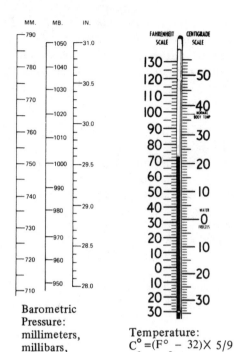

Barometric Pressure: millimeters, millibars, inches

Temperature:
$$C^\circ = (F^\circ - 32) \times 5/9$$
$$F^\circ = C^\circ \times 9/5 + 32$$

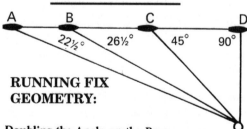

RUNNING FIX GEOMETRY:

Doubling the Angle on the Bow
1. Angle DCO = 45°; Angle CDO = 90°;
   True distance run (CD) = distance DO.
2. Angle DAO = $22\frac{1}{2}^\circ$; Angle DCO = 45°;
   True distance run (AC) = Distance CO.

Other Useful Bow Bearings
3. Angle DBO = $26\frac{1}{2}^\circ$; Angle DCO = 45°;
   True distance run (BC) = distance DO.
4. Example 3 also works with angles of 25° and 41°; 32° and 59°; 35° and 67°; 37° and 72° when distance run will be distance DO.

Sailing by the Book
by Jake Lundberg

You probably haven't heard the one about the *Coast Pilot* and the Bible. It was making the rounds in 1875, when *Eldridge* was in its infancy. It went like this: a packet schooner working the route between Penobscot and Boston is caught in a storm, and the captain is seeking shelter. Thinking he might tuck in to the Annisquam River on Cape Ann, he asks a passenger—a parson—to go below and fetch the Coast Pilot. When the parson comes back on deck with the Bible, the captain says, "a very good book, Elder, but it won't show me the way into 'Squam."

Seafaring has always been defined by a certain tension between the practical and the sacred, the ordinary and the sublime, the destination, and the journey. This was particularly true in the nineteenth century, when the relentless rise of global commerce meant more ships, more routes, and more passages. Many of those who took to the sea also took up their pens, producing works that both guided and interpreted their voyages.

Some of these works were eminently practical. Edmund March Blunt's *American Coast Pilot*, Nathaniel Bowditch's *American Practical Navigator*, and, eventually, *Eldridge*, offered eminently useful aids. Properly applied, these texts could help mariners figure out where they were, where they were going, and what to do when they got there. Reliability and precision were their watchwords—such that seafarers could, and did, stake their lives on them. No fuzzy abstraction here; just hard numbers and lots of practical good advice.

Bowditch was known as a mathematical genius capable of near otherworldly feats of computation—a sort of Good Will Hunting in knee breeches. But when it came to his great work, he downplayed all that. The *Navigator* was, he told a European friend, not a work of high scholarship, but instead "written…according to the method of instruction used in our country, where we prefer in these matters practice to theory." It was a method of instruction, in other words, that put complex navigational calculations within the reach of even non-mathematical geniuses.

Blunt, too, boasted of "practical utility." In his *American Coast Pilot*, he provided careful descriptions of the country's "marine boundaries," noting that ships faced their greatest peril when moving from sea to coast. The knowledge contained in his book would enable the mariner to "set the rock-bound shore at defiance," as he put it in the preface to the 1822 edition. Better to follow Blunt's instructions than to learn the hard way—in a wreck. Better indeed. If we can assume that the parson aboard that packet schooner dove back below and swapped out Gospel for guide, the captain would have found all that he needed to know for someone in just his predicament. After admonishing all "masters of vessels" to be "generally acquainted with the harbour of Squam," Blunt duly offered instructions for "when a stranger is obliged to run for [that] harbour." And so it was that mariners sailing by the book could meet the many perils of coast and sea.

But the perils also had their poets. The foul conditions, the tireless gales, the rocky shores, and dangerous approaches were not merely hazards to be cataloged and defied; they were trials to be met, endured, and, ultimately, described. And so the nineteenth century was the last heyday of a different kind of sea writing in English, when sea scribes worked to capture the majesty, mystery, and misery of life offshore.

And therein rested the tension. Where the navigational guide sought order and clarity—to demystify and disenchant—the sea writers worked in the opposite direction, reveling in the unknown, the mystical, and the enchanted. Theirs was a sea of sublime wonders and mystical contemplation. Herman Melville offered a cheeky assessment of the problem in the "Mast-Head" chapter of *Moby-Dick*. There, his narrator Ishmael cops to being a terrible lookout for whales, too preoccupied as he is with his ocean reveries to be of much use to the ship. "Let me in this place movingly admonish you, ye ship-owners of Nantucket," he warns. "Beware of enlisting in your vigilant fisheries any lad with lean brow and hollow eye; given to unseasonable meditativeness; and who offers to ship with the Phædon instead of Bowditch in his head." Beware, that is, of shipping a "sunken-eyed Platonist" like Ishmael, who is more tuned into idealistic reflections on the soul (the subject of Plato's dialogue, the *Phaedo*) than the practical demands of ship and voyage.

The dreamers like Ishmael could hardly be blamed; like the practical-minded captain consulting his navigational guide, they, too, were sailing by the book. Going as far back as the seventeenth century, sea writing had been filling young men's heads with certain notions about life aboard ship and on the open ocean. For the contemplative or spiritual, the encounter with the ocean's vastness—the "howling infinite," Melville called it—was a kind of existential ordeal, in which the individual was forced to confront his puny insignificance in the face of the world's great forces.

For the bold and the daring, meanwhile, there was the promise of adventure and romance captured in pirate and explorer tales. The wildly popular *Pirate's Own Book*, first published in 1837, gathered and repackaged old buccaneering yarns that dangled enticing visions of desires fulfilled and restraints removed. "The pirate is truly fond of women and wine," the book's preface instructed. His was a life of "rich plunder, caskets of buried jewels, chests of gold ingots, bags of outlandish coins, secreted in lonely, out of the way places, or buried about the wild shores of rivers, and unexplored sea coasts." For young men leaving behind the green fields for clerical and factory work in increasingly crowded cities, who wouldn't want to sign up for all that?

From this vantage, the sea was a place of freedom, and the ship a means of escape. So it is with Ishmael, who leaves behind the "carking cares of earth" and the "slavish shore" for the unencumbered vastness of the deeps. And so it could be—even more powerfully—for the actually enslaved. In one of the most vivid scenes of his first autobiography (1845), Frederick Douglass described the soul-stirring experience of gazing out at the Chesapeake, "whose broad bosom was ever white with sails from every quarter of the habitable globe." Those ships "moving off to the mighty ocean" represented both a torment to Douglass—why couldn't he break free like that—and enacted his own aspiration. Not long after, he would escape to freedom—dressed as a sailor.

The only trouble was that the ship was rarely an actual vehicle of liberation, nor the sea always a hospitable venue for actual contemplation. Dream and reality were mismatched. Richard Henry Dana wrote his classic account *Two Years before the Mast* (1840) as a cautionary tale for anyone—sunken-eyed dreamers and otherwise—who might regard sea life with undue romance. The ship, Dana was keen to demonstrate, was less a place of wonder and contemplation than one of brutality and misery. The sailor's lot was defined by unending toil, bad food, worse smells, rigid hierarchies, and tyrannical, crazed captains wielding arbitrary power—what the sea writer Nathaniel Ames called "the generally overbearing, tyrannical, inhuman conduct of Yankee skippers." On the latter point, Melville's fictional Ahab looms large, but the captain of Dana's ship, the *Pilgrim*, was real—and really crazy. Few readers of *Two Years* will forget the captain's soliloquy, "I'm Frank Thompson, all the way from 'down east.' I've been through the mill, ground and bolted, and come out a regular-built down-east johnny-cake, when it's hot, damned good, but when it's cold, damned sour and indigestible;— and you'll find me so!"

Before getting a taste of the regular-built down-east johnny-cake, Dana, too, suffered from misconceptions about going to sea. He was the scion of a Brahmin family—the "Duke of Cambridge," as he was sometimes called—and hardly the type for the miseries and deprivations of the forecastle. But some combination of a self-described "weakness of the eyes," misplaced romance, and restlessness with elite society led him to swap out "tight dress coat, silk cap, and kid gloves of an undergraduate at Cambridge" (he dropped out of Harvard in 1832) for "the loose duck trousers, checked shirt and tarpaulin hat of a sailor." Dana hoped his trials might dissuade others from suffering similar ones, and that his book would generate sympathy for those who went to sea by necessity rather than choice. To add to his case, he followed up *Two Years* with the *The Seamen's Friend*, a book filled with help and practical information for mariners.

At one level, it seemed to work. Reviews of *Two Years before the Mast* lauded its clear-eyed realism. Any reader would be forced to give up his "false fancies" of sea life before he should chance to "enter this den of horrors." The idea was not new, of course. The English writer Samuel Johnson had famously pronounced back in the eighteenth century, that "no man will be a sailor who has contrivance enough to get himself into jail; for being in a ship is being in a jail, with the chance of being drowned." Johnson, though, was a man of the armchair rather than the foredeck and topyard. Dana had actually been there, and that lent weight to an account that promised to "dissipate all the illusions about the sea, which most young men are wont to cherish." When the book was an unlikely success—who knew you could have a bestseller about the sea without the romance?—a wave of imitators gathered, and the whole genre of sea writing seemed to shift toward the real and true. The spirit of the navigational guide and the sea book seemed almost to be coming into alignment.

Except, that's not exactly how it went. The world wasn't quite ready to let go of the mystique. One perceptive reader of *Two Years* saw in an instant that Dana's effort would not succeed in "diminishing the attractiveness of a sailor's life by telling the naked homely truth." Dana, he said, had "told his story too well. He has made the witchery of the sea more a witchery than ever." Much the same could be said for many of Dana's followers, whose real stories remained really compelling. With time, even Dana himself succumbed to the mystique of his own story and traded the realism back in for the romance. In a reflective essay called "Twenty-Four Years After," he confessed, "How softening is the effect of time! It touches us through the affections. I almost feel as if I were lamenting the passing away of something loved and dear."

Dana's surrender to the romance, and the stubborn witchery of the sea, bring us to the critical point: perhaps the ordinary and the sublime are not so far removed after all. No matter how precise the calculation, how clear the instructions, how reliable the tables, the sea itself never surrenders, and can never be contained or controlled. Certain laws and knowable patterns might pertain, but the sea keeps its own mysteries. Sometimes, this manifests itself in awesome, destructive power. "However baby man may brag of his science and skill," Melville wrote in *Moby-Dick*, "for ever and for ever, to the crack of doom, the sea will insult and murder him, and pulverize the stateliest, stiffest frigate he can make." The romance resides in that possibility, and, God-willing, in the defiance of that possibility. To perform that feat, you might want the *Coast Pilot*, your *Bowditch*, your *Eldridge*—and the Bible, too.

Jake Lundberg teaches American history at the University of Notre Dame.

Erica M. Szuplat

How to Contact the U.S. Coast Guard

U.S. Coast Guard Rescue Coordination Centers (RCCs)
24-hour Regional Contacts for Emergencies

RCC Boston, MA – (617) 223-8555 Maine to Northern New Jersey

RCC Norfolk, VA – (757) 398-6231 New Jersey to border of N. Carolina and S. Carolina

RCC Miami, FL – (305) 415-6800 S. Carolina to Key West including much of Caribbean

USCG Navigation Information Service (NIS) Watchstander, (24/7): (703) 313-5900

USCG National Response Center (NRC): (800) 424-8802

USCG Marine Safety Center: (202) 795-6729, msc@uscg.mil

INTERNET: USCG - www.navcen.uscg.gov/ Canada - www.notmar.gc.ca/

U.S. Coast Guard Boardings

The U.S. Coast Guard has the authority to enforce federal laws by making inquiries, examinations, inspections, searches, seizures, and arrests on the waters over which the United States has jurisdiction. Unlike law enforcement regulations ashore, the U.S. Coast Guard does not need probable cause to board your vessel.

The U.S. Coast Guard personnel are armed and may use necessary force to compel compliance. They are charged with the enforcement of laws dealing with safety, water pollution, drug smuggling, illegal immigration, and the 200-mile fishery conservation zone. In nearly half the boardings, they find some kind of non-compliance with regulations. A civil penalty may be imposed for failure to comply with equipment or numbering regulations, navigation rules, accident reporting procedures, etc.

A boat underway that is hailed by a U.S. Coast Guard vessel or patrol boat is required to follow the boarding officer's instructions, which may be to stop, to continue at reduced speed, or to maneuver in such a way as to permit boarding. Instructions will depend on sea conditions. The Coast Guard follows a standard procedure before boarding, and the boarding team will provide as explanation before the actual boarding. If the boarding party has full cooperation from you, the inspection will be completed quickly.

The editors wish to thank the U.S. Power Squadrons (USPS) for permission to reprint this article from their Seamanship Manual.

Free Supplement
Available June 1 — Changes and updates through May 15, 2024

Download or sign up to receive a copy via email at http://eldridgetide.com/updates/, or mail a self-addressed, stamped envelope to the address on the front cover.

Radio Telephone Information—VHF System

Calling Guidelines: Avoid excessive calling. Make calls as brief as possible. Give name of called vessel first, then "This is (name of your vessel)," your call sign (if you have a Station License), and the word "Over." If station does not answer, delay your repeat call for 2 minutes. At the end of your message, sign off with "This is (your vessel's name)," your call sign, and "Out."

Range and Power: Operation is essentially line-of-sight. Since the elevation of antennas at both communications points extends the "horizon," range may be 20 to 50 miles on a 24-hour basis between a boat and a land station. Effective range between boats will be less because of lower antenna heights. 25 watts is the maximum power permitted.

Interference factor: Most VHF-FM equipment has 6 or more channels, so it is possible to shift to a clear channel. Like the FM in your home radio, the system is practically immune to interference from ignition noise, static, etc., except under unusual conditions.

Channelization: A minimum of 3 channels is required by the FCC. Two are mandatory: Channel 16 (156.800 MHz), the International Distress frequency; and Channel 06 (156.300 MHz), the Intership Safety Frequency. The Coast Guard *strongly* recommends that you have Channel 22A as your third channel.

Note: designations for channels that previously ended with "A" have changed. To convert to the new format, prepend "10" and drop the "A" – e.g., 22A becomes 1022. The table below includes both new and old designations. Frequencies are not changing; older VHF radios will function as before the change.

Channel	Purpose and Comments
16 156.800 MHz **Vessels are required to maintain a watch on this channel.**	**Distress and Safety**: Ship to Shore and Intership. Guarded 24 hours by the Coast Guard. No routine messages allowed other than to establish use of a working channel. See pp. 270-271 for distress calling procedure. **Calling**: Ship to Shore and Intership. Use Ch. 16 to establish contact, then switch to a working channel (see below). Calling Channel: New England waters. Commercial and pleasure.
09 156.450 MHz	**Boater Calling:** Commercial and Non-Commercial
06 156.300 MHz	**Intership Safety:** No routine messages allowed. 06 is limited to talking with the Coast Guard and others at the scene of an emergency, and to information on the movement of vessels.
22A/1022 157.100 MHz (**21 in Canada** 161.65 MHz)	**Maritime Safety Information** channel. Not guarded by the CG, but after a vessel makes contact with the CG for non-distress calls on Ch. 16, they will tell you to switch to and use *only* 22A for communicating. Also used for CG weather advisories and Notices to Mariners; times of these broadcasts given on Ch. 16.
12, 14, 20A/1020, 65A/1065, 66A/1066, 73, 74, 77	**Ship to Shore and Intership:** Port operations, harbormasters, etc. Your electronics dealer should have local frequencies.
08, 67, 88	**Commercial (intership only):** For ocean vessels, dredges, tugs, etc.
07A/1007, 10, 11, 18A/1018, 19A/1019, 79A/1079, 80A/1080	**Commercial only**
13 156.650 MHz	**Intership Navigation Safety:** (bridge to bridge). Ships > 20 m length maintain a listening watch on this channel in US waters.
68, 69, 71, 72, 78A/1078	**Ship to Shore and Intership, pleasure craft only:** Shore stations, marinas, etc. The best channels for general communication.
70 156.525 MHz	**Digital Selective Calling (DSC)**. Special equipment required.
81A/1081 157.075 MHz **83A/1083** 157.175 MHz	**Keyed Fog Signals**. Key microphone 5–10 times consecutively to activate fog signal (see note on p.173).
AIS 1 161.975 MHz **AIS 2** 162.025 MHz	**Automatic Identification System** (AIS)

VHF Call Scripts

16 | HAILING

PENDRAGON, PENDRAGON, *this is* **BALLARD, BALLARD** *calling* **PENDRAGON,** *repeat,* **PENDRAGON.** *Come in* **PENDRAGON. OVER.**

NAME of VESSEL being called, repeat 2X ---------- pause →

this is ----- vessel type and NAME, repeat 2X ---------- pause →

Come in hailed vessel NAME ---------- **OVER.**

When vessel responds, name another channel, leave Channel 16.

UNKNOWN VESSEL
CONTAINER SHIP EXITING THE CAPE COD CANAL
This is the sailing Ketch **LOLLIPOP** *off your port bow, calling to state our intentions.* **OVER.**

16 | SECURITÉ HAZARD TO NAVIGATION

[see-kyoor-ih-TAY], SECURITÉ, SECURITÉ This is the motor vessel **TRANQUIL,** *the* **MV TRANQUIL** *calling* **WOODS HOLE COAST GUARD** *to report a hazard to navigation: a section of wooden dock is floating awash near beacon 1A east of Woods Hole.* **OVER.**

SECURITÉ, SECURITÉ, SECURITÉ. pause →

This is ----- vessel type and NAME, repeat 2X ---------- pause →

calling COAST GUARD STATION NEAREST pause →

to warn of specific nature of hazard and location pause →

Coast Guard please copy. **OVER.**

Repeat until Coast Guard responds, discuss hazard on channel required by Coast Guard communications.

VHF Call Scripts

16 | PAN-PAN REQUEST FOR ASSISTANCE

[pawn-pawn], PAN-PAN, PAN-PAN This is the sport fisherman **TORO**, *repeat,* **TORO**, *requesting medical assistance for minor injuries, possible broken bone. We are under way heading NNE off Mosquito Island, near can 15.* **OVER.**

PAN-PAN, PAN-PAN, PAN-PAN.

This is ___ vessel type and NAME, repeat 2X ___ → pause

requesting nature of required assistance ___ → pause

we are docked, anchored, under way, specific location → pause

Coast Guard please copy. **OVER.**

Repeat until Coast Guard responds, confirm request and rendezvous on channel required by Coast Guard.

16 | MAYDAY URGENT EMERGENCY, LIFE THREAT

MAYDAY, MAYDAY, MAYDAY This is the sloop **LADY HELEN**, *repeat,* **LADY HELEN**. *Fire aboard. We are abandoning ship, repeat, abandoning ship, two miles west of Serpent Island, two miles west of Serpent Island. Need immediate assistance. Coast Guard please respond. This is a MAYDAY.* **OVER.**

MAYDAY, MAYDAY, MAYDAY.

This is ___ vessel type and NAME, repeat 2X ___ → pause

declaring emergency ___ nature of emergency ___ → pause

we are docked, anchored, under way, specific location → pause

This is a MAYDAY. **OVER.**

Repeat until Coast Guard responds.

Index To Advertisers

For more information about **ELDRIDGE** advertisers and links to their websites, visit:

www.eldridgetide.com

Erica M. S

272